This book is updated and the latest information on Avon collecting is released to the public about every 2 to 3 years. Send your name and address to Bud Hastin to be first to know when the next book will be released.

Bud Hastin's

Avon Bottle Collector Encyclopedia™

The official Guide For
Avon Bottle Collectors

11th Edition

Published, Written, Photographed and Researched by
Bud Hastin
P.O. Box 43690 Las Vegas, Nevada 89116

Bud Hastin is in no way responsible for buying, selling or trading Avon bottles at the prices quoted in this guide book. It is published only as a guide and prices vary from state to state as much as 90%. Most prices quoted are top prices in mint condition and it is not uncommon for prices to be quoted differently, usually being lower. Bud Hastin does not solicit Avon bottles to buy or sell. The current values in this book should be used only as a guide. They are not intended to set prices, which vary from one section of the country to another. Auction prices as well as dealer prices vary greatly and are affected by condition as well as demand. Neither the Author nor the Publisher assumes responsibility for any losses that might be incurred as a result of consulting this guide.

The Bud Hastin's Avon Bottle Collectors Encyclopedia™ is recognized by Avon Collectors and Avon Representatives as the official and most complete collector's guide in print.

Acknowledgements & Credits

Bud Hastin personally thanks all the Avon collectors across the nation who have permitted him to photograph their collection to update this book. Much credit goes to all the following people for their assistance and help, be it big or small. For without them there would never have been an Avon Encyclopedia.

Dwight & Vera Young, MO
Sara June & Bill Lloyd, CA
Eola Clark, Canada
Dick Pardini, CA
George Gaspar, Ill
Rosie Anderson, MO
Jerry Fink, IL
Lenny Talys, PA
Bud Hoover, OR
Sunny Lyman, CA
Jenny Stanley, OH
Doris Singer, IN
Phil & Ogreta Simmons, KS
Marge McGraw, TX
Ruth Hershberger, Canada
Ralphi Lintz, CA
Sue Metheney, OH

Pat O'Leary, OH
Phyllis Lehner, OH
Mary Adams, OH
Bob & Arlene Cherry, NJ
Ray Potter, IL
Gerry Ruchy, NJ
Sharon Hardifer, NJ
Kitty Stinson, DE
Jo Olsen, MI
Linda Watson, GA
Grace Powers, GA
Dorothy Rudolph, CA
Clark Popham, WA
Jim & Sally Herrema, MI
Ivan & Joan Norris, Canada
Gerardo Diaz, TX

Garnett Harter, IN
Mabel Patterson, OH
Pat Alderson, OH
Ed Bea, NJ
Lara Nell Stout, KS
Tony Jotautas, PA
Ron Federico, CA
Debbi Coppock, Canada
Gladys & Bob Dwyer, NJ
Margaret Helm, PA
Jerry Graham, IA
Mary Rose Brown, OK
Darleen Sisson, CA
Dorothy Chamberlin, IL
Dolores Yunker, IL
Marci & Nick Latoof, NJ

"Avon Calling" is a registered trade mark of Avon Products

The phrase "Avon Calling" rings 'round the world' as the signature of a firm devoted to the manufacture and sales of high quality cosmetic and toiletry items for all members of the family.

From its start in 1886 as the California Perfume Company, Avon has grown steadily, expanding its operation throughout the world. Today fourteen manufacturing laboratories and twenty-five distribution branches, all using the most modern and efficient equipment and all staffed by well trained and experienced employees, produce a vast variety of ever changing, imaginative products.

The Avon representative, focal point of the company, employs the oldest method of distribution in the world . . . direct-to-the-home selling. This means she brings the latest news in beauty and grooming, the finest products, and the most personal kind of service directly to her customers in their homes.

Avon's growth from a one room laboratory in down town New York to the current world wide network of manufacturing laboratories and distribution branches is a success story based on quality . . . quality of product, quality of service, quality of relationships with people.

Avon is the worlds largest manufacturer and distributor of cosmetics, fragrances and costume jewelry. Its products are sold by more than 1,600,000 active Representatives to customers in the home in the United States and other countries. Plus their products are sold in almost every country in the world.

1969

1970

1971

1971

1972

1972

1974

1976 & 1979

1981 & 1982

Bud Hastin was born in Butler, Missouri. He grew up in Butler, where he graduated from Butler High School. He spent three years in the United States Air Force. Bud went into the auto glass business in 1964 and sold Mobile Auto Glass of Kansas City in 1971 to devote full time to preparing Avon Collector Guides for the collector.

Bud says his father is responsible for getting him interested in the bottle hobby when someone gave him some fancy cut glass bottles and Bud liked them so much that he started collecting.

The Avon hobby as a whole, covers a tremendous volume of material. Avon collectables include bottles, tin containers, jars, soaps, samples, candles, plates, prizes, catalogs, magazine advertisements, Outlooks, and many more. There is far too much to collect for the average person to work on all catogories. **No.1 Rule in Avon Collecting:** "Set a goal for your hobby and collect only what you want to collect." You rule the hobby, it doesn't rule you. Decide what part of the overall hobby appeals to you, set your goal and work hard toward that goal. Ask yourself some questions. How much room do I have? How much can I spend each month? What do I enjoy most about Avon Collecting? Base your goal on the answer.

Since 1969 Bud has sold over 620,000 copies of his Avon Collectors book. This book is the 11th book in the Avon collecting by Bud Hastin. The first, being sold in 1969, was the Avon Collectors Guide, Vol. 1, then followed the 1970 Avon Collectors Guide Vol. II, The Avon Collectors Encyclopedia, the 1971 Avon Collectors Guide for Beginners, the 1972 Avons Collectors Encyclopedia, the 1972 Avon Beginners Guide, the 1974 Avon Collectors Encyclopedia, and the Avon Collectors Encyclopedia special hardbound edition for collectors. Only 1,000 were printed and each was signed by Bud.

The 1976-77 Avon Collectors Encyclopedia - There were 500 hardbound copies of the 1976 Avon Collectors Encyclopedia - There were 350 special hardbound collectors editions of the 1979 Encyclopedia, 1982-83 Encyclopedia, 1984, Encyclopedia. Many people are starting to collect the older Avon books published by Bud.

Bud's personal views on collecting are: "I think the Avon collecting hobby is the best hobby around today. It is one of the few hobbies that you will probably never find all of them and that's what collecting is all about, the challange to find something you don't have. The thrill is finding a high priced Avon bottle in a flea market or garage sale for a low price. You see very few Avon collections the same and this always makes the challenge greater to find the one that your friend has. Avon collecting is one of the biggest hobbies in the U.S. I wonder how many of the old and rare C.P.C. and Avon bottles are lying around in somebodies attic and cellars just waiting to be discovered by some informed collector ? Garage sales, rummage sales, etc. are the gold fields and it is almost as big a thrill to find a $100.00 C.P.C. as it was for the treasure hunters of old to find gold. Avon collecting is for all ages, both young and old. It's a hobby for the entire family.

NATIONAL ASSOCIATION OF AVON COLLECTORS

Bud was chairman of the Board of the National Association of Avon Collectors Clubs, and was the founder of the National Organization in 1971 to 1986. The N.A.A.C. is not a club, but an organization to help promote Avon collecting in the United States. The N.A.A.C. is run by an elected board of Directors. The N.A.A.C. is ready to help anyone start a new Avon collectors club in your area. For information on starting a new Avon Collectors Club, write to N.A.A.C. in care of Bud Hastin and we will see all N.A.A.C. material is sent to you. At present there are 100 active Avon Collectors Clubs in the N.A.A.C. A National Convention is held each year along with a National Avon Bottle Show. Each year it is held in a different section of the U.S. The N.A.A.C. is a non-profit organization and fifanced by the sale of the N.A.A.C. club bottle easch year. See the N.A.A.C. section of this book for N.A.A.C. Club Bottles. These club bottles are very limited editions and have skyrocketed in price after they were released. Profits from the sale of the club bottles are used to send a delegate from the member clubs to the National Convention each year.

NEW PRODUCTS 1984 and NEWER. HOW THEY ARE PRICED & WHAT IS TRULY COLLECTABLE.

Avon collecting has matured and is in for some adjustment and a little regulation. Avon Products has expanded their product lines to include many products that do not seem to fit into a Avon collection. They are making a number of household products, decorator items, and etc., that are not marked Avon or have a Avon trademark on them or lables. We suggest that this type of products be purchased for the purpose it was intended and not as a collectable. If we include everything in the book that Avon is mass producing, this book would be 1000 pages thick and most of it with little or no value.

I, along with many others I have talked to in the last couple of years, agree that unless it is marked Avon on the product, don't collect it to put in an Avon collection. It will never have any real value. We have also found little or no interest in cosmetic fragrance lines newer than 1975. This applies both to men's and women's products. For this reason we have taken out all fragrance lines 1975 or newer. The only products in these lines to collect are soaps, sets, and awards after 1975. These products are produced in the millions of pieces. There will never be a resale market for this type of product in our lifetime.

DEMO PRICE. All new collectables added to this book 1984 or newer is marked at DP which is the demo price that the more than 400,000 avon representatives are paying for each product. We feel this is a fair price to pay for a new collectable. In this manner of pricing for current market value (CMV) which is the same as the DP, we feel you won't have to wait as many years for a collectable to raise in value in the future.

We want Avon Collecting to be as exciting as possible but for the prices to be fair to all concerned.

WHAT IS HOT AND WHAT IS NOT IN AVON COLLECTING.

For the absolute best investment in avon collecting, nothing can beat something old and in new condition. This of course is the California Perfume Company products. This is the original Avon Product's name from the late 1800's to 1939 when the name was changed to Avon Products Inc. as it remains today. Almost anything in mint condition with the CPC label will sell quickly and usually bring a good price. It's like any other collectable, the older the better. DECANTURS, FIGURINES, both mens and womens, SOAPS, KID'S TOYS, SETS, AVON REPRESENTATIVE AWARDS, OLD FRAGRANCE LINES both mens and womens, PER-FECTION PRODUCTS, OLD MISC. BOTTLES 1935 or older. These are the collectables that are hot if they are older and in mint condition.

WHAT NOT TO COLLECT FOR FUTURE RESALE.

We have removed from this book all items listed because they are mass produced in the millions of pieces and will never have a value for resale. We have left only the older items in each category that is truly rare or harder to find for a collection. Any new items will not be included in this book in the future as collectors just do not want them. We suggest you dispose of them.

Items not to collect are all tubes, tin cans, misc. bottles, any plastic bottle unless it is part of a set or a children's toy unless it is listed in this book. This goes both for American and Canada and Foreign products. All fragrance lines from 1975 on should be avoided as there is little or no resale market for them.

Collect only what you truly enjoy for yourself. You may collect any of the things I have listed as not collectable as long as you understand that there is not a resale market for them. Otherwise when you are done with them, dispose of them. Happy collecting.

HELPFUL HINTS AND MEANING OF TERMS IN BOOK

The 11th Avon Collectors Encyclopedia has been complied by Bud Hastin. To best understand this book and its contents, please read this before starting through the book.

All items from 1929 to 1984 will give the first year and the last year date that the items were sold by the Avon Company. Dates will read, for instance, 1930-36. This means this item was introduced sometime in 1930 and was discontinued for the last time in 1936. Dates like 1970-71 mean the item sold in both years, but is very possible it sold for less than one year selling time. An item dated for three years like 1958-60 means it sold in all three years, but could have only been on the market for a period of about two years total time. All items dated 1886 to 1928 mean the first and last year sold. All dates from 1929 to 1983 with only one year given, means this item was sold during that one year only and usually for a very short period. These items are usually considered a short-issue and hard to find. 1984 and up gives only the issue date.

O.S.P. means Original Selling Price. This is the full value price Avon puts on an item. It does not represent a special selling price which is from 20% to 50% off the O.S.P.

S.S.P. means Special Selling Price (reduced in price). The O.S.P. or S.S.P. price may vary as Avon may have put a different special selling price each time it was offered and the O.S.P., may have been changed from the time it was introduced to the time it was taken off the market because of rising cost to make the product. Prices quoted are just to give you an idea of what the item sold for from Avon.

C.M.V. means Current Market Value that most collectors are willing to pay for that particular item. Many items priced in this book are priced both item only and item in box. Items in the original box need not be full.

The collectors price is for an empty bottle. If it is current and full, and in the box, then you can expect to pay full retail price or the special selling price that Avon sells this item for. Only after Avon stops selling the item and it has been placed on the annual discontinued list Avon prints each year of items that will not be offered for sale again on its original design, will Avon be considered as a Collectors item and the value could start to increase.

B.O. means bottle only (mint), no box. **M.B.** means mint and boxed in perfect condition.

All Avon tubes priced in this book are for full mint condition tubes. If a tooth paste tube or other type tube has been used then it would not be mint. Tubes and soaps are the only items in this book that have to be full to be mint condition. Most all other items are priced empty unless otherwise stated. In most cases all older items will bring as much empty as they would full.

This book has been compiled from original CPC and Avon Catalogs. Original California Perfume Company catalogs used in the 11th Avon Collectors Encyclopedia have been copied completely and all items pictured in these original catalogs are pictured in this book. The CPC was used from the years 1896 to 1929. From 1916 to 1929 the CPC sales catalogs were black leather type covers. 1916 to 1923 these books were hard bound. 1924 to 1929 the same size books were soft cover bound. January, 1929, was the introduction of Avon Products with the Avon name first appearing on a number of CPC products.

The CPC sales catalogs 1896 to 1906 were smaller booklet type with soft covers measuring 6 5/8" x 4 3/4". the 1915 book is dated and measures 4" x 7 1/8". 1930 through 1935 the Avon sales catalogs had CPC/Avon Products in them in a 6 3/4" x 10" dark blue soft cover book. 1936 through 1957 the sales catalogs are the same size only with a green cover.

An entire set of Avon sales catalogs from 1930 to 1987 were used to compile the Avon Collectors Encyclopedia. A complete set of Avon Sales Outlook or Avon Calling from 1905 to 1987 were also used. Special Christmas sales catalogs from 1934 to 1987 were also used showing many special sets sold only at Christmas time each year.

Grading Condition of Avons

People have asked me **WHAT A BOTTLE IS WORTH WITHOUT A LABEL.** If it's an old bottle where the label is the main thing that identifies the bottle and it is missing, then it's worth whatever you can get, which is usually not too much. If it is a new figural bottle, then it will usually take a few dollars off the price.

MINT CONDITION means items must be in new condition as orginally sold, with all labels bright and correct, and cap and/or stopper. Items need not be full or boxed, but will bring a higher price in most cases if they are in the box. All items in the book are priced empty in mint condition only with the right cap and all labels. Bottles with no cap or label are of little or no value.

TEST BOTTLES & COMPS

Test bottles have been removed from this book only to discourage the theft of test bottles from the factory that make them for Avon. Test and comps are still considered very collectable, but we will no longer print pictures or prices on them in this book.

GRADING EXAMPLES
A Guide for Selling Or Buying

1969-73 Gold Cadillac... Chipped paint, deduct 50% to 90% from CMV. Don't buy it.

1966-67 Casey's Latern. Chipped paint, broken bail ears, deduct 70% to 90% from CMV

1971 French Telephone.. Gold chip on handle, deduct 40% to 70% CMV, label off handle, deduct 40% CMV. Don't buy chipped product.

1961-63 Cotillion Cologne. Cap turning grey, deduct 25 - 50% CMV, lettering faint.

1947-56 Golden Promise Cologne.... Letters or printing gone, deduct 70-90% CMV. Gold off cap, deduct 40-90% CMV. Don't buy it.

1948-50 Quaintance Perfume.. Letters gone on printing, deduct 40-90% CMV

1963 Topaze Perfume Oil for Bath..... Letters fading in printing, deduct 70-90% CMV

1958 "Old 99" Soap..... Chip on soap, deduct 70% CMV. Box torn, deduct 10 - 50% CMV

1961-62 Avon Slugger.. Crack in handle, deduct 60-90% CMV. Don't buy it.

1896-1908 French Perfume... Torn or damaged label, deduct 20 -70% CMV

Painted Figurals (Gold Cadillac, Casey's Lanterns, French Telephone, Red VW, Silver Warrior, etc.): One or two tiny chips, deduct 40%. Larger flakes that are visible, deduct 50%. They have little or no value. Throw them away.

Other Figurals: Bottom label missing or damaged, deduct 20%. Poor cap, deduct 20%. Both, deduct 50% or more.

Fragrance Line Bottles with Painted Labels (Nearness, Forever Spring, Quaintance, etc.) One or two letters mis-placed or missing, deduct 10%. If more than that, deduct 25-90%. Faint writing on gold painted labels, deduct 20-80%. Front paper labels (To A Wild Rose, Nearness, Old Cotillion, etc.) if intact but faded, deduct 10-30%; if torn or damaged, deduct 30-75%.

CPCs (very few are absolutely mint), deduct 10-85% for poor caps, damaged labels, scratched bottles, chips, etc.

Soaps: Chips, deduct 20-85%. White spots, some are natural, use your judgement. Boxes dirty, stained or torn, deduct 50-75%. If used even once, take a bath with it.

Children's Toys.. Paint missing, deduct 25-95%. Cracked, holes, or teeth marks, deduct 80-95%. Bottom label missing or damaged, deduct 20%.

If any Avon is damaged in any way - I would not buy it. Collect only mint Avons and throw away the less than mint ones in the Avon Line.

IF ANYTHING IS TOO BADLY DAMAGED, DON'T BUY IT OR SELL IT!

CPC bottles may have the same shape but with different labels. Be sure to check labels and boxes to get the right date on your bottles.

All items are dated in this book from actual old Avon catalogs I have in my possession. They did not change the bottles for many years in the early days of CPC. 1896 was the first year a CPC catalog was printed.

TO BUY AND SELL AVONS. Garage sales, flea markets, antique shops, bottle shops are the best places to buy and sell Avon bottles locally. To sell Avons in your own town, place a small ad in your local paper and say Avon bottles for sale with your address or phone number. Have a garage sale and put Avon bottles on your sign. People will come to you. If you have no luck locally, **The Avon Times is the number one spot in the U.S. to sell those extra Avons.** The Avon Times is the largest in the world and Avon ads get the best result anywhere. Write Avon Times, P.O. Box 9868, Kansas City, MO 64134, for a sample copy of this club magazine. Send 40c in stamps to cover postage.

There are several reasons for pricing all items empty. After Shave bottles are known to explode in sun light or heat. Full bottles sitting on glass shelves increase the chance of the shelves breaking. After a few years, the contents become spoiled or unsafe to skin and dangerous in the hands of children. I feel if you buy the item new, use the contents and you will still have the pretty bottles.

PRICING CURRENT MARKET VALUE

Pricing Current Market Value

All pricing in this book for CMV has been set by several qualified Avon bottle dealers and collectors across the United States. The prices reflected are what the item is actually selling for in their respective areas. While many items have increased in value, some have been lowered, only slightly. This in no way reflects a fall out in the market of Avon collecting. It is stronger today than ever and we are trying to reflect the approximate true collector's value; or what a collector will actually pay for the item in Mint condition. All items are priced empty unless otherwise stated. On the pricing of new Avon products dated 1978 to 1984, the CMV is usually the same as the Special Selling Price Avon sold it for, or it is priced a little under the SSP. The future CMV on these products may very well fall somewhat in future issues of this book to reflect the true collector's value. Remember, the price paid to the Avon Representative is not a collector's price, but a new product price. You are paying for the contents. After you use the product, the price usually goes down and it becomes a used item. After you buy the item from Avon it is a used item. It takes some time for the item to become scarce on the collector's market before you see a true collector's price.

WHAT IS CMV?

Current Market Value - Definition: A willing buyer and a willing seller with neither under duress to make the transaction.

What makes an Avon valuable? Shape, color, unusual design, scarcity and how well it will display:

    a. Too big - takes too much room
    b. Too small - gets lost in collection
    c. Odd shapes - doesn't fit shelves, also takes too much room

Condition: Refer to coin collectors. Mint means perfect condition, unused, exceptional and undamaged. Mint means Mint, commands top dollar:

a. Boxes were made to protect the container, keeping it clean and brilliant. Boxes advertise the product and instruct the user. Boxes tell a story. When you say original condition, that was with a box. Boxes (especially men's) were usually thrown away immediately. A good clean, crisp box will help make the item bring a premium.
b. Grading and condition become even more important for an item with a CMV over $25.00.
c. Example: 1966-67 Tall Pony Post. The box is probably the hardest to find of the modern figurals. Box should have a premium price.

Sets - The bug-a-boo of Avon grading!! Many sets have a premium value because they display so well. They are packaged in unusual ways and are much harder to find with perfect box and superior contents. I agree with the statement: Poor box - poor set, subtract 50% to 75% of listed value.

A mint box is at least twice as hard to obtain as the mint bottle that came in it. As good as Avon is in packing - order 10 items of the same thing and only 4 will be truly mint boxes and containers. That is: creased or crushed box, corner of label not securely glued.

Several people ask about **INSURANCE ON BOTTLE COLLECTIONS.** Bottle insurance is available through your home owners policy. Check with your local agent.

Bottles will differ in color shades due to various dates in manufacture. It is difficult to get exactly the same color each time. Unless a bottle comes out in a completely different color, it will be of the same value.

THE SILVER METAL SALT & PEPPER SHAKERS WITH AVON PAT.DATE 1926-28, is not Avon Cosmetic Co. items. **THE AVON NAME WAS NOT USED UNTIL 1929.** The name Avon has been used by several companies and still is. Only the name Avon Products Incorporated is copyrighted.

IF YOU ARE AN AVON REPRESENTATIVE, AND WOULD LIKE TO SELL THIS BOOK TO YOUR CUSTOMERS, see volume prices in back of book or write Bud Hastin, P.O. Box 43690, Las Vegas, NV 89116.

HOW TO INVEST
RULES FOR COLLECTING

"The hunger to find a tin toy for $30.00, rather than a good night's sleep drives a painter to wake up at three in the morning in his Brooklyn home. He's rushing to Renneger's flea market in Pennsylvania by the time the rosy fingers of dawn peak over the tents." Does this sound familiar? Of course it does, if you're an Avon collector. How many foolish things have you ever done while seeking that hoped-for bargain or very much sought after item? People are doing this kind of thing in every part of America - and they are doing it for almost anything you could name; be it a tin toy or a campaign button. In today's market, anything is colllectible if it has aesthetic vitality, if it's pleasing to the eye and to the senses. However, we are interested in Avon and California Perfume. . . and Avon collecting is now a big collecting field. For the new collectors and to refresh seasoned collectors - we have found collecting, like other investments, has rules to follow for the best results:

- If you don't like an item, don't buy it no matter how much of a bargain it seems to be. The only good investments are those that are enjoyed.
- The old goes up in value, or at least retains its resale value. New items take longer to increase in value and stay around longer. Of course, we all know, there are more collectors today.
- Buy it when you see it. Avons don't stay put . . .some don't have a very long shelf life.
- If you don't know your dealers, be sure you know your Avons. Fakes can be convincing (don't we all know that!).
- It is acceptable to haggle - it cannot hurt to ask if there is a lower price. Often in a booth or flea market there will be a better price available - don't be timid.
- Start small and learn the market. Browse, study the guides and learn all you can before you start buying.
- Measure your space - don't be the collector who buys a lot of items only to bring them home with no place to put them (ha, ha).
- Don't change your item in any way - don't paint it, add lettering, etc. . .this may destroy the value.

The above rules are good ones to keep in mind - the advice I've found most helpful is to have FUN while collecting . . .whether it be at a flea market, garage sale or convention.

A HISTORY OF THE
CALIFORNIA PERFUME CO.
NOW AVON PRODUCTS INCORPORATED

Written by the Founder, D. H. McConnell, Sr., in 1903

To give you a sketch or history of the birth and growth of the *California Perfume Company is, in a measure, like writing an autobiography. Our lives have become so identical and so interwoven that it seems almost impossible to separate us, even in history. I will ask you, therefore, to pardon whatever personal reference I may make of myself in describing to you how the California Perfume Company has become the largest of its kind, not only in the United States, but I believe, in the entire world.

In 1878, when but a mere lad, I left my father's farm located near Oswego City, New York State. Here I spent my boyhood days, and through hard work and proper training developed a good, strong, hardy, rugged constitution. When I started out in the world "to make my fortune", I had this positive advantage over many who were less favored.

My first experience in the business world was as a book agent. I took this up during my school vacation, and developed quite a faculty for talking, which I have since learned is quite essential, and has stood me well in hand many times.

My success in canvassing was such as to invite me into the same field the following year, and after two years hard work in the canvass, I was promoted from local canvasser to that of General Traveling Agent. As General Agent I traveled in nearly every state east of the Rocky Mountains; this gave me a valuable knowledge regarding the country. And my experience, both as canvasser and as General Agent, gave me a good insight into human nature.

It is uninteresting to you to follow me through the different work from Chicago to New York and from New York to Atlanta, Georgia, and back to Chicago, and finally back to New York. During all these years I represented in different ways the same publishing company with which I originally started as a canvasser; canvassing, appointing and drilling agents; starting and drilling General Agents, and corresponding with both after they once entered the field. My work as a canvasser and on the road taught me not to enter right into the everyday work of the canvasser and advise and encourage, so as to obtain the best results. If I learned to be anything, I learned to be practical.

The book business was not congenial to me, although I was, in every sense, successful in it, but there were many things that were not pleasant.

On my return from Chicago, I purchased the entire business from my employer and managed it myself for sometime. During this time the one thing I learned successfully was how to sell goods to the customer.

My ambition was to manufacture a line of goods that would be consumed, used up, and to sell it through canvassing agents, direct from the factory to the consumer.

The starting of the perfume business was the result of most careful and thorough investigation, guided by the experience of several years successful operation in the book business. That is, in selling goods direct to the consumer or purchaser. I learned during this time that the proper and most advantageous way of selling goods was to be able to submit the goods themselves to the people. In investigating this matter nearly every line of business was gone over, and it seemed to me, then, as it has since been proved, that the perfume business in its different branches afforded the very best possible opportunity to build up a permanent and well established trade. Having once decided that the perfume business was the business, the question naturally presented itself, "By what name are these perfumes to be known: by what name is this company to be called?" The gentleman who took me from the farm as a boy became in the past years, not only my employer but my personal friend, and after buying him out he moved to California, and while there wrote me glowing accounts of the country, and to him belongs the idea of the name California, as associated with this business.

I started the perfume business in a space scarcely larger than an ordinary kitchen pantry. At first I manufactured but five odors: Violet, White Rose, Heliotrope, Lily-of-the-Valley, and Hyacinth. I did much experimental work in making these odors, and the selling price to the first batch of perfumes I made did not cover one-half the actual cost of the goods, but experience is a great teacher, and I applied myself to the task of making perfumes with the same vim and energy that I had in selling books and after a short time, I fancied that I could produce as fine an odor as some of the old and tried perfumes. At least my perfumes pleased my customers; they were the natural perfumes of the flower, made in the most natural way and by the process employed by the large French perfumers.

I soon found it necessary to increase the odors, and to add to the line other articles for the toilet. Among those first put out were: Shampoo Cream, Witch Hazel Cream, Almond Cream Balm, Tooth Paste, which afterwards was made into the Tooth Tablet, Toilet Waters, etc.

As the business increased the laboratory must, of necessity grow, so that at the end of two years I was occupying one entire floor in this building for manufacturing purposes alone.

It is perhaps unfair to note the progress of one side of the business without carrying with it the natural development on the other.

My ambition was to manufacture a line of goods superior to any other, to be moneyed value into the goods themselves, and just enough money in the package to make them respectable, and as stated above, take these goods through canvassing agents direct from the laboratory to the consumer.

While in the book business I had in my employ as *General Traveling Agent, a Mrs.

P.F.E. Albee, of Winchester, NH. Mrs. Albee was one of the most successful General Agents

Mrs. P.F.E. Albee
1st CPC-Avon Sales Lady

I had in the book work, and it was in her hands I placed the first sample case, or outfit, in the perfume business. Mrs. Albee was the only General Agent employed for the first six months of the business. During that time she secured a number of good workers, some of whom are with us today. It is, therefore, only befitting that we give her the honorary title of Mother of the California Perfume Company. For the system that we now use for distributing our goods is the system that was put in practical operation by Mrs. Albee.

As the business grew, through the work of our agents, we were forced from time to time to increase our laboratory space, and in 1895 we built our own laboratory in Suffern, New York, 32 miles out on the main line of the Erie Railroad. This building has been enlarged and remodeled three different times, until today we have a building 120 feet long, main building 50 feet wide and the wing 30 feet, all three stories and basement giving us four working floors, each floor having 4,800 square feet of floor space, or a total floor capacity of 17,200 feet. This building is equipped with the best possible machinery, the latest devices for bottling goods and so on, until I feel we can truthfully say that there is not a plant of our kind in the country so large and so well fitted for our business, as the laboratory of the California Perfume Company.

As well directed efforts and hard work must eventually win their way to the front, so the manufacturing end of the California Perfume Company grew out of my hands; that is to say, I found that it was almost impossible for me to manufacture, to give the personal attention to both manufacturing and correspondence which the merits of each required. Therefore, in 1896, I secured the services of the best perfumer I could find, a gentleman who had been in the perfume business himself for 25 years and had the reputation in New York and vicinity for making the finest perfumes on the American market. In order to secure his services I was obliged to buy out his business and close up his laboratory, and he now has full charge of the manufacturing of every ounce of goods we put out.

My object in locating the laboratory at Suffern was that as Suffern is my home I can give much more personal attention and supervision to the affairs of the laboratory than if it was located in New York. So that every day in the year, unless when I am out on one of my trips, visiting agents and general agents, I am at the laboratory every morning, and spend an hour with our chemist, going over his work and see that every ounce of goods, every package in every department is made and put up in the best possible shape.

Contrast, if you please, the appearance of our office today with that of when Mrs. Albee first started out with the California Perfume Company's goods. Then, I had one stenographer, and I myself filled the position of correspondent,, cashier, bookkeeper, shipping clerk and office boy, anf manufacturing chemist. Today we have on our weekly payroll over 125 employees. Mrs. Albee for the first six months was the only general agent on the road. Today we have 48 general agents traveling over this country and selecting and drilling agents for this work. The first six months we had perhaps 100 agents in the field, today we have over 10,000 good, honest, industrious and energetic Depot Managers. All of you have your own customers, so that it is difficult to accurately estimate today the vast number of families that are using our goods. If each of you have 100 customers, or sell goods to only one different family, we are supporting goods to at least one million families in the United States. This will give you an idea of the magnitude of our business.The growth of the California Perfume Company only emphasizes what energy and fair dealing with everyone can accomplish. We propose first to be fair to our customers - your customers - by giving them they very best goods that can be made for the money. We propose to be fair and just, even liberal, with you who form the bone and sinew of our business.

Avon Representatives in the early days of the California Perfume Company were called Agents or Depot Managers.

Gallery Originals by Avon are not considered a collectors item. Only Avon Products are considered collectibles by most Avon Collectors.

David Hall McConnell

Founder

CPC - Avon Products

David Hall McConnell, manufacturer, was born in Oswego, NY, July 18, 1858, son of James and Isabel (Hall) McConnell, who came from Calvin County, Ireland, in 1845 and settled in Oswego, where James McConnell became a farmer and brick manufacturer. Brought up on a farm, David Hall McConnell attended a district school and the Oswego State Normal School and was planning to become a mathematics teacher, but instead entered business life in 1879 as a salesman for a New York book selling agency. In 1880 he joined the Union Publisheing Co. of Chicago and three years later was placed in charge of the southern territory, making his home in Atlanta, GA. He decided that, if books could be sold house-to-house, perfumes could also. Out of this conception grew his California Perfume Co. At first he manufactured his own perfumes at home and went out during the day selling them along with books until the enterprise grew and he had to discontinue his book selling and establish a perfume laboratory in Suffern, NY. Other toiletries and cosmetics were soon added to his line of products which he sold under the name of CPC, standing for California Perfume Co. Later the company also began to manufacture flavoring extracts and other household articles sold under the brand name, Perfection. From the onset McConnell effected distribution of his products through housewives and other women who could devote only a portion of their time to the work. The years brought steadily increasing success and at the time of his death his sales force had grown to over 30,000 agents and the volume of sales was measured in the millions. The California Perfume Co. was incorporated in January 1916, and through subsequent changes in name it became Allied Products, Inc., and later Avon Allied Products, Inc., with the following subsidiaries: Avon Products, Inc, distributors of Avon cosmetics and toiletries, the trade name Avon having been adopted in 1929 because of the similarity of the landscape surrounding the laboratories in Suffern, NY to that of Avon, England; Perfection Household Products; Avon Products of Canada, Ltd., incorporated in 1924, being an outgrowth of the California Perfume Company of Canada, Ltd., which was started in 1906; Hinz Ambrosia, Inc., and Technical Laboratories, Inc. McConnell was president, chairman of the board and principal owner of Avon Allied Products, Inc., and its affiliated companies until his death. He was also treasurer of G.W. Carnrick & Co., manufactureres of pharmaceautical supplies in Newark, NJ, and a director of the Holly Hill Fruit Products, Inc., a large orange grove and canning enterprise of Davenport, FL. He was one of the founders of the Suffern National Bank of which he became vice president in 1901, president in 1922 and chairman of the board in 1927. He was again elected chairman of the board and president in 1933 and continued in one or the other office until his death. For varying periods he was superintendent of schools in Suffern; president of the Suffern Board of Education, and treasurer of the Rockland County Republican committee. During the First World War he was chairman of the Rockland County selective service board. A Presbyterian in religion, he was instrumental in starting and played a major part in building the Suffern Presbyterian Church and for many years was superintendent of its Sunday school. He was a Mason and a member of the Union League Club of New York city, the Ormond Beach Club of Florida, the Arcola, NY Country Club and Houvenkoph Country Club of of Suffern, NY. Fishing, golf and horseback riding were his recreations. He was married in Chicago, March 31, 1885, to Lucy Emma, daughter of Ward Hays of Le Porte, IN, and had three children: Edna Bertha, who married William Van Allen Clark; Doris Hall, who married Edward Hall Faile; and David Hall McConnell, Jr. His death occurred in Suffern, NY, January 20, 1937.

Avon Miscellanea

EARLY DAYS

The company's name suggest a likely California beginning, but it has no such meaning; the manufacturing, shipping, and office work in the beginning was done at 126 Chambers St., New York City. The name followed a suggestion made by a friend of Mr. McConnell's who had just visited California and returned to New York greatly enthused over the gorgeous flowers he had seen there. Since only perfumes were being sold, he suggested that the name of the company be "The California Perfume Company".

A LARGE LINE

By 1915 we had a large line. Our products were well and favorably known among our customers but were not known to the public at large. No advertising was done. The customers told their friends about these splendid products and the CPC Representatives' service. From the beginning all products were sold under the CPC trademark. All were offered to customers by Representatives (our products have never been sold through stores) and, always the products were unconditionally guaranteed. This was most unusual in the early days.

THE PANAMA PACIFIC EXPOSITION

We were invited to exhibit at the Panama Pacific Exposition in San Francisco in 1914-1915. This was a World's Fair, and prizes were given for the best articles exhibited in various classifications. Our entire line of perfumes, toilet articles and household products was entered in competition with like products from all over the world, and were awarded the Gold Medal, both for the quality of the products, and the beauty of the packages. This Gold Medal appeared on all packages until it was replaced by the seal that is reconized and followed throughout the world as a consumer's guide to the highest quality of merchandise - The Good Housekeeping Seal of Approval.

NEW NAMES - NEW PACKAGES

Through the years, our chemists were following every avenue of research, improving products wherever possible, and discovering new ones that in every way measured up to the standards of the first one. Manufacturing methods were improved to the point that every product was the sum of perfection as to blending and handling. Then in 1929, the chemist suggested an entirely new line of cosmetics. They had it ready, the managers agreed, and the Avon line was presented to Representatives and customers. The household line was named "Perfection" and given its own trademark.

GOOD HOUSEKEEPING'S SEAL OF APPROVAL

In 1931, the first group of Avon Cosmetics were approved by Good Housekeeping, and from that time on, other groups were sent, tested, approved, and the Seal added to our packages. By 1936, our 50th Anniversary year, Good Housekeeping completed their tests and approved all Avon and Perfection products which came within their scope. All products added since that time bear the Seal of Approval.

A NEW POLICY - NATIONAL ADVERTISING

Steadily increasing business over a period of years without any advertising was a remarkable record, but with the celebration of a Golden Jubilee we changed our policy and began to advertise. All during 1936 and 1937, our advertisements appeared in Good Housekeeping. They are appearing now, telling the public that Avon products are unconditionally guaranteed and that our Representatives give the Avon service. We tell readers how convenient shopping the "Avon Way" is for them.

Calendar of Events

Late 1800's
David McConnell starts the California Perfume Company, at the age of 28, in a room in downtown Manhattan. He and his wife, Lucy, create and manufacture the first products. It is sold by the first Representative, Mrs. P.F.E. Albee, who recruits others to sell at the same time.

1894
Mr. McConnell expands to four floors in the Manhattan building.

1896
The first catalog is issued on Nobember 2. Text only (no pictures).

1897
The first laboratory is built, a three story wooden structure in Suffern.

1902
10,000 Representatives are now selling the company's products.

1903
The first branch is opened in Kansas City, Missouri.

1905
The first Outlook is published, with news and selling tips for Representatives.

1906
The first company advertisement appears. The product: Roses perfume. The magazine: Good Housekeeping.

1912
Over 5,000,000 products are sold during this year.

1914
A Canadian office is opened in Montreal.

1915
The company wins the Panama-Pacific International Exposition gold medal for quality and packaging.

1920
Sales reach the $1,000,000 mark.

1928
A line of new products, called "Avon" is introduced. It includes a toothbrush, cleaner and talc.

1932
Three week selling campaigns begin in August. Up to this time, Representatives have been asked to send in orders every month. As a result of the change, sales increase by over 70% during America's bleak Depression years. The first Specials also appear with products sold at less than regular prices.

1935
The company sponsors a national radio program, called "Friends", a twice weekly show of music and chatter.

1936
An important step is taken to reach customers in urban and suburban areas. Site of this experiment is the Midwest, where several cities, Kansas City, Wichita and Oklahoma City, are divided into territories. Each Territory is to be covered by a Representative with a manager in charge. Later, after the war, this is to become the universal Avon sales structure.

1937
The home office moves to 30 Rockefeller Plaza in New York City. David McConnell dies at age 79.

1939
On October 6, the California Perfume Company changes its name to Avon Products, Inc.

1942-45
The company joins the war effort, with over 50% of the Suffern plant converted to production for the Armed Forces. Among the items manufactured are insect repellent, pharmaceuticals, paratrooper kits and gas mask canisters.

1949
Avon now has 2,500 employees. 1,175 shareholders, 65,000 Representatives and $25 million in sales. The company has facilities in New York City, Suffern, Kansas City, Middletown, Chicago and Pasadena.

1951
The Atlanta distribution branch opens.

1952
The Newark distribution branch opens.

1954
On TV advertising, the "Ding-Dong, Avon Calling" bell is heard for the first time. Avon goes international with its entry into Puerto Rico and Venezuela.

1955
Sales brochures are introduced to support campaign selling.

1956
The Morton Grove shipping facilities opens.

1959
Monrovia shipping and warehousing facilities open.

1960
The Rye branch opens.

1964
On April 2, the New York Stock Exchange starts trading Avon stock. The "advance call-back" brochure selling plan is adopted, with Representatives leaving mini-brochures at customers homes, then returning for the orders.

1965
The Springdale laboratory distribution facilities open. A new research and development laboratory is completed in Suffern.

1968
Two week selling is introduced in the U.S. The first car decanter appears, launching our most successful decanter series.

1970
The Glenview distribution branch opens.

1971
Jewelry is first introduced in the U.S.

1972 to Present
Avon moves into new world headquarters at 9 West 57th Street in New York City. Sales top the billion dollar mark. Sales continue to climb worldwide. Avon continues to open new operations around the world each year.

Avon Products, Inc.

Pictured here are two contrasting buildings that have housed Avon through the years. On the left is the 1900 California Perfume Factory and on the right is the present Avon World Headquarters (50 stories) at 9 West 57th St., New York, NY.

1890s - TRADEMARKS OF QUALITY - 1988

It is interesting to see the changes that have been made over the years in the Avon trademark. As you may know, in the early days your Company was called the California Perfume Company. The founder, Mr. D. H. McConnell, selected this name for his flourishing perfume business because he had heard so many glowing accounts of the great beauty and abundance of flowers in the state of California. This name, however, was changed in the early 1930s to Avon . . .a name that today is known and respected in all parts of the world.

These labels and trademarks are given as reference only. Some dates may vary. Some early CPC products also have Chicago on the label. This label is very rare.

1888-1904

1904-1911

1911-1930

1929

1930-1936

1936-53

1940's

1953

1976

1978. . .

TOOTH TABLETS

TOOTH TABLET 1936-40
Aluminum lid on white glass bottom. Avon Tulip "A" on lid. OSP 36c, **CMV $55. mint, $75. MB.**

TOOTH TABLET 1934-36
Aluminum lid on white glass bottom. OSP 36c, **CMV $60., $80. MB.**

TOOTH TABLET 1921-23
(Left) Aluminum lid & clear glass bottom. OSP 25c, **CMV $60. mint.**
TOOTH TABLET 1923-24
(Right) Aluminum lid with white glass bottom. OSP 36c, **CMV $55. mint.** Both have same lid, different bottoms. Add $20. each in MB.

TOOTH TABLET 1906-1921
Painted metal top with clear glass bottom embossed with Calif. Tooth Tablet in glass. 2 different boxes. 1906 to 1921 lid is painted just under New York with Food & Drug Act 1906. OSP 25c, **CMV $70. mint, $90. MB each.**

CALIFORNIA TOOTH TABLET 1896-1905
Blue and white painted metal lid. Clear glass bottom has embossed California Tooth Tablet, Most Perfect Dentifrice. OSP 25c, **CMV $95. mint, 110. MB.**

FRAGRANCE JARS

AMERICAN BEAUTY FRAGRANCE JAR 1923-33
(Far Left) - Clear glass jar & lid. Red ribbon around neck. OSP, $2.95, **CMV, $75.**
LAVENDER FRAGRANCE JAR 1914-23
3 different sizes. Left - 5 1/2" high, 3" wide base. Center - 5 7/8" high, 3" wide base.

Right - 7" high, 3 9/16" wide base. OSP $2.50 each, **CMV $90. each size.** One on far right is 1st issue. Add $25. MB each.

AMERICAN BEAUTY FRAGRANCE JAR 1934-43
6 oz. glass jar and stopper. Red tassel around neck. OSP $2.75, **CMV $25. jar only mint, with tassel $40. MB.**

FRAGRANCE JAR 1946
Made of pink ceramic, white flower on pink lid. Very short issue. Does not say "Avon" on it. Also came with white, blue and green flowers on lid. OSP $2.75, **CMV $60., MB. Jar only mint $40.** Also came with white flowers on white lid.

AMERICAN BEAUTY FRAGRANCE JAR CUBES 1923
4 oz. can. OSP 48c, **CMV $50. mint.** Front and back view shown.

FRAGRANCE JAR CUBES 1943-49
3 oz. jar. OSP 85c, **CMV $25., $35. MB.**

ROSE FRAGRANCE JAR 1948-57
6 oz. 1st issue came out with clear rose shaped glass stopper. 1949 issue had frosted rose glass stopper. Both had red silk neck ribbon. OSP $3.50, **CMV $20.** clear stopper, $15. with stopper. Add $10. MB. each.

FRAGRANCE JAR LIQUID 1921
(Left) 4 oz. cork stopper, brown label. OSP 96c, **CMV $100., $115. MB.**
AMERICAN BEAUTY FRAGRANCE JAR LIQUID 1925
4 oz. bottle, brown label, metal cap. OSP 96c - **CMV $85. MB, $75. BO.**

FRAGRANCE JAR LIQUID 1934-36
6 oz. bottle, aluminum cap. Silver and blue label. OSP $1.75, **CMV $45. mint, $50. MB**
FRAGRANCE JAR LIQUID 1955-57
7 oz. white cap, gray label. OSP $1.39. **CMV $15., $20. MB.**

ROSE FRAGRANCE JAR TEST 1948
Dark amber glass. Was not sold. Test bottle at factory. **CMV $100.**

ROSE FRAGRANCE JAR SET 1948-57
Box contains one 6 oz. fragrance jar liquid. One 3 oz. fragrance jar cubes. One 8 oz. empty fragrance jar. **CMV $90. set MB.**

AMERICAN IDEAL

AMERICAN IDEAL PERFUMES 1911
Introductory size glass stoppered bottle with green neck ribbon and pink paper label with ladies face, in green box. OSP 60c, **CMV $160. MB, $120. BO mint.**

AMERICAN IDEAL INTRODUCTION LETTER 1914
Given to customers on trial size bottle of perfume. **CMV $20.**

AMERICAN IDEAL PERFUME "INTRODUCTORY SIZE" 1910
Glass stopper in round screw on wood box, gold label. OSP 75c, **CMV $120. BO.** Bottle in wood box, **$225. mint.**

AMERICAN IDEAL PERFUME 1913 only
(Right) Introductory size octagonal shaped glass stoppered bottle fits in wood box with screw on wood lid, paper label with ladies face. OSP 75c, **CMV $120. mint, $225. MB.** Both came with neck ribbons.

AMERICAN IDEAL PERFUME 1917
Glass stoppered bottle came in green box. 1 and 2 oz. size, gold neck and front label. Green neck ribbon. OSP $2.50 and $4.75. **CMV $180. MB, $140. BO.**

AMERICAN IDEAL PERFUME 1917
1/2 oz. glass stoppered bottle, green box, gold label on front and neck. Green neck ribbon. OSP 75c, **CMV $125. MB, $100. BO mint.**

AMERICAN IDEAL PERFUME 1910
Wood case with dark velvet lining holds 1 oz. glass stoppered bottle with green and gold label with ladies face. Neck ribbon matches inside of box. OSP $2., **CMV $200. MB, $150. BO mint.**

AMERICAN IDEAL PERFUME 1911
1 and 2 oz. size bottles, glass stopper. Ladies face on paper label in green box. OSP $2.50 and $4.75. **CMV $165. MB, $125. BO mint each.**

AMERICAN IDEAL PERFUME 1919
1 oz. with frosted flower embossed glass stopper. Green label. OSP $2.40. **CMV $125., $150. MB.**

AMERICAN IDEAL PERFUME 1930-33
1 oz. clear glass bottle with frosted glass stopper. In silver box. Label on top of bottle. OSP $2.40. **CMV $145. MB., $110. BO.**

AMERICAN IDEAL PERFUME 1925
Flaconette size embossed bottle with brass cap over long dabber glass stopper. OSP $1.10. **CMV $90. BO, $110. MB.**

AMERICAN IDEAL PERFUME 1941
1/8 oz. clear glass bottle, gold cap. Gold and blue label. OSP 75c. **CMV $35. BO, $55. MB.**

AMERICAN IDEAL PERFUME 1908
Glass Stoppered bottle came in 1 and 2 oz. size. Velvet lined wood box. Neck ribbon on bottle, gold front and neck label. OSP $2. and $3.75. **CMV $200. MB, $150. BO.**

AMERICAN IDEAL PERFUME 1925
1 oz. bottle with wide flat glass stopper. Green neck ribbon and gold and green label. OSP $2.40. **CMV $150. MB, $125. BO mint.**

AMERICAN IDEAL SACHET 1910
Box holds ribbed sided bottle with brass cap and ladies face on green and gold label. OSP 50c. **CMV $125. MB, $100. BO mint.**

AMERICAN IDEAL PERFUME 1941 only
3 dram glass stopper, paper neck tag. Name was changed to Apple Blossom in 1941. OSP $2.25. **CMV $120. ∫ø with tag, $150. MB.**

AMERICAN IDEAL POWDER SACHET 1923
(Right) Glass bottle, brass cap, green label. OSP $1.20. **CMV $120. BO mint - $115. MB.**

AMERICAN IDEAL SACHET 1908
Glass bottle with metal cap. 2 piece gold label. OSP 50c. **CMV $105. BO mint, $125. MB.**

AMERICAN IDEAL TALCUM 1911
Pink can with gold top. OSP 35c. **CMV $90., $115. MB.**

AMERICAN IDEAL TOILET SOAP 1911
Pink and gold metal can holds 1 bar of soap wrapped in same design as can. OSP 50c. **CMV can only $60., with wrapped soap $100 mint.**

AMERICAN IDEAL POWDER SACHET 1911
Large size sachet bottle with brass cap and lady on paper label. OSP $1. **CMV $65. BO Mint $85. MB.**

AMERICAN IDEAL TALCUM POWDER 1917
3 1/2 oz. glass jar, gold metal lid and gold label. OSP 75c. **CMV $90. BO, $115. MB.**

AMERICAN IDEAL COMPACT 1920
Contains face powder or rouge. Brass container with mirror on lid. OSP 59c. **CMV $65., compact only $50. mint.**

AMERICAN IDEAL FACE POWDER 1923
Green and gold box with green and gold label. OSP 96c. **CMV $50. MB, $45. powder box only mint.**

AMERICAN IDEAL SOAP 1923
One bar toilet soap in white paper with gold label. OSP 48c. **CMV $60. mint.**

AMERICAN IDEAL DOUBLE COMPACT 1921
Contains face powder and rouge. Made of solid brass. OSP $1.17. **CMV $70. MB. Compact only $60. mint.**

AMERICAN IDEAL TALCUM 1923-28
3 1/2 oz. glass jar, brass cap, gold and green label. OSP 72c. **CMV $90. BO mint, $115. MB.**

AMERICAN IDEAL FACE POWDER 1915
Green and gold box. OSP 75c. CMV $65.
MB, powder box only $50. mint.

AMERICAN IDEAL FACE POWDER 1922
Green box holds green and gold paper
container. OSP 96c. CMV $45., $60. MB.

AMERICAN IDEAL TALCUM 1928
Frosted glass bottle with brass lid, gold &
green label. OSP 75c. CMV $75. MB - $70.
BO.

AMERICAN IDEAL FACE POWDER 1925
Green & gold box. OSP 96c. CMV $45. mint,
$60. MB.

AMERICAN IDEAL CREAM DELUXE 1923
White glass jar with CPC on metal lid. Gold &
green label. OSP 96c. CMV $55. MB - $40.
jar only mint.

AMERICAN IDEAL PERFUME 1929
1 oz. glass stoppered bottle in green satin lined
box. Paper label on top of bottle. OSP $2.20.
CMV $150. MB - $110. BO mint.

AMERICAN IDEAL TOILET SOAP 1920
White box, green label. OSP 48c. CMV $75.
MB.

AMERICAN IDEAL TOILET SOAP 1925
Green box holds 2 bars. OSP 96c. CMV $90.
MB.

(Left to Right)
AMERICAN IDEAL PERFUME 1919
1 & 2 oz. glass bottle with glass stopper, green
& gold label, green box, green neck ribbon.
OSP $2.40 $ $4.65. CMV $150. MB - $125.
BO.

AMERICAN IDEAL PERFUME 1923
Introductory size bottle. Glass bottle &
stopper. Green label & neck ribbon. OSP 75c.
CMV in green box $135. BO, $110. mint.

Also came with octagonal glass stopper set in
cork with long dabber. Same CMV.

AMERICAN IDEAL SACHET POWDER 1919
Glass bottle with brass cap, green label. OSP
$1.20. CMV $80. BO - $110. MB.

AMERICAN IDEAL TOILET WATER 1923
2 & 4 oz. glass stoppered bottle with green
front & neck label & neck ribbon. Green box.
OSP $1.50 & $2.85. CMV $140. MB - $115.
BO mint.

AMERICAN IDEAL LIPSTICK 1929
CPC on green metal tube. OSP $1. **CMV $35. tube only, $45. MB.**

AMERICAN IDEAL SET 1919
Green silk lined box holds 1 oz. glass stoppered American Ideal perfume, powder sachet, bottle of talcum powder & toilet soap. All have green labels. OSP set $5.50. **CMV $450. MB.**

AMERICAN IDEAL BOX C SET 1911
Flip top box holds glass stoppered perfume & powder sachet. OSP 50c. **CMV $300. MB.**

AMERICAN IDEAL FOURSOME SET 1925
Green box holds 1 oz. bottle with glass stopper of perfume, glass bottle of talcum, green box of face powder & white jar of vanishing cream. OSP $6.50. **CMV $400. MB.**

AMERICAN IDEAL SET 1911
Large fancy box with green lining holds American Ideal talcum powder, powder sachet, 1 oz. glass stoppered perfume & bar of toilet soap in pink soap can. OSP $4. **CMV $500. MB.**

AMERICAN IDEAL THREESOME 1923
Green box contains 2 oz. toilet water, bottle of sachet & glass bottle of talc. Green & gold label. OSP $3.95. **CMV $350. MB.**

AMERICAN IDEAL PERFUMES
Shown for the different sizes of bottles, glass stoppers. **CMV same as bottles listed with the same labels.**

AMERICAN IDEAL PERFUME "INTRODUC-TORY SIZES" 1913
2 different size glass stopper bottles & labels are different size. **CMV $120. each Mint.**

AMERICAN IDEAL POWDER SACHET 1917
2 piece label on front. Rare with this label. Metal cap. **CMV $125. Mint.**

ARIEL THREESOME 1932-33
Blue & silver compact, blue & silver Avon face powder & Ariel flaconette with brass cap. In silver & blue box. OSP $3.12. **CMV $145. MB.**

ARIEL PERFUME "RIBBED" 1933-36
(Left) 1/2 oz. ribbed glass bottle with black octagonal cap & gold label. Came in Gold Box Set. **CMV $45. mint.**
ARIEL PERFUME 1933-36
(Right) Small six sided octagonal shaped bottle with black octagonal cap. Came in Little Folks set and Handkerchief set. Has silver label. **CMV $45. mint.**

ARIEL BATH SALTS 1933-37
8 1/2 oz. ribbed glass, navy blue cap. Silver & blue label. OSP 63c. **CMV $60. MB - $40. BO mint.**
ARIEL BATH SALTS 1929-30
10 oz. clear glass with chrome cap, silver & blue label. **CMV $60. BO - $75. MB.**

ARIEL POWDER SACHET 1932-36
(Left) 1 1/4" oz. ribbed glass. Dark blue cap. OSP 78c. **CMV $28. - $33. MB.**
ARIEL SACHET 1930-32
(Right) Metal cap, silver & blue label. OSP 78c. **CMV $60. mint - $75. MB.**

ARIEL PERFUME 1930
(Right) 1 oz. glass stoppered bottle with small silver label. Silver box. OSP $2.50. **CMV $120. BO - $150. MB.**
ARIEL PERFUME FLACONETTE 1930
(Left) Brass cap over glass stoppered embossed bottle. OSP 84c. **CMV $90. BO mint - $115. MB.**

ARIEL BATH SALTS SAMPLE 1933-37
Small ribbed glass bottle with dark blue or black octagonal shaped cap. Silver label. **CMV $60. mint.**
ARIEL TOILET WATER 1930-35
2 oz. glass stoppered bottle, small label on top of bottle. Came in silver & blue box. OSP $1.75. **CMV $110. B) - $135. MB.**

ARIEL PERFUME 1930
1 oz. glass stoppered bottle, large silver & blue label. Came in silver box. OSP $2.50. **CMV $105. BO mint - $135. MB.**

ARIEL FACE POWDER 1930-36
Silver & blue round box in special issue 1935 red Christmas box. OSP 78c. **CMV $12. container only mint - $16. MB as shown in Christmas box - or $13. In regular issue box on left.**

ARIEL SET NO.2 1931-33
(Right) Silver & blue round box in special issue 1935 red Christmas box. OSP 78c. **CMV $12. container only mint - $16. MB as shown in Christmas box - or $13. in regular issue box on left.**

DAPHNE

DAPHNE TALCUM 1931-36
Silver and blue can with blue cap. OSP 35c.
CMV $20., $30. MB. Same can in gold color.
CMV $35. Silver and blue can in large 1 Lb.
family size. OSP $1. **CMV $30. can only.**
$40. MB.

DAPHNE TALCUM CHRISTMAS BOX 1943
Pale blue and pink outer box issued only at
Christmas 1943 with cardboard large size talc
with top & bottom cover caps. OSP 98c. **CMV**
$40. MB as shown. Talc only $30. mint.

DAPHNE TALCUM 1936-43 THEN 1946-50
(Right) 2.75 oz. turquoise & white can,
turquoise cap. OSP 37c. **CMV $8., MB $10.**
DAPHNE TALCUM 1936-43 THEN 1946-50
(Left) 14.5 Turquoise and white can, turquoise
cap. OSP $1.19. **CMV $20. MB $25.**

DAPHNE TALCUM
Silver can in 2 special boxes. 49 Year box on
left 1935 & 50th Year box on right 1936. OSP
20c. **CMV mint & boxed only in either box**
$50. each. Also came in gold can in 50th year
box. **CMV $60. MB.**

DAPHNE TALCUM CHRISTMAS PACKAGE
1940-41
Outer sleeve fits over short issue blue
Christmas box with white Christmas tree.
Holds large size 14.5 oz. metal talc turquoise
and white can of Daphne Talcum. Can only
sold 1936-50. OSP 89c. **CMV $40. MB as**
shown.

DAPHNE PERFUME 1925
1 and 2 oz. glass bottle with flat glass stopper.
Bottle and top of stopper have embossed
flowers. Came in green and gold box, gold
label and green neck ribbons. OSP $1.95 and
$3.45. **CMV $135. BO $175. MB.**

DAPHNE TALCUM 1933-36
(Left) Metal can came in sets only. **CMV $35.**
mint.
DAPHNE TALCUM 1943-46
(Right) Turquoise & white paper box. No top
cover, bottom cover, cap only. Family size.
OSP $1.19. **CMV $30. MB.**

DAPHNE TALC 52nd ANNIVERSARY 1938
only
Turquoise & white can in special box sold for
10c during 52nd anniversary campaign. **CMV**
$32.50 in box shown.

DAPHNE TALCUM 1937 only - 51st
ANNIVERSARY
Special box was given to Avon customers with
any purchase. **CMV $25. MB as shown.**

DAPHNE

DAPHNE TALC MAY POLE BOX 1940 ONLY
Yellow box with dancing girls around May Pole holds regular issue 2.75 oz. Daphne Talc. can. Sold in May 1940 for 10c with regular order from Avon lady. CMV $30. MB as shown.

DAPHNE POWDER SACHET 1922
Brass cap, green and gold square label. OSP 96c. CMV $90. BO mint, $115. MB.

DAPHNE PERFUME 1925-30
Clear glass, brass cap, box is brown, yellow & green. Came in Jack & Jill Jungle Jinks Set. CMV $60. MB.

DAPHNE GLYCERINE SOAP 1925
Green box & wrapping with gold labels. Two bars of soap. OSP 72c. CMV $90. MB.

DAPHNE FACE POWDER VANITY COMPACT 1917
Green box, came in white, pink & brunette tints. OSP 75c. CMV $45. MB. Same box also came in Daphne Rouge. Same CMV, $30. compact only mint.

DAPHNE PERFUME 1916
1 & 2 oz. bottles shown with frosted glass stoppers. Also came in 1/2 oz. size. Each came in green box. OSP $1., $1.90 & $3.50. CMV $120. BO, $145. MB.

DAPHNE TOILET WATER 1923
Green box holds 2 or 4 oz. size bottle with frosted glass stopper, gold front & neck label, green neck ribbon. OSP $1.20 & $2.25. CMV $105. BO, $135. MB. Came with 2 different glass stoppers set in cork as pictured & outer box. CMV for both boxes $140. MB.

DAPHNE DOUBLE VANITY COMPACT 1917
Contained face powder & rouge. Green compact with mirror on lid. OSP $1. CMV $60., $50. compact only mint.

DAPHNE VANITY COMPACT 1917
Face powder, came in white, pink & brunette. Green compact with mirror on lid. OSP 50c. CMV $45. MB, $35. compact only mint.

DAPHNE DERMA CREAM 1925
White glass jar 1/2" thick green lid. Came in Septette Gift box. CMV $40. mint.

DAPHNE CERATE 1925
1/2" thick white glass jar, green lid. Came in Septette gift box. CMV $40. mint. Also came in large size jar.

DAPHNE POWDER SACHET 1920
Brass cap & gold label. OSP 96c. CMV $80. mint, $100. MB.

DAPHNE PERFUME 1922
1/4 oz. vial given to customers for each $5.
order in March 1922. **CMV $155. MB, $130.
BO mint.**

DAPHNE TALCUM POWDER 1923
4 oz. green can, brass cap. OSP 48c. **CMV
$75, MB, $65. can only.**
**DAPHNE ROLLING MASSAGE CREAM
1923**
White glass jar with CPC on metal lid, gold
label. OSP 69c. **CMV $45., $50. MB.**

DAPHNE CERATE 1923
White glass jar with CPC on metal lid, gold
label. Small & large size jars. OSP 72c &
$1.35. **CMV $45., $50. MB.**
DAPHNE DUPLEX COMPACT 1923
Green compact & puffs, mirror on lid. OSP
98c. **CMV $45., $55. MB.**

DAPHNE CERATE 1926
1/2" thick white glass jar, solid green lid says
Daphne CPC Cerate on top. Also came in
Daphne Derma Cream. Came in Septette gift
box set. **CMV $35. each mint.**

DAPHNE THREESOME 1923
Green box contains 2 oz. toilet water, bottle of
sachet & can of talc. OSP $3.20. **CMV $325.
MB.**

DAPHNE LIPSTICK 1919
Metal case. Daphne on case. OSP 50c. **CMV
$50. mint - $60. MB.**

DAPHNE CREAMS 1929
Square white glass jars with ribbed sides &
CPC on aluminum lids & gold labels. Came in
Daphne Cerate, Daphne Derma Cream &
Daphne Rolling Massage Cream. OSP 75c.
CMV $50. each MB, $40. jar only.
DAPHNE BATH SALTS 1925
Ribbed glass jar with brass lid, gold label.
OSP 98c. **CMV $65. MB, $50. BO.**

DAPHNE SET 1918
Green box holds Daphne Perfume in 1 oz. glass stoppered bottle, green box of Daphne Face Powder & green box of Daphne rouge. OSP $3.50. **CMV $210. MB.**

DAPHNE LIPSTICK 1925
2-1/8" metal lipstick has embossed name & CPC on side. OSP 39c. **CMV $25. mint, $35. MB.**

DAPHNE CREAMS 1926
Large & small size glass jars with gold and green labels and green lids. Came in Daphne Derma Cream & Daphne Rolling Massage Cream. Came in large size jars only. OSp 72c. **CMV $50. each MB, $45. jar only.**

DAPHNE EYEBROW PENCIL 1925
Metal tube in box. **CMV $25. mint, $35. MB.**

DAPHNE POWDER SACHET 1915
Brass cap, brown flower label. Flower box. **CMV $90. BO, $115. MB.**

DAPHNE TALCUM 1944-46
Turquoise and white paper container. Plastic cap. OSP 39c. **CMV $20. mint.**

MISSION GARDEN

DAPHNE SEPTETTE GIFT BOX 1925
Green box holds jar of Derma Cream, jar of Cerate, green box of face powder, rouge compact, can of talcum, 1 oz. bottle of toilet water & flaconette of perfume. All in Daphne fragrance. OSP $2.95. **CMV $500. MB.**

MISSION GARDEN PERFUME 1922-25
1 1/2 oz. bohemian glass bottle with frosted sides & frosted glass stopper. Satin lined tan box. OSP $4.95. **CMV $200. MB, $150. BO mint.**

MISSION GARDEN TOILET WATER 1922
2 & 4 oz. glass bottle with frosted glass stopper. Gold label on front & neck. OSP $2.25 and $4.35. **CMV $135. BO, $165. MB.**

MISSION GARDEN DOUBLE COMPACT 1922
Contains face powder & rouge. Made of solid brass. OSP $1.45. **CMV $45., $55. MB.**

MISSION GARDEN PERFUME 1925
Flaconette size, gold box, embossed glass bottle with glass stopper. Brass cap over stopper. OSP $1.20. **CMV $95. BO, $115. MB.**

MISSION GARDEN PERFUME 1925
1 oz. glass bottle, flat embossed glass stopper. Satin lined gold box. OSP $2.85. **CMV $110. BO, $140. MB.** Also came in 2 oz. size. **$150. MB.**

MISSION GARDEN COMPACT 1925
Mission Garden CPC on edge of compact. Embossed brass case in single or double compact. OSP 98c and $1.48. **CMV $60. each MB, $45. compact only.**

MISSION GARDEN FLACONETTE 1926
Glass tube of perfume in brass case. Sold at Easter time. OSP 98c. **CMV $100. MB. Tube in case only $85.**

MISSION GARDEN TALC 1925
4 oz. red & gold can, brass cap. Came in Mission Garden Threesome Set only. **CMV $85. mint.**

MISSION GARDEN SACHET POWDER 1922
Glass bottle with brass cap & gold label. OSP $1.75. **CMV $90. BO, $110. MB.**

MISSION GARDEN FLACONETTE 1922
Brass tubes and cap with gold label on the tube. Holds clear glass vial with blue stripes and steel cap, glass stopper. OSP 98c. **CMV $100. mint as shown. Metal case only $60. mint.**

MISSION GARDEN TALC SET 1923
2 cans of Mission Garden Talc was a gift set to CPC employees. Red and gold silk lined box. **CMV $225. MB.**

MISSION GARDEN THREESOME 1925
Satin lined gold box holds 1 oz. Mission Garden Perfume, Talc & gold compact. OSP $7. **CMV $325. MB.**

NATOMA - NATOMA ROSE

NATOMA ROSE PERFUME 1914-15
1/2 oz. glass stoppered bottle with front & neck label. Green ribbon, green snap shut box. OSP 40c. **CMV $175. MB, $140. BO.**

NATOMA ROSE PERFUME 1915
1 oz. glass stopper bottle, green front and neck label. Green neck ribbon in green felt box. OSP 40c. **CMV $140. BO mint, $175. MB.**

NARCISSUS

NARCISSUS PERFUME 1929-30
1 oz. glass stoppered bottle. Came in silver, blue & gold box. Blue label on top of bottle. OSP $2.20. **CMV $110. BO, $175. MB.**

NARCISSUS PERFUME 1925
1 oz. glass bottle with frosted embossed glass stopper. Bottle in blue & gold box, blue label & neck ribbon. OSP $2.19. **CMV $120. BO mint, $175. MB.**

NARCISSUS PERFUME 1931-34
1 oz. glass stoppered bottle came in silver & blue box, label on top of bottle. Same as 1929 perfume only box is changed. OSP $2.25. **CMV $115. BO, $150. MB.**
NARCISSUS PERFUME FLACONETTE 1925
Embossed bottle with glass stopper with long glass dobber under brass cap. OSP 84c. **CMV $95. BO mint, $115. MB.**

NATOMA ROLLING MASSAGE CREAM 1918-21
Metal screw on lid, green paper label. OSP 75c. **CMV $135., $160. MB.**

NATOMA MASSAGE CREAM 1911
1st issue glass jar, cork lid stopper. Side, neck & lid labels. OSP 75c. **CMV $125., $150. MB.**

NATOMA ROSE PERFUME 1915
1 oz. bottle, glass stoppered, front and neck label. OSP 60c. **CMV $140. BO mint, $165. MB.**

NATOMA ROSE ART OF MASSAGE BOOKLET 1913
10 page booklet on giving a massage with Natoma Massage. **CMV $20.**

NATOMA TALCUM POWDER 1915
(Left) 2" tall Brass top. Came in 1915 Juvenile Set only. **CMV $175.** Also came 3 1/2 oz. regular size on right. OSP 33c. **CMV $125. mint.**

NATOMA ROSE PERFUME 1916
(Left) 1/2 oz. glass stoppered bottle, green riibbon on neck, green neck & front label. Green box. OSP 40c. **CMV $140. BO mint, $175. MB.**

NATOMA ROSE PERFUME 1914-21
(Right) 1 oz. clear glass, glass stopper, green label. OSP $1.40. **CMV $175. MB, $140. BO mint.**

NATOMA ROSE PERFUME 1914-21
Green box , holds 1,2 or 4 oz. size glass stoppered bottle with green front & neck label with green neck ribbon. OSP $1.40, $2.75 & $5.25. **CMV $175. MB, $150. BO.**

NATOMA TALCUM POWDER 1911
3 1/2 oz. metal can. Brass cap. Label and cap a little different from 1915 issue. OSP 25c. **CMV $150. MB as shown. Can only mint, $125.**

NATOMA ROLLING MASSAGE CREAM 1914-17
Glass stoppered jar with front & neck label. OSP 50c. **CMV $165. mint, $190. MB.**

NATOMA LEATHER TABLE COVER 1913
Full size sheep skin leather cover with Natoma Indian head or male Indian head in center. Laid out like a baseball field. Given to Reps for meeting sales goals. **CMV $350.**

NATOMA ROSE TALCUM 1914-21
4 oz. green can with pink roses, brass cap. 3 different. 1 has green sifter cap, one brass cap and one has flowers painted on top of can and brass cap. **CMV flower top can $130., $155. MB.** OSP 25c. **CMV $110. mint, $125. MB.**

NATOMA ROLLING MASSAGE CREAM 1912
Green front label, white label on back side. Aluminum lid. Label does not say NATOMA, only Indian Head & CPC. 5 oz. white glass jar. Rare. **CMV $150. mint.**

NATOMA ROSE SAMPLE
1 oz. bottle with atomizer. Green Natoma labels. Back label says bottle is a free sample. Rare. **CMV $175. mint.**

TRAILING ARBUTUS PERFUME 1923
(Left) 2 oz. glass stoppered bottle. Basket design front label and neck label. OSP $2.10. **CMV $125. BO mint, $150. MB.**
TRAILING ARBUTUS PERFUME 1933-36
(Right) Small 6 sided octagonal bottle and black cap came in Little Folks Set and Handkerchief set. Silver label. Came with CPC or CPC Avon Products, Inc. division label. **CMV $45. mint.**

TRAILING ARBUTUS

TRAILING ARBUTUS PERFUME 1928-29
Came in 1 & 2 oz. glass stoppered bottle with blue label. Blue box. OSP $1.20 & $2.10. **CMV $160., MB $120. BO.**

TRAILING ARBUTUS PERFUME 1915
Fancy embossed box holds glass stoppered bottle with front & neck label. Came in 1, 2 & 4 oz. size. OSP $1.10, $2.10 & $4. **CMV $175. MB $140. BO mint.**

TRAILING ARBUTUS PERFUME FLACON 1926
Frosted ribbed glass with long glass stopper under CPC embossed brass cap. Front paper label. OSP 59c. **CMV $90. mint with brass cap and label, $110. MB.**
TRAILING ARBUTUS TALCUM REFILL CAN 1918
1 lb. metal can with brass finish. Front paper label. **CMV $75. mint in new condition.**

TRAILING ARBUTUS PERFUME 1940-42
3/8 oz. bottle, gold octagonal cap. Gold speckled box. OSP $1.50. **CMV $60. BO mint, $85. MB.**

TRAILING ARBUTUS TOILET WATER 1933-34
2 oz. ribbed glass, black cap. Silver label. OSP 75c. **CMV $50. BO mint. $60 MB.**
TRAILING ARBUTUS TOILET WATER 1915
2 oz. clear glass bottle with blue & gold front & neck label. Metal crown stopper set in cork. OSP 35c. **CMV $140. BO mint, $155. MB.**

TRAILING ARBUTUS VEGETABLE OIL SOAP SAMPLE 1925
Small 2" X 1 1/8" size sample bar. **CMV $50. mint.**

TRAILING ARBUTUS COLD CREAM SAMPLE 1925
Small sample tube in box marked sample. Came with CPC instruction sheet. **CMV $65. MB $40. tube only mint.**

TRAILING ARBUTUS PERFUME 1923 ONLY
1 oz. travelers bottle, gold labels. Metal cap over glass stopper. Short issue. OSP 78c. **CMV $150., $175. MB.**

TRAILING ARBUTUS PERFUME 1930
1/2 oz. bottle with frosted glass stopper, silver label. **CMV $95. mint.**

TRAILING ARBUTUS PERFUME 1941-45
1/8 oz. bottle, white paper label, brass cap. OSP $1. **CMV $35. BO mint., $40. MB.**

TRAILING ARBUTUS SACHET 1915
Brass cap, flowered label, clear glass, 2 different labels. OSP 60c. **CMV $90. BO mint each, $115. MB.**

TRAILING ARBUTUS ROUGE 1928-29
Blue box. OSP 40c. **CMV $35. in box.** Rouge only $30. mint.

TRAILING ARBUTUS FACE POWDER 1928-29
Blue & pink box. OSP 35c. **CMV $45. in box. $35. powder box only mint.**

TRAILING ARBUTUS FACE POWDER 1925
Blue box. OSP 33c. **CMV $55. MB., $40. powder box only mint.**

TRAILING ARBUTUS BATH POWDER 1925
Blue 1 lb. size can with brass cap. This label says only "Trailing Arbutus Bath Powder". OSP 89c. **CMV $95. MB, $80. can only mint.**

TRAILING ARBUTUS TALCUM POWDER 1920
16 oz. Blue can, brass cap. OSP 89c. **CMV $85. MB, $70. can only mint.**

TRAILING ARBUTUS VEGETABLE OIL SOAP 1925
Blue box holds 3 embossed soap bars. OSP 39c. **CMV $110. MB.**

TRAILING ARBUTUS COLD CREAM CAN 1925-30
Came in Jack & Jill Jungle Set, gold can with blue and pink lid. Box is brown, yellow and green. Also came in plain brown CPC box. **CMV $40. MB.**

TRAILING ARBUTUS TALCUM POWDER, 1914
4 oz. blue can. 1914-17 can had brass sifter cap with grooved edge. **CMV $85. MB, $70. can only.** 1917-29 can came with removable brass cap. OSP 33c. **CMV $70. MB, $45. can only.** Both came with "The Story of Italian Talc" in box. 2 different labels on can. With the top section of can all gold, rare - $110.

TRAILING ARBUTUS TALCUM POWDER SAMPLE 1914
Small blue sample can, gold cap. Front of box in English and back side in French. **CMV $85. mint, $105. MB.**

TRAILING ARBUTUS CREAMS 1928-29
Large & small round white glass jars with CPC on blue lids. Came in cold cream & vanishing cream. OSP 33c & 59c. **CMV $55. MB, jar only $45. each.**

BRILLANTINE 1923
A hair dressing with Trailing Arbutus perfume scent. Glass bottle with frosted glass stopper. Blue front & neck label. OSP 39c. **CMV $125. BO mint, $150. MB.**

TRAILING ARBUTUS PERFUME 1925
1 and 2 oz. sizes. Ribbed bottle with glass stopper. Came in blue box. Front and neck lael. OSP $1.17 and $2.10. **CMV $115. BO, $140. MB.**

TRAILING ARBUTUS POWDER SACHET 1925
Brass cap and blue & green label with pink flowers. Rare label is all pink with black border. Same CMV. OSP 72c. **CMV $90. BO mint, $110. MB.**

TRAILING ARBUTUS TOILET WATER 1925
2 and 4 oz. sizes. Ribbed bottle with metal and cork cap. OSP 59c and $1.08. **CMV $80. BO., $100. MB.**

TRAILING ARBUTUS BATH POWDER 1925-29
4 3/4 oz. blue can and cap. OSP 35c. **CMV $80. MB, $65. can only mint.**

TRAILING ARBUTUS BATH POWDER 1925-29
1 lb. size blue can with brass cap. OSP 89c, 2 different labels on front and top of can. This can says only "Bath Powder". **CMV $100. MB, $80. can only mint.**

TRAILING ARBUTUS SEXTETTE BOX 1925
Box only showing label in center of box. **CMV box only $40. mint.**

TRAILING ARBUTUS CREAMS 1925
Large and small white glass jars of Cold
Cream and Vanishing Cream. CPC on blue or
plain aluminum metal lids. OSP 33c and 59c.
CMV $55. each MB, jar only $45. mint.
**TRAILING ARBUTUS COLD CREAM TUBE
1925**
Large and small size. Blue tubes. OSP 23c
and 45c. **CMV $45. MB, tube only $35. mint.**

TRAILING ARBUTUS THREESOME 1923
Blue box contains 2 oz. bottle of toilet water, 4
oz. can of talcum & bottle of sachet powder.
OSP $1.85. **CMV $300. MB.**

TRAILING ARBUTUS GIFT BOX 1915
Red, green & pink box contains Trailing
Arbutus talcum can, powder sachet & 4 oz.
toilet water. OSP $1.25. **CMV $350.**

TRAILING ARBUTUS SEXTETTE SET 1925
Large blue box holds white glass jar of Trailing
Arbutus Cold Cream & Vanishing Cream. Both
have blue lids. Blue can of Talcum Powder,
blue box of Face Powder & 2 bars of
Vegetable Oil Soap. OSP $1.59. **CMV $365.
MB.**

**TRAILING ARBUTUS SEXTETTE GIFT BOX
1928-29**
Blue box holds 2 bars Vegetable Oil Soap,
Cold Cream jar & Vanishing Cream jar, box of
Face Powder & can of Talcum Powder. All are
trimmed in blue & have Trailing Arbutus labels.
OSP $1.60. **CMV $350. MB.**

VERNAFLEUR
All CPC'S MUST BE NEW MINT CONDITION
FOR CMV

ATOMIZER PERFUME 1928
2 oz., 5 3/4" tall. Green frosted bottle with gold
plated top. Came in Vernafleur Perfume. Is
not marked Avon or CPC. OSP $2.50. **CMV
$80. BO. mint, $110. MB.**
VERNAFLEUR TOILET WATER 1928
4 oz. Ribbed glass - CPC brass crown top,
front & neck label. OSP $1.35. **CMV $90. BO.
mint, $110. MB.**

VERNAFLEUR PERFUME 1931-33
1 oz. bottle with plastic sealed cork stopper,
silver and blue label. Silver box. **CMV $70.
BO. mint, $100. MB.**

VERNAFLEUR

VERNAFLEUR PERFUME FLACON 1925
(Left) Brass cap over glass stopper with long glass dabber. OSP 69c. **CMV $90. - $110. MB.**

VERNAFLEUR PERFUME 1933-36
(Right) 2 1/4" tall - six sided bottle with black octagonal cap. Silver label. Came in sets only. **CMV $45. mint.**

VERNAFLEUR PERFUME 1928
1 oz. ribbed clear glass bottle, frosted glass stopper, front label, neck ribbon. OSP $1.17. **CMV $110. BO. mint, $135. MB.**

VERNAFLEUR SAMPLES 1923
3 different small glass vials with cork stoppers. one is 1 1/2" the other is 2" high & the fat one is 1 3/4" high. Not for sale on label. **CMV $75. each mint.**

VERNAFLEUR BATH SALTS 1927-29
Clear glass, brass cap. Sent to Representatives to give to each customer that orders $2. worth of merchandise. Representative must attain $45. in customer sales on January 1927 order. Offer expired Jan. 31, 1927. (Not a sample) Rare. **CMV $150. mint. $175. MB as shown with paper.**

VERNAFLEUR TOILET SOAP 1936-39
Turquoise & white box & wrapping holds 3 violet colored bars. OSP 77c. **CMV $60. MB.**

VERNAFLEUR BATH SALTS 1946
9 oz. jar, turquoise lid. Short issue. Special blu & white label. OSP 63c. **CMV $40. - $55. MB.** See Bath Salts Misc. section for regular issue.

VERNAFLEUR TOILET SOAP 1925-28
Gray box & wrapping holds 3 bars. OSP 69c. **CMV $110. MB.**

CHRISTMAS CHEER 1929
Red, white & blue boxes of Vernafleur Sachet Powder. Came in sets of 4 boxes. OSP $1.20. **CMV $50. each box.**

ATOMIZER GIFT SET 1933
Blue box with green & red holly leaves holds 1 oz. bottle of Vernafleur perfume with small silver label & 1 oz. red glass bottle with spray atomizer. OSP $2.86. **CMV $185. MB.**

VERNAFLEUR TOILET SOAP 1931-36
Lavender in color, in white wrapper. Box of 3 bars. OSP 75c. **CMV $60. MB.**

VERNAFLEUR FACE POWDER SAMPLE 1928
Adherent Powder sample. Came several in a box. OSP 48c per box of samples. **CMV $25. per box.**

VERNAFLEUR PERFUME EXTRACT 1923
1/4 oz. glass bottle with glass stopper. Neck label & ribbon. OSP 48c. **CMV $100. MB.,** **$80. BO.**

VERNAFLEUR ADHERENT POWDER 1923
Gray metal can. OSP 48c. **CMV $45. MB.,** **$35. can only.**

VERNAFLEUR PERFUME 1923
Gray box holds 1 oz. ribbed glass bottle with frosted glass stopper. Front & neck label. Green ribbon on neck. OSP 1 oz. size $1.44., 2 oz. size $2.70. **CMV $110. BO., $135. MB.**

VERNAFLEUR TOILET WATER 1923
2 & 4 oz. glass bottle with metal & cork shaker cap. OSP 74c & $1.35. **CMV $110. MB., $90. BO. mint.**

VERNAFLEUR TOILET WATER 1925
2 & 4 oz. Ribbed glass bottle with metal & cork cap. OSP 74c & $1.35. **CMV $85. BO., $100. MB.**

VERNATALC 1922
4 oz. can of Talc Powder. Gray. OSP 30c. **CMV $60. MB. Can only $50.**

VERNAFLEUR TISSUE CREAM 1923
White glass jar with ribs on sides. CPC on metal lid. Large & small size jars. OSP 48c & 89c. **CMV $45. MB. Jar only $35.**

VERNAFLEUR NUTRI CREAM 1923
Large & small white glass jar with ribs on sides. CPC on metal lid. OSP 48c & 89c. **CMV $45. MB, $35. Jar only.**

VERNAFLEUR BATH SALTS 1925
10 oz. glass bottle with brass lid, ribbed glass sides. OSP 75c. **CMV $85. MB, $70. Jar only mint.**

VERNAFLEUR PERFUME FLACON 1925
Flaconette size frosted ribbed bottle with glass stopper, brass cap over stopper. Small front label. CPC on cap. Comes in yellow & green box. OSP 70c. **CMV $90. with cap, $110. MB.**

VERNAFLEUR TISSUE CREAM 1928
Small & Large size white glass jar with ribbed sides. Came with or without CPC on aluminum lid. OSP 50c & 90c. **CMV $55. MB, $40. Jar only.**

VERNAFLEUR PERFUME 1928
1 oz. glass stoppered bottle, blue, yellow & black box. OSP $1.45. **CMV $150. MB, $110. BO. mint.**

VERNAFLEUR COMPACT 1928
Silver compact with Vernafleur on lid. Single & double compact. OSP $1. & $1.50. **CMV $45. MB, $35. compact only mint.**

VERNAFLEUR THREESOME GIFT BOX 1928
Gray box holds 2 oz. bottle of Vernafleur Toilet Water, jar of Vanishing Cream & can of Face Powder. OSP **$2.10. CMV $225. MB.**

VERNA TALC 1928
4 oz. multi-colored can, brass cap. OSP $1.15. **CMV $75. mint, $90. MB.**
VERNAFLEUR NUTRI CREME 1928
Large & small white glass jar with ribbed sides. CPC on aluminum lid. OSP 50c & 90c. **CMV $50. MB, $40. jar only mint.**
VERNAFLEUR TOILET SOAP 1928-31
Box holds 3 bars of soap in blue paper. OSP 75c. **CMV $90.**
VERNAFLEUR FACE POWDER 1925
Blue, yellow & black metal can. OSP 48c. **CMV $30. MB, $20. can only mint.** This was also called Vernafleur Adherent Powder.

VERNAFLEUR QUINTETTE SET 1929
Blue, black & gold box holds Vernafleur Tissue Cream & Nutri-Cream, Face Powder, Talc & Flaconette of Perfume. OSP $2.25. **CMV $350. MB.**

VERNAFLEUR BATH SET 1929
Black & gold box holds bottle of Vernafleur Bath Salts, Dusting powder in gold & black striped can & 1 bar of Vegetable Oil Soap. OSP $3.50. **CMV $250. MB.**

VIOLET
SEE MISCELLANEOUS CPC JARS
FOR OTHER VIOLET PRODUCTS.

VERNAFLEUR NUTRI-CREME SAMPLE 1925
(Left) Multi-colored tube, says on back side "not for Sale Sample." **CMV $50. MB, $40. tube.**
VERNAFLEUR FACE POWDER SAMPLE 1925
(Right) 1 1/2" small paper box used as sample. **CMV $50. mint.**

VIOLET ALMOND MEAL 1912
(Right) Glass jar with metal shaker lid. Came in 3 1/2 oz. & 3 3/4 oz. size. Two different labels. OSP 50c. **CMV $110., $130. MB.**

VIOLET ALMOND MEAL 1893
8 oz. glass jar with metal lid. OSP 50c. **CMV $145. MB, $125. jar only mint.**

VIOLET TOILET WATER 1915
(Left) 2 oz. bottle, metal crown stopper in cork, front & neck label. OSP 35c. **CMV $100. BO. mint, $125. MB.**

VIOLET TOILET WATER 1915
(Center) 1/4 oz. clear glass, cork stopper. Came only in 1915 Juvenile Set. Rare. **CMV $125. mint.**

VIOLET PERFUME 1915
(Right) Front & neck label, glass crown stopper in cork. OSP 50c. **CMV $175. mint.**

VIOLET WATER 1908
8 oz. glass bottle, glass stopper. Eureka Trade Mark label in color. Neck ribbon. **CMV $150.**

VIOLET TALCUM POWDER 1912
Blue paper sides, metal shaker top & metal bottom. Eureka Trade Mark label. **CMV $75. mint.**

VIOLET ALMOND MEAL 1908
(Left) 8 oz. Glass jar with metal lid. OSP 50c. **CMV $115. jar only mint, $135. MB.** 1910 issue same only Eureka Trade Mark in place of CP at top of label.

VIOLET PERFUME 1915
1 oz. size, cork stopper. Used with spray atomizer. Came in 1915 Violet Gift Box H set only. **CMV $100. mint.**

VIOLET TALCUM 1923
(Left) 3-1/3" oz. Violet & green colored can, brass cap. OSP 23c. **CMV $75. mint, $90. MB.**

VIOLET TOILET WATER 1916
(Right) 2 oz. bottle with metal crown pour cap in cork. Colorful front and neck label. OSP 35c. **CMV $100. BO. mint, $125. MB.**

VIOLET NUTRI-CREME 1912
(Left) Small & large size white glass jars with aluminum lid. OSP 50c & 90c. **CMV $55. each MB. $45. jar only mint.**

VIOLET NUTRI-CREME 1923
(Right) Large & small white glass jars with CPC on metal lid. OSP 49c & 89c. **CMV $45. each, $55. MB.**

VIOLET PERFUME 1896
New York label. Eureka trade mark. Round glass stopper. Colored flower box. **CMV $175. BO., $200. MB.**

VIOLET GIFT SET H 1915
Green, white & purple box contains bottle of Violet Talcum, 1 oz. Perfume bottle with cork stopper & Atomizer, Violet Powder Sachet. OSP $1.35. **CMV $435. MB.**

VIOLET ALMOND MEAL 1923
4 oz. sifter top metal can. 2 different labels.
OSP 48c. **CMV $60., $75. MB.**

VIOLET ALMOND MEAL 1907
8 oz. Clear glass - metal shaker top. OSP 50c.
CMV $110. jar only mint, $140. MB.

VIOLET THREESOME SET 1923
Contains 2 oz. bottle of Toilet Water, 3 & 1/3
oz. can of Talcum & bottle of Sachet Powder in
violet colored box. OSP $1.40. **CMV $325.
MB.**

VIOLET NUTRI-CREME 1910
White glass jar, aluminum lid. Paper label all
around jar. Bottom pat. Dec. 9, 1890. OSP
50c. **CMV $55. mint, $65. MB.**

BABY ITEMS - CPC

BABY SET 1923
Yellow box contains 2 oz. bottle of Toilet
Water, bar of Baby Soap & can of Baby
Powder. OSP 99c. **CMV $350. MB. - CMV
Toilet water only $125. mint.**

BABY SET 1910
Box with kids playing on lid holds 1905 Baby
Powder can, 2 oz. bottle of Violet Toilet Water
and box of Baby Soap. OSP 75c. **CMV $325.
MB.**

VIOLET TALCUM POWDER 1915
(Left) 3 1/2 oz. Glass jar, OSP 25c. **CMV
$110. MB, $90. BO.**
VIOLET TALCUM POWDER 1908
(Right) 3 1/2 oz. Glass jar with metal cap has
2 variations of labels. OSP 25c. **CMV $110.
Jar only mint $135. MB.**

California Baby Soap
Manufactured only by
CALIFORNIA PERFUME CO.
NEW YORK

CALIFORNIA BABY SOAP 1902
Box of one bar. OSP 15c. **CMV $75. mint.**

BABY POWDER 1898
Metal can. Eureka Trade Mark on label. OSP 25c. CMV $120. mint, $145. MB.

BABY SET 1925
Yellow box holds 4 oz. bottle of Supreme Olive Oil, 4 oz. yellow can of Baby Powder, yellow box of Boric Acid $ 5 oz. yellow cake of genuine imported Castile Soap. OSP $1.78. CMV $350. MB.
SUPREME OLIVE OIL FOR BABY'S 1925
4 oz. bottle with yellow label & cork stopper. Came in Baby Set only. CMV $100. mint.
CASTILE SOAP FOR BABY'S 1925
5 oz. cake wrapped in yellow paper. Came in Baby Set only. CMV $75. mint.
BORIC ACID FOR BABY 1925
Yellow Box with soldiers on top. OSP 33c. CMV $50.
BABY POWDER 1923
4 oz. Yellow can. OSP 29c. CMV $85. MB, can only $70.

CALIFORNIA BABY SOAP 1905
4 oz. white embossed bar in wrapping. OSP 15c. CMV $75. MB., $50. soap only.

BABY POWDER 1905
(Left) Metal can lift off cap 1905. 1906 cap has sifter top, CP in center of Trade Mark. 1910 same can sifter cap a little different and Eureka trade mark in place of CP. CMV $115., $135. MB.
BABY POWDER 1912-16
(Right) Metal can. OSP 25c. CMV $110. mint, $130. MB.

BABY POWDER 1916
(Top) Blue & pink can. OSP 25c. CMV $120. MB, $100. can only, mint.
BABY SET 1916
(Bottom) Baby set box holds can of baby Powder as pictured above, without box, bar of Baby Soap & 2 oz. bottle of Violet Toilet Water. OSP 75c. CMV $350. MB.

BAY RUM - CPC

ALSO SEE AVON BAY RUM SECTION.
ALL BOTTLES PRICED MINT.

BAY RUM 1896
(Left) 4 oz. glass stoppered bottle. OSP 40c. CMV $150. Also came in 8 & 16 oz. size with glass stoppers. OSP 75c & $1.25. CMV $150. each BO $200. MB.
BAY RUM 1905
(Right) 16 oz. size glass stopper. OSP $1.25. CMV $150. mint, BO $200. MB.

BAY RUM 1930-36
8 oz. clear glass bottle, black cap, green & black label. OSP 89c. CMV $40. BO mint, $50. MB.

BAY RUM 1898
4 oz. clear glass square bottle. Glass stopper. colored label. OSP 40c. CMV $190., $220. MB.

BAY RUM

BAY RUM 1908
(Left) 4 oz. glass stoppered bottle. OSP 40c.
CMV $135., BO $160. MB. Also came in 8 &
16 oz. size glass stoppered bottles. CMV
$140. each mint., $165. MB.

BAY RUM 1912
(Right) 4 oz. glass stoppered bottle. Also
came in 8 & 16 oz. size glass stoppered
bottles. OSP 40c. CMV $140. each mint,
$165. MB.

BAY RUM 1927
4 oz. metal & cork CPC embossed stopper.
Front & neck label. Also came in 8 "shown on
right" & 16 oz. size with cork stopper. OSP
50c. CMV $100. BO 4 oz., $120. 8 & 16 oz.
Add $25. for box, mint.

BAY RUM 1929
(Left) 16 oz. size with metal cap. OSP $1.44.
CMV $95. BO, $110. MB.

BAY RUM 1923
(Right) 4 oz. bottle, metal shaker cap in cork.
OSP 47c. CMV $95. MB, $85. BO. Also came
in 8 oz. OSP 84c, 32 oz. $2.40. CMV $95. BO
each, $110. MB.

LEFT TO RIGHT
BAY RUM 1915
4 oz. with crown metal & cork stopper. OSP
25c. CMV $125. mint. $150. MB.

BAY RUM 1921
4 oz. front & neck label. Cork stopper. OSP
47c. CMV $175. MB, $125. BO.

BAY RUM 1898
4 oz. cork stopper. 126 Chambers St. on label
where CPC started. Very rare. CMV $200. -
$240. MB.

BAY RUM 1920
4 oz. clear glass botle, glass stopper. CMV
$110. mint, $135. MB.

BAY RUM 1912
16 oz. clear glass, cork stopper. RARE. CMV
$150., $175. MB.

BAY RUM 1915
(Left) 4 oz. glass stopper. CPC logo label.
CMV $125. mint.

BAY RUM SUPERIOR 1898
4 oz. botle, 126 Chambers St., New York
address on label. Chrome crown stopper in
cork. CMV $175. mint.

BAY RUM 1930-36
4 oz. Ribbed glass bottle with black cap &
green label. OSP 50c. CMV $50. MB, $45.
BO. Also came in 16 oz. size OSP 89c. CMV
$50. BO $60. MB.

BAY RUM 1905
4 oz. glass stopper. CMV $140. mint.

BAY RUM 1936
4 oz. bottle sold 1930-36. Yellow label, Black
cap. Shown with red & green Christmas box.
Good House Keeping on label. CMV $50. BO,
$65. MB as shown.

CPC BOTTLES - MISC.

LAIT VIRGINAL 1900
2 oz., cork stopper. OSP 60c. **CMV $115. - $140. MB.**

BENZOIN LOTION 1915
(Left) 2 oz. size, metal crown stopper in cork. Flowered label. OSP 75c. Also came in 4 oz. size $1.50. **CMV $100. each mint - $125. MB.**
BENZOIN LOTION 1923
(Right) 2 oz. bottle with metal & cork stopper. OSP 59c. **CMV $75. - $100. MB.**

LIQUID SHAMPOO 1923
6 oz. front & neck label. Metal shaker cap in cork. OSP 48c. **CMV $90., $110. MB.**

FACE LOTION 1896
(Left) Glass bottle with cork stopper. OSP $1. **CMV $110. - $135. MB.**
FACE LOTION 1908
(Right) Glass bottle, cork stopper, front & neck label. OSP $1. **CMV $110. - $135. MB.**

BENZOIN LOTION 1925
(Left) 2 oz. ribbed glass bottle with metal & cork stopper, blue & gold label. OSP 59c. **CMV $75. BO, $90. MB.**
LAIT VIRGINAL 1896
(Right) 2 oz. size, ribbed glass bottle has ribbed glass stopper set in cork. OSP 65c. **CMV $150. mint, $175. MB.**

FACE LOTION 1912
(Left) 6 oz. clear glass botle, cork stopper. Front & neck label. Came in white & pink shades. OSP $1. **CMV $100. BO, $125. MB.**
LIQUID SHAMPOO 1914
(Right) 6 oz. glass bottle with metal cap. OSP 35c. **CMV $95. BO, $120. MB.**

FACE LOTION 1918
(Left) 6 oz. glass bottle has cork stopper, green front & neck label. Came with small sponge tied to neck. OSP $1. **CMV $80, $100. MB.**
FACE LOTION 1923
(Right) 6 oz. glass bottle, blue label, cork stopper. OSP 97c. **CMV $80, $100. MB.**

CUTICLE REMOVER OR SOFTENER 1929-30

(Left) 1/2 oz. bottle with brown label & cork stopper with glass dabber. Also came in Boudoir Set. OSP 35c. **CMV $70. BO, $85. MB.**

CUTRANE 1924

(Center) Glass bottle with cork stopper with camel hair brush on stopper. Gold & black label. OSP 30c. **CMV $70. BO mint, $85. MB.**

LIQUID FACE POWDER 1920

(Right) 6 oz. clear glass, cork stopper. Has green front & neck label. OSP 97c. **CMV $80. mint BO, $100. MB.**

EAU DE QUININE HAIR TONIC 1905

Glass stopper in cork. Eureka Trade Mark on neck label. OSP 65c. **CMV $125. - $150. MB.**

LAIT VIRGINAL 1910

2 oz. shown, metal crown in cork stopper. ALso came in 4 and 8 oz. size. Front and neck labels. OSP 65c, $1.25 and $2. **CMV $100. mint, $125. MB.**

EAU DE QUININE 1915

(Left) 6 oz. glass bottle with metal crown & cork cap. OSP 65c. **CMV $100. BO, $125. MB.**

EAU DE QUININE 1923

(Right) 6 oz. glass bottle, metal shaker cap in cork. OSP 69c. **CMV $90. BO, $110. MB.**

EAU DE QUININE 1900

(Left) 6 oz. bottle with sprinkler top. OSP 65c. **CMV $125. - $150. MB.**

EAU DE QUININE 1908

(Right) Glass bottle has cork stopper with metal cap. Front & neck label. Label has Eureka CP Trade Mark. OSP 65c. **CMV $125. - $150. MB.**

WITCH HAZEL 1924

Both bottles on left 8 oz. size, same label. Left is cork stopper and right is glass stopper. **CMV $85. cork stopper round bottle. $110. for glass stopper & square bottle.** Bottle on right is 1910, 8 oz. size glass stopper. **CMV $125. mint.**

WITCH HAZEL 1910

16 oz. clear glass, glass stopper. OSP 75c. **CMV $150. - $175. MB.**

WITCH HAZEL 1896
(Left) 4 & 8 oz. bottles came with sprinkler top. OSP 25c & 45c. **CMV $100.** Pint bottle came with glass stopper. OSP 75c. **CMV $150. mint, $200. MB.**

WITCH HAZEL 1905
(Right) 16 oz. size, glass stopper. OSP 75c. **CMV $150. mint, $200. MB.**

WITCH HAZEL 1915
(Left) 4 oz. glass bottle with cork stopper. OSP 25c. **CMV $90.** 8 & 16 oz. size with glass stopper. OSp 45c & 75c. **CMV $125. each mint, $145. MB.**

WITCH HAZEL 1924
(Center & Right) 4 oz. clear glass bottle, cork stopper. Front & neck label. 3 different labels. 2 shown. OSP 39c. **CMV $75. BO mint, $90. MB.**

ROSE WATER GLYCERINE AND BENZOIN 1930
4 oz. ribbed glass, black screw on cap. color label. **CMV $75.**

WITCH HAZEL 1908
(Left) 16 oz. size glass stopper. OSP 75c. **CMV $150. mint, $200. MB.**

WITCH HAZEL 1908
(Right) Came in 4, 8 & 16 oz. bottles with glass stopper. Eureka Trade Mark on label. OSP 25c, 45c & 75c. **CMV $150. mint, $200. MB.**

WITCH HAZEL 1920
(Left) 16 oz. clear glass, cork stopper. Front label. Rare. OSP 75c. **CMV $135. mint, $160. MB.** Also came in 8 oz. size with metal crown & cork stopper. OSP 45c. **CMV $100. Mint, $125. MB.**

WITCH HAZEL 1930
(Right) 4 oz. ribbed glass bottle, black cap, green label. Rare. **CMV $80. - $90. MB.**

WITCH HAZEL 1923
(Left) 4 oz. bottle with cork stopper, green front & neck label. OSP 39c. **CMV $75.** Also came in 8, 16 & 32 oz. size. OSP 69c, $1.20 & $2.25. **CMV each, $75. mint, add $25. MB each.**

WITCH HAZEL 1925
(Right) 4 oz. bottle with cork stopper, green label on front & neck. OSP 39c. **CMV each $75. mint, add $25. MB each.**

ROSE WATER GLYCERINE AND BENZOIN SAMPLE 1925
Small sample bottle on 1st introduction of this product in January 1925. Rare. **CMV $75., $85. MB.**

TOOTH WASH 1921
(Left) 2 oz. glass bottle, brass & cork stopper. OSP 25c. **CMV $100., $125. MB.**

TOOTH WASH 1923
(Right) 2 oz. glass bottle, metal and cork cap. Front & neck label. OSP 33c. **CMV $85., $110. MB.**

LOTUS CREAM 1917
12 oz. bottle has glass stopper. OSP $1.23.
CMV $160. 4 oz. bottle has cork stopper.
OSP 48c. CMV $120. Add $25. MB. each.
Both have front & neck labels. Also came in 1
quart, 1/2 & 1 gallon size.

TOOTH WASH 1908
(Left) Glass bottle has cork stopper with metal
crown top. Eureka Trade Mark on neck label.
OSP 25c. CMV $140. MB - $115. MB.

TOOTH WASH 1915
(Right) Glass bottle with metal & cork cap.
Back side of bottle is embossed California
Tooth Wash. OSP 25c. CMV $105. with label
mint. Embossed bottle only $25. - $130.
MB.

**ROSE WATER GLYCERINE & BENZOIN
1923**
(Left) 6 oz. clear glass bottle. Glass stopper
set in cork. Print front & neck label. OSP 60c.
CMV $100. - $125. MB.

**ROSE WATER GLYCERINE & BENZOIN
1924-25**
(Right) 6 oz. bottle with cork stopper. Front &
neck label. This was a very short issue bottle.
OSP 60c. CMV $100. BO, $125. MB.

**ROSE WATER GLYCERINE & BENZOIN
SAMPLE 1924**
Glass bottle, cork stopper. CMV $75. MB,
$60. BO mint.

**ROSE WATER GLYCERINE & BENZOIN
1929 ONLY**
(Left) 4 oz. clear glass ribbed bottle with black
cap. Bottle came from Avon with small sample
pink label marked not for resale. Bottle with
this label rare. CMV $100. mint BO.

**ROSE WATER GLYCERINE & BENZOIN
1926**
(Right) 4 oz. ribbed bottle with cork stopper,
front & neck label. OSP 50c. CMV $75. mint,
$90. MB.

LOTUS CREAM SAMPLE 1917
Blue and white box holds 1/2 oz. sample bottle
with cork stopper. Blue label. CMV $80. MB,
$65. BO. mint.

CALIFORNIA NAIL BLEACH 1900
Eureka Trade Mark New York label. Glass
stopper. 1 oz. size. CMV $135.

LOTUS CREAM 1925
4 oz. ribbed bottle with cork stopper, front &
neck label. OSP 48c. **CMV $85. BO mint,
$100. MB.**

**GERTRUDE RECORDON'S PEACH LOTION
1929 ONLY**
Clear glass. Box states "This merchandise
sent free for demonstration purposes or
personal use. It must not be sold." **CMV $100.
MB., $85. BO.**

BRILLIANTINE 1930 ONLY
(Left) 2 oz. bottle with frosted glass stopper in
cork. Silver label. OSP 50c. **CMV $75. mint,
$95. MB.**
DEODORANT 1930 ONLY
(Right) 2 oz. bottle with corked frosted glass
stopper. OSP 50c. **CMV $80. - $100. MB.**

HAIR TONIC EAU DE QUININE 1931-36
(Left) Ribbed glass bottle with black cap &
silver label. OSP 90c. **CMV $40. bottle only,
$45. in box.** Also came in 16 oz. size. OSP
$1.75. **CMV $50. BO mint, $55. MB.**
NULODOR 1928
(Right) Bottle has clear stopper, front & neck
label. OSP 35c. **CMV $120. mint. Rare.**

NAIL BLEACH - 1 OZ. 1912
(Left) 1 oz. bottle, cork stopper. OSP 25c.
CMV $100. - $115. MB.
DEPLIATORY 1915
(Right) 1 oz. bottle with cork stopper. OSP
50c. **CMV $100. - $120. MB.**

ROSE POMADE 1914
(Left) White glass jar. Top & side label. OSP
25c. **CMV $65.**
NAIL BLEACH - 2 OZ. 1912
(Right) 2 oz. clear glass round bottle, cork
stopper, front & neck label. OSP 25c. **CMV
$95. BO, $110. MB.**

NAIL BLEACH 1914
2 oz. round bottle with glass stopper, front
paper label. 2 different labels shown. OSP
25c. **CMV $90. BO, $110. MB. each.**

NAIL BLEACH 1916
2 oz. glass stopper, square bottle. Rare. OSP
25c. **CMV $125. BO, $150. MB.**

ROUGE 1908
Rouge powder can. **CMV $50., $70. MB.**
LIQUID ROUGE
Bottle. **CMV $100., $125. MB.** OSP each 25c.
Eureka trademark on both labels and CP in
center of early label instead of Eureka.

ROUGE 1916
(Left) Rough. OSP 25c. **CMV $45., $60. MB.**
LIQUID ROUGE 1916
(Right) Glass bottle, cork stopper. OSP 25c.
CMV $80. BO, $100. MB.

SHAVING SOAP 1905
(Left) 1 bar of soap. OSP 20c. **CMV $70. in wrapper, mint.**
BAYBERRY SHAVING STICK 1923
(Right) Three piece nickel metal container holds shaving soap. OSP 33c. **CMV $55. mint.**

SHAVING CREAM STICK 1915
Gold or silvertone metal can. Came with soap stick, CPC on lid. OSP 25c. **CMV $55. MB., $30. can only mint.**

CPC JARS

AUTOMASSAGE SHAVING BRUSH 1915
Automassage on handle. Rubber center of brush as shown. This was not made for CPC but sold by CPC on a special offer with CPC shaving powder. OSP 25c. **CMV $50. MB, $30. brush only.**

LAVENDER SALTS 1890s
(Left) Teal green glass, octagonal shaped bottle. Ground glass stopper. Rare. OSP 35c. **CMV $275. - $300. MB.**
LAVENDER SALTS - METAL TOP 1890s
(Right) Emerald green glass, glass stopper with screw on metal top. Rare. OSP 35c. **CMV $275. - $300. MB.**

LAVENDER SALTS 1893
(Left) Emerald green glass bottle with green glass stopper with leather liner. OSP 35c. **CMV $200. mint, $225. MB.**
LAVENDER SALTS 1915
(Right) Glass stoppered bottle. OSP 35c. **CMV $115. mint, $140. MB.**

LAVENDER SALTS 1923
Glass stoppered bottle, front & neck label. OSP 49c. **CMV $110. mint, $135. MB.**

LAVENDER SALTS 1910
Emerald green glass. Same label only 1 bottle is 1/8" bigger than the other. Green glass stoppers set in rubber. OSP 35c. **CMV $200. each mint, $225. MB.**

MASSAGE CREAM 1896
Glass jar with glass stopper. OSP 75c. **CMV $150. mint, $175. MB.**

SHAMPOO CREAM 1896
4 oz. glass jar. Man's picture, washing his hair on lid. Rare. OSP 35c. **CMV $125. - $150. MB.**

LAVENDER SALTS 1912
(Left) Glass stoppered bottle. OSP 35c. **CMV $110. - $135. MB.**

LAVENDER SALTS 1908
(Right) Green glass bottle has green glass stopper with rubber base. OSP 35c. **CMV $160. mint, $185. MB.**

LEMONOL CLEANSING CREAM 1926-30
Frosted glass jar with brass lid. OSP 50c. **CMV $75. MB, $65. jar only.**

DERMOL MASSAGE CREAM 1923
(Left) White glass jar with ribbed sides. CPC on metal lid. OSP 96c. **CMV $50. - $60. MB.**

VIOLET NUTRI-CREME 1926
(Right) White glass jar with flowered label. OSP 89c. **CMV $50. - $60. MB.**

MASSAGE CREAM 1916
Glass jar has glass stopper, green ribbon on neck. OSP 50c. **CMV $125. mint, $145. MB.**

SHAMPOO CREAM 1896
4 oz. white glass jar, metal lid. OSP 35c. **CMV $90., $110. MB.**

SHAMPOO CREAM 1905
4 oz. white glass jar. OSP 35c. **CMV $85. jar only mint, $105. MB.**

DERMOL MASSAGE CREAM 1920-23
Glass jar with metal screw on lid. OSP 96c. **CMV $75. mint, $90. MB.**

TOOTH POWDER 1908
White glass bottle with metal cap. OSP 25c. **CMV $110. mint, $130. MB.**

SHAMPOO CREAM 1908
4 oz. white glass jar with metal lid. OSP 35c. **CMV $75. jar only, $95. MB.**

SHAMPOO CREAM 1912
4 oz. white glass jar, metal lid, with or without CPC on lid. Early issue 1912 has Eureka trademark on box - 1915 one does not. OSP 35c. CMV $80. jar only $95. MB for Eureka trademark, $10. less without it.

BANDOLINE HAIR DRESSING 1923-30 - 4 OZ.
Tall 4 oz. clear glass with cork stopper. Comes with neck label to be mint. OSP 45c. CMV $75. BO mint, $90. MB.

BANDOLINE 1908
2 oz. glass bottle, cork stopper. OSP 25c. CMV $110. MB, $90. BO.

SHAMPOO CREAM SAMPLE 1915
Small 1"size aluminum round bottom container. Rare. CMV $50. mint.

BANDOLINE HAIR DRESSING 1923-30
(Left) 2 oz. yellow label & cork stopper, clear glass jar. OSP 24c. CMV $60. mint, $75. MB.
BANDOLINE HAIR DRESSING 1923-30
(Right) 4 oz. size. Glass bottle, cork stopper, front & neck label. OSP 45c. CMV $65. BO, $80. MB.

COLD CREAM 1896
White glass jar with metal lid. Eureka trademark on label. OSP 25c. CMV $90. mint, $110. MB.

COLD CREAMS 1915
Large & small white glass jars with CPC on metal lid. OSP 25c & 45c. CMV $75. MB. each, $60. jar only, mint.

CALIFORNIA COLD CREAM 1908
2 oz. white glass jar with metal lid. OSP 25c. CMV $95. MB, $80. jar only mint.

BANDOLINE 1915
(Left) Glass bottle with cork stopper. OSP 25c. CMV $75. mint, $90. MB.
BANDOLINE 1930-35
(Right) Frosted glass or clear glass bottle with blue wrapped cork stopper. OSP 37c. CMV $60. BO, $70. MB.

COLD CREAM 1926
White glas jar with CPC on aluminum lid. OSP 63c. CMV $50. mint, $65. MB.

CPC COLD CREAM 1912
Large white glass jar with metal lid. OSP 45c.
CMV $60. jar only, $75. MB.

ROSE POMADE 1900
(Left) Eureka Trademark. Same in CPC sets.
1914 on right. Both white glass, top & side
paper labels. **CMV $55. each mint.**

DERMOL MASSAGE CREAM 1923
1 lb. white glass jar. Aluminum lid, colored
front label. Very rare. 4 1/4" high. **CMV $100.
mint** SHown next to 1915 Cold Cream jar
regular size, for size comparison.

CALIFORNIA SHAMPOO CREAM 1900
Both 4 oz. glass jars, metal lids are different
sizes. 1 plain - 1 with man washing his hair &
CPC. Both has plain paper flower design front
labels. **CMV $125. with man's head lid,
$100. for plain lid.**

CPC PERFUMES - MISC.

TRAVELERS PERFUME 1 OZ. 1917
1 oz. octagonal shaped bottle with glass
stopper & screw on nickel lid. OSP 90c.
CMV $135. BO mint, $160. MB.

TRAVELER'S PERFUME 1900-1923
1/2 oz. size. Metal cap over glass stopper.
Gold label. Bottle is octagonally shaped.
Came in all fragrances of 1896-1908. Red
flowered box. OSP 50c. **CMV $125. BO mint,
$150. MB.** Also came in 1 oz. size on left.
RARE. **CMV $150. - $175. MB.**

PERFUME FLACONETTE 1925
Flaconette size embossed glass bottle with
glass stopper. Brass cap over stopper. Came
in Mission Garden, American Ideal, Narcissus,
Daphne, Jardin D' Amour. OSP $1.10. **CMV
$90. BO, mint with brass cap. 120. MB.**
The cap has fragrance on it.

PERFUME FLACONETTE 1923
Octagonal shaped bottle with long glass
stopper, neck label. Came with & without
brass cap with CPC on cap. Came in Daphne,
Crab Apple, Vernafleur, Trailing Arbutus, White
Rose, Carnation, Violet, White Lilac,
Heliotrope, Roses, Lily of the Valley, Mission
Garden. OSP 49c. **CMV with brass cap
$90., without cap $75. - $1010. MB.**

PERFUME FLACONETTE 1930-35
(Left) Embossed clear glass stopper, brass
cap over glass stopper. Avon on cap. Came
in all perfumes of 1930-35. OSP $1.10. **CMV
$90. each mint, $110. MB.**
ROSE PERFUME SAMPLE 1900
(Right) 1/2 oz. size, cork stopper. Came in all
fragrances of 1900. **CMV $125. mint.**

1896 TO 1914 PERFUMES

The following list of perfumes were sold by CPC from 1896 to 1914. Use this list to identify misc. perfumes.
The regular line of CP Floral extracts consists of thirty odors, in the following range of prices and sizes:

Roses
Lily of the Valley
White Rose
Violet
White Lilac
Sweet Peas
Hyacinth

Heliotrope		
Carnation	1 ounce bottle	$ .60
Bouquet Marie	2 ounce bottle	1.10
New Mown Hay	4 ounce bottle	2.00
Marie Stewart	1/2 pint bottle	3.75
Rose Geranium	1 pint bottle	7.00
Stephanotis		

Ylang Ylang
Jack Rose
Tube Rose
Treffle
California Bouquet

Crab Apple Blossom	1 ounce bottle	$ .75
Trailing Arbutus	2 ounce bottle	1.40
Frangipanni	4 ounce bottle	2.75
May Blossom	1/2 pint bottle	5.25
Jockey Club	1 pint bottle	10.00
White Heliotrope		

Lou Lillie	1 ounce bottle	$ .50
Musk	2 ounce bottle	.90
Golf Club	4 ounce bottle	1.75
Venetian Carnation	1/2 pint bottle	3.25
Golf Violet	1 pint bottle	6.00

1915 TO 1921 PERFUMES

The very extensive CPC line gives a wide range of selection, and among the 27 different odors there is sure to be one or more to satisfy the most fastidious and exacting.
The prices are according to the cost of production and the value of the goods offered. All perfumes are in attractive bottles, put up in beautiful lithographed boxes, as illustrated.

Concentrated Floral Odors Triple Extracts

Violet
White Rose
Carnation
Heliotrope

Lily of the Valley	1 ounce bottle	$ .50
White Lilac	2 ounce bottle	.90
Hyacinth	4 ounce bottle	1.75
California Bouquet	1/2 pint bottle	3.25
Roses	1 pint bottle	6.00

New Mown Hay
Sweet Pea
Treffle
Rose Geranium
Jack Rose

Quadruple Extracts

Crab Apple Blossom	1 ounce bottle	$ .60
Trailing Arbutus	2 ounce bottle	1.10
Jockey Club	4 ounce bottle	2.00
Honeysuckle	1/2 pint bottle	3.75
White Heliotrope	1 pint bottle	7.00

Extra Concentrated Odors

Natoma Rose	1 ounce bottle	$.75
Venetian Carnation	2 ounce bottle	1.40
Golf Violet	4 ounce bottle	2.75
Musk	1/2 pint bottle	5.25
	1 pint bottle	10.00

PERFUME SPRAY ATOMIZER 1928
1 is green opaque over clear glass & 1 is green painted over clear, gold plated top. **CMV $90. each.**

PERFUME 1918
1/2 oz. bottle with crown glass stopper set in cork. Front & neck label. Came in all fragrances of 1918. OSP 50c. **CMV $100. BO mint, $125. MB.**

CPC PERFUME 1918
(Left) 1/2 oz. glass & cork stopper. Came in 1918 Gift Box A Set. **CMV $110. mint.**
1/2 OZ. PERFUME 1919
(Right) 1/2 oz. glass crowned shaped stopper in cork. Came in all 1919 fragrances. OSP 75c. **CMV $100. mint, $125. MB.**

WHITE ROSE PERFUME 1918
2 oz. size, RARE, cork stopper. Front & neck label with neck ribbon. OSP $1. **CMV $125. mint.**

LITTLE FOLKS PERFUMES 1908
2" high small bottles with cork stoppers came in early 1900s Little Folks gift sets. Came in Heliotrope, Rose, Carnation, and Violet. Front labels and neck ribbons. **CMV $75. each mint.**

LITTLE FOLKS PERFUME 1915
(Left) Small gem size bottle with front label & ribbon on neck. Cork stopper. Came in 1915 Little Folks Set only. Came in Carnation, Violet, White Rose, Heliotrope. **CMV $75. each mint.**
LITTLE FOLKS PERFUME 1910
(Right) 2" high, cork stopper. Came in Little Folks Set only from 1910 to 1915. Both bottles pictured came in same fragrances. **CMV $75. mint.**

PERFUME FLACONETTE 1926
Frosted ribbed glass bottle with long glass stopper. Small paper label on front. Came with brass cap with CPC on cap. Came in Crab Apple, Daphne, Trailing Arbutus, Vernafleur, American Ideal, Carnation, Heliotrope, White Rose, Violet, Lily of the Valley. OSP 59c. **CMV with brass cap $90., $70. BO, $110. MB.**

LITTLE FOLKS PERFUME 1925-32
(Left) 1/2 oz. bottle with brass screw on cap. Came in 1925 Little Folks Set only. Came in Violet, Carnation, Heliotrope, White Lilac, Daphne, Vernafleur, Trailing Arbutus. **CMV $65. each mint.**
LITTLE FOLKS PERFUME 1896
(Right) 2" high. Came in 1896 & 1906 Little Folks Set only in Rose, or White Rose, Heliotrope, Violet, & Carnation. Cork stopper. **CMV $75. each mint.**

PERFUMES 1906
1 oz. round bottles came in Atomizer Perfume Set with cork stopper. Came in all fragrances of 1908. CMV $110. each mint.

1/2 OZ. PERFUME 1915
(Left) 1/2 oz. bottle with glass stopper set in cork. Front and neck label. Came in Violet, White Rose, Carnation, White Lilac, Heliotrope, Lily of the Valley. Two different stoppers as shown on left. OSP 25c. CMV $110., $135. MB.

1 OZ. EXTRA CONCENTRATED PERFUMES
(Right) 1 oz. size, front and neck label. Came in Golf Violet, Musk, Crab Apple Blossom, Natoma, Rose, Venetian Carnation. OSP 75c. CMV $175. MB, $135. BO.

FRENCH PERFUMES 1900
(Left) Trial size 1/4 oz. on left. 2 oz. size on right. Cork stoppers. CMV $125. BO trial size mint, CMV $200. 2 oz. size mint, add $25. MB.

FRENCH PERFUMES 1916
(Right) 2 different embossed glass bottles. Cork stoppers. Trial size. OSP 25c. CMV $150. BO mint, $175. MB.

PERFUME 1896
1 oz. octagonal shaped bottle, front & neck label with Eureka Trade Mark. Came in Atomizer Perfume Set with cork stopper. Came in all fragrances of 1896. CMV $165. mint.

EXTRACT ROSE GERANIUM PERFUME 1896
1 oz. glass stopper, paper label. OSP 40c. CMV $200. mint.

PERFUMES 1923
1/2 oz. bottle with crown glass stopper set in cork. Front & neck label. Crab Apple, Blossom, White Rose, Trailing Arbutus, Rose Carnation, Heliotrope, Violet, White Lilac & Lily of the Valley. Came in red box, 2 different bottles as shown. OSP 59c. CMV $110. BO, $135. MB.

FRENCH PERFUMES 1900
(Left) 1/4 oz. bottle with glass stopper. Came in Le Perfume Des Roses, L' Odeur de Violette, Peau d'Espagne. OSP 25c. CMV $125. BO, $150. MB.

FRENCH PERFUMES 1896
(Right) 1/4 oz. glass bottle, cork stopper. Came in Le Perfume Des Roses, L'Odeur de Violette, Peau d'Espagne. OSP 25c. CMV $125. BO mint, $150. MB.

ATOMIZER PERFUME 1908
(Left) 1 oz. 6 sided bottle with cork stopper. Green neck & front label. Came in all fragrances of 1908. Came only in CPC Atomizer Sets. Used with Spray Atomizer. OSP 50c. CMV $100. mint.

ATOMIZER PERFUME 1914
(Right) 1 oz. bottle with green & gold front & neck label, cork stopper. Came in 1918 Atomizer Box Set only. Used with Spray Atomizer. Came in all 1918 perfumes. OSP 50c. CMV $100. BO mint.

JOCKEY CLUB PERFUME 1908
Green front and neck label and green neck ribbon. OSP 50c. **CMV $100. mint, $130. MB.**

PEAU D'ESPAGNE PERFUME 1896
(Left) 4" high flaconette size, cork stopper. CPC French perfume. OSP 25c. **CMV $160. mint, $180. MB.**

CRAB APPLE BLOSSOM PERFUME 1910
(Center) 1 oz. glass stopper, front & neck label. CPC on label. **CMV $110. mint, $135. MB.**

WHITE ROSE PERFUME 1896
(Right) 1 oz. glass stopper. Bottom part of label is missing on bottle shown. OSP 40c. **CMV $150. BO, $200. MB.**

PERFUME 1908
(Left) 1 oz. glass stopper, gold label. Eureka Trade Mark on label. Came in all fragrances of 1908. **CMV $180. MB, $150. BO. mint.** Also came in several different glass stoppers. 2 different shown on left.

PERFUME 1906-1918
(Right) 4 oz. glass stoppered bottle, gold embossed front and neck label. Came in all perfumes of the period. See list on front of this section. OSP $2.75. **CMV $150. BO, $200. MB.**

CPC PERFUME 1906
1 oz. perfume, gold front & neck label. Came in all 1908 perfumes. **CMV $200. MB, $150. BO.**

CHRISTMAS BOX NO. 5 PERFUME 1906
(Left) White leather covered box holds 3 oz. glass stoppered perfume. OSP $1.50. **CMV $175. BO mint, $225. MB.**

MUSK PERFUME 1896
(Right) 1 oz. size, glass stoppered. Came in all fragrances, with Chicago label. RARE. **CMV $125. mint, $150. MB.**

VIOLET PERFUME 1900
Eureka Trade Mark. Neck ribbon, neck label is plain. **CMV $165. BO mint.**

CUT GLASS PERFUME 1915-20
2 oz. bottle with cut glass stopper. 2 different labels in embossed gold. White leatherette box. Came in Trailing Arbutus & Crab Apple Blossom. OSP $2.25. **CMV $225., $265. MB.** Octagonal label on bottom is 1911 issue. Same CMV.

PERFUME & ATOMIZER 1918
1 oz. bottle with atomizer came in black box. Bottle has cork stopper & green front & neck label. Came in all fragrances of 1918, including American Ideal & Daphne. OSP $1.50. **CMV $150. MB with atomizer. $100. BO mint.**

CHRISTMAS PERFUME 1905
2 oz. glass stopper perfume. OSP 75c. CMV
$150. BO, $200. MB.

EXTRACT PERFUMES 1905
1 oz. glass stopper, white paper label. Came
in all fragrances of 1896. OSP 50c. CMV
$215. MB, $175. BO mint.

EXTRACT PERFUMES 1896
(Left) 2 oz. round glass stopper. New York,
Chicago, San Francisco on label. Came in all
fragrances in 1908. OSP 90c to $1.40. **CMV**
$150. BO, $200. MB.

FRENCH PERFUME 1896-1908
(Right) 1/2 oz. bottle with glass stopper.
Eureka Trade Mark in center of label. Came in
Le Perfume des Roses, Peau d'Espagne,
L'Odeur de Violette. OSP 55c. **CMV $150.
BO, $200. MB.**

PERFUME "FLORAL EXTRACTS" 1908
1 oz. glass stoppered bottle with Eureka CP
Trade Mark on label. Came in all 1908
perfumes. OSP 50c. **CMV $150. BO, $200.
MB.** Also came in 2, 4, 8 & 16 oz. bottles.
CMV same as 1 oz. size.

CPC PERFUME 1916
3 different glass stoppers shown. 1 & 2 oz.
sizes. OSP 50c. **CMV $135. BO mint, $175.
MB.**

WHITE ROSE PERFUME 1908
2 oz. Extract of White Rose perfume. Neck
ribbon & glass stopper. OSP 90c. **CMV $150.
BO mint, $200. MB.**

1 OZ. PERFUMES 1908
1 oz. glass stoppered bottle. Eureka Trade
Mark on label. In gray flowered box. Cane in
all fragrances of 1908. OSP 50c to 75c. **CMV
each $200. MB, $150. BO.** Each fragrance
came with different flower on label. Heliotrope
on left and Crab Apple Blossom on right.

PERFUME 1915
(Left) 1 oz. clear glass bottle with glass
stopper. Came in all 1915 fragrances. OSP
75c. **CMV $150. mint, $175. MB.**

CRAB APPLE BLOSSOM 1905
(Right) 1 oz. clear glass bottle, glass stopper,
label has CPC Eureka Trade Mark. Came in
all 1908 fragrances. Bottle came with different
shaped stopper also. OSP 50c - 75c. **CMV
$150. BO, $200. MB.**

FRENCH PERFUME 1905
Glass stoppered bottle came in 1/2, 1, 2 & 4
oz. sizes in these fragrances: Le Perfume des
Roses, L'Odeur de Violette & Peau d'Espagne.
1 oz. size pictured. OSP 25c to $3.75. **CMV
$165. BO, $215. MB.**

CPC PERFUME SAMPLE SET 1922
Black carrying case with "California Perfume Co." on front. 4 glass flaconette with gold cap & fits into gold case. **CMV $350. MB, $75. each flaconette.**

2 OZ. PERFUME 1916
2 oz. glass stopper either faceted or round. Front & neck label. Came in all fragrances of 1915. OSP $1.10. **CMV $200. MB, $150. BO.**

PERFUMES 1923
1 & 2 oz. bottle in same shape & design with glass stopper. Front & neck label with gold basket design. Beige box. Came in Carnation, Roses, Heliotrope, Violet, White Lilac, Lily of the Valley, Crab Apple Blossom, Trailing Arbutus, White Rose. OSP $1.17 & $2.10. **CMV $135. BO, $170. MB.** Also came in 4 oz. size.

PERFUMES 8 OZ. 1905
(Left) 8 oz. glass stoppered bottle. Came in California Bouquet, shown. Violet, White Rose, Carnation, Heliotrope, Lily of the Valley, White Lilac, Hyacinth, Roses, New Mown Hay, Sweet Pea, Treffle, Rose Geranium, Jack Rose, front paper label and also came with neck label. OSP $3.25 each. **CMV $175. each BO, $225. MB.**

PERFUME 1923
(Right) 1 oz. glass stoppered bottle is ribbed. Came in Carnation, Crab Apple Blossom, Heliotrope, Lily of the Valley, Violet & White Rose. Front & neck label. OSP $1.17. **CMV $135. BO, $160. MB.**

PERFUMES 1915
2 oz. on left & 1 oz. on right, different labels & diamond cut shaped glass stoppers. **CMV $125. each mint.**

TRIAL SIZE PERFUMES
Shown for different size glass stoppers, bottles & labels. **CMV same as listed now.**

WHITE ROSE PERFUME 1896
1 oz., round glass stopper, long neck. Square round shoulder bottle.

SWEET PEA PERFUME 1896
1 oz. only has cork stopper. Bottle is shorter than one on left. **CMV $150. each mint.**

WHITE ROSE PERFUME 1930
Silver & blue box holds 2 oz. bottle with flat glass stopper, pink neck ribbon & red paper rose label. RARE. **CMV $150. MB, $115. BO mint.**

WHITE ROSE PERFUME FLACONETTE 1926
CPC brass cap over glass stopper ribbed bottle. Red paper rose label. **CMV $90. mint.**

CARNATION PERFUME 1890s
(Left) 1 oz, glass stopper. Plain paper label. **CMV $150.**

FRENCH PERFUME ROSES 1897
(Right) 1/4 oz. bottle, cork stopper. **CMV $140. mint.**

PERFUMES 1908
The 6 glass stoppered 1 oz. bottles shown on left came in California Bouquet, Carnation, Heliotrope, Hyacinth, Lily of the Valley, New Mown Hay, Rose Geranium, Sweet Pea, Treffle, Violet, White Lilac & White Rose. OSP 50c. **CMV $150. BO, $195. MB.**

PERFUME SAMPLE SET 1931
Four 3 dram ribbed & frosted glass bottles with clear ribbed stoppers. Black carrying case. Came in Daphne, Trailing Arbutus, Vernafleur, American Ideal, Crab Apple, Carnation, Heliotrope, White Rose, Violet & Lily of the Valley. **CMV set $315. mint.** Came with card on proper way to demonstrate perfumes. **Add $10. for card.**

PERFUME SAMPLE SET - SILVER LABELS 1931
Same CPC black case & bottles, only has very rare silver & blue labels on bottles. **CMV $400. set, mint.**

CPC PERFUME SAMPLE SET 1923
Black box holds 4 glass stoppered perfume samples. Box has California Perfume Co. on front, 3 dram size. Each has neck labels. Labels read Daphne, Vernafleur, American Ideal, Trailing Arbutus or Roses. **CMV $75. each bottle, $335. set MB.**

APPLE BLOSSOM PERFUME 1908
(Left) 1 oz. glass stopper. Special Christmas box. OSP 70c. **CMV $225. MB.**

HELIOTROPE PERFUME 1908
(Right) 1 oz. glass stopper. Special Christmas box. OSP 70c. **CMV $225. MB.**

FRENCH PERFUMES 1910
Bottle on left is 1 oz., center is 1/4 oz.
trial size, right is 1/2 oz. size. Each has
glass stopper. Came in L'Odeur De
Violette, Le Perfume Des Roses & Peau
de'Espagne. Also came in 2 & 4 oz
size. OSP 25c, 55c, $1., $1.90 & $3.75.
**CMV bottle 1/2 oz. size to 4 oz. $150.
BO each 1/4 oz. size $125. BO., $175.
MB.**

PERFUME CHRISTMAS BOX 4 OZ. 1905
Fancy flowered box holds 4 oz. glass
stoppered bottle. Front & neck label. OSP
$1.50. **CMV $175. - $225. MB.**

PERFUME CHRISTMAS BOX 8 OZ. 1905
Embossed paper box, satin lined. Holds 8 oz.
glass stoppered bottle with neck ribbon. OSP
$3.50. **CMV $200. - $275. MB.**

PERFUME CHRISTMAS BOX 4 OZ. 1905
Embossed paper box, satin lined. Holds 4 oz.
glass stoppered bottle with neck ribbon. OSP
$2. **CMV $175. - $250. MB.**

CPC TOILET WATER

WHITE ROSE WATER 1910
4 oz. clear glass stopper. Eureka trademark
on label. OSP 35c. **CMV $150. mint, $190.
MB.**

FLORIDA WATER 1905
(Left) 1 1/2 oz. size, glass crown & cork
stopper. OSP 35c. **CMV $175. mint, $200.
MB.**
EAU DE COLOGNE FOR THE TOILET 1896
(Right) 2 oz. ribbed glass bottle. Front & neck
label with Eureka trademark. Glass stopper in
cork. OSP 35c. **CMV $175. BO mint, $210.
MB.**

TOILET WATER 1906
(Left) 2 oz. clear ribbed glass bottle & glass corked stopper. Pure food act 1906 on label. Came in Violet Water, White Rose, Lavender Water, Florida Water, California Sweet Cologne & Eau de Cologne. OSP 35c. **CMV $175. mint, $210. MB.**

TOILET WATERS 1896
(Right) 2 oz. ribbed glass bottle, glass stopper in cork. Front & neck label has Eureka trademark. Came in California Sweet Cologne, Violet Water, White Rose, Lavender Water & Florida Water. OSP 35c. **CMV $175. BO, $210. MB.**

TOILET WATERS 1908
(Left) 2, 4, 8 & 16 oz. sizes. Glass stoppered bottle. Came in Violet, White Rose, Lavender, Florida, California Sweet Cologne & Eau De Cologne. Bottle shown in 2 oz. size. OSP 35c, 65c, $1.25 & $2. **CMV each $150. BO, $200. MB.**

LAVENDER WATER 1910
(Right) 2 oz. glass stoppered bottle with Eureka trademark on label. Also came in Violet, White Rose, Florida Water, California Sweet Cologne & Eau De Cologne. Also came in 4 & 8 oz. & 1 pint sizes with glass stopper. OSP 35c. **CMV $150. BO mint, $190. MB.**

TOILET WATER 1916
4 oz. bottle with metal & cork stopper. Came in red & gold box. Came in California Sweet Cologne, Carnation, Eau De Cologne, Florida Water, Lavender Water, Trailing Arbutus, Violet, White Lilac, White Rose & Crab Apple Blossom. OSP 65c. **CMV $120. BO, $150. MB.**

TOILET WATERS 1922-25
Came in 2, 4 & 8 oz. sizes in Violet, Vernafleur, Lavender, White Lilac, Lily of the Valley, Carnation, White Rose, Trailing Arbutus, Crab Apple Blossom & Eau De Cologne. 2 & 4 oz. size same as pictured. Front & neck labels. Metal crown stopper in cork. OSP 59c, $1.08 & $1.95. **CMV $90. BO, $115. MB.**

TRIPLE EXTRACT TOILET WATER 1896
(Left) 4 oz. & 8 oz. size glass stopper, label has Eureka trademark. Came in Violet Water, White Rose, Lavender Water, Florida Water, Eau De Cologne, California Sweet Cologne. OSP each 65c. **CMV $200. MB, $150. BO mint.**

FLORIDA WATER 1900
(Right) 2 oz. botle, glass stopper. OSP 35c. **CMV $175. mint, $210. MB.**

TOILET WATER 1910
8 oz. bottle with glass stopper. Front & neck label. Came in all fragrances of 1916 in Toilet Waters. OSP $1.25. **CMV $175. BO mint, $225. MB.**

TOILET WATER 1910
2 oz. bottle with metal pour cap in cork, 1916 up. California Sweet Cologne, Lait Virginal, Eau De Cologne, Trailing Arbutus, White Rose, Violet, White Lilac, Lavender Water, Florida Water, Crab Apple Blossom & Carnation. Front & neck label in 2 styles. OSP 35c. **CMV $115. BO, mint, $140. MB.** Also came with brass crown and cork stopper in 1910.

TOILET WATER 1910
2 oz. size with metal crown cork stopper.
Came in either of 2 labels shown in Carnation,
Florida Water, Trailing Arbutus, White Lilac,
White Rose, Violet, Lavender Water, Eau De
Cologne, California Sweet Cologne. OSP 35c.
CMV $115. each Bo, $140. MB.

LILAC VEGETAL 1928-29
(Left) 2 oz. ribbed glass bottle with crown
metal top in cork. Pink front & neck label. This
bottle with CPC on front label came in Humidor
Shaving Set only. **CMV $80. - $100. MB.**
LILAC VEGETAL 1925-30
(Right) 2 oz. ribbed glass bottle with metal
stopper in cork. Pink front & neck label. OSP
$1.08. **CMV $80. BO, $100. MB.**

TOILET WATER 1923-29
(Left) 2 or 4 oz. metal crown cork stopper,
ribbed bottle, front & neck label. Came in Lily
of the Valley, Violet, White Rose, Carnation,
Crab Apple Blossom. OSP 59c. **CMV $80.
each mint, $100. MB.**
BABY TOILET WATER 1923
(Right) 2 & 4 oz. size bottles. Red soldier on
front label, blue neck label. Brass & cork
stopper. OSP 48c & 89c. **CMV $125. BO,
$145. MB.**

CPC POWDERS

WHITE LILAC TALCUM 1917
2 sizes, both 4 oz. 2 different metal shaker
tops. Both lavender paper sides. **CMV $75.
each, $90. MB.**

TOOTH POWDER 1915 ONLY
(Left) Small metal can came in 1915 Juvenile
Set. **CMV $75. mint.**
TOOTH POWDER 1908
(Right) Metal can. OSP 25c. **CMV $85. MB,
$70. can only mint.**

ELITE POWDER 1915
Glass jar, metal sifter lid in CPC box. OSP 25c. **CMV $80. BO mint, $95. MB.**

PYROX TOOTH POWDER 1925
(Left) Blue metal can. OSP 24c. **CMV $75. MB, $60. can only mint.**
CALIFORNIA ROSE TALCUM 1923
(Right) 4 oz. pink can with brass cap. OSP 33c. **CMV $90., $110. MB.**

ELITE POWDER 1923
(Left & Center) 1 lb. blue can with English & French label. 2 different brass caps & narrow & wide blue band around top. OSP 89c. CMV $85. each, $95. MB.
ELITE POWDER REGULAR ISSUE 1923
(Right) Pictured for size comparison.

SWEET SIXTEEN FACE POWDER 1916
(Left) Yellow, pink & green box. OSP 25c. **CMV $50. mint.**
CALIFORNIA NAIL POWDER 1916
(Right) Paper sides. Came bright green or beige in color. OSP 25c. **CMV $45. mint.**

ELITE FOOT POWDER 1919
Paper side round container. Sold for 25c each after WWI from the Army & Navy kits. RARE. **CMV $85. - $100. MB.**

ROSE TALCUM POWDER ANTISEPTIC 1907
Metal can with brass sifter cap. OSP 25c. **CMV $100. mint, $120. MB.**

CALIFORNIA ROSE TALCUM 1921
3 1/2 oz. glass jar with brass cap. OSP 33c. **CMV $85. jar only, $105. MB.**

ELITE POWDER 1911
(Left) Glass jar with aluminum lid. OSP 25c. **CMV $80. mint, $100. MB. Brown glass jar $150.**
ELITE POWDER 1923
(Right) Blue metal can with sifter cap. OSP 24c. **CMV $50. MB, $35. can only mint.** Came in 2 different sifter caps & 2 variations in labels. **Same CMV.**

WHITE LILAC TALCUM 1919
(Left) 4 oz. blue metal can, blue sifter cap. OSP 24c. **CMV $75. mint, $90. MB.**
WHITE LILAC TALCUM 1917
(Right) 4 oz. paper box, purple in color. OSP 25c. **CMV $70. mint, $90. MB.**

WHITE LILAC TALCUM 1920
4 oz. blue metal can with brass take off cap. Box came with paper on the Story of Italian Talc. OSP 24c. **CMV $75. can only mint, $90. MB as shown.**

RADIANT NAIL POWDER 1924-29
(Left) Small gold & black can. All 3 pieces came in 1924 Manicure Set. **CMV $35.**
CUTI CREME OR NAIL CREAM 1924-29
(Center) Small gold & black can. **CMV $15.-$30.**
NAIL WHITE 1924-29
(Center Top) Small gold & black can. **CMV $15. - $30. MB.**

DEPILATORY 1914
A metal can of hair remover. OSP 50c. **CMV $90. MB, $75. mint.** Came with brass lift off cap.

SMOKERS TOOTH POWDER 1918
(Left) 2 3/4 oz. bottle with metal & cork stopper also comes with metal crown stopper. OSP 50c. **CMV $105. BO, $130. MB.**
SMOKERS TOOTH POWDER 1920
(Right) 2 3/4 oz. metal & cork stopper. OSP 50c. **CMV $105. BO, $130. MB.**

CALIFORNIA BATH POWDER 1910
Gold, white & green can. Came with sifter cap & take off cap. OSP 25c. **CMV $65. - $85. MB.**

HYGIENE FACE POWDER 1906
Leatherette box trimmed in gold. OSP 50c. **CMV $85. mint.**

SMOKERS TOOTH POWDER 1925-33
4 oz. cream colored can. Label in French & English. OSP 50c. **CMV $80. MB, $60. can only mint.**

HYGIENE FACE POWDER 1918
Green, gold & red powder box. OSP 50c. **CMV $90. mint.**

RADIANT NAIL POWDER 1923
(Left) Blue & pink can. 2 different labels. OSP 24c. **CMV $65. mint each, $80. MB.**
SHAVING POWDER 1915
(Right) 2 oz. metal can. OSP 25c. **CMV $70. mint, $85. MB.**

SACHET POWDER 1890s
Small envelope of powder. "CPC Eastern Agency - 7 Summer St., Bradford, Mass." on envelope. RARE. **CMV $50. mint.**
AMERICAN IDEAL CARD 1915
Small white card. **CMV $10.**

SACHET POWDER ENVELOPE 1910
Paper packet of sachet in Violet, White Rose or Heliotrope. OSP 25c. **CMV $30. mint.**

CALIFORNIA NAIL POWDER 1916 (LEFT), 1900 (RIGHT)
2 different labels & 1 has paper lift off top or metal sifter top. 1 only comes with paper top. OSP 25c each. **CMV $45. mint each.**

SWEET SIXTEEN FACE POWDER 1905
Paper box with outer box. OSP 25c. **CMV $55. - $75. MB.**

CPC BODY POWDER 1928-29
Yellow, black & maroon colored metal can. CPC New York, Montreal on bottom. Came in Trailing Arbutus, Daphne & Baby Powder. OSP $1.19. **CMV $50. mint, $65. MB.**

POWDER CAN REFILL 1920
1 lb. gold tone can. Came in several fragrances as a refill. **CMV $75. in new condition.**

HYGIENE FACE POWDER 1915
(Right) Green paper box. OSP 50c. **CMV $60. mint.**

POWDER SACHETS - MISC.
ALL CPC'S MUST BE IN NEW MINT CONDITION FOR CMV

POWDER SACHET 1923
(Left) Brass cap, dark flowered label. **CMV $95. BO, $110, MB.**
HELIOTROPE POWDER SACHET 1919
(Right) Clear glass bottle, gold cap, label yellow with lavender flowers and green leaves. Came in other fragrances. Rare. **CMV $110. BO, $125. MB.** Both bottles cam ein Carnation, Heliotrope, White Rose, Violet, White Lilac.

SACHET POWDER 1890s
Heliotrope violet or white rose sachet in box.
Metal cap. OSP 25c. **CMV $110. MB, $90.
BO mint.**

POWDER SACHET 1922-25
Large & small bottles with brass caps. Came
in Carnation, Heliotrope, Violet, White Rose &
Trailing Arbutus. OSP 49c & 72c. **CMV $100.
BO, $115. MB each size.**

SACHET POWDER 1890s
Eureka Trade Mark on label. Maroon Box
contins powder in Violet, White Rose,
Heliotrope. OSP 25c. **CMV $75. per box,
mint.**

POWDER SACHET 1905
(Left) Round glass bottle, aluminum lid. Came
in Violet, Lilac, Rose, White Rose & Heliotrope.
Came in sets only. **CMV $100. BO mint.**
POWDER SACHET 1890s-1912
(Right) Clear glass, gold cap, front label.
Came in French Odors of Le Parfume de
Roses, L'Odour de Violette, Peau D'Espagne.
OSP 25c. **CMV $110. MB, $90. BO mint.**

SACHET POWDER BOXED 1908
In Violet, White Rose & Heliotrope. OSP 25c.
CMV $75. MB.

FACE POWDER LEAVES 1916
Small book of 72 sheets of scented paper.
Came in Rose, White, Rachel. OSP 20c.
CMV $50. mint.

POWDER SACHET 1890s-1912
Silver or gold cap on glass bottle with front
label. Came in Lilac, Rose, White Rose,
Violet, Heliotrope. OSP 25c. **CMV $110. MB,
$90. BO mint.** Each one has different label.

CPC SAMPLE CASES

EARLY 1900s SAMPLE CASE
Plain wood box with brass handle. CMV
$100. mint with CPC price list. Case was
used by CPC Reps to sell products.

POWDER SACHET 1915
Gold cap, paper label on glass bottle. Came in
Carnation, White Rose, Violet, White Lilac &
Heliotrope. 2 different - Boxes 7 labels as
shown. OSP 25c. **CMV $65. mint BO, $85.
MB.**

CPC SALES CASE 1920
Black case with red velvet lining. California
Perfume Co. on chrome handle. Used by
Reps to show products. Case measures 14
1/2" long X 8" wide, 3 1/2" high. **CMV $100.
mint.**

EARLY 1900s SAMPLE CASE
Plain wood box with leather handle. Red felt
lining, printed paper price list inside lid. **CMV
$75. mint with list.**

CPC SAMPLE CASE 1915
Straw basket weave case & leather handle &
trim. Measures 11 X 17. The large CPC black
catalogs fit inside perfectly. A CPC label is
inside lid stating all contents that came in
sample case. **CMV $100. with CPC label.**

CPC SAMPLE CASE 1890s
Small wood case, 6 1/2" X 12 1/2". Red felt
lining. List of CPC products inside of lid. **CMV
$100. mint.**

SAMPLE CASE 1900
Black leather covered case with leather strap.
Case came with CPC list of all products glued
inside lid of case. Case was carried by CPC
Reps to show products. **CMV Case mint full
of products, $1,500.** Case only mint $100.
with list.

CPC SETS

WARNING!! Grading condition is paramount on sets. CMV can vary 50% to 90% on grade.

CALIFORNIA IDEAL HAIR TREATMENT SET 1915
Box holds 4 oz. glass stoppered Bay Rum White Jar of Shampoo Cream, 6 oz. Eau De Quinine. All products in set came in separate boxes in set with pamphlet on the 3 products. OSP $1.35. **CMV $500. MB as shown.**

ATOMIZER BOX SET 1908
Three 1 oz. bottles with cork stoppers & atomizer. Came in all fragrances of 1915. Green box. Each bottle has green front & neck labels. OSP $1.50. **CMV $350. MB complete set.**

ATOMIZER SET 1896
Box holds atomizer & three 1 oz. bottles with cork stoppers. 2 bottles are round & center bottle is octagonal shape. Each has front & neck labels. OSP $1.35. **CMV $450. MB, completed set.** Came in all fragrances of 1896.

JUVENILE SET 1915 ONLY
Box holds miniature size cans of Natoma Talcum Powder, Tooth Powder, small bottle of Violet Water with cork stopper & small cake of Savona Bouquet Soap. Each item is about 2" high. OSP 50c. **CMV $450. MB.**

ATOMIZER SET 1906
Box holds three 1 oz. bottles of perfume with cork stoppers & atomizer. Came in all fragrances of 1908. OSP $1.50. **CMV $400. MB.**

JACK & JILL JUNGLE JINKS SET 1925-30
Brown decorated box holds 1 can Superite Trailing Arbutus Talcum, 1 bottle of Daphne Perfume, 1 cake of Apple Blossom soap, 1 can Trailing Arbutus Cold Cream, 1 tube Sen-Den-Tal Cream, 1 imported juvenile size tooth brush. OSP $1.50. **CMV $335. MB metal box only $75. mint.**

MANICURE SET 1900
Box holds bottle of Nail Bleach with glass stopper. **CMV $100. White jar of Rose Pomade. CMV $70.** & paper box of Nail Powder, **CMV $50.** OSP each 25c. OSP complete set 65c, CP on center of labels. Replaced with Eureka Trade mark in 1910. **CMV set $250. MB.**

MANICURE SET 1912
Gray box contains buffer, scissors, file, Nail Bleach, Nail Powder & Rose Pomade. OSP $3. CMV $265. MB.

CPC ATOMIZER SET 1929
Black box with green liner & gold tone lid holds green glass, lift off lid jar & 2 oz. green glass spray atomizer bottle. Both have gold tone lide. Does not say CPC on it or box. CMV $150. MB.

BOX A SET 1909
Holly green, red & gold box holds two 1/2 oz. perfumes with glass stoppers. OSP 50c. CMV $325. MB.

MANICURE SET 1916
(Left) Box holds glass stoppered bottle of Nail Bleach, jar of Rose Pomade and paper container of Nail Powder. OSP 65c. CMV complete set $250.

MANICURE SET BOX 1924-30
Gold and black stripped metal can. CMV $25., metal box only, mint.
LOVELY HANDS BOOKLET 1924-30
Came in Manicure Set shown. CMV $10. booklet mint only.

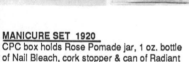

MANICURE SET 1920
CPC box holds Rose Pomade jar, 1 oz. bottle of Nail Bleach, cork stopper & can of Radiant Nail Powder. OSP 65c. CMV $250. MB.

GIFT BOX A 1915
Same pattern as Holly Pattern set. Green & red holly box. Two 1/2 oz. glass stoppered perfumes in choice of Violet, White Rose, Carnation, hite Lilac, Heliotrope & Lily of the Valley. OSP 50c. CMV $300. MB.

GERTRUDE RECORDON'S FACIAL TREATMENT SET 1929 ONLY
4 oz. bottle of astringent with cork stopper, $85. 4 oz. bottle of peach lotion with cork stopper, $85. Ribbed white glass jar with CPC on metal lid each in cleansing cream & skin food. Each jar $60. OSP $4. CMV complete set $350. MB.

MANICURE SET 1923
White box holds can of Radiant Nail Powder, bottle of Nail Bleach with glass stopper, orange wood stick & jar of Rose Pomade. OSP 72c. CMV $250. MB.

MANICURE SET 1924-28
Gold & black striped metal can holds gold & black can of Radiant Nail Powder, 1 can each of Nail White & Cuti-cream & nottle of Cutrain with cork stopper. OSP $1.20. CMV $165. MB.
BOUDOIR MANICURE SET 1929-30
Same set as 1924 Manicure Set with name changed and has bottle of Cuticle Softener or Cuticle Remover, & small can of Nail Cream, Nail White & Radiant Nail Powder. All in same design. OSP $1.20 CMV $175. MB. Set came with Lovely Hands Booklet.

GERTRUDE RECORDON'S INTRODUC-TORY FACIAL TREATMENT SET 1928-29
Box holds white jars of Gertrude Recordon's cleansing cream & skin food. **CMV each jar $60.** 2 bottles with cork stoppers of peach lotion & astringent. **CMV each bottle $60. & roll of facial tissues. CMV set mint $300. MB.**

HOLLY PATTERN BOX A 1921
Set has two 1/2 oz. glass & cork stoppered perfume bottles. Came in Carnation, Lily of the Valley, Violet, White Rose, White Lilac & Heliotrope. OSP 50c. **CMV $300. set MB.**

HOLLY SET 1912
Holly pattern design box holds 2 - 1/2 oz. size glass & cork stopper bottles. OSP 50c. **CMV $300. MB.**

GIFT BOX NO. 3 1918
Box holds 2 half ounce bottles of perfume. Crown glass stopper set in cork. Came in all fragrances of 1917-18 period. **CMV $300. MB.**

HOLLY SET 1910
Holly design holds 2 half ounce bottles with glass & cork stoppers. Gold front & neck labels. Choice of Violet, White Rose, White Lilac, Carnation, Heliotrope, Lily of the Valley perfume. OSP 50c. **CMV $325. MB.**

CHRISTMAS BOX SET NO. 3 1906
Roses on box, 2 perfumes, glass stoppered. Gold labels. Box is 5 1/4 X 4 3/4 inches. OSP 65c. **CMV $335. MB.**

CHRISTMAS BOX SET NO. 4 1906
Box holds Hygiene Face Powder, Savona soap & glass stoppered perfume. Box is 6 3/4" square. OSP $1. **CMV $300. MB.**

MEMORIES THAT LINGER SET 1913
3 glass stoppered perfumes in book shaped box. Box is 8 X 5 1/2 inches. Violet, White Rose & Carnation Perfume. OSP $2. **CMV $450. MB.**

CHRISTMAS BOX SET NO. 2 1906
Babies on box, 2 glass stoppered perfumes. Gold labels. OSP 50c. **CMV $335. MB.**

DRESSING TABLE VANITY SET 1926-30
Orange & gold two-section box has brass lipstick & eyebrow pencil & rouge compact in top half of box & bottom half is full of Jardin D'Amour or Ariel Face Powder. OSP $2.25. **CMV $150. MB.**

GIFT BOX NO. 2 1915
Box holds 1/2 oz. perfume with glass & cork stopper & powder sachet in Carnation, White Lilac, Heliotrope, Violet & White Rose. OSP 50c. **CMV $275. MB.**

CHRISTMAS SET NO. 4 1905
Fancy box holds 1 oz. glass stoppered of perfume. Round bottle of Powder Sachet, screw on cap & 1 wrapped bar of Savona Bouquet soap. OSP $1. **CMV $425.**

PERFUME SET NO. 2 1905
Lithographed box holds 2 crown sahped glass stoppered in cork bottles. Front & neck labels. OSP 50c. **CMV $350. MB.**

GIFT BOX NO. 2 1922
1/2 oz. bottle of perfume & bottle of sachet. Came in Violet, White Rose, Carnation, Heliotrope & White Lilac. OSP 97c. **CMV $250. MB.**

PERFUME SET NO. 5 1905
Holly Christmas Box holds two 1 oz. glass stoppered bottles. OSP $1. **CMV $350.**

GIFT BOX NO. 2 1915
Yellow & purple box holds 1/2 oz. perfume & powder sachet. Choice of Carnation, Heliotrope, White Lilac, Violet & White Rose. OSP 50c per set. **CMV set $275. MB.**

LITTLE FOLKS SET

LITTLE FOLKS SET 1906
4 small bottles of Violet, Carnation, White Rose or Rose & Heliotrope perfume. Birds & kids on lid & edge of box. OSP 40c. **CMV $350. MB.**

LITTLE FOLKS SET 1905
Boy & girl with dog inside lid of box. Four gem sized perfume bottles of Violet, Carnation, White Rose & Heliotrope. Bottles had cork stoppers & ribbons on neck. Flower on labels. Box size is 5 1/2" X 3 1/4". OSP 40c. **CMV $400. for set, mint, $75. each bottle.**

LITTLE FOLKS SET 1908
Four gem sized bottles of perfume came in Violet, Carnation, Rose & Heliotrope. Cork stoppers. Same bottles & labels as 1905 Little Folks s=Set. OSP 50c. **CMV $75. each bottle, $350. for set, mint.**

LITTLE FOLKS SET 1912
Same box as 1906 set only different labels. Birds & kids on lid. OSP 40c. **CMV $350. MB.**

LITTLE FOLKS SET 1915-23
Contains 4 gem bottles of perfume with Violet, Carnation, White Rose & Heliotrope. OSP 50c. **CMV $75. each bottle, $350. for set, MB.**

LITTLE FOLKS SET 1932 ONLY
Same box as 1923-32 Little Folks Set. Holds 4 octagonal shaped bottles. Silver labels, black caps. Came in Ariel, Bolero, Gardenia & Trailing Arbutus. OSP 90c. **CMV $275. set MB.**

LITTLE FOLKS SET 1904
Small red border box & 4 small cork stopper perfumes. Sleeping boy with red hat on lid. Sleeping girl in bed on inside lid. **CMV $400. mint.**

LITTLE FOLKS SET 1932-36
Four small bottles, choice of Ariel, Vernafleur, Gardenia or Bolero, 391 & Trailing Arbutus perfume with black caps, silver labels. OSP 90c. **CMV $200. MB, $225. MB with outer turquoise box as shown.**

LITTLE FOLKS SET 1937-39
Fancy box has four bottles of perfume in Gardenia, Cotillion, Narcissus & Trailing Arbutus. 2 dram size. OSP 94c. **CMV $165. MB, each bottle $25.**

LITTLE FOLKS SET 1910
Same box as 1908 set, same bottles & labels as 1912 set. OSP 50c. **CMV $350. MB.**

LITTLE FOLKS SET 1903
Blue flowers & farm house on inside lid. Boy in 1700 style clothes in blue coat holding white flowers on outside lid. 4 gem size perfumes: Violet, Rose, Carnation, Heliotrope. **VERY RARE. Light blue box. CMV $400.**

LITTLE FOLKS SET 1923-32
Blue box contains four gem size bottles of Floral perfumes in Daphne, Vernafleur, Trailing Arbutus & Carnation, Violet, Heliotrope or White Lilac. All have brass caps. OSP 69c. **CMV $300. for set, mint, $65. each bottle.**

CPC MEN'S SETS

HUMIDOR SHAVING SET 1928-29
Gold & black metal box holds 4 oz. bottle Bay Rum, 2 oz. bottle Lilac Vegetal, styptic pencil, green tube Menthol Witch Hazel cream, green tube Bayberry shave cream & can of either White Lilac talcum or Avon Talc for Men. OSP $2.25. **CMV $350. complete set MB.**

HUMIDOR SHAVING SET 1930-32
Gold & black metal box holds 4 oz. ribbed bottle of Bay Rum, 2 oz. bottle of Lilac Vegetal with crown cork stopper, styptic pencil, green tubes of Menthol Witch Hazel cream & Bayberry shaving cream & green can of Talc for Men. OSP $2.50. **CMV $300. MB.**

HUMIDOR SHAVING SET 1930-33
Gold & black metal box holds 4 oz. ribbed glass Bay Rum, 2 oz. ribbed glass Lilac Vegetal (black cap), styptic pencil, green tubes of Bayberry shaving cream & green can Talc for Men. OSP $2.50. **CMV $265. MB.**

HUMIDOR SHAVING SET BOX 1928-30
Metal gold striped box only. Measures 9 1/4" wide X 5 3/4" X 3" deep. Does not say CPC pn box. Picture of ship on lid. **CMV box only mint $40.**

HUMIDOR SHAVING SET BOX 1925-29
Maroon & gold metal box only. Measures 9 1/4" wide X 5 3/4" X 3" deep. Bottom says Metal Packaging Corp. of New York. **CMV box only mint $40.**

SHAVING SET BOX 1914
Black cardboard box. CPC label inside lid. Contents list on lid.. **CMV $20. Box only.**

GENTLEMEN'S SHAVING SET 1923
Box contains Bayberry shave cream tube, White Lilac talcum, White Lilac toilet water, styrtic pencil, Bay Rum, Menthol Witch Hazel & shaving pad. OSP $1.95. **CMV $375. MB.**

HUMIDOR SHAVING SET 1925-28
Wood grained box trimmed in gold & black holds 2 oz. bottle of Lilac Vegetal, 4 oz. bottle of Bay Rum, blue can of White Lilac talcum, Trailing Arbutus cold cream, tube of Menthol Witch Hazel cream, Bayberry shave cream tube & styptic pencil. OSP $1.95. **CMV $360. MB.**

ARMY & NAVY KIT 1918
Heavy cardboard box holds 2 bars of peroxide toilet soap, styptic pencil, Elite foot powder, cream shaving stick, dental cream. OSP $1.25. **CMV $275. MB.**

GENTLEMEN'S SHAVING SET 1917
Brown box holds cream shaving stick, Menthol Witch Hazel cream tube, 50 sheet shaving pad, 2 oz. bottle of White Lilac toilet water, styptic pencil, 4 oz. bottle of genuine Bay Rum with glass stopper & box of White Lilac talcum or jar of Violet talcum. OSP $1.50. **CMV $450. MB complete set.**

GENTLEMEN'S SHAVING SET 1919
Box contains blue can of White Lilac talcum, green tube of Menthol Witch Hazel cream, can of cream shaving stick, 4 oz. Bay Rum with cork stopper, styptic pencil, 2 oz. bottle of White Lilac toilet water & 50 sheet shaving pad. OSP $2.25. **CMV $450. MB.**

GENTLEMEN'S SHAVING SET 1915
Box holds glass bottle of Violet talcum powder, can of cream shaving stick, tube of Menthol Witch Hazel cream, styptic pencil, 4 oz. glass stoppered bottle of Bay Rum, 2 oz. White Lilac toilet water & 50 sheet shaving pad. OSP $1.50. **CMV $460. MB.**

WHAT'S HOT AND WHAT'S NOT IN WOMEN'S FRAGRANCE LINES

IMPORTANT - READ THIS

We suggest you do not collect any women's fragrance lines 1975 or newer as there is little to no collector demand. Only Soaps, Sets and Avon Representative awards are collectable. All fragrance line awards will be found in the Award section of this book. Mass production and way over supply means there will be no resale demand to collectors for fragrance lines in the future. Some children's fragrance lines might be added because of the cuteness of the product and some collector's interest in this type of product. We suggest you buy the newer fragrance products, use them and dispose of them. They will have no future value. The older fragrance lines are very collectable. The older the better for resale, just like any collectable. All fragrance line products 1975 or newer have been removed because of no value to most collectors. The following fragrance lines have been removed from this book.

FRAGRANCE LINES DROPPED

Ariane
Avon Hire Blue
Candid
Come Summer
Country Breeze
Delicate Daisies
Emprise
Foxfire
Lemon Violet
Mineral Spring
Odyssey
Patchwork
Private World
Queens Gold
Raining Violets
Sea Garden
Sportif
Sun Blossom
Sweet Honesty
Tasha
Tempo
Tender Blossoms
Timeless
Toccara
Tracy
Unspoken
Zany

APPLE BLOSSOM

APPLE BLOSSOM PERFUME 1941-42
1/8 oz. gold cap. OSP 75c. **CMV in box $45.,
$27.50 BO.** This bottle has two different gold
labels and round or flat top caps.

APPLE BLOSSOM BEAUTY DUST 1946
Special short issue box holds regular issue
beauty dust. OSP $1.10. **CMV $25. MB as
shown.**

BLUE BIRD SET WITH PERFUME 1941
Blue satin lined box holds Apple Blossom
Perfume and Apple Blossom Body Powder.
OSP $1.65. **CMV $90. MB.**

APPLE BLOSSOM TOILET WATER 1941-42
2 oz. pink, white and blue. OSP $1.04. **CMV
$30. BO, $40. MB.**

COLONIAL SET 1941-42
Satin lined box holds Apple Blossom Perfume
with gold cap and blue feather box of Face
Powder. OSP $1.35. **CMV $80. MB.** Also
came with perfume on right side of box.

BLUE BIRD SET WITH LIPSTICK 1941
Satin lined box holds Apple Blossom, Body
Powder, blue feather box of Face Powder and
turquoise and gold lipstick. OSP $2.25. **CMV
$80. MB.**

APPLE BLOSSOM PERFUME 1941-43
Box holds 1/8 oz. bottle with gold cap and
label. OSP 75c. **CMV $27.50 BO mint, $40.
MB as shown.**

**APPLE BLOSSOM MOTHERS DAY BEAUTY
DUST 1942-43**
Special issue blue, pink and white lace design
box. Holds feather design Apple Blossom
beauty dust..Sold at Mothers Day only in this
special box. OSP $1.10. **CMV $30. MB as
shown.**

APPLE BLOSSOM COLOGNE 1941-43
6 oz. bubble sided bottle with pink cap. OSP
$1. **CMV $45. BO, $60. MB.**

**APPLE BLOSSOM COMPLEXION SOAP
1925**
Yellow and pink wrapping on 3 bars of soap.
OSP 69c. **CMV $85. MB.**

APPLE BLOSSOM BEAUTY DUST 1941-48
6 oz. blue and white paper box. OSP $1.10.
**CMV $20. MB, $15. for Beauty Dust only
mint.**

APPLE BLOSSOM BODY POWDER 1941-44
Blue feather design, flat sifter top container in special issue box as shown. OSP 65c. **CMV $25. MB as shown. Can only $22.50 mint.**

PETAL OF BEAUTY SET 1943-44
Blue flowered box, pink satin lining, holds 6 oz. Apple Blossom cologne, pink cap and blue feathered Apple Blossom Beauty Dust. OSP $2.20. **CMV $100. MB.**

ATTENTION TOILET WATER 1942 ONLY
Special issue Christmas box holds 2 oz. Attention Toilet Water with purple cap and label. OSP 25c. **CMV $45. MB as shown, $30. BO.**

APPLE BLOSSOM BEAUTY DUST 1941-48
6 oz. size blue and white feather design paper container. OSP $1.10. **CMV $18. mint.** The Feather Plume outer box shown was issued Christmas 1942 only. **Add $7. for this box.**

SCENTIMENTS SET 1945 ONLY
Box holds 6 oz. Attention Cologne and 2 satin sachet pillows. OSP $2.50. **CMV $90. MB.**

FLOWERTIME SET 1943-45
Box holds 6 oz. Attention cologne and Attention Body Powder. OSP $1.65, 1943 set is green satin lined box with flower carts on lid. **CMV $90. MB.** 1944 set in plain box with flower design on lid. **CMV $90. MB.** 1945 set in white box with boy and girl in 1700 style dress under a tree. **CMV $90.**

APPLE BLOSSOM BEAUTY DUST 1943-45
Blue and white feather design paper box. OSP $1.10. **CMV $35. mint, $40. MB.** Outer box pictured in 1943 Christmas issue only. This is rare. **CMV $45. MB as shown.**

SCENTIMENTS SET 1943 ONLY
2 oz. clear bottle toilet water, gold foil label, white cap or gold cap. White and pink satin sachet pillows. OSP $1.85. **CMV $75. MB.**

FLOWERTIME SET 1943
Green satin lined box with flower carts on lid. Holds 6 oz. Apple Blossom cologne and Apple Blossom Body Powder. OSP $1.65. **CMV $90.**

FLOWERTIME SET 1944
Box with flowers on lid holds 6 oz. Attention cologne and Attention body powder. OSP $1.65. **CMV $85. MB.**

ATTENTION TOILET WATER 1942 ONLY
(Left) 2 oz. purple cap. OSP 25c. **CMV $40. BO, $45. MB.**
ATTENTION TOILET WATER 1943-46
(Right) 2 oz. bottle, came with gold ribbed cap or plastic cap. OSP $1.04. **CMV $25. BO mint, $35. MB.**

ATTENTION SACHET CHRISTMAS BOX 1942
1 1/4 oz. bottle with turquoise cap sold 1942-48. Regular issue box in Misc. Powder Sachet section. The box pictured here is special issue for Christmas. OSP 25c. **CMV $18. MB as shown. $12. BO mint.**

ATTENTION BODY POWDER 1941-43
Pink box, flat sifter top on paper container. OSP 65c. **CMV $25. MB, can only $20. mint.**

ATTENTION COLOGNE 1943-47
6 oz. bubble sided bottle with pink tall or short cap. OSP $1.50. **CMV $50. BO, $65. MB.**

ATTENTION SACHET 1942
Special 1st issue blue box as shown. 1 1/4 oz. bottle, turquoise cap. OSP $1.04. **CMV $20. MB as shown in this box.** See Misc. Powder Sachet section for further details on regular issue bottles and box.

ATTENTION SACHET 57th ANNIVERSARY BOX 1943
Special issue purple and pink box with flowers. Holds regular issue Attention powder sachet. Sold for 25c, to celebrate Avons 57th Anniversary. **CMV $20. as shown ,MB.**

ATTENTION BATH SALTS 1943-44, THEN 46-48
Tulip "A" box holds 9 oz. or 8 1/2 oz. glass jar with turquoise lid. OSP 63c. **CMV $25. MB, $15. BO mint.**

PINK RIBBON SET 1943-45
Blue and pink box holds blue and pink can of Attention Body Powder and paper box of Attention Bath Salts. OSP $1.61. **CMV $75. for set in box.**
ATTENTION BODY POWDER 1943-45
Blue and pink cardboard container. Came in Pink Ribbon set only. **CMV $30.**
ATTENTION BATH SALTS 1943-45
9 oz. blue and pink cardboard container. Came in Pink Ribbon set only. **CMV $30.**

ATTENTION BODY POWDER 1943-47
Blue and white carboard with feather design. OSP 65c. **CMV $25. MB, container only $20. mint.**

AVON COLOGNE

AVON COLOGNE 1941
6 oz. flat sided bottle. Soon after Avon Cologne was introduced, the name was changed to Orchard Blossoms Cologne. OSP 60c. **CMV $50. BO, $65. MB.**

AVON COLOGNE REPRESENTATIVE GIFT 1943
6 oz. clear bottle, maroon and gold label, blue cap. Bottom label reads "This is a gift to our representatives and must not be offered for sale." Came in blue and pink box, pink ribbon on box and bottle. 57th Anniversary Campaign card. **CMV bottle only $100. mint, $150. MB as shown.**

AVONSHIRE BLUE SOAP DISH & SOAP 1972
6" long blue dish trimmed in white with white bar of soap. Came with oval soap and round soap. OSP $4.50. **CMV $8. oval, $23. round soap MB.**

BABY PRODUCTS

Baby products 1975 or newer are not collectable except soaps & sets.

BABY CREAM 1961-64
2 oz. blue and white tube. OSP 89c. **CMV $4.**
BABY SOAP 1961-64
Blue and white wrapper. OSP 39c. **CMV $8.**
TOT 'N TYKE BABY SHAMPOO 1959-64
6 oz. cwhite plastic bottle, blue cap. OSP 98c. **CMV $6. BO, $7. MB.**
BABY LOTION 1958-64
6 oz. white plastic bottle, blue cap. OSP 98c. **CMV $5.**
BABY OIL 1960-64
6 oz. white plastic bottle, blue cap. OSP 98c. **CMV $6.**
BABY POWDER 1955-64
9 oz. blue and white can. OSP 79c. **CMV $10.**

AVONSHIRE BLUE

AVONSHIRE BLUE PRODUCTS 1971-74
Wedgewood blue and white over clear glass.
COLOGNE DECANTER
6 oz. Comes in Field Flowers, Brocade, Elusive, Charisma. SSP $5. **CMV $6. MB, $3. BO.**
PERFUME CANDLE
Holds Patchwork, Sonnet, Moonwind, Bird of Paradise, Charisma, Wassail, Roses Roses, Bayberry, Frankincense & Myrrh. SSP $8. **CMV $8. MB, $6. CO.**
BATH OIL DECANTER
6 oz. holds Skin So Soft or Field Flowers, Bird of Paradise. SSP $6. **CMV $6. MB, $4. BO.**
SOAP
3 bars, 2 oz. blue soap. SSP $2. **CMV $6. MB**

BABY TALC 1951-55
Blue and white box and can. OSP 52c. **CMV $18. in box, $13. can only.**
LANOLIN BABY SOAP 1951-55
Blue and white box and wrapping, holds 2 bars. OSP 69c. **CMV $25. in box.**
BABY LOTION 1951-55
4 oz. white plastic bottle, blue cap. OSP $1. **CMV $12. MB, $8. BO.**

BABY POWDER 1954-56
2 oz. pink can and cap with paper label around can. Came in Little Lamb set. RARE. **CMV $25.**
BABY POWDER 1954-56
2 oz. blue, white and pink can, pink cap. Came in Little Lamb set. **CMV $20.**

BABY OIL 1955-60
8 oz. bottle with indented sides, white cap. OSP 79c. **CMV $15.**

BABY PRODUCTS

BABY LOTION 1955-57
8 oz. bottle with indented sides, white cap.
OSP 89c. **CMV $12.50 BO, $15. MB.**

BABY & ME SET 1957-58
Clear glass bottle baby lotion, white cap and
Cotillion Toilet Water gold cap, pink paper
around neck. Box white, blue and pink. OSP
$1.98. **CMV $45. MB.**

SWEETEST ONE BABY SET 1962-64
Pink and white box holds 1 bar Baby Soap,
Baby Powder and Lotion or Oil. Bar of soap
came with blue ends, white center and white
ends with blue center. OSP $2.07. **CMV $40.
MB.**

TREE TOTS SET 1966
Box holds white plastic hair brush, 3 oz. plastic
tube Non-Tear Gel Shampoo, 3 oz. Baby Soap
with Lanolin and 6 oz. Nursery Fresh Room
Spray. OSP $3. **CMV $20. MB.**

TOT 'N TYKE BABY SHAMPOO 1959-64
Special issue box as shown. **CMV $12. MB as
shown.**

BABY PRODUCTS 1968-75
SHAMPOO 1969-74
Blue, white and pink, 6 oz. plastic bottle. OSP
98c. **CMV $1.**
NURSERY FRESH ROOM SPRAY 1968-79
6 oz. blue, white and pink can. OSP $1.50.
CMV $1.50. Also came with upside-down
label. **CMV $8.**
BABY POWDER 1969-72
9 oz. blue, white and pink plastic bottle. OSP
98c. **CMV $2.**
BABY CREAM 1969-75
2 oz. tube, blue, pink and white. OSP 98c.
CMV $1.
BABY SOAP 1969-75
3 oz. bar wrapped in blue, pink and white
paper. OSP 59c. **CMV $2.**
BABY LOTION 1969-75
6 oz. blue, white and pink plastic bottle. OSP
98c. **CMV $1.**

BABY SHAMPOO 1964-68
6 oz. white plastic bottle with blue cap. OSP
98c. **CMV $5.**
BABY LOTION 1964-68
6 oz. white plastic bottle with blue cap. OSP
98c. **CMV $5.**
BABY CREAM 1964-68
2 oz. blue and white tube with blue cap. OSP
98c. **CMV $3.**
BABY POWDER 1964-68
9 oz. white plastic bottle, blue cap. OSP 98c.
CMV $5.
BABY OIL 1964-66
6 oz. white plastic bottle with blue cap. OSP
98c. **CMV $6.**
TOT 'N TYKE BABY SOAP 1964-68
Blue and white wrapper, white cake of baby
soap. OSP 39c. **CMV $7.**

C.P.C. BABY BOOK 1915
CMV $30. mint.

LANOLIN BABY SOAP 1946-50
Pink box holds 2 wrapped bars. OSP 86c.
CMV $45. MB, $20. each bar.

BABY SOAP 1955-61
Blue and white box holds Castile & Lanolin white cake baby soap. OSP 29c. **CMV $12. MB.** Also came with "Castile with Lanolin" on box and printed on soap horizontally. **Same CMV.**

BABY SOAP 1962-64
White ends and blue center line. **CMV $8. mint.**

BABY LOTION SAMPLES 1964-68
White foil with pink and blue design. Came 10 to a box. **CMV $6. box or 50c per sample.**

BALLAD

BALLAD AWARD PERFUME 1945
Avon label on bottom, Ballad label across top, glass stopper. **CMV $375. mint box.**

BALLAD PERFUME 1945-53
Gold and white box holds 3 dram glass stoppered bottle with gold neck cord and gold label at base of bottle. OSP $3.50. **CMV $130. in box, $90. bottle only.**

BALLAD PERFUME 1939-45
3 dram glass stoppered bottle with gold neck cord and gold label at base of bottle. Front of box lays down. OSP $3.50. **CMV $130. in box. Bottle only $90.** See misc. perfume for 1 dram Ballad Perfume.

BALLAD PERFUME 1945 ONLY
3 dram, clear glass with gold neck cord and label, box gray, white and gold. OSP $3.50. **CMV $135. in this box, $90. bottle only.**

BIRD OF PARADISE

BIRD OF PARADISE PERFUME ROLLETTE 1970-76
1/3 oz. bottle with gold cap, turquoise and green box. OSP $3. **CMV $1. MB.**
BIRD OF PARADISE COLOGNE DECANTER 1970-72
8" high 5 oz. clear glass with gold head. OSP $6. **CMV $5. BO, $7. MB.**

BIRD OF PARADISE BATH BRUSH & SOAP 1970-71
Blue box holds blue plastic bath brush and blue soap. OSP $6. **CMV $8. MB.**

BATH OIL EMOLLIENT 1969-75
6 oz. gold cap and neck tag. OSP $7.50 **CMV $1.**

COLOGNE 1969-72
4 oz. gold cap & neck tag. OSP $5. **CMV $2.**

BEAUTY DUST 1969-74
6 oz. turquoise and gold paper box. OSP $5. CMV $3., $5. MB.

COLOGNE MIST 1970-76
3 oz. blue plastic coated bottle with gold cap and neck tag. OSP $7. **CMV $1.**

CREAM SACHET 1969-75
.66 oz. blue glass with gold lid. OSP $3. **CMV 50c.**

SOAP 1970-76
3 oz. bars blue soap in blue & turquoise box. 1st issue no flower on soap. 1972 soap had flower. SSP $3. **CMV $. MB, no flowers $6. MB.**

BIRD OF PARADISE PERFUMED SKIN SOFTENER 1973-76
5 oz. blue plastic jar, gold and blue lid. OSP $3. **CMV 25c.**

SOAP 1975
3 oz. blue bar with blue wrapper and floral center. OSP $1. **CMV $1. mint.**

SOAP 1976-78
3 oz. blue bar with blue wrapper. OSP $1. **CMV $1. mint.**

BIRD OF PARADISE PERFUME GLACE RING 1970-72
(Left) Gold ring with turquoise top. Perfume glace inside. OSP $10. **CMV $7.**

COLOGNE 1970-72
(Right) 1/2 oz. bottle with gold cap. OSP $2. **CMV $2. MB.**

BIRD OF PARADISE PERFUMED TALC 1971-78
2 different labels. Left and center same labels but top is turquoise on one and dark blue on the other. One on right is dark blue label and top. Each is 3 1/4 oz. size. OSP $1.35. **CMV 50c.** Also came with upside down label. **CMV $4.**

BRISTOL BLUE

BRISTOL BLUE COLOGNE 1975
5 oz. translucent blue glass filled with Moonwind, Sonnet or Imperial Garden Cologne. OSP $6. **CMV $4. BO, $5. MB.**

BATH OIL 1975-76
5 oz. blue opaline glass decanter with plastic inner bottle that holds Skin So SOft bath oil. OSP $6. **CMV $4. BO, $5. MB.**

SOAP DISH & SOAP 1975-76
Translucent blue opaline glass dish with Moonwind, Sonnet or Imperial Garden soap. OSP $5. **CMV $6. MB.**

BIRD OF PARADISE PERFUMED SKIN SOFTENER 1971-73
(Left) 5 oz. blue glass jar with blue & gold lid. OSP $4. **CMV $1.**

COLOGNE FLUFF 1969-72
(Center) 3 oz. blue plastic coated bottle with gold top. Blue & gold neck tag. OSP $5. **CMV $1.**

PERFUMED POWDER MIST 1971-77
(Right) 7 oz. blue and gold can, gold cap. OSP $4. **CMV $1.**

BIRD OF PARADISE SCENTED HAIR SPRAY 1971-72
(Left) 7 oz. blue can & lid. OSP $1.50. **CMV $3.**

FOAMING BATH OIL 1971-74
(Right) 6 oz. blue plastic bottle with gold cap and blue & gold neck tag. OSP $4. **CMV $1.**

BLUE LOTUS	BRIGHT NIGHT

BLUE LOTUS AFTER BATH FRESHENER 1967-72
6 oz. glass bottle with blue cap. OSP $3. CMV $2.

CREAM SACHET 1968-72
.66 oz. blue frosted glass with blue cap. OSP $2.50. CMV $1.50.

FOAMING BATH OIL 1970-73
6 oz. plastic bottle with blue cap. OSP $3.50. CMV $1.50.

CREAM LOTION 1969-72
5 oz. plastic bottle with blue cap. OSP $2. CMV $1.50.

DEMI STICK 1969-73
.19 oz. white plastic with blue and green center. OSP $1. CMV $1.

BLUE LOTUS PERFUME SOAP 1967-71
3 oz. blue, white and purple wrapper. OSP 75c. CMV $2.

PERFUMED TALC 1967-71
3 1/2 oz. cardboard container with plastic shaker top. OSP $1.10. CMV $2.

BRIGHT NIGHT BEAUTY DUST 1959-61
White plastic box with gold stars on lid. OSP $2.95. CMV $8. CO, $12. MB.

BRIGHT NIGHT COLOGNE 1954-61
4 oz. gold speckled cap with gold neck cord and white paper label. OSP $2.50. CMV $20. MB, $14. BO mint.

BRIGHT NIGHT TOILET WATER 1955-61
2 oz. gold speckled cap with white paper label on gold neck cord. OSP $2. CMV $20. MB, $14. BO.

BRIGHT NIGHT BEAUTY DUST 1957-58
(Top) White cardboard box trimmed in gold. Came at Christmas with 5/8 dram Snowflake Perfume bottle with white ribbon and cap. OSP $2.50. CMV $30. MB.

BRIGHT NIGHT BEAUTY DUST 1956
(Bottom) Same as above. Came at Christmas 1956 with long neck perfume bottle with white cap and ribbon. OSP $2.50. CMV $30. MB.

BRIGHT NIGHT BEAUTY DUST 1954-59
Same powder box without perfume. OSP 75c. CMV $18. mint.

BRIGHT NIGHT PERFUME 1954-59
Gold and white box holds 1/2 oz. glass stoppered bottle with white label on gold neck cord. OSP $7.50. CMV $120. MB., $75. BO. Also came with 1 dram perfume in felt wrapper on top of lid. Add $15. for 1 dram perfume with ribbon around box.

BRIGHT NIGHT COLOGNE MIST 1958-61
3 oz. white plastic coated over clear glass. Gold speckled cap, gold neck cord with white paper label. Came with 2 different caps. OSP $2.75. CMV$20. MB, $14. BO.

BRIGHT NIGHT GEMS 1957
Gold & white flip open box holds Bright Night 2 oz. toilet water in top & cream sachet in pull-out drawer in bottom. OSP $3.50. CMV $45. mint.

BRIGHT NIGHT POWDER SACHET 1955-61
(Left) .9 oz., 1 1/4, 1 1/2 oz. white glass jar with stars on white lid. Front paper label. OSP $1.50. **CMV $8. bo, $12. MB.** 1 1/2 oz. rare. **CMV $20. MB, $16. BO.**

BRIGHT NIGHT CREAM SACHET 1954-61
(Right) White glass jar with stars on white lid. OSP $1.50. **CMV $6. MB, $8.**

MELODY SET 1955-56
Gold & white box holds Bright Night 1 dram perfume, cream sachet, 4 oz. cologne & beauty dust. OSP $8.75. **CMV $85.**

BROCADE PERFUME GLACE 1967-72
Gold case. OSP $5.50. **CMV $6. MB, $9.**

GOLDEN BEAUTY 1957
Gold base box lined with gold acetate with gold plastic lid, holds Bright Night Beauty Dust, 4 oz. cologne, cream sachet and 1 dram perfume. OSP $8.95. **CMV $85.**

GOLDEN GLAMOUR SET 1958
Gold & white box holds Bright Night cologne mist, 1 dram perfume, cream sachet & beauty dust. OSP $8.95. **CMV $95. MB.**

MAGIC HOURS SET 1956
Gold & white box holds Bright Night 2 oz. toilet water & white cologne stick. OSP $3.50. **CMV $45.**

BROCADE 4 OZ. COLOGNE 1967-72
(Left) Frosted ribbed glass with brown & white cap. OSP $6. **CMV $2,MB $3.**

BROCADE COLOGNE MIST 1967-72
(Center) 3 oz. ribbed frosted glass with brown & white cap. Some lids have design only & some say Brocade on top. OSP $6. **CMV $2. BO, $3. MB.**

BROCADE COLOGNE MIST REFILL 1967-72
(Right) 3 oz. brown plastic coated bottle, white cap. OSP $4. **CMV $3. BO, $4. MB.**

BROCADE PERFUMED TALC 1969-72
(Left) 3 1/2 oz. brown & white cardboard. OSP $1.25. **CMV $1.50.**

SCENTED HAIR SPRAY 1969-72
(Right) 7 oz. brown & white can. OSP $1.50. **CMV $3.**

BROCADE PERFUME OIL 1967-69
(Left) 1/2 oz. frosted brown glass with gold cap. OSP $6. **CMV $5, MB $7.**
BROCADE 1/2 OZ. COLOGNE 1970-71
(Right) Ribbed clear glass with gold cap. OSP $2. **CMV $2. MB, $1. BO.**

BROCADE DELUXE GIFT SET 1967
Brown & white box with white lining holds Brocade beauty dust, perfume rollette & cream sachet. OSP $12.95. **CMV $35. MB.**

BROCADE COLOGNE SILK 1968-70
(Left) 3 oz. frosted bottle with gold cap. OSP $4.50. **CMV $2. MB, $4.50**
BROCADE FOAMING BATH OIL 1968--72
(Right) 6 oz. plastic bottle with gold cap. OSP $4. **CMV $2.**

BROCADE BEAUTY DUST 1967-71
(Left) Brown ribbed plastic, patterned lid. OSP $6. **CMV $6, MB $9.**
BROCADE BEAUTY DUST 1971-75
(Right) Pattern printed cardboard, non-refillable. OSP $5. **CMV $4. CO, $5. MB.** Also came with upside down lettering. **CMV $6.**

BROCADE SOAP 1968
Brown & white wrapper. Came in Perfume Pair only. **CMV $4. mint.**

BROCADE PERFUME ROLLETTE 1967-72
(Left) Brown frosted glass, gold cap with 4A design. Ribs horizontal. OSP $3. **CMV $3.**
(Inside Left) Same as above only no 4A design. OSP $3. **CMV $3.**
(Inside Right) Brown carnival glass, gold cap. Vertical ribs. OSP $3. **CMV $8.**
(Right) Brown frosted glass, brown & white paper band on cap. Ribs horizontal. OSP $3. **CMV $5.**

BROCADE PERFUMED SKIN SOFTENER 1969-72
(Left) 5 oz. ribbed sides, brown glass, designed top. OSP $4. **CMV $2. BO, $3.MB.**
BROCADE PERFUMED SKIN SOFTENER 1968-69
(Center) 5 oz. ribbed sides, brown glass, label printed on top. OSP $4. **CMV $5. MB, $3. BO.**
BROCADE PERFUMED SKIN SOFTENER 1968 ONLY
(Right) Manufactured during glass strike, 5 oz. round smooth brown glass, label painted on top. OSP $4. **CMV $15. mint.**

BROCADE PERFUME POWDER MIST 1967-74
(Left) 7 oz. brown & white painted can with gold cap. OSP $4. **CMV 50c.**
(Right) 7 oz. brown & white paper label with gold cap. OSP $4. **CMV $3.** Some came with 7 oz. weight in center label and some at bottom of can in front.

MANAGER'S BROCADE DEMO KIT 1969
Brocade box holds round Brocade talc & cologne mist. **CMV $27.50 MB.**

BROCADE CREAM SACHET 1968-75
(Left) .66 oz. brown ribbed glass, designed cap. OSP $3. **CMV 50c.**
BROCADE CREAM SACHET 1967-68
(Center) .66 oz. brown ribbed glass, label on top. OSP $3. **CMV $2. BO, $3. MB.**
BROCADE TALC 1968
(Right) 2 3/4 oz. metal talc, brown, white and gold. Sold only in Perfume Pair set. **CMV $2.**

BUTTONS 'N BOWS

BUTTONS 'N BOWS NAIL POLISH 1961-63
(Left) Pink and white box holds nail polish with white cap. OSP 69c. **CMV $8. in box, $6. bottle only.**

BUTTONS 'N BOWS LIPSTICK 1961-63
(Right) Pink and white box holds pink and white striped lipstick. OSP 89c. **CMV $7. in box, $4. tube only.**

BUTTONS 'N BOWS COLOGNE 1960-63
(Left) 2 oz. clear glass, white cap, lettering pink, came with pink ribbon bow around neck. OSP $1.35. **CMV $12. MB, $9. BO.**

BUTTONS 'N BOWS COLOGNE MIST 1960-63
(Center) 2 1/2 oz. pink plastic with white cap. Bottom is 2 shades of pink. OSP $2.25. **CMV $9., $12. MB.**

BUTTONS 'N BOWS ROLL-ON DEODORANT 1962-63
(Right) 1 3/4 oz. white and pink painted label on clear glass, pink cap. OSP 89c. **CMV $8. BO, $12. MB.**

BUTTON BUTTON SET 1961-62
Pink & white box holds Buttons 'N bows 2 oz. cologne & beauty dust. OSP $3.60. **CMV $40. MB.**

BUTTONS 'N BOWS CREAM LOTION 1962-63
(Left) 4 oz. pink plastic bottle with white cap, OSP $1.35. **CMV $6, MB. $10.**

BUTTONS 'N BOWS BUBBLE BATH 1962-63
(Right) 4 oz. pink plastic, white cap, pink lettering. OSP $1.35. **CMV $6, $10. MB.**

BUTTONS 'N BOWS
Cream lotion & bubble bath both came in solid pink plastic & clear frosted plastic bottle. Pink has pink letters. Frosted has white letters.

PRETTY CHOICE SET 1962-63
2 oz. frosted plastic bottle cream lotion, white cap. Cologne, clear glass, white cap, light pink ribbon on neck. Had choice of cream lotion or bubble bath. OSP $2.70. **CMV $30. MB.**

CUTE AS A BUTTON SET 1961-63
Pink & white box holds Buttons 'N Bows nail polish with white cap and pink & white lipstick. OSP $1.58. **CMV $17. MB.**

BUTTONS 'N BOWS SOAP 1961-63
Pink box & soap. OSP $1.35. Some buttons have thread through holes. **CMV $25. MB no threads, $27.50 with threads.** Two boxes are shown. Each box holds 2 bars. Boxes are same.

BUTTONS 'N BOWS BEAUTY DUST 1960-63
(left) Pink & white cardboard box with clear plastic lid. OSP $2.25. **CMV $16.**

BUTTONS 'N BOWS CREAM SACHET 1960-63
(Right) Pink glass jar with white & pink lid. OSP $1.35. **CMV $9. BO, $12. MB.**

CAMEO

CAMEO SOAP ON A ROPE 1969
(Top Left) Blue box holds blue soap on white or blue & white rope. OSP $1.75. **CMV $7. - $12. MB.**

CAMEO SACHET 1961-63
(Top Right) Gold metal base holds pink painted over milk glass jar with white lid with lady's face. Came in Topaze, Cotillion, Somewhere. OSP $3.25. To A Wild Rose OSP $2.75. Persian Wood & Here's My Heart. OSP $3. **CMV $7. BO, $11. MB.**

CAMEO BROCH 1965
(Bottom) Gold brooch with pink & white lady's face. Came in Cameo Set only. **CMV $15. MB, $9. brooch only.**

CAMEO SET 1965
White, gold & green box holds Cameo compact, lipstick & Cameo brooch. OSP $6.50. **CMV $30.**

CAMEO LIPSTICK 1965-66
White lipstick with gold base & lady's face on top. OSP 98c. **CMV $2. - $3. MB.**

CAMEO COMPACT 1965-66
White plastic with gold edge & pink lady's face on top. OSP $2.50. **CMV $6. CO, $8. MB.**

CAMEO SET 1973-74
Reddish brown plastic with white Cameo beauty dust 6 oz. Came in Sonnet, Moonwind, Hana Gasa, Charisma, Unforgettable, Rapture, Somewhere, Cotillion, Here's My Heart, Topaze, Occur!, To A Wild Rose. SSP $4. **CMV $4. BRUSH & COMB SET. CMV $3. MIRROR. CMV $2.**

CAMEO SOAP 1966
Blue & white box holds 4 white Cameo soaps. OSP $2. **CMV $20. MB.**

CHARISMA

CHARISMA SKIN SOFTENER 1969-71
(Top) 5 oz. dark red glass jar has red & gold metal caps, or red & silver metal caps. Bottom labels are red with gold lettering. OSP $4. **CMV $1. BO, $2. MB.**

CHARISMA SKIN SOFTENER 1972
(Top) 5 oz. light red glass, caps are red & gold metal. Paper labels on bottoms are white with red lettering. OSP $4. **CMV $2. MB, $1. BO.**

COLOGNE 1969-72
(Bottom Left) 4 oz. red glass, some are silver tip (rare) with red plastic cap trimmed in gold. OSP $6. **CMV $3.**

COLOGNE MIST 1968-76
(Bottom Right) 3 oz. red plastic coated, trimmed in gold. OSP $8. **CMV $1.**

PERFUME ROLLETTE 1968-76
(Bottom Center) .33 oz. red glass trimmed in gold. OSP $4.50. **CMV $1.**

CHARISMA TRAY 1968-70
(Left) Dark red plastic with gold trim. 11" diameter. This one used as introduction. **CMV $8. MB.**
(Right) Lighter red plastic with gold rim. 10" diameter. OSP $3. **CMV $3. - $5. MB.**

CHARISMA CREAM SACHET 1968-76
(Left) .66 oz. red glass jar with red & gold lid. OSP $4.50. **CMV 50c.**

COLOGNE 1969-72
(Center) 1/2 oz. red glass, gold cap. OSP $1.75. **CMV $2.**

BEAUTY DUST 1968-76
(Right) 6 oz. red plastic powder box trimmed in gold. OSP $10. **CMV $6. MB, $3. CO.**

CHARISMA COLOGNE SILK 1970-71
(Left) 3 oz. clear glass, red cap. OSP $4.50.
CMV $2. BO, $3. MB.
COLOGNE SILK 1969
(Right) 3 oz. frosted glass, red cap. OSP
$4.50. CMV $4. MB, $3. BO.

CHARISMA SCENTED HAIR SPRAY 1970-72
(Left) 7 oz. red can. OSP $1.50. CMV $3.
PERFUMED TALC 1970-76
(Inside Left) 3 1/2 oz. red cardboard. OSP
$1.35. CMV 50c.
PERFUME POWDER MIST 1971-76
(Inside Right) 7 oz. red & gold can, gold top,
painted label. No longer boxed. OSP $5.
CMV $1.
PERFUMED POWDER MIST 1969-70
(Right) 7 oz. red & gold can, gold top, has
paper label. Also came boxed. OSP $3.50.
CMV $3.

CHARISMA SOAP 1975
(Top) 3 pink Charisma soap in special
Christmas 1975 design box. OSP $3. CMV
$8. MB.
CHARISMA SOAP 1970-76
(Bottom) Red box holds 3 bars. OSP $3.50.
CMV $6. MB.

CHARISMA FOAMING BATH OIL 1970-71
(Left) 6 oz. red plastic bottle with red band on
gold cap. Red paper label with gold lettering
on bottom. OSP $3.50. CMV $1.
FOAMING BATH OIL 1971-73
(Center) Same as above only cap has no red
band. Bottom label is white with red lettering.
OSP $4. CMV $1. MB.
FOAMING BATH OIL 1973-74
(Right) Same as above only front lettering
says Foaming Bath Oil. Bottom label has
number in red. OSP $4. CMV $1. MB.

COTILLION

**All white caps on 1961-74 Cotillion bottles will turn dark gray when exposed
to sunlight. The gray or faded caps are not considered to be in mint condition.**

COTILLION PERFUME 1951-52
3 dram glass stoppered swirl glass bottle.
White, pink & blue flower design around
neck with neck tag. Pink & white box. OSP
$3.50. CMV $125. MB, BO with tag &
flower design $100.

COTILLION SWIRL PERFUME 1948-50
3 dram glass stoppered is swirl glass design,
gold neck tag. Purple & white flowered box.
Osp $3. CMV $75. mint, $100. MB.

COTILLION PERFUME 1935 ONLY
1/4 oz. gold cap, green and yellow label & box.
For 77th birthday of D. H. McConnell. OSP
20c. CMV $80. MB, $60. BO.

COTILLION PERFUME 1945-47
3 dram glass stopper bottle with gold neck tag.
Came in blue, pink & white box as shown.
OSP $3. CMV $100. BO mint, $125. MB.

COTILLION PERFUME 1939 ONLY
2 dram, ribbed cap with "A" on cap. Sold for one campaign only for 20c with purchase of other Avons. **CMV MB $75., $55. BO.**

COTILLION PERFUME 1936 ONLY
2 dram, gold ribbed cap. Sold for 20c July 7-27, 1936 only, with purchase of other Avons. In honor of mr. McConnell's 78th birthday. **CMV $80. MB, $60. BO.**

COTILLION TULIP PERFUME CHRISTMAS BOX 1935
Red & green Christmas box holds 1/4 oz. glass stoppered perfume with gold label. This bottle sold 1934-39. With this box 1935 Christmas only. OSP $1.04. **CMV $90. MB as shown.** See Misc. perfumes for other fragrances in same bottles.

COTILLION PERFUME 1934
1/4 oz. metal cap. First Cotillion bottle issued in honor of Mr. McConnell's birthday. OSP 20c. **CMV $55. BO, $75. MB.**

COTILLION PERFUME 1937
2 dram, gold cap. OSP 20c. **CMV $70. MB, $50. BO.**

COTILLION TOILET WATER 1938-39
Flowered box & label. 2 oz. bottle, white plastic cap. Sold for 20c with purchase of other Avons. May 2-22, 1939. CPC on box and back side of label. **CMV $52.50 MB, $37.50 BO mint.**

COTILLION PERFUME 1940 ONLY
2 dram, ribbed gold cap with "A" on top. Also came plain gold cap. Sold for 20c with purchase of other Avons. **CMV $75. MB, $55. BO.**

COTILLION TOILET WATER 1946-49
2 oz. pink, gold or white cap. OSP $1.19. **CMV $35. MB, $25. BO mint.**

COTILLION BATH OIL 1962
(Left) 6 oz. pink & white plastic bottle. Came in Bath Bouquet set only. **CMV $6.**
COTILLION COLOGNE 1949-50
(Right) 2 oz. pink cap. OSP $1.25. **CMV $22.50 - $25. MB.** Toilet water in same design bottle & label. 2 oz. size, pink cap. **Same CMV.**

COTILLION PERFUME 1950
1/8 oz. pink cap. Very rare. OSP $1. **CMV $70.BO, $85.MB.**

COTILLION CREAM SACHET 1951-53
(Left) White glass jar with pink & white lid.
OSP $1.25. CMV $15.
COTILLION TOILET WATER 1950-53
(Right) 2 oz. pink cap, pink & white label &
white box. Box came solid & with open
window so label shows through. OSP $1.25.
CMV $22. MB, $18. BO.

COTILLION BEAUTY DUST 1950-53
Pink & white container. OSP $1.75. CMV $20.
mint, $25. MB.

COTILLION SOAP 1950-53
Pink & white box holds pink bars. OSP 69c.
CMV $37.50 MB.

COTILLION BATH OIL 1950-53
6 oz. pink & white label & pink cap. Pink &
white box. OSP 95c. CMV $22. MB, $18. BO.

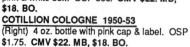

COTILLION CREAM LOTION 1950-53
(Left) 6 oz. pink & white label, pink cap and
pink & white box. OSP 89c. CMV $22. MB,
$18. BO.
COTILLION COLOGNE 1950-53
(Right) 4 oz. bottle with pink cap & label. OSP
$1.75. CMV $22. MB, $18. BO.

COTILLION SOAP 1953-61
Pink & white box holds 3 pink or white bars.
OSP 89c. Box came as sleeve top with round
edge white soaps. 1953-56 CMV $35. MB.
1956-61 came sleeve top box with 3 flat edge
pink soaps. CMV $32.50 MB.

COTILLION SOAP 1961-67
Gold & white box holds 3 bars with gold
centers. OSP $2. CMV $22.50 MB.

COTILLION TALC 1950-53
(Left) Pink & white can with pink cap. OSP
43c. CMV $12., MB $15.
COTILLION BODY POWDER 1950-53
(Right) 5 oz. pink & white paper box, sifter top
with metal lid & bottom. OSP 75c. CMV $17.,
MB $20.

COTILLION TALCUM 1947 ONLY
(Left) Pink paper box, white shaker top. OSP
39c. CMV $25., MB $30.
COTILLION TALCUM 1942-46
(Center) 2.75 oz. turquoise & white all paper
box. War time. Paper top fits over top of box,
shaker top. CMV without top $20. in mint.
OSP 39c. CMV $25. mint.
COTILLION TALCUM 1944-46
(Right) Turquoise & white paper box, plastic
octagonal cap. OSP 39c. CMV $25. mint.

COTILLION TALCUM BOX 1941 ONLY
Blue box with fan. 2.75 oz. can. Sold to Reps
for 10c to use as a demonstrator. CMV $30.
MB as shown.

53rd ANNIVERSARY COTILLION TALCUM 1939 ONLY
Special 53rd Anniversary box to first introduce Cotillion talcum. May 23 to June 12, 1939. 2.75 oz. turquoise & white can. This can sold 1939-43 then 1946-50. OSP 37c. **CMV can only $10, in special 53rd box $25.**

COTILLION TALCUM 1938-50
2.75 oz. turquoise can. Box marked 2 3/4 oz. size. Can sold 1938-43 then 1946-50. OSP 37c. **CMV $10. can only, $15. MB mint.**

COTILLION COLOGNE 1946-50
(Left) 6 oz. pink cap. OSP $1.50. **CMV $50. BO, $65. MB.**
COTILLION BODY POWDER 1946-50
(Center & Right) 4.5 oz. light pink cardboard. Blue metal sifter top. OSP 75c. **CMV $15., Mb $20.** Came in sets 5 oz. size with pink & white plastic sifter top. **Same CMV.**

COTILLION TALCUM 1940-43 THEN 1946-50
(Left) 14.5 oz. metal can, turquoise & white. OSP $1.05. **CMV $20., add $5. for CPC label.**
COTILLION TALCUM 1943-46
(Right) 14.5 oz. paper box used during war. Rare. OSP $1.19. **CMV $35.**

COTILLION TALCUM CHRISTMAS BOX 1943
Pale blue & pink outer box issued only at Christmas 1943 with cardboard large size talc. OSP 98c. **CMV $35. MB as shown.**

COTILLION BEAUTY DUST 1962-63
Gold & white paper box with clear plastic lid with 4A design on lid. Came in 1962-63 Fragrance Magic sets only. **CMV $17. mint.**

COTILLION BEAUTY DUST 1959-61
Pink plastic bottom, white plastic top with gold center. OSP $2.95. **CMV $6. CO, $12. MB.**

COTILLION PERFUMED TALC 1956-61
White can with pink cap & design. Also came just talc. OSP 69c. **CMV $8. MB, CO $5.**

COTILLION TALCUM CHRISTMAS BOX 1940-41
Special issue blue & white Christmas box holds regular issue metal can of Cotillion talcum in large size. OSP 89c, RARE. **CMV $30. MB as shown.**

COTILLION BEAUTY DUST 1953-59
Pink paper sides with pink & white tin top. OSP $1.95. **CMV $12., MB $16.**

COTILLION FACE POWDER 1939-42
Gold & turquoise powder box. OSP 78c. **CMV**
$8., MB $10. Add $3. for CPC label.

COTILLION SACHET 1946-47
(Left) 1 1/4 oz. pink glass & cap with painted
label. (Rare) Sold only in Cotillion Garland
Set. Same set in 1947 was called Cotillion
Duet. **CMV $20., MB $22.**
SACHET 1946-49
(Center) 1 1/4 oz. clear glass, pink cap, paper
label. OSP $1.15. **CMV $16., MB $18.**
SACHET 1939-44
(Right) 1 1/4 oz. turquoise cap, clear glass,
paper label. OSP $1.04. **CMV $12. BO, $16.
MB.**

COTILLION CREAM SACHET 1961-75
(Left) .66 frosted glass with pink & white lid,
gold or silver lettering. OSP $2. **CMV 25c.**
POWDER SACHET 1961-67
(Center) 9/10 oz. frosted glass with pink &
white cap. OSP $2. **CMV $8. MB, $6. BO.**
SACHET 1944-45
(Right) 1 1/4 oz. paper box, pink plastic
flowers on lid. OSP $1.15. **CMV $20. MB,
$18. BO mint.**

COTILLION SACHET SPECIAL ISSUE BOX
1939
Special issue box is blue with lace design.
Holds regular issue powder sachet. OSP 20c.
CMV $18. MB as shown.

COTILLION SACHET 1937-38
1 1/4 oz. ribbed glass bottle with turquoise cap.
OSP $1.04. **CMV $24. MB, $18. BO mint.**

COTILLION POWDER SACHET 1950-53
(Left) 1 1/4 oz. pink cap and pink & white
label. OSP $1.19. **CMV $15., MB $20.**
POWDER SACHET 1957-61
(Center) 1 1/4 oz. or .9 oz. pink cap & pink
bottom with painted label. Came light or dark
pink bottom & also white or pink painted
lettering. OSP $1.50. **CMV $9., MB $13.**
POWDER SACHET 1953-56
(Right) 9/10 oz. or 1 1/4 oz. clear glass, pink
cap & pink painted label. Also white lettering
(rare). OSP $1.25. **CMV $8., MB $12. White
lettering $18.**

COTILLION SACHET BOX 1941 ONLY
Special issue box to Avon ladies only, for 20c.
Holds regular issue Cotillion sachet, 1939-44.
CMV $20. MB as shown.

COTILLION SACHET VALENTINE BOX
1952
1 1/4 oz. pink cap. Came in gold, pink and
white Valentine box. Rare in this box. **CMV
$25. MB as shown.**

COTILLION VALENTINE SACHET 1952
1 1/4 oz. white cap. OSP 98c. **CMV $25. MB.**
See Misc. Powder Sachet section for nox.
CMV $18. BO mint.

COTILLION SACHET 1937
(Left) Red & green box sold Christmas only for
25c, CPC on box & bottle. **CMV $25. MB, $18.
BO mint.**
SACHET 1937
(Right) Blue & white box special issue. **CMV
$25. MB.** Bottle only, ribbed glass, turquoise
cap, sold 1937-38. OSP $1.04. **CMV $18. BO
mint.**

COTILLION SACHET CHRISTMAS BOX 1957

.9 oz. pink painted glass, pink cap. Bottle sold 1957-61. Pink, green and blue triangle box sold 1957 only. OSP $1.50. **CMV $15. MB as shown.**

COTILLION TALC 1953-54

4 oz. clear glass bottle with pink cap & pink or white (rare) painted label. 1955 was called Talcum in painted label, pink & white box. OSP $1. **CMV $15. each MB, $10. BO.**

COTILLION TALC 1950 ONLY

(Left) 2 oz. white cardbaord, pink top & bottom. Came in Always Sweet set only. **CMV $15.**

COTILLION PERFUMED BATH OIL 1959-61

(Right) 8 oz. pink plastic, pink cap. OSP $2.50. **CMV $10.**

COTILLION POWDER SACHET-NO LABEL 1957-61

Pink paint over clear glass, pink cap. Rare issue came with no painted label. Plain pink all over. **CMV add $5. to price of regular issue.**

COTILLION BATH OIL 1954-59

(Left) 4 1/2 oz. pink cap, pink painted label, pink & white box. OSP $1.35. **CMV $15. MB, $9. BO.**

CREAM LOTION 1954-61

(Right) 4 1/4 oz. pink cap & pink painted label, pink & white box. OSP 95c. **CMV $12. MB, $8. BO.**

COTILLION COLOGNE MIST 1959-61

(Left) 3 oz. pink plastic coated bottle with white cap & paper label. OSP $2.95. **CMV $12. BO, $17. MB.**

COLOGNE MIST 1958-59

(Center) 3 oz. pink plastic coated bottle. OSP $2.50. **CMV $16. - $20. MB.**

COLOGNE MIST 1958 ONLY

(Right) Rare 3 oz. pink plastic bottle. OSP $2.50. **CMV $42.50 BO, $52.50 MB.**

COTILLION TOILET WATER 1953-61

(Left) 2 oz. gold cap, pink band around neck, pink painted label. OSP $1.50. **CMV $15. MB, $10. BO.** Some have white painted label.

4 OZ. COLOGNE 1953-61

(Right) Gold cap, pink band around neck, pink painted label. OSP $2. **CMV $15. MB, $10. BO mint.** Some have white painted label.

COTILLION TALC 1956-58

(Left) 3 oz. frosted glass with pink lid & paper label, pink & white box. OSP $1. **CMV $14. MB, $9. BO.**

BODY POWDER 1958-59

(Right) 3 oz. frosted glass with pink lid & paper label, pink & white box. OSP $1. **CMV $15. MB, $11. BO.**

COTILLION CREAM SACHET 1953-57

(Left) Pink lid, white glass bottom. OSP $1.25. **CMV $8., MB $10.**

CREAM SACHET 1957-61

Pink lid, pink glass bottom. OSP $1.50. **CMV $7., MB $9.**

COTILLION COLOGNE 1957 ONLY
(Left) 3 dram, white cap. Came in Fragrance Rainbow set only. **CMV $8. BO, $10. with neck bow.**
COLOGNE 1961 ONLY
(Right) 2 oz. gold cap, pink band around neck, painted label. OSP $1.50. **CMV $20. - $22. MB.**

THE COTILLION SET 1950-52
Pink & white box with green lining holds Cotillion cream lotion & cologne. OSP $2.60. **CMV $60.**

COTILLION ENCHANTMENT SET 1951
Pink, white & green box holds Cotillion toilet water & cream sachet. OSP $2.50. **CMV $60. MB.**

COTILLION PERFUME TALC 1974-77
(Left) 3.5 oz. pink & gold cardboard. OSP $1. **CMV $1.**
CREAM SACHET 1975-78
(Inside Left) .66 oz. clear glass with gold & pink cap. OSP $2. **CMV 50c.**
PERFUME DEMI STICK 1975-78
(Center) .19 oz. white with pink & gold. OSP $1. **CMV 50c.**
COLOGNE MIST 1961-74
(Inside Right & Right) 3 oz. white plastic coated bottle with white cap. OSP $4. **CMV $1.** Same bottle with yellow plastic coated bottom. **CMV $10. MB, $7. BO.** 1975-76 issue has white cap, pink top & pink painted label. OSP $5. **CMV $1.**

COTILLION COLOGNE 1969-72
(Left) 1/2 oz. white cap, clear glass. OSP $1.50. **CMV $1. BO, $2. MB.**
PERFUMED OIL 1964-69
(Center) 1/2 oz. frosted glass with white cap. OSP $4. **CMV $5. BO, $7. MB.**
PERFUMED OIL FOR THE BATH 1963-64
(Right) 1/2 oz. frosted glass with white cap. OSP $4. **CMV $7. BO, $9. MB.**

JOLLY SURPRISE SET 1951-52
Pink & white box holds Cotillion powder sachet & 1 dram perfume in pink net lining. OSP $1.99. **CMV $42. set.**

COTILLION PERFUMED BATH OIL 1961-66
(Left) 6 oz. pink plastic bottle, white cap. OSP $2.50. **CMV $6.**
FAOMING BATH OIL 1966-74
(Right) 6 oz. pink plastic bottle, white cap. OSP $2. **CMV $2. BO, $3. MB.**

COTILLION BATH BOUQUET SET 1956 ONLY
Pink & white box holds 2 oz. Cotillion cologne, 2 oz. Cotillion bath oil & 1 bar of Cotillion soap. OSP $2.25. **CMV $55.**

COTILLION COLOGNE 1960 ONLY
4 oz. clear glass, gold cap, pink paper band around neck with pink painted label. Pink & gold box. OSP $2.50. **CMV $22. in this box.**

COTILLION BOUQUET SET 1958
Pink & white box holds Cotillion cologne mist & pink glass cream sachet. OSP $3.95. **CMV $65. MB.**

COTILLION BEAUTY DUST 1961-70
(Left) White frosted plastic bottom with clear plastic lid. OSP $4. **CMV $3. - $5. MB.** Some with yellow plastic bottom. **CMV $6. - $8. MB.**
PERFUMED TALC 1961-74
(Center) 2.75 oz. bright pink can with white cap. OSP $1. **CMV $1.**
PERFUMED SKIN SOFTENER 1964-73
(Right) 5 oz. pink glass jar with gold & white lid. Some came with silver lid. OSP $3.50. **CMV gold 50c, silver $1.** Regular issue came pink painted over clear glass. **CMV 50c.** Some came pink painted over white milk glass. **CMV $5.**
PERFUMED SKIN SOFTENER 1973-75
(Not Shown) 5 oz. pink plastic with white & gold cap. OSP $3.50. **CMV 50c.**

COTILLION COLOGNE 1961-71
(Left) 2 oz. frosted glass with white cap. OSP $2. **CMV $1. - $2. MB.**
COLOGNE 1961-63
(Right) 4 oz. frosted glass with white cap. OSP $3. **CMV $3.**

COTILLION CREAM LOTION 1961-68
(Left) 4 oz. pink plastic, white cap. OSP $1.50. **CMV $3.50.**
COTILLION BODY POWDER 1961-64
(Right) 4 oz. pink plastic, white cap. OSP $2.25. **CMV $6., MB $8.**

COTILLION DUET SET 1953-55
Pink & white flowered box with pink satin lining holds Cotillion 4 oz. cologne & Cotillion talc. OSP $3. **CMV $42. MB.**

COTILLION DELUXE SET 1953-55
Pink & white box flips open in center. Holds Cotillion 1 dram persume, 4 oz. cologne, powder sachet & talcum. Same set also came with lift off lid. OSP $6. **CMV $60. MB.**

THE COTILLION SET 1957
Pink & white box holds Cotillion beauty dust, cream sachet with white glass bottom & 4 oz. cologne. OSP $4.95. **CMV $45.**

COTILLION CAROL SET 1956
Pink & white box holds Cotillion cream sachet with white glass bottom & Cotillion talc. OSP $2.25. **CMV $35.**

COTILLION SCENTED HAIR SPRAY 1966-70
(Left) 7 oz. pink can. OSP $1.50. **CMV $3.**
PERFUMED POWDER MIST 1966-72
(Center) 7 oz. (1966-70) pink can has paper label & pink cap & came in white box lined in pink. OSP $3.50. **CMV $2.**
(Right) 7 oz. (1970-71) pink can, pink cap. Label was painted. Not boxed. OSP $3.50. **CMV $1.**

COTILLION BATH OIL 1955-56
(Left) 2 oz. clear glass bottle with pink cap, label pink & white. Came in That's For Me set only. CMV $15.
HAND LOTION 1949
(Right) 2 oz. clear glass bottle with pink & blue label, blue cap. Came in Your Charms & Hair-Ribbons set. CMV $15.

COTILLION TREASURES SET 1957
Gold, white & pink box holds 3 oz. bottles of Cotillion bath oil & cologne with gold caps, 1 pink bar of Cotillion soap. OSP $2.75. **CMV $75. MB.**

COTILLION PERFUME MIST 1964-68
(Left) 2 dram, pink & white metal with gold band. OSP $3.25. CMV $6. - $7. MB.
SPRAY PERFUME 1961-63
(Center) 2 dram, pink & white metal with gold band. OSP $3.50. CMV $10. MB, $8. BO.
SPRAY PERFUME 1960-61
(Right) Rose, white & gold box holds rose & gold metal spray container. OSP $2.95. CMV $10. BO, $16. MB.

COTILLION GARLAND SET 1954-55
Pink & white box holds 4 1/2 oz. Cotillion bath oil & cream lotion. OSP $2.15. CMV $37.50 MB.

COTILLION PRINCESS SET 1956
Pink, white & gold box holds Cotillion beauty dust & 4 oz. cologne. OSP $3.95. CMV $40.

ENCHANTMENT SET 1953-56
Pink & white box holds Cotillion powder sachet & 1 dram perfume. OSP $3. CMV $37. MB.

COTILLION TALC 1948
(Left) White, pink & blue paper container came in Hair Ribbon set only. CMV $12.
TALC 1951
(Right) 2 oz. blue, white & pink paper container. Came in 1951 Always Sweet set. CMV $12.

1 OZ. COTILLION COLOGNE 1957 ONLY
(Left) Pink cap. Came in Beautiful Journey set. CMV $15.
COLOGNE 1956 ONLY
(Center) 2 oz. white caps. Came in Bath Bouquet only. CMV $20. mint.
BATH OIL 1956 ONLY
(Right) 2 oz. white caps. Came in Bath Bouquet only. CMV $20. mint.

COTILLION DUO SET 1964
White, pink & gold box holds Cotillion powder sachet & 1 dram perfume. OSP $4.50. CMV $22.50. MB.

DEBUTANTE SET 1963
Pink, white & gold box holds Cotillion cologne mist & beauty dust. Comes in 2 different inner boxes. OSP $8.50. **CMV $20. MB.**

COTILLION DUET SET 1947-48
Pink box holds 2 oz. Cotillion toilet water with gold cap & powder sachet. OSP $2.39. **CMV $70. MB.**

ALWAYS SWEET SET 1951
White, blue & pink box with girls hat on lid, holds straw handbag containing Cotillion talc, 5/8 dram perfume & cream lotion with blue cap. OSP $3. **CMV $95. MB.**

HAIR RIBBONS SET 1948-49
Pink & white box has bottle of Avon hand lotion, Cotillion talc, 5/8 dram bottle of Cotillion perfume. Also came, this box, with hand lotion & Cotillion talc from 1949 Your Charm set. Set came with or without perfume. OSP $1.59. **CMV $65. with perfume, $50. without perfume.**

SOMEONE LIKE YOU SET 1961-62
Pink & white box holds Cotillion 2 oz. cologne & cream sachet. OSP $4. **CMV $22.**

COTILLION BATH ENSEMBLE SET 1950-52
Pink & white box holds 2 drawers with Cotillion talc, powder sachet & 2 bars of pink soap in top drawer. Bottom drawer holds Cotillion cream lotion, toilet water, bath oil & 1 dram perfume. OSP $8.25. **CMV $175. MB.**

COTILLION DEBUT SET 1961-62
White & gold box holds Cotillion beauty dust, cream sachet & cologne mist, in satin lined flip open compartment. OSP $10. **CMV $35.**

YOUR CHARMS SET 1949
White, blue & pink box with or without ribbon band around lid came with gold heart & arrow charm on lid. Box contains pink & blue paper box of Cotillion talc, 2 oz. Avon hand lotion, pink & blue label with blue cap, 5/8 dram Cotillion perfume with blue cap. Set came with & without perfume. OSP $1.59. **CMV $65. with perfume, $50. without perfume.**

COTILLION GARLAND SET 1950
Pink, white & green box holds Cotillion talc & 2 oz. toilet water. OSP $1.85. **CMV $52.50.**

ALWAYS SWEET SET 1950
Pink & white box holds straw handbag with green & yellow ribbon & pink flower. Holds bottle of cream lotion with blue cap, Cotillion talc & 5/8 dram Cotillion perfume. OSP $2.39. **CMV $95. MB.**

COTILLION CLASSIC SET 1940-41
Satin lined box with people dancing on lid holds 2 oz. Cotillion toilet water & gold box of Cotillion talc. OSP $1.50. **CMV $67.50 MB.**

COTILLION FANTASY SET 1952
Pink & white Cotillion body powder with cream sachet on top under clear plastic lid. OSP $1.95. **CMV $40. MB.**

COTILLION CLASSIC SET 1946-47
Pink flowered box holds Cotillion 6 oz. cologne & body powder. OSP $2.48. **CMV $95.**

COTILLION ENCHANTMENT SET 1938-39
White box with satin lining holds Cotillion 2 dram glass stoppered perfume, 2 oz. Cotillion toilet water & powder sachet. OSP $2.95. **CMV $150. MB.**

COTILLION ENCHANTMENT SET 1940-43
Silk lined gold & green box holds Cotillion powder sachet, 2 oz. toilet water & 1 dram perfume with gold cap. OSP $2.85. **CMV $95. MB.**

COTILLION GARLAND/COTILLION DUET SET 1946
Pink round box holds Cotillion toilet water & pink painted powder sachet. This set was introduced as Cotillion Duet then changed to Cotillion Garland for Christmas 1946. OSP $2.84. **CMV $80. MB.**

COTILLION PERFUME 1953-58
3 dram bottle with gold cap, pink band around neck with painted label. In pink & white box. OSP $4.50. **CMV $100. MB, $65. BO.** Came with perfume 1 dram smooth glass with gold scroll cap in gold wrapper with pink snap and white & gold ribbon. OSP $6. **CMV $12. Complete set CMV $115. with white & gold ribbon.**

COUNTRY
GARDENS

COUNTRY GARDEN FOAMING BATH OIL 1971-73
4" high, 6 oz. white glass bottle, white cap, green ribbon on neck. Came in Bird of Paradise, Elusive or Charisma. OSP $5.50. **CMV $5. MB, $3. BO.**

SOAP DISH & SOAP 1971-72
4" long white soap dish with bar of Country Garden soap. OSP $4.50. **CMV $6. MB.**

BEAUTY DUST 1971-72
4 1/2" high, 5 oz. white glass jar with white lid & greeen ribbon. Came in Bird of Paradise, Elusive or Charisma. OSP $6. **CMV $6. MB, $4. BO.**

POWDER SACHET 1971-73
3" high, 1 1/4 oz. white glass jar with white lid & green ribbon. Came in Bird of Paradise, Elusive or Charisma. OSP $4.50. **CMV $4. MB, $2. BO.**

COUNTRY KITCHEN

COURTSHIP PERFUME 1940-44
Box holds 1/8 oz. bottle, gold cap and label. OSP 75c. **CMV $25. mint, $35. MB as shown.**

COUNTRY KITCHEN MAGNETS & NOTE PADS 1981
Box holds Country Kitchen design fragranced note pads & packet of sachet. Three small metal magnets. SSP $6. **CMV $6. MB.**

COUNTRY KITCHEN CERAMIC TRIVET 1980-82
(Left) 7 1/2" long, made in Brazil. SSP $10. **CMV $6. MB.**
MOISTURIZED HAND LOTION
(Inside Left) 10oz. glass with pump dispenser. SSP $8. **CMV $3. MB.**
CERAMIC SALT & PEPPER SHAKERS
(Center & Inside Right) Made in Brazil. 4" high. SSP $10. set. **CMV $6. set MB.**

COURTSHIP

COURTSHIP PERFUME 1937 ONLY
2 dram, gold cap. Sold for 20c with other purchase during Founders Campaign, July 6-26, 1937. **CMV $60. MB, $40. BO mint.** See Misc. Perfumes & Toilet Water for other Courtship bottles.

CRIMSON

CARNATION

COURTSHIP PERFUME 1938 ONLY
2 dram bottle, gold cap. OSP 20c. **CMV $60. MB, $40. BO mint.**

CRYSTALIQUE

CRIMSON CARNATION TOILET WATER 1946-48
2 oz. gold or plastic caps. OSP $1.19. **CMV $40. BO, $55. MB.**

CRIMSON CARNATION PERFUME 1946-47
Blue & white box holds 3 dram bottle with white cap. OSP $3.75. **CMV $100. MB, BO $60.** See misc. perfumes for other Crimson Carnation perfumes.

CRYSTALIQUE BEAUTY DUST 1972
(Left) Clear crystal plastic powder box & lid with gold base. OSP $8. **CMV $5. - $7. MB.**
CRYSTALIQUE BEAUTY DUST 1972
(Right) Clear glass came with choice of powder. Moonwind, Charisma, Regence, Elusive, Rapture, Occur!, Somewhere, Topaze, Cotillion, Unforgettable or Here's My Heart, with matching puffs. SSP $7. **CMV $11. - $13. MB.**

CRYSTAL BEAUTY DUST 1966
(Left) All glass powder dish. OSP $5. CMV $20. - $22.50 MB.
CRYSTAL COLOGNE 1966-70
(Right) 4 oz., 5 1/2" high glass bottle with matching plastic cap, gold trim. Came in Unforgettable, Rapture, Occur!, Somewhere, Topaze, Cotillion, Here's My Heart or To A Wild Rose. OSP $3.50. CMV $3. BO, $5. MB.

CRYSTALIQUE BEAUTY DUST 1979-80
Clear glass, holds all beauty dust refills. (Sold empty.) OSP $5. CMV $5. MB.

DAISIES WON'T TELL

DAISIES WON'T TELL BEAUTY DUST 1957
(Left) Blue, white & yellow paper powder box with girl on lid. OSP $1.29. CMV $20. - $25. MB.
DAISY FLUFF-ON 1959-60
(Right) Blue paper powder box with Daisy Puff & clear plastic lid. OSP $1.98. CMV $12. - $16. MB.

DAISIES WON'T TELL BEAUTY DUST 1956
Yellow, white & blue paper box. Short issue. OSP $1.29. CMV $20. mint, $25. MB. Also came with blue sided container.

HEARTS 'N DAISIES 1958
(Left) Blue & white box holds 2 oz. Daisies Won't Tell cologne & pink pomade lipstick. OSP $1.59. CMV $22. MB.
LOVE ME - LOVE ME NOT 1959
(Right) Blue, white & green box holds Daisies Won't Tell spray cologne & cream sachet in pink glass. OSP $2.50. CMV $30.

DAISIES WON'T TELL CREAM SACHET 1963-64
(Left) Pink glass jar with white plastic lid. OSP $1.10. CMV in box $11., jar only $9.
CREAM SACHET 1959-61
(Right) Pink glass jar with floral metal lid. OSP $1.19. CMV $11., MB $13.

DAISY SHAMPOO 1959-61
4 oz. white plastic bottle & cap. OSP $1.19. CMV $10. BO, $12. MB.

DAISIES WON'T TELL BEAUTY DUST 1958
Blue & white box holds blue & white paper powder box with white daisy on top. OSP $1.49. CMV $23. MB, beauty dust only $18. mint.

DAISIES WON'T TELL COLOGNE 1958-62
(Left) 2 oz. white cap & painted label. OSP
$1.19. CMV $7. - $10. MB. Same bottle came
in Bubble Bath & Cream Lotion in sets only.
Same CMV.
BUBBLE BATH 1956-57
(Center) 4 oz. bottle with rib around center.
Painted label, white flower cap. OSP $1.10.
CMV $8., MB $10.
COLOGNE 1957-58
(Right) 2 oz. cologne with rib around center in
One I Love set and Daisies Won't Tell set.
CMV $12.

**DAISIES WON'T TELL CREAM LOTION
1956-57**
(Left) Yellow & white box holds 2 oz. bottle
with rib around center & white flower cap,
painted label. OSP 69c. **CMV $12. MB, $10.
bottle only.**
HAND CREAM 1962-64
(Right) Pink tube with white flower cap. In
pink & blue box. OSP 59c. **CMV $7. in box,
$5. tube only.**

**DAISIES WON'T TELL COLOGNE WITH
ATOMIZER 1956**
Yellow, white & pink box holds 2 oz. bottle with
rib around middle, white & gold spray atomizer.
Short issue. OSP $1.25. **CMV $15., MB $20.**

DAISY DUST 1958-61
(Left) 2 oz. white plastic bottle & cap. OSP
$1.19. **CMV $10. BO, $12. MB.**
DAISY CREAM LOTION 1958-61
(Center) 4 oz. white plastic bottle & cap. Two
different labels. Newer has large letters &
painted address at bottom. Older one is
smaller letters & embossed address at bottom.
OSP $1.19. **CMV $10. BO, $12. MB.**

**DAISIES WON'T TELL SPRAY COLOGNE
1958-60**
(Left) Pink plastic coated bottle with white cap.
OSP $1.59. **CMV $10. BO, $12. MB.**
SPRAY COLOGNE 1957 ONLY
1 1/2 oz. blue plastic coated bottle with white c
& painted label. OSP $1.59. **CMV $13., MB
$15.**
COLOGNE 1962-64
(Right) 2 oz. glass bottle, white cap & painted
label. OSP $1.19. **CMV $6. BO, $9. MB.**

**DAISIES WON'T TELL COLOGNE MIST
1962-64**
(Left) 2 oz. white plastic coated bottle with
white cap and blue painted label. OSP $2.25.
CMV $7. BO, $9. MB.
CREAM LOTION 1962-64
(Right) 4 oz. white plastic bottle and cap. Blue
painted label. OSP $1.19. **CMV $6. BO, $8.
MB.**

DAISY SOAP ON A ROPE 1963-64
(Left) Pink, white & yellow box holds white
soap with yellow center on a white rope. OSP
$1.19. **CMV $20. MB.**
DAISY SOAP ON A ROPE 1959-62
(Right) Blue, white & pink flowered box holds
white Daisy soap with yellow center, on a blue
rope. OSP $1.19. **CMV $20. MB.**

FAIRY TOUCH 1958
Blue and white box holds 2 blue & white tubes
with yellow caps of Daisies Won't Tell hand
cream. OSP 79c. **CMV $16. MB.**

GAY DAISIES SET 1960
Blue, white & pink box holds daisy soap on a blue rope & choice of daisy bubble bath, daisy dust, cream lotion or daisy shampoo. OSP $2.35. **CMV $35. MB.**

FIRST RECITAL SET 1962-64
Pink & blue fold-over box holds Daisy soap on rope & choice of Daisy cream lotion, bubble bath or Daisy dust. OSP $2.38. **CMV $35. MB.**

DAISIES WON'T TELL BUBBLE BATH 1962-64
(Top Left) 4 oz. white plastic bottle & cap with blue painted label. OSP $1.19. **CMV $6. BO, $8. MB.**

DAISY DUST 1962-64
(Bottom Left) 2 oz. white plastic bottle & cap with blue painted label. OSP $1.19. **CMV $6. BO, $8. MB.**

HAND CREAM 1958-61
(Right) Blue & white box holds blue & white tube with both flat or tall yellow cap. OSP 49c. **CMV $6. in box, $4. tube only.** 2 oz. Bubble Bath is same type bottle. Came in One I Love set & Daisies Won't Tell set. **CMV $8.**

DAISY POMADE 1958-59
Blue & white flowered holder holds pink daisy pomade. Also came in lime green color. OSP 59c. **CMV $12.50 in holder, $2. pomade only.**

PICK A DAISY SET 1963-64
Pink & blue box holds daisy soap on a rope & Daisies Won't Tell cream sachet. OSP $2.38. **CMV $32.50 MB.**

WEE TWO SET 1956
(Left) Blue, white & yellow box has two tubes with yellow caps of Daisies Won't Tell hand cream & cream shampoo. OSP 89c. **CMV $18.**

DAINTY HANDS SET 1957
(Right) Pink, white & yellow box holds 2 tubes with pink hearts & yellow caps of Daisies Won't Tell hand cream. OSP 79c. **CMV $18. MB.**

ONE I LOVE SET 1957 ONLY
Floral box contains 2 oz. cologne, cream lotion & bubble bath in Daisies Won't Tell. White flower caps with yellow centers. Any sets you find with pink caps are taken off Cotillion bottles and not considered a mint set. OSP $2.49. **CMV $50. MB.**

DAISY CHAIN GIFT SET 1963-64
Pink & white box holds 2 oz. Daisies Won't Tell cologne & pink tube of daisy hand cream. OSP $1.78. **CMV $22. MB.**

FIELD OF DAISIES SET 1958
Blue & white flowered box holds 2 oz. bottles of Daisies Won't Tell cologne, cream lotion with red ribbon & bubble bath. OSP $2.19. CMV $50. MB.

LITTLE CHARMER SET 1956
Black & white plastic basket with flowers on top holds Daisies Won't Tell 2 oz. cologne, gold pomade & tube of Daisy hand cream. OSP $3.50. CMV $65. MB.

BLOSSOMS SET 1956
Daisy box holds 2 oz. Daisies Won't Tell cologne with blue ribbon & gold pomade. OSP $1.59. CMV $27.50 MB, gold pomade $5.

DAISIES WON'T TELL SET 1957
Box holds 2 oz. each in bubble bath, cream lotion & cologne. White & yellow daisy caps. OSP $2.49. Came with outer sleeve. Also came Daisy Talc can in place of cream lotion. CMV $60. MB.

DAISY PETALS SET 1957
Yellow & white box with pink hearts holds 2 oz. Daisies Won't Tell cologne & lime yellow pomade lipstick in corner of box. OSP $1.59. CMV $25. MB.

DAISY BOUQUET SET 1959-60
Blue & white flowered box holds 4 oz. Daisy cream lotion, Daisy bubble bath & 2 oz. Daisy dust. OSP $3.50. CMV $37.50 MB.

DAISY TREASURES SET 1959
Pink box with yellow slide open cover with it. Light blue ribbon on daisy flower. Holds 3 bottles of nail polish with white caps & nail file. OSP $2.75. CMV $60. MB.

PRETTY BEGINNER SET 1961
Blue, white & yellow box holds Daisies Won't Tell 2 oz. cologne & choice of Daisy soap, Daisy dust, cream lotion, shampoo or bubble bath. OSP $2.38. CMV $25, with soap $35. MB.

DAISIES WON'T TELL SET 1956
Daisy box holds 2 oz. Daisies Won't Tell cologne & bubble bath with center rib on each & can of 3 1/4 oz. Daisy talc. OSP $2.25. CMV talc can only $20., $60. MB with outer sleeve.

MISS DAISY SET 1956
Daisy box holds Daisies Won't Tell 2 oz. cologne & beauty dust. Top of bottle sticks through top of box. OSP $2.35. CMV $40.

DAISY BOUQUET SET 1957
Blue, white & yellow box holds Daisies Won't Tell 2 oz. cologne, beauty dust & lime yellow pomade. OSP $2.95. **CMV $45. MB, yellow pomade $5.**

PLAYMATE SET 1956
Daisies carrying case holds Daisies Won't Tell 2 oz. cologne, cream lotion & gold or black pomade with plastic doll with movable arms with satin & net dress. Eyes open & shut, red hair. OSP $3.95. **CMV $90. MB.**

DAISY POMADE LIPSTICK 1962-64
Pink box holds pink with gold base lipstick. OSP 59c. **CMV $4. MB.**

FIRST WALTZ SET 1960
Blue & white Daisies Wont't Tell box holds First Waltz nail polish & pink pomade. OSP $1.25. **CMV $20. MB.**

DAISY DARLING SET 1958
Blue box with daisies & red ribbon holds Daisies Won't Tell spray cologne & beauty dust. OSP $2.98. **CMV $42.50 MB.**

MY DOLLY SET 1957
White, yellow & green box holds Daisies Won't Tell 2 oz. cream lotion, cologne, pink or yellow pomade & plastic doll with movable arms, brown hair, blue hat, yellow dress trimmed in pink satin. OSP $3.95. **CMV $90. MB.**

DAISY PINK NAIL POLISH 1960
(Left) Blue & white box holds Daisies Won't Tell nail polish, white cap. OSP 69c. **CMV $8. MB, $6. BO mint.**
FIRST WALTZ NAIL POLISH 1960
(Not Shown) Blue & white box holds Daisies Won't Tell nail polish, white cap. OSP 69c. **CMV $8. MB, $6. BO mint.**
DAISY POMADE LIPSTICK 1960-61
(Right) Blue & white box holds pink & gold pomade in shades of 1st Waltz or Daisy Pomade. OSP 69c. **CMV $6. MB.**

FIRST WALTZ LIPSTICK 1960
Blue flowered box holds pink lipstick. Came in Daisies Won't Tell. OSP 50c. **CMV $6. MB.**

DAISY PINK SET 1960
Daisies box holds Daisy pink nail polish, white cap & pink metal pomade in box. OSP $1.25. **CMV $20. MB.**

DELFT BLUE

ELEGANTE BEAUTY DUST 1956-59
(Left) Red paper sides with tin top & bottom. Silver letters on lid. OSP $2.25. **CMV $15., MB $20.**

ELEGANTE COLOGNE 1956-59
(Inside Left) Red & silver box holds 4 oz. bottle with silver cap & neck tag & red ribbon. OSP $2.50. **CMV $40. MB, $20. BO with neck tag & ribbon.**

ELEGANTE TOILET WATER 1957-59
(Center) Red & silver box holds 2 oz. bottle with silver cap & neck tag & red ribbon. OSP $2. **CMV $40. MB, BO with tag & ribbon $20.**

ELEGANTE POWDER SACHET 1957-59
(Inside Right) 9/10 oz. bottle with silver cap. OSP $1.50. **CMV $12. BO, $17. MB.**

ELEGANTE CREAM SACHET 1956-59
(Right) .66 oz. jar with silver cap. OSP $1.50. **CMV $8. BO, $13. MB.**

DELFT BLUE 1972-74
White milk glass with blue flowers.
SKIN-SO-SOFT SOFTENER
5 oz. SSP $4. **CMV $5. BO, $6. MB.**
FOAMING BATH OIL
5 oz. holds Patchwork, Moonwind or Sonnet. SSP $6. **CMV $7. MB, $6.BO.**
PITCHER & BOWL
5 oz. SSP $8. **CMV $10. MB, $7. BO & bowl**
SOAP DISH & SKIN-SO-SOFT SOAP
3 oz. SSP $4. **CMV $6. MB.**

ELEGANTE

SPARKLING BURGUNDY SET 1957
Round neck & silver box with red satin lining. Holds Elegante 4 oz. cologne, cream sachet, 1 dram perfume & beauty dust. OSP $8.95. **CMV $115. MB.**

ELEGANTE PERFUME 1956-59
Red & silver box holds 1/2 oz. bottle with silver cap & neck tag with red ribbon. OSP $7.50. **CMV $125. MB, $75. BO with neck tag & ribbon.**

SNOW DREAMS SET 1957
White box with red ribbon holds Elegante 2 oz. toilet water, cream sachet & 1 dram perfume in red wrapper. OSP $5.50. **CMV $75. MB.**

ELUSIVE

ELUSIVE BEAUTY DUST 1969-74
Pink plastic with gold or silver trim. OSP $6.
CMV $3. - $5. MB.
ELUSIVE SAMPLES 1969-74
10 samples to a box. **CMV 50c.**
ROLLETTE 1969-75
.33 oz. frosted glass. OSP $3. **CMV 75c.**
PERFUMED DEMI STICK 1970-73
Paper center, white cap. OSP $1.75. **CMV $1.**
1/2 OZ. COLOGNE 1969-75
1/2 oz. pink frosted glass. OSP $2. **CMV $1.**
CREAM SACHET 1969-75
Pink frosted glass. OSP $3. **CMV 50c.**
PERFUMED SKIN SOFTENER 1970-72
Pink frosted glass. Lid came with gold or silver trim. OSP $4. **CMV $1.**
ELUSIVE TRAY 1970-71
Pink plastic, gold trim. OSP $4. **CMV $6. MB, $4. tray only.**

ELUSIVE SCENTED HAIR SPRAY 1970-72
(Back Left) 7 oz. pink can & cap with gold letters. OSP $1.50. **CMV $3.**
PERFUMED POWDER MIST 1971-74
(Back Inside Left) 7 oz. pink painted label. OSP $4. **CMV 50c.**
PERFUMED POWDER MIST 1970-71
(Back Center Left) 7 oz. pink paper label. OSP $4. **CMV $2.**
PERFUMED TALC 1971-74
(Back Center Right) 3 1/2 oz. pink paper container. OSP $1.35. **CMV 50c.**
COLOGNE MIST 1969-74
(Back Inside Right) 3 oz. pink plastic coated bottle. OSP $6. **CMV 50c.**
ELUSIVE FOAMING BATH OIL 1970-72
(Back Right) 6 oz. pink plastic with pink cap. OSP $3.50. **CMV $2.**
PERFUMED SOAP 1970-74
(Front) 3 pink bars in pink box. OSP $3.50. **CMV $5. MB.**

ENGLISH PROVINCIAL

ENGLISH PROVINCIAL 1972-74
White milk glass with blue & pink flowers & aqua blue lid with flowers. Came in Charisma, or Bird of Paradise.
FOAMING BATH OIL
(Left) 8 oz. SSP $5. **CMV $2. MB, $1. BO.**
COLOGNE
(Inside Left) 5 oz. SSP $5. **CMV $2. MB, $1. BO.**
POWDER SACHET
(Inside Right) 1.25 oz. SSP $4. **CMV $2. MB, $1. BO.**
SOAP DISH & SOAP
(Right) 1.25 oz. SSP $4. **CMV $4. - $5. MB.**

ELUSIVE COLOGNE MIST 1969-74
(Left) Pink painted bottle with pink & gold cap. Paint doesn't go to bottom.
(Right) Later issue pink plastic coated bottle, pink & gold cap. OSP $6. **CMV painted $1., plastic coated 50c.**

FIELD FLOWERS

FIELD FLOWER PRODUCTS

COLOGNE MIST 1971-76
3 oz. green plastic coated over glass, yellow cap. OSP $7. **CMV $1.**

COLOGNE GELEE 1971-72
3 oz. green ribbed glass & orange cap. OSP $4. **CMV $1.50**

PERFUMED SKIN SOFTENER 1971-73
5 oz. green glass, bright or pale blue cap. OSP $4. **CMV $1.**

CREAM SACHET 1971-75
.66 oz. green ribbed glass with purple cap. OSP $3. **CMV 50c.**

PERFUMED POWDER MIST 1971-76
7 oz. green, white & pink can. OSP $4.50. **CMV 50c.** Also came with upside down label. **CMV $4.**

SOAP 1971-76
Flowered box holds yellow, pink 7 green flower bars. OSP $5. **CMV $6. MB.**

FOAMING BATH OIL 1971-72
6 oz. green plastic bottle with pink flowered cap. OSP $4. **CMV $1.**

SCENTED HAIR SPRAY 1971-72
7 oz. pink & green can with green cap. OSP $1.50. **CMV $3.**

AFTER BATH FRESHENER 1971-75
Green plastic, blue cap. **CMV 50c.**

COLOGNE ICE 1976
1 oz. tube. **CMV $1.**

FIELD FLOWERS PERFUMED TALC 1970-73
(Left) 3 1/2 oz. green paper label. OSP $2. **CMV $1.** 1973-77 Perfumed Talc had pink label. **CMV 50c.**

DEMI STICK 1970-78
(Inside Left) Green paper band, white cap. OSP $2. **CMV 50c.**

FRAGRANCE SAMPLES 1970-77
(Inside Right) 10 samples in a box. **CMV 50c.**

COLOGNE SAMPLE 1970-78
(Right) Clear glass, white cap. **CMV 25c.**

FLOWER TALK

FLOWER TALK 1972-73
White with orange, blue, yellow, green & purple designs.

PERFUMED TALC
3.5 oz. SSP $1. **CMV $1.**

COLOGNE MIST
3 oz. SSP $4. **CMV $1.**

ROLLETTE
.33 oz. SSP $1. **CMV $1.**

DEMI STICK
.19 oz. SSP $1. **CMV 50c.**

SAMPLE FLOWER TALK
CMV 25c.

CREAM SACHET
.66 oz. SSP $2. **CMV $1.**

FIELD FLOWERS BATH BRUSH & SOAP 1971-72
Pink brush approx. 16" long & 5 oz. flower embossed pink soap. OSP $6. **CMV $8. MB.**

FLOWERTIME

VALENTINE GIFT SACHET 1952
In special red & white gift box. Came in Flowertime, Golden Promise, Quaintance or Cotillion. OSP 98c. **CMV $15. MB as shown, $10. BO mint.**

FLOWERTIME POWDER SACHET 1950-53
(Left) 1 1/2 oz. with indented pink cap. OSP $1.19. **CMV $15. MB, $10. BO.**

FLOWERTIME TALC 1949-53
(Right) 5 oz. bottle with brass shaker top. OSP 89c. **CMV $20. MB, $15. BO.**

FLOWERS IN THE WIND SET 1950-52
Blue & silver flip-open box with pink satin lining holds Flowertime cologne talc, powder sachet & 1 dram perfume. OSP $5.50. **CMV $95. MB.**

DOUBLY YOURS SET 1949
White & blue swing open box holds 2 oz. bottles of cologne with pink caps in Cotillion & Flowertime. OSP $2.10. **CMV $65. MB.**

FLOWERTIME COLOGNE 1949-53
(Left) 4 oz. pink cap. OSP $1.75. **CMV $15. MB, $10. BO.** Same bottle came in 2 oz. size in sets only. **CMV $10.**

FLOWERTIME TOILET WATER 1949-53
(Center) 2 oz. pink cap. OSP $1.25. **CMV $15. MB, $10. BO.**

FLOWERTIME POWDER SACHET 1949-50
(Right) 1 1/4 oz. bottle has flat or indented pink cap. OSP $1.19. **CMV $15. MB, $10. BO.**

FOREVER SPRING

FOREVER SPRING PERFUME 1956-59
Yellow & white box with purple base holds 1/2oz. bottle with blue bird on yellow cap & painted label. OSP $5. **CMV MB $100, BO with bird $85.**

FOREVER SPRING BEAUTY DUST 1951-56
(Left) Green & white can. OSP $1.75. **CMV $20. - $25. MB.**

FOREVER SPRING BEAUTY DUST 1956-59
(Right) Yellow & white paper box with tin top & bottom. OSP $1.95. **CMV $16. - $20. MB.**

FLOWER CLUSTER SET 1949
Blue & gold box contains box of face powder, gold lipstick & 1 dram Flowertime perfume. OSP $3. **CMV $50. MB.**

FOREVER SPRING PERFUME 1951-56
Yellow & green box with blue & green ribbon holds 3 dram glass stoppered bottle with blue ribbon on neck & neck tag. OSp $5. **CMV $100. in box, $85. bottle only with tag & ribbon.**

FOREVER SPRING COLOGNE 1951-56
(Left) 4 oz. with yellow tulip cap & green painted label. Came in green box. OSP $2.25. **CMV $20. MB, $15. mint, BO.**

FOREVER SPRING POWDER SACHET 1953-56
(Right) 1 1/4 oz. bottle with yellow cap & green painted label. Came in green box. OSP $1.25. **CMV $15. MB, $10. BO.**

FLOWERTIME SET 1949-52
Turquoise & gold box with satin lining holds 4 oz. Flowertime cologne & talc. OSP $2.75. **CMV $60. MB.**

FOREVER SPRING 1 DRAM PERFUME 1951-52
(Left) 1 dram, ribbed glass, gold cap. Came in green felt folder. OSP $1.75. **CMV $15. in sleeve, $10. BO.**

FOREVER SPRING POWDER BOX COLOGNE 1956
(Right) 1/16 oz. size bottle came in special beauty dust box set only. Came tied to silk ribbon. **CMV $5. BO mint, $10. mint with ribbon.**

FOREVER SPRING TOILET WATER 1951-56
2 oz. yellow tulip cap & green painted label. Came in green box. OSP $1.50. **CMV $20. MB, $15. BO mint.**

FOREVER SPRING CREAM SACHET 1956-59
(Left) Yellow glass bottom & cap with flowers on all 3 lids shown. OSP $1.25. **CMV $8. - $11. MB.**

FOREVER SPRING POWDER SACHET 1956-59
(Center) 9/10 oz. yellow glass & cap. OSP $1.25. **CMV $9. - $12. MB.**

FOREVER SPRING BODY POWDER 1956-59
(Right) Frosted glass jar with flowered cap, painted label. OSP $1. **CMV $12. BO, $17. MB.**

SPRING MOOD SET 1956
Yellow & white box holds Forever Spring body powder & 4 oz. cream lotion in green glass. OSP $1.95. **CMV $40. MB.**

FOREVER SPRING COLOGNE 1956-59
4 oz. bottle with blue bird on yellow cap, painted label, yellow & white flowered box. OSP $2. **CMV $20. MB, BO with bird $15.**

SPRINGTIME SET 1956
Yellow & white box holds Forever Spring beauty dust & 4 oz. cologne. OSP $3.95. **CMV $50.**

FOREVER SPRING CREAM LOTION 1956-59
(Left) 4 oz. clear glass with yellow cap, painted label. No bird on cap. Came in yellow & white box. OSP 95c. **CMV $14. MB, $12. mint BO.**

FOREVER SPRING TOILET WATER 1956-59
(Center) 2 oz. yellow cap with tiny blue bird, painted label. Came in yellow & white flowered box. OSP $1.50. **CMV MB $20., BO with bird $15. mint.**

FOREVER SPRING CREAM SACHET 1951-56
(Right) Green box holds white glass jatr with green lid. OSP $1.25. **CMV $12. MB, $7. jar only mint.**

MERRY MERRY SPRING SET 1956
Yellow, white & blue box holds Forever Spring 2 oz. toilet water and cream sachet. OSP $2.75. **CMV $37.50 MB.**

FOREVER SPRING CREAM LOTION 1956-59
4 oz. green painted over clear glass bottle with yellow cap. OSP 95c. **CMV $18. BO mint, $25. MB.**

SPRING GODESS SET 1957
Yellow & white box holds Forever Spring
beauty dust, cream sachet & 4 oz. cologne.
OSP $4.95. **CMV $50. MB.**

FOREVER SPRING SET 1953
Green & white box with green net lining holds
Forever Spring boby powder, cream sachet &
1 dram perfume in green felt sleeve. OSP
$3.95. **CMV $55. MB.**
FOREVER SPRING SET 1952
Is same as above only did not have 1 dram
perfume. OSP $2.75. **CMV $37.50 MB.**

SPRING MELODY SET 1952-53
Forever Spring body powder & cream sachet
setting on top under clear plastic lid. OSP
$1.95. **CMV $35. MB.**

**FOREVER SPRING REPRESENTATIVE GIFT
SET 1951**
CMV $80. MB.

SPRING SONG SET 1953
Blue & green box holds Forever Spring 4 oz.
cologne & 1 dram perfume. OSP $3.50. CMV
$40. MB.

APRIL AIRS SET 1956-57
Yellow & white box with blue ribbon top holds
Forever Spring body powder & cream sachet.
OSP $2.25. **CMV $40. MB.**

SPRING CREATION SET 1953
Green box with net lining holds Forever Spring
cream sachet & 1 dram perfume. OSP $2.75.
CMV $40. MB.

SPRING CORSAGE SET 1951-52
Green box with clear plastic lid & bouquet of
flowers holds Forever Spring 4 oz. cologne & 1
dram perfume. OSP $4.50. **CMV $50.**

**FOREVER SPRING BODY POWDER 1951-
56**
(Left) Green & white paper container. OSP
95c. **CMV $15.**
**FOREVER SPRING PERFUMED TALC 1957-
59**
(Right) 2.75 oz. yellow & white can, yellow
cap. OSP 69c. **CMV $10., MB $12.**

GARDEN OF LOVE

GARDENIA

GOLDEN PROMISE

GARDEN OF LOVE SWIRL PERFUME 1948 ONLY
3 dram glass stoppered bottle is swirl glass design with gold neck tag. Purple and white flowered box. OSP $3. **CMV $90. BO mint, $120. MB.**

GARDENIA PERFUME 1940-42
Gold speckled box holds 3/8 oz. bottle with gold octagonal cap. OSP $1.50. **CMV $50. BO mint., $80. MB.**

GOLDEN PROMISE BEAUTY DUST 1947-56
(Left) Standard issue gold and white can. OSP $1.50. **CMV $18. CO mint, $22. MB.**
GOLDEN PROMISE BEAUTY DUST 1947-51
(Right) Smaller than regular issue. Came in sets only. **CMV $20. mint.**

GARDENIA PERFUME "RIBBED" 1933-36
1/2 oz. ribbed glass with black octagonal cap. Came in gold box set. **CMV $45. mint.**
GARDENIA PERFUME "OCTAGONAL" 1933-36
6 sided bottle and black octagonal cap. Came in Little Folks set and Hankerchief set. **CMV $45. mint**

GARDEN OF LOVE POWDER SACHET 1946-48
(Left) 1 1/4 oz. turquoise ribbed plastic cap and flowered label. OSP $1.19. **CMV $20. in box, $17. bottle only.**
GARDEN OF LOVE SACHET 1944-45
(Center) 1 1/4 oz. pink paper sachet. Came with pink plastic flower on lid. OSP $1.15. **CMV $18. mint, $23. MB.**
GARDEN OF LOVE POWDER SACHET 1940-46
(Right) 1 1/4 oz. bottle with black or turquoise metal cap. OSP $1.04. **CMV $20., $15. bottle only.**

GOLDEN PROMISE PERFUME 1949 ONLY
(Left) 1/4 oz. glass bottle fits in gold metal case. Came in Golden Duet & Evening Charm Sets. **CMV $25.**
GOLDEN PROMISE CREAM SACHET 1953-56
(Center) White glass, square base with yellow flowered top. OSP $1. **CMV $9. BO, $13. MB.**
GOLDEN PROMISE BODY POWDER 1947-56
(Right) Gold and white shaker top can. OSP $1.50. **CMV $16. CO mint, $20. MB.**

GARDEN OF LOVE PERFUME 1940-44
Orange lid, gold base box holds 3 dram glass stoppered bottle with gold neck tag. OSP $2.50. **CMV $100. mint BO, $125. MB.**

GARDENIA PERFUME 1948-52
3/8 oz. or 3 dram bottle with flowered cap, paper or painted label. Came in satin lined box with clear plastic lid. OSP $2.50 each. **CMV $80. MB, $40. BO mint.**

GOLDEN PROMISE POWDER SACHET 1952-56
(Left) 1 1/4 oz. yellow plastic cap. OSP $1.25. **CMV $12. MB, $9. BO.**
GOLDEN PROMISE POWDER SACHET 1951-52
(Center) 1 1/4 oz. gold cap. OSP $1.25. **CMV $12. MB, $9. BO.**

GOLDEN PROMISE

GOLDEN PROMISE SACHET 1948
Special gold box, 62nd Anniversary issue. 1 1/4 oz. ribbed gold plastic cap or threaded brass cap. OSP $1.25. **CMV $18.50 MB as shown.**

GOLDEN PROMISE PERFUME 1947-50
Gold and white flip open box holds 1/2 oz. bottle with gold cap and painted label. OSP $3.95. **CMV $175. in box. Bottle only $100. mint.**

GOLDEN PROMISE PERFUME 1950-54
Gold & white box holds 3 dram glass stoppered bottle with gold base label and neck cord. OSP $4. **CMV $125. in box, bottle with label and cord $100.**

GOLDEN PROMISE COLOGNE 1947-56
4 oz. painted label, gold cap. OSP $2.25. **CMV $18., MB $24.**
GOLDEN PROMISE TOILET WATER 1953-56
2 oz. gold cap & painted label. OSP $1.50. **CMV $20., MB $24.**

GOLDEN PROMISE PERFUME 1954-56
Gold and white box holds 1/2 oz. bottle with flat glass stopper and gold & white label. OSP $3.95. **CMV $125. in box., $90. bottle only mint.**

GOLDEN PROMISE 3 PIECE SET 1947-49
Gold and white box holds Golden Promise 1 dram perfume, 4 oz. cologne, and beauty dust. OSP $4.95. **CMV $85. MB.**

GOLDEN PROMISE PERFUME GIFT 1947
Clear bottle, gold cap. Label is gold with red lettering, says "Golden Promise Perfume with Best Wishes of Avon Products Inc., Pasadena, Cal." Came in gold box with same statement. **CMV $75. MB, $50. BO.**
GOLDEN JEWEL 1953-54
White and gold box with gold jewel on front. Holds Golden Promise 2 oz. Toilet Water and 1 dram Perfume. Toilet Water cap fits through top of box. OSP $2.75. **CMV $40. MB.**

GOLDEN PROMISE BODY POWDER CHRISTMAS DEMO 1947
Regular issue talc in gold box given to Avon ladies in special Merry Christmas demo box. OSP $1.50. **CMV $30. MB with outer box shown.**

GOLDEN PROMISE SET 1950-51
Gold box with clear plastic cover and gold tie down ribbon holds Golden Promise 4 oz. cologne and beauty dust. OSP $3.95. **CMV $60. MB.**

GOLDEN PROMISE 2 PIECE SET 1947-49
Gold and white box holds Golden Promise 4 oz. cologne and body powder. OSP $2.95. **CMV $60. MB.**

GOLDEN PROMISE DELUXE SET 1952-54
Gold box with clear plastic lid and gold satin lining holds Golden Promise 4 oz. cologne, powder sachet, 1 dram perfume and body powder. Gold ribbon around box. OSP $6.25. **CMV $100. MB.**

GOLDEN DUET SET 1949
Small gold purse holds Lipstick and gold metal case with 1/2 dram bottle of Golden Promise perfume inside. OSP $2.50. **CMV $35. mint, $40. MB.**

HANA GASA

HANA GASA GIFT NOTES 1970-71
Yellow with pink flowers, has 15 notes and envelopes. 18 seals. OSP $2. **CMV $3.**

HANA GASA FRAGRANCE SAMPLES 1970-74
10 in a box. **CMV 50c box.**
HANA GASA COLOGNE SAMPLE 1970-74
Sample bottle, white cap. **CMV 25c.**
COLOGNE 1970-75
1/2 oz. clear glass, yellow cap. OSP $2. **CMV $1, $1.50 MB.**
PERFUME ROLLETTE 1970-74
Yellow painted glass, yellow cap. OSP $3. **CMV $1.**
CREAM SACHET 1970-75
.66 oz. yellow painted over milk glass with yellow lid. OSP $3. **CMV 50c.**
HANA GASA BEAUTY DUST 1970-76
6 oz. yellow plastic. OSP $8.50. **CMV $3. CO, $5. MB.**

HANA GASA HAIR SPRAY 1971
7 oz. yellow can, OSP $1.50. **CMV $3.**
HANA GASA PERFUME POWDER MIST 1971-74
7 oz. yellow can. OSP $4. **CMV $1.**
PERFUME TALC 1971-74
3 1/2 oz. yellow cardboard. OSP $1.35. **CMV $1.**
FOAMING BATH OIL 1971-77
6 oz. clear plastic bottle, also yellow plastic bottle, yellow cap. OSP $4.50. **CMV $1.**
COLOGNE MIST 1970-76
3 oz. yellow plastic coated glass, yellow cap. OSP $6. **CMV $1.**
HANA GASA SOAP 1971-75
3 yellow bars in pink and yellow box. OSP $5. **CMV $5. MB.**
HAPPY HOURS SET 1948-49
Pink and blue box holds Happy Hours Talc, Cologne and Perfume. OSP $2. **CMV $115. MB.**

HAPPY HOURS

HAPPY HOURS TALC 1948-49
2 3/4 oz. metal shaker cap. Sold in sets only. **CMV $20. mint.**
HAPPY HOURS COLOGNE 1948-49
1 oz. plastic cap. Came in sets only. **CMV $20. mint.**
HAPPY HOURS PERFUME 1948-49
3 drams, pink cap. Rare. Came in sets only. **CMV $50. mint.**

MEMENTO SET 1948-49
Blue and pink box holds Happy Hours Cologne and Perfume. OSP $1.50. **CMV $95. MB.**

STAR BOUQUET SET 1948-49
Green and pink box holds Happy Hours Talc and Cologne. OSP $1.25. **CMV $67.50 MB.**

HAWAIIAN WHITE GINGER

HAWAIIAN WHITE GINGER TALC 1968 ONLY
(Left) 2.75 oz. green and white talc sold in perfume pair only. **CMV $2.**

TALC 1968-73
(Center) 3.5 oz. multi-colored cardboard, gold letter label. OSP $2. **CMV $1.** 1974-77 Talc came with pink letter label. **CMV 50c.**

BEAUTY DUST 1972
(Right) Multi-colored cardboard. OSP $3. **CMV $4. mint, $5. MB.**

HAWAIIAN WHITE GINGER CREAM SACHET 1968-72
Both .66 oz. green frosted jars and flowered caps. Short jar 1967, same as Lily of the Valley jar. OSP $2. **CMV $2.** Tall green jar in 1969. **CMV $1.**

BATH FRESHENER 1967-72
(Left) 6 oz. glass bottle with white cap. OSP $2.50. **CMV $2.**

HAWAIIAN WHITE GINGER FOAMING BATH OIL 1968-76
(Center) 8 oz. plastic bottle. OSP $3. **CMV 50c.**

CREAM LOTION 1969-72
5 oz. plastic bottle. OSP $2. **CMV 75c.**

HAWAIIAN WHITE GINGER AFTER BATH FRESHENER 1972-76
8 oz. white plastic bottle with white cap. OSP $5. **CMV 50c.**

COLOGNE MIST 1971-72
2 oz. Light green glass bottle with white cap. OSP $4.25. **CMV $1, $2. MB.**

AFTER BATH FRESHENER 1965-67
5 oz. bottle with white painted label and cap. Also came with and without gold 4A design. OSP $2. **CMV $6. in box, $5. bottle only.**

HAWAIIAN WHITE GINGER COLOGNE MIST 1972-76
2 oz. clear glass bottle with clear plastic cap with inner cap of green, red and white. OSP $5. **CMV 75c.**

ROLLETTE 1972-74
.33 oz. clear bottle, white cap with colored band. OSP $2.50. **CMV 50c.**

DEMI STICK 1970-78
.19 oz. green, red & white, white cap. OSP $1.75. **CMV 50c.**

CREAM SACHET 1973-78
.66 oz. glass jar, white, green and red cap. This has 3 different lid labels. Early one - no zip code. .66 oz. Next - zip but no numbers. Doesn't have weight on lid. Later ones have zip and numbers but no weight on lid. OSP $2.50. **CMV 50c.**

FLORAL DUET HAWAIIAN WHITE GINGER SET 1972-73
Came with Rollette and bar of soap. OSP $3.25. **CMV $5. MB.**

HAWAIIAN WHITE GINGER SOAP 1970-78
3 oz. single bar soap (same as shown in set). OSP $1. **CMV $1.**

FRAGRANCE KWICKETTES 1969-75
(Not shown) Box holds 14 packettes. OSP $1.50. **CMV $1. box.**

HELLO SUNSHINE

HELLO SUNSHINE PRODUCTS 1979-80

LIP BALM
Pink, white and yellow. **CMV 50c.**

HAND CREAM
White, yellow and pink. 1.5 oz. tube. Green cap. **CMV 50c.**

FUN SHINE NAIL TINT
.5 oz. clear glass, pink cap. **CMV 75c MB.**

COLOGNE
2.5 oz. clear glass, yellow cap. Yellow and pink decal on glass. **CMV $1.**

HELLO SUNSHINE SOLID PERFUME 1980-83
Yellow plastic jar, white flowered top. SSP $2.50. **CMV $1. MB.**

BRUSH
White plastic, 6 1/2" long. SSP $4. **CMV $1. MB.**

HER PRETTINESS

HER PRETTINESS LIP KISSES 1970-71
Lip Pomade, tubes blue and white, pink and white, orange and white in cherry, chocolate or peppermint. Mirror on back side of cap. OSP $1.95. **CMV $2. each, $3. MB.**

HER PRETTINESS ENCHANTED COLOGNE MIST 1969-72
Brown tree base holds 3 oz. cologne mist in green bubble top and green bird spray button. OSP $5. **CMV $6., $7. MB.**

MAGIC MUSHROOM CREAM SACHET 1969-72
Green, pink and blue plastic. OSP $3. **CMV $4.**

LADY BUG FRAGRANCE GLACE 1969-72
Red, black and green plastic bug. OSP $3. **CMV $3., $4. MB.**

LOVE LOCKET FRAGRANCE GLACE 1969-71
Gold locket and chain, in yellow, gold and pink box. OSP $4.50. **CMV $10. MB.**

SECRET TOWER ROLLETTE 1969-72
Red cap on bottle. OSP $1.75. **CMV $3. MB.**

PRETTY ME DOLL 1969-71
5 oz. plastic bottle with gold hair, cap and pink neck ribbon. Holds Powdered Bubble Bath. 6 1/2" high. OSP $6. **CMV $8., $6. BO.**

FLOWER BELLE COLOGNE MIST 1969-72
Blue top with yellow base has 2 oz. Her Prettiness Cologne Mist. OSP $3.50. **CMV $4.**

BRUSH AND COMB SET 1969-72
Pink box with yellow comb and brush. OSP $3.50. **CMV $5.**

BUNNY PUFF 1969-72
3 1/2 oz. white plastic rabbit with pink fluff tail. Holds Her Prettiness Talc. OSP $3.75. **CMV $5.**

BUNNY FLUFF PUFF 1976
Reissued - Same except holds Pink & Pretty. OSP $4. **CMV $4.** Also has R on bottom for reissue. 1979 reissue in yellow rabbit. It is shown in children's toy section.

ROYAL FOUNTAIN CREME SACHET 1970
Blue base with silver and gold fountain top. Contains Her Prettiness Creme Sachet. OSP $3. **CMV $5. MB.**

HER PRETTINESS TALC 1970-71
3 1/2 oz. flowered box. OSP $1. **CMV $2.**

HER PRETTINESS ART REPRODUCTION PRINT 1969-70
14" x 18" pink, green and white, was free purchase of any Her Prettiness products. Came in cardboard tube with Her Prettiness sticker and a poem "Her Prettiness Serves Ten in The Garden". **CMV $8., three pieces. $4. print alone.**

HER PRETTINESS COLOGNE SAMPLE 1969-72
1/8 oz. clear glass white cap. Painted label. Came in envelope. **CMV $1. mint in envelope.**

HERE'S MY HEART

HERE'S MY HEART PERFUME 1946-48
1/2 oz. glass stoppered bottle with painted label and pink neck ribbons. Bottle is tied to pink satin heart shaped base and box. OSP $7.50. **CMV $140. MB. BO with ribbon, $100. mint.**

HERE'S MY HEART PERFUME 1948-49
1/2 oz. glass stoppered heart shaped bottle. Painted label, pink satin ribbon and heart shaped box and base. Very rare. OSP $7.50. **CMV $125. BO mint, $175. MB.**

HERE'S MY HEART PERFUME OIL FOR THE BATH 1963
1/2 oz. painted label and white beaded cap. Came in blue and white box. OSP $3.50. **CMV $15. MB, BO$12.**

1/2 OZ. COLOGNE 1970-71
1/2 oz. painted label, white beaded cap, blue and white box. OSP $1.50. **CMV $1. BO, $1. MB.**

HERE'S MY HEART COLOGNE SPECIAL ISSUE 1961
Blue and white box (short issue) holds 4 oz. cologne. OSP $3. **CMV $16. MB as shown.**

HERE'S MY HEART PERFUME OIL 1964-68
1/2 oz. painted label and white beaded cap. Came in blue and white box. OSP $3.40. **CMV $8. MB, $6. BO.**
LOTION SACHET 1958-61
1 oz. blue plastic coated bottle with white beaded cap and painted label. Blue and white box. OSP $2. **CMV $8. MB, $5. BO.**
2 OZ. COLOGNE 1961-68
2 oz. white beaded cap and painted label, blue and white box. First introduced in red and white rose box. OSP $1.75. **CMV in rose box $8.** In blue box $3., $1. BO.
COLOGNE MIST 1958-76
3 oz. blue plastic coated bottle with white beaded cap and painted label. Blue and white box. OSP $7. **CMV $1.**

HERE'S MY HEART PERFUMED BATH OIL 1960-66
6 oz. blue plastic, white beaded cap. OSP $2.25. **CMV $2. BO, $4. MB.**
FOAMING BATH OIL 1966-68
6 oz. blue plastic, white beaded cap. OSP $2.75. **CMV $2. BO, $4. MB.**

HERE'S MY HEART COLOGNE MIST 1957-58
3 oz. blue plastic coated bottle with indented heart, 2 hearts on gold cap. Also plain lid. OSP $3. **CMV $18. BO mint, $23. MB.**

HERE'S MY HEART TOILET WATER 1959-62
2 oz. painted label and white beaded cap. Came in blue and white box. OSP $2.50. **CMV $5. MB, $2. BO.**
4 OZ. COLOGNE 1960-63
4 oz. bottle with white beaded cap and painted label. Came in blue and white box. OSP $3. **CMV $5. MB, $2. BO.**

POWDER SACHET CHRISTMAS BOX 1959
Blue box with gold butterflies sold Christmas only 1959 with choice of powder sachet in Here's My Heart, Persian Wood, Nearness, Cotillion (pink painted), Bright Night and To A Wild Rose. OSP $1.50 - $1.75. **CMV $15. each MB as shown.**

HERE'S MY HEART PERFUME ROLLETTE 1967-68
.33 oz. ribbed glass, smooth gold cap. OSP $3. **CMV $3.**
PERFUMED CREAM ROLLETTE 1963-65
.33 oz. 4A embossed bottle with gold cap. OSP $1.75. **CMV $3. mint.**
HERE'S MY HEART POWDER SACHET 1960-66
9/10 oz. blue glass, white beaded plastic cap. OSP $2. **CMV $8., $10. MB.**
POWDER SACHET 1958-60
Blue and white plastic squeeze bottle with white beaded cap. OSP $1.75. **CMV $10., $12. MB.**
DEMI STICK 1975-78
.19 oz. blue and white, white cap. OSP $1. **CMV 25c.**
CREAM SACHET 1976-77
.66 oz. clear glass, gold, blue and white lid. OSP $2. **CMV 25c.**

LOTION SACHET 1958
1/2 oz. clear glass fan shaped bottle with blue cap. Came in Here's My Heart and Persian Wood. Came in Wishing set only. **CMV $8. each MB, $4. BO.**
HERE'S MY HEART BODY POWDER 1961-63
4 oz. blue plastic bottle with white beaded cap, painted label. OSP $1.95. **CMV $8. MB, $5. BO.**

HERE'S MY HEART SOAP 1962-65
Blue and white box holds 2 white heart shaped soaps. OSP $1.29. **CMV $24. MB.**

HERE'S MY HEART CREAM LOTION 1958-68
4 oz. bottle with painted label and white beaded cap. OSP $1. **CMV $2. BO, $3. MB.**

SPRAY PERFUME 1958-63
Blue, white and gold box holds blue tin container with gold cap with hearts on top. OSP $3.50. **CMV $12. MB, $8. BO.**

HERE'S MY HEART PERFUME SAMPLE 1950
With gold lid. **CMV $30.**

HERE'S MY HEART LOTION SACHET 1957-58
1 oz. blue plastic coated bottle with hearts on gold cap, painted label. OSP $2. **CMV $10. MB, $5. BO.**

SENTIMENTAL HEART SET 1961
Blue box with blue satin lining holds Here's My Heart cologne mist and beauty dust. OSP $6.50. **CMV $32.50. MB.**

HERE'S MY HEART PERFUMED SOAP 1965-66
3 oz. white soap in blue and white wrapper. OSP 39c. **CMV $3.**

PERFUME MIST 1964-68
2 dram blue and white metal with gold band. OSP $3. **CMV $5, $6. MB.**

FRAGRANCE SAMPLE
10 foil samples in a box. **CMV 75c box.**

POWDER SACHET SAMPLE 1960-66
CMV $1.

ROMANTIC MOOD SET 1960
Blue and white box with blue satin lining with Here's My Heart cologne mist, cream sachet and beauty dust.. OSP $8.25. **CMV $40. MB.**

HEART FELT SET 1964
Blue and white box holds Here's My Heart 2 oz. cologne and cream sachet. OSP $3.50. **CMV $22.50 MB.**

HERE'S MY HEART SOAP 1966-67
Blue and white box holds 3 heart shaped bars. OSP $1.75. **CMV $22.50 MB.**

HERE'S MY HEART PERFUMED TALC 1958-62
2.75 oz. blue and white can, white beaded cap. OSP 79c. **CMV $1. CO, $3. MB.**

SCENTED HAIR SPRAY 1966-70
7 oz. blue and white can, 4A on cap. OSP $1.50. **CMV $3.**

PERFUMED TALC 1962-72
2.75 oz. blue and white can with white cap. OSP 79c. **CMV $1.**

HERE'S MY HEART CREAM SACHET 1959-75
.66 oz. white beaded cap. Came blue painted over clear glass. **CMV 50c or blue paint over white milk glass.** OSP $3. **CMV $1.**

PERFUMED SKIN SOFTENER 1964-73
5 oz. painted over milk glass or clear glass jar with gold and white lid. OSP $3. **CMV $1.**

HERE'S MY HEART BEAUTY DUST 1958-70
White plastic powder box with beaded edge. Some with yellow lid and white handle. **CMV $10.** OSP $3. white issue. **CMV $3. CO, $5. MB.**

HEARTS IN BLOOM SET 1964
Blue and white box holds Here's My Heart cologne mist, cream sachet and cream lotion. OSP $6.50. **CMV $37.50 MB.**

HERE'S MY HEART SOAP 1959-64
Blue and white box, holds 2 white heart shaped bars. OSP $1.29. **CMV $24. MB.**

SWEETHEARTS SET 1958
Blue and white heart shaped box with white satin lining and white rose on lid. Holds Here's My Heart cologne mist, and plastic powder sachet or lotion sachet. OSP $5. **CMV $45. MB.**

HEART O'MINE SET 1959
Blue and white box with blue heart on lid with white rose and blue satin lining. Holds Here's My Heart cologne mist, cream sachet, beauty dust and spray perfume. OSP $11.95. **CMV $45. MB.**

NEW REMEMBRANCE SET 1963
Blue and white box holds Here's My Heart cologne mist and beauty dust. OSP $6.95. **CMV $30. MB.**

TWO HEARTS GIFT SET 1961
Blue and white box holds 2 oz. Here's My Heart cologne and cream sachet. OSP $3.50. **CMV $25. MB.**

HONEYSUCKLE

HONEYSUCKLE FLORAL DUET SET 1972-73
Box came with Rollette and bar of soap. OSP $3.25. **CMV $5. MB.**

HONEYSUCKLE AFTER BATH FRESHENER 1967-72
8 oz. bottle with orange cap and center band label. OSP $3. **CMV $1.**
AFTER BATH FRESHENER 1972-76
8 oz. yellow plastic bottle with yellow cap. OSP $5. **CMV 50c.**
FOAMING BATH OIL 1967-76
8 oz. plastic bottle with orange cap. OSP $4.50. **CMV $1.**
CREAM LOTION 1969-72
5 oz. yellow plastic bottle. OSP $2. **CMV 50c.**
PERFUMED TALC 1967-77
3 1/2 oz. yellow and white paper container. OSP $2. **CMV 50c.**
SOAP 1968-69
6 sided box holds 3 yellow bars. OSP $3. **CMV $9. MB.**
PERFUMED DEMI STICK 1970-74
.19 oz. yellow, green and white. Yellow cap. OSP $1.75. **CMV $1.**
COLOGNE MIST 1971-72
2 oz. yellow glass bottle, yellow cap. OSP $4.25. **CMV $1.**
CREAM SACHET SAMPLE
Sample in foil. **CMV 25c.**
KWICKETTES 1971-73
Box holds 14 Kwickettes. OSP $1.75. **CMV $1.**
PERFUMED SOAP 1967-78
3 oz. bar in yellow and orange wrapper. OSP $1.25. **CMV $1.25.**
CREAM SACHET 1967-75
.66 oz. yellow frosted glass with orange lid. OSP $2.50. **CMV 50c.**

IMPERIAL GARDEN

IMPERIAL GARDEN COLOGNE MIST 1973-77
3 oz. white with orange flowers and gold stems. 2 different designs as pictured. OSP $8. **CMV $1. each.**

IMPERIAL GARDEN CERAMIC VASE TEST 1973
Test vase from factory never sold by Avon. Has gold band around top of cap and bottom is glazed over Avon. Blue and green flowers on front different from regular issue. **CMV $25.**

IMPERIAL GARDEN PERFUME TALC 1974-76
3.5 oz. white, gold and orange, cardboard.
OSP $1. **CMV 50c.**

IMPERIAL GARDEN BEAUTY DUST 1974-ONLY
6 oz. white plastic with orange and gold. OSP $5. **CMV $6., $7. MB.**

IMPERIAL GARDEN PERFUMED SOAP 1974-76
Three 3 oz. cakes white soap. Came in white and orange box. SSP $6. **CMV $7. MB.**

PERFUMED POWDER MIST 1974-77
7 oz. orange painted can, white lid. OSP $5. **CMV 50c.**

PERFUMED SKIN SOFTENER 1974-76
5 oz. orange plastic, white and gold cap. OSP $5.50.

IMPERIAL GARDEN COASTERS 1973
4 white plastic, orange design. **CMV $25. MB set.**

JARDIN D'AMOUR
See Misc. Perfume & Powder Section for additional Jardin D'Amour bottles.

IMPERIAL GARDEN CERAMIC VASE 1973-75
Some came with short neck and tall cap and some with long neck and short caps. White with orange flowers and gold stems. 18 oz. ceramic vase. Bath crystals. 7" high. SSP $16. **CMV $16. MB.**

COLOGNE MIST 1973-77
3 oz. SSP $8. **CMV $1.**

CREAM SACHET 1973-77
.66 oz. SSP $4.50. **CMV 50c.**

ROLLETTE 1973-77
.33 oz. SSP $4.50. **CMV 25c.**

SAMPLE BOTTLE COLOGNE 1973-77
CMV 25c.

SAMPLE 1973-77
CMV 25c box. Box of 10 samples.

JARDIN D'AMOUR PERFUME 1930s
1 oz. clear glass bottle with frosted glass stopper. Silver & blue CPC label. Very rare. CMV $150. mint.

JARDIN D'AMOUR SACHET 1926-30
Brass cap, silver & blue label. Rare. **CMV $85. mint.**

JARDIN D'AMOUR PERFUME 1929-33
2 oz. glass stoppered bottle. Orange box. Label on top of bottle. OSP $6.50. **CMV $100. BO mint, $135. MB.**

JARDIN D'AMOUR PERFUME 1926-33
Orange box with gold base for 1 oz. glass stoppered bottle. Black label at neck. OSP $3.50. **CMV $100. BO, $135. MB.**

JARDIN D'AMOUR PERFUME SET 1954 ONLY
Blue & gold bucket with gold tie down cord. Holds 1 1/2 oz. bottle with gold label, clear plastic cap with blue stone in gold set. Bottom of bucket holds 1 dram perfume. Came in blue, white & gold lay down box. OSP $15. **CMV in box complete $200, 1- 1/2 oz. bottle in bucket mint $175, 1 dram perfume $15, 1 1/2 oz. bottle only $50. mint.**

JARDIN D'AMOUR VANITY COMPACT 1926-32
Silver compact. OSP $2.25. **CMV $40. in box, compact only $35. mint.**

JASMINE SOAP 1936-45
Turquoise & gold box holds 3 embossed bars. OSP $1.02. **CMV $47.50 MB.**

JASMINE & ROYAL JASMINE

JARDIN D'AMOUR SACHET 1932-36
1 1/4 oz. ribbed glass jar, black cap. OSP $1.04. **CMV $25. mint BO, $30. MB.**

JASMINE SOAP 1934-36
Beige & gold box holds 3 bars. OSP $1.02. **CMV $50. MB.**

ROYAL JASMINE SOAP 1954-59
Box holds 3 bars, with round or flat edges. Box lid lifts off. OSP $1.69. **CMV $25. MB.**
ROYAL JASMINE SOAP 1959-66
Same box only lid flips back and not off. The soap has flat edges. **CMV $22. MB.**

JARDIN D'AMOUR TALC 1926-36
Frosted glass with brass shaker top. Front paper label. OSP $1.04. **CMV $60. BO mint, $75. MB.**

JASMINE GIFT SOAP 1966-67
Floral box contains 3 yellow Jasmine soaps. OSP $2. **CMV $20. MB.**

JASMINE SOAP 1946-53
Black flowered box holds 3 bars. OSP $1.25. **CMV $40. MB.**

JASMINE SOAP 1948-49
Christmas only. Black flowered box holds 3 white bars. OSP $1.28. **CMV $40. MB.**

JASMINE SOAP 1939 ONLY
Gold striped box holds 3 bars. Avon on back of soap. OSP $1.25. CMV $60. MB.

JASMINE BATH SALTS 1936-44
9 oz. glass jar, turquoise lid. OSP 63c. CMV $20. BO mint, $25. MB.

JASMINE POWDER SACHET 1946-50
(Left) 1 1/4 oz. bottle with black cap & label. Came in black box. OSP $1.19. CMV $20. MB, $15. BO.
JASMINE DUSTING POWDER 1947-50
(Right) 13 oz. black & gold tin can with pink flowers on lid. OSP $1.50. CMV $25., MB $30.

JASMINE TOILET WATER 1946-48
2 oz. gold cap, also came in black flowered box. Turquoise box shown. OSP $1.19. CMV MB $40., $30. BO.

JASMINE AFTER BATH FRESHENER 1964-68
8 oz. glass bottle with yellow cap & painted label. Yellow flowered box. OSP $2.50. CMV $2. BO, $3. MB.
FOAMING BATH OIL 1966-70
8 oz. frosted plastic bottle with yellow cap, green or white painted label, yellow box. OSP $2.50. CMV $1.50.
PERFUMED BATH OIL 1964-66
8 oz. plastic bottle, green cap. Green or white painted label. OSP $2.50. CMV $2.50.
PERFUMED TALC 1964-68
3 1/2 oz. yellow flowered paper container with plastic shaker top. OSP 89c. CMV $2.
FRAGRANCE KWICKETTES 1967-72
14 foil towellettes in box. OSP $1.25. CMV $1. box.
PERFUMED SOAP 1964-67
3 oz. bar in yellow flowered wrapping. OSP 39c. CMV $2.
CREAM SACHET 1967-72
.66 oz. yellow frosted glass with gold & white lid. OSP $2.50. CMV 50c.

ROYAL JASMINE BATH OIL 1957-59
Yellow, white & green box holds 8 oz. bottle with yellow cap and flowered label. OSP $1.95. CMV $25. MB, $20. BO.

ROYAL JASMINE BATH SALTS 1954-57
Yellow & white flowered box holds 8 oz. bottle with yellow cap. OSP 89c. CMV $25. MB, $20. BO.

FANTASY IN JASMINE SET 1942-44
Green box holds 2 bars Jasmine soap & 9 oz. Jasmine bath salts with turquoise lid. OSP $1.35. CMV $70. MB.

FANTASY IN JASMINE 1946-47
Black box with pink flowers holds 2 bars of Jasmine soap & 9 oz. bottle of Jasmine bath salts. OSP $1.95. CMV $75 MB. Set also came with 2 bottles in boxes of 1 1/4 oz. Jasmine sachet in place of soaps. **CMV with boxed sachets $100. MB.**

JASMINE BATH SALTS 1945-52
9 oz. clear glass with black cap & label. Label came with either a large or small pink flower on front. Came in black box. OSP 75c. CMV $40 MB, $30. BO.

FANTASY IN JASMINE SET 1945 ONLY
Black box with pink flowers holds Jasmine bath salts & 2 Jasmine soaps. OSP $1.60. CMV $77.50 MB.

BATH ENSEMBLE SET 1940-43
Blue flowered flip open box holds Jasmine bath salts, Jasmine 2 oz. toilet water, 2 bars of Jasmine soap & can of dusting powder. OSP $3.50,. CMV $150. MB set.

FANTASY IN JASMINE SET 1956-57
White box with yellow flowers holds 2 bars Royal Jasmine soap & 2 oz. Royal Jasmine bath oil with white cap & black label. OSP $1.95. CMV $45. MB, 2 oz. bath oil $25. BO.

FANTASY IN JASMINE SET 1940
Blue box with flowers holds 9 oz. Jasmine bath salts & 2 bars soap or 2 Powder Sachets boxed. OSP $1.35. CMV $100. MB.

ROYAL JASMINE SET 1954-57
Yellow & white flowered box holds 8 oz. Royal Jasmine bath salts & bar of Royal Jasmine soap. OSP $1.39. CMV $37.50.

FANTASY IN JASMINE SET 1948
Black box with pink flowers holds 2 bars Jasmine soap & 2 oz. Jasmine toilet water. OSP $2.39. CMV $75. MB.

JASMINE POWDER SACHET 1949
(Left) 1 1/2 oz. clear glass bottle, black cap & label. OSP $1.25. CMV $20. - $25. MB.
JASMINE TOILET WATER 1949
2 oz. black cap & label. OSP $1.25. CMV $35., MB $40.

LAVENDER

LAVENDER SACHET 1944-45
Beige box holds 2 lavender wrapped cakes of sachet. One set is wrapped in clear cellophane with a flowered band. The other set is wrapped in lavender flowered paper, no band. OSP 79c set. Some boxes have label printed on box & some boxes plain. CMV $25. MB.

LAVENDER BLOSSOMS 1935-38
Lavender & pink box holds package of Lavender Blossoms. OSP 50c. CMV $40. MB.

LAVENDER SACHET CAKES 1946-48
(Top) Box holds 2 flower design wrapped cakes of sachet. OSP 79c. CMV $25. MB.
LAVENDER SACHETS 1945-46
(Bottom) Beige box holds 2 foil wrapped cakes of sachet. Plain band. OSP 79c. CMV $25. MB.

LAVENDER SOAP 1935 ONLY
Box holds 3 lavender bars of soap. OSP 67c. **CMV $75. MB.**

LAVENDER TOILET WATER 1938-43
(Left) 4 oz. lavender cap. OSP 78c. **CMV $35. BO, $40. MB. CPC on box, 1938-39 add $5.**
LAVENDER TOILET WATER 1945-46
(Right) 4 oz. lavender cap. OSP 89c. **CMV $40. BO, $45. MB.**

LAVENDER SOAP SET 1945
Pink box holds 3 Lavender embossed bars. OSP 85c. **CMV $60. MB.**

LAVENDER SOAP SET 1946 ONLY
Box holds 3 lavender bars of soap. OSP 85c. **CMV $50. MB.**

LAVENDER TOILET WATER 1946-48
(Left) 4 oz. pink cap. OSP $1.19. **CMV $35. BO, $40. MB.**
LAVENDER TOILET WATER 1934-37
(Right) 4 oz. ribbed bottle with blue or gold cap. Lavender label, box shown used 1934-36. OSP 75c. **CMV $45. mint BO, $55. MB.**

LAVENDER TOILET WATER 1934-37
4 oz. ribbed glass, gold cap, pink & lavender box. Box shown used 1936-37. OSP 75c. **CMV $45. BO, $55. MB.**

LAVENDER POWDER SACHET 1961-68
.9 oz. pink & white label & neck band, glass & plastic stopper. **CMV one with 4A design in place of size $4. BO, $7. MB. CMV on 9 oz. $20. MB, $15. BO.** Box on right is 1965, box in center is regular issue.

LAVENDER ENSEMBLE SET 1941 ONLY
Box holds 2 Lavender sachet cakes, bottle of Lavender toilet water & 2 Lavender bars of soap. OSP $1.50. **CMV $85. MB set.**

LAVENDER ENSEMBLE SET 1934-38
Lavender box holds 4 oz. Lavender toilet water, 2 bars Lavender soap & package of Lavender Blossoms. OSP $1.50. **CMV $125. MB set, Lavender Blossoms only $50. MB.**

LAVENDER BOUQUET SACHET PILLOWS 1977-78
Pink box holds 6 satin lavender filled sachet pillows. Came with pink ribbon around them. SSP $4. **CMV $4.**

LAVENDER ENSEMBLE SET 1938 ONLY
Lavender flip open box holds 4 oz. Lavender toilet water with same label as 1934 Lavender toilet water, 2 bars of Lavender soap, 2 Lavender sachet cakes. OSP $1.50. **CMV $100. MB, $45. BO.**

LAVENDER / LILAC

LAVENDER ENSEMBLE 1938-40
Lavender flip open box with cardboard liner holds 4 oz. Lavender toilet water, 2 bars of Lavender soap wrapped in lavender paper & 2 sachet cakes with lavender band around them. OSP $1.50. **CMV $80. MB.**

LAVENDER ENSEMBLE SET 1940-43
Lavender flowered box with satin lining holds 4 oz. Lavender toilet water, 2 bars of Lavender soap & 2 Lavender sachet cakes. OSP $1.75. **CMV $90. MB.**

LAVENDER ENSEMBLE SET 1946-48
Blue & pink flowered flip open box holds 4 oz. bottle, pink cap of Lavender toilet water, 2 pink bars of Lavender soap & 2 paper wrapped cakes of sachet. OSP $2.75. **CMV $90. MB.**

LAVENDER ENSEMBLE SET 1945-46
Blue, pink & white with silver bottom holds 4 oz. Lavender toilet water, 2 bars Lavender soap & 2 sachet cakes. OSP $1.95. **CMV $90. MB.**

LAVENDER SET 1939
Yellow box with lavender, green & pink flowers holds 4 oz. Lavender toilet water, 2 cakes Lavender soap & 2 sachet cakes with plain lavender color paper ribbons. **CMV $125. MB.**

LAVENDER ENSEMBLE 1946
Blue, pink & green flowered box with satin lining holds 2 bars of Lavender soap, 4 oz. bottle of Lavender toilet water & 2 flower wrapped cakes of sachet. OSP $2.75. **CMV $95. MB.**

LILAC

LILAC TOILET WATER 1940
2 oz. gold ribbed cap with "A" on top, gold label. Blue box. Has Avon Products Inc. label. OSP 78c. **CMV $35. BO mint, $40. MB.** Same bottle sold 1934 to 1939 only bottom of label says Toilet Water & does not say Avon Products. CPC pn backside of label. **Same CMV as above.**

LILAC AFTER BATH FRESHENER 1964-68
8 oz. glass bottle with pink cap & pink or white painted label. Pink box. OSP $2.50. **CMV $2.**

PERFUME BATH OIL 1964-66
8 oz. frosted plastic bottle with pink cap & painted label, pink box. OSP $2.50. **CMV $1.**

PERFUMED TALC 1964-76
3 1/2 oz. pink paper container with plastic shaker top. OSP $2. **CMV $1.**

FRAGRANCE KWICKETTES 1971-73
Box holds 14 towellettes. OSP $1.75. **CMV $1.50 MB.**

PERFUMED DEMI STICK 1970-76
.19 oz. lavender label with white cap & bottom. OSP $1.75. **CMV 50c.**

PERFUMED DEMI STICK 1968-70
.19 oz. lavender label & cap & bottom. OSP $1.75. **CMV $1.**

PERFUMED SOAP 1964-67
1 bar in pink flowered wrapping. OSP 39c. **CMV $2.50 MB.**

CREAM SACHET 1967-75
.66 oz. purple frosted glass with gold & white lid. OSP $2.50. **CMV 50c.**

CREAM SACHET 1975-76
.66 oz. clear glass, white cap with lilacs on top. OSP $3. **CMV 25c.**

FOAMING BATH OIL 1966-75
8 oz. plastic bottle, pink cap. OSP $2.50. **CMV 50c.**

LILAC SOAP 1966
Lavender box holds 3 piece lavender soap in cellophane wrapper. OSP $2.50. **CMV $15. MB.**

LILAC SOAP 1968-77
Box holds lavender bars. OSP $5. **CMV $7.**

LILY OF THE VALLEY

LILY OF THE VALLEY TOILET WATER 1949-52
2 oz. white cap. OSP $1.25. **CMV $45. MB, $35. BO.**

LILY OF THE VALLEY TOILET WATER 1934-40
2 oz. gold ribbed cap, "A" on top. Gold front label. OSP 78c. **CMV $35. BO, $40. MB.**

LILY OF THE VALLEY TOILET WATER 1946-49
Green box holds 2 oz. bottle with gold cap & label. OSP $1.19. **CMV $40. MB, $30. BO.**

LILY OF THE VALLEY PERFUME 1948-52
3 dram bottle with flower cap. Came in satin lined box with clear plastic lid. OSP $2.50. **CMV $80. MB, $40. BO.**

LILY OF THE VALLEY PERFUME 1952-54
3 dram, white cap, white satin lined box. OSP $3.75. **CMV $85. MB, $40. BO.** Also came in Gardenia.

LILY OF THE VALLEY SCENTED PILLOW 1979
10" x 10" lace green & white scented pillow. SSP $11.99. **CMV $8. MB.**

LILY OF THE VALLEY FOAMING BATH OIL 1966-70
8 oz. white plastic, green label & cap. OSP $2.50. **CMV $2.**

CREAM SACHET 1967-75
.66 oz. frosted green glass jar with gold & white lid. OSP $2.50. **CMV 50c.**

KWICKETTES 1964-68
Box of 14 fragrance samples. OSP $1.25. **CMV $2. MB.**

LILY OF THE VALLEY SOAP 1966-68
Green box holds 2 green cakes. OSP $2. **CMV $18.50 MB.**

LILY OF THE VALLEY AFTER BATH FRESHENER 1964-68
8 oz. glass bottle with green cap, painted label in green or white letters, green box. OSP $2.50. **CMV $2. MB, $1. BO.**

PERFUMED BATH OIL 1964-66
8 oz. frosted plastic bottle with green cap, painted label in green or white letters, green box. OSP $2.50. **CMV $1.**

PERFUMED TALC 1964-70
3 1/2 oz. green paper container with plastic shaker top. OSP 89c. **CMV $1.50.**

PERFUMED SOAP 1964-67
3 oz. bar with green & white flowered wrapping. OSP 39c. **CMV $$3. MB.**

123

LILY OF THE VALLEY CREAM SACHET
1974 ONLY
(Left) .66 oz. clear embossed glass with white cap with flowers. First issued with this jar. OSP $1.25. **CMV $1.**
CREAM SACHET 1975-76
(Center) .66 oz. clear ribbed glass with white cap with flowers. OSP $1.25. **CMV $1.**
PERFUME DEMI STICK 1974-76
(Right) .19 oz. white with flowers. OSP $1. **CMV $1.**

LILY OF THE VALLEY PRODUCTS 1979-80
COLOGNE ICE STICK
(Left) Yellow & green plastic. SSP $2.49. **CMV 50c.**
PERFUMED TALC
(Center) 3.5 oz. cardboard sides, plastic bottom & top. SSP $1.29. **CMV 25c.**
CHATEAU OF FLOWERS BOOK
(Right) Green hardback book on story of Lily of the Valley. Book does not say Avon on it. Must be in Avon box cover as shown. SSP $2. **CMV $2. MB.**

LITTLE BLOSSOM

LITTLE BLOSSOM & FRIENDS 1983-84
Shaker talc with puff sets. 2 oz. talc & small hand puff. Choice of
LITTLE BLOSSOM
Pink
DAISY DREAMER
Yellow
SCAMPER LILY
Orange
SSP $4. each. **CMV $4. each set.**
MINI DOLLS
2 1.4" high soft plastic, choice of Little Blossom, Daisy Dreamer, Scamper Lily. SSP $4. each. **CMV $2. each.**
DAB O COLOGNE
.45 oz. rollette, choice of Little Blossom in Whisper Soft, Daisy Dreamer in Secret Wishes & Scamper Lily in Sparkle Bright. SSP $3. each. **CMV $2. each.**

LITTLE BLOSSOM LIP & NAIL TINT 1982-83
Lip tint on left, pink cap, no box. Nail tint in .5 oz. plastic bottle, white cap, boxed. **CMV $1. each.**

LITTLE BLOSSOM FINGER PUPPET WITH DEMI STICK SET 1982-83
(Left) box holds small finger puppet & blue, white & pink Demi Stick. SSP $4. **CMV $4. MB.**
LITTLE BLOSSOM LIGHT SWITCH COVER
(Right) Box holds blue & green light switch plate with pink flowers. SSP $4. **CMV $4. MB.**

LITTLE BLOSSOM WHISPER SOFT COLOGNE 1981-82
1.5 oz. clear glass painted decor. Pink cap. SSP $3.75. **CMV $2. MB.**
CHEEKY ROSE BLUSH 1981-82
Pink & white plastic jar. SSP $2.25. **CMV $1. MB.**
CHEERFUL LIP TINT 1981-82
White flowered tube, pink cap. SSP $1.25. **CMV $1. mint, no box.**
LITTLE BLOSSOM SCENTED PICTURE FRAME 1981-82
Pink plastic frame 4 1/2" x 4 1/2" has scented fabric picture of little blossom. SSP $6. **CMV $6. MB.**

LITTLE BLOSSOM BUBBLE BATH PACKETS 1983
Flowered box holds 10 packets. SSP $2. **CMV $1. MB.**

LITTLE BLOSSOM & FRIENDS IRON ON DECALS 1983
Package of 3 T-shirt decals. SSP 70c. **CMV 75c. set of 3.**

LUCY HAYS

LUCY HAYS PERFUME 1936 ONLY
2 dram, gold cap. Sold for 20c with other purchase to celebrate Mr. & Mrs. McConnell 51st wedding anniversary. Lucy Hays was Mrs. McConnell's maiden name. Sold March 3 to 23, 1936 only. **CMV $85. MB, $65. mint BO.**

LULLABYE SET 1955-56
Blue & pink box holds baby oil & baby powder. OSP $1.39. **CMV $45. MB.**

LULLABYE

LULLABYE BABY TALC 1946-50
5 oz. pink paper container with pink & white plastic top & bottom. OSP 65c. **CMV $35. MB, $30. talc only mint.**

LULLABYE BABY OIL 1946-50
6 oz. clear glass bottle, back side flat. Pink cap & painted label. OSP $1. **CMV $50. MB, $40. BO.**

LULLABYE BABY CREAM 1946-50
White milk glass jar with pink lid & label. OSP 89c. **CMV $30. MB, $25. jar only.**

LULLABYE BABY SOAP 1946-50
Plastic wrapper with pink painted bow & flowers on wrapper. OSP 39c. **CMV $25. mint.**

LULLABYE BABY SET 1951-55
Blue, pink & white box holds baby lotion, baby talc, lanolin baby soap. OSP $2.35. **CMV $65. MB.**

LULLABYE BABY SET 1946-50
Pink box holds Lullabye baby oil, Lullabye baby soap, Lullabye baby cream & Lullabye baby talc. OSP $3.55. **CMV $150. MB.**

LULLABE BABY SET 1964-66
Pink & blue box holds 2 bars baby soap & choice of Tot 'N Tyke baby oil, baby lotion or baby shampoo. OSP $1.96. **CMV $27.50 MB.**

LUSCIOUS

LUSCIOUS PERFUME AWARD 1950
(Left) Gold & purple box holds 3 dram, ribbed glass stopper. Stopper different from regular issue. Given when Luscious was first issued. **CMV $150. MB, $100. BO.**

LUSCIOUS PERFUME 1950
(Right) 1 dram clear bottle with gold cap & cap. Came in brown felt wrapper. OSP $1.75. **CMV $12. BO, $18. in wrapper.**

LUSCIOUS PERFUME 1950-55
(Left) 1 dram, painted label with smooth gold cap. Came in felt wrapper. OSP $1.75. **CMV in wrapper $15., $10. mint BO.**

LUSCIOUE PERFUME 1955-56
(Right) 1 dram, painted label, embossed gold cap. Came in felt wrapper. OSP $1.75. **CMV in wrapper $15., $8. BO.**

LUSCIOUS PERFUME 1950
3 dram glass stoppered bottle, came with painted label or with gold neck tag label. OSP $2.25. **CMV $125. MB, $100. BO.**

MARIONETTE

MARIONETTE PERFUME 1940-44
(Left) 1 dram bottle, plastic cap. OSP 75c.
CMV $25. BO, $30. MB.
MARIONETTE PERFUME 1938
(Right) 1/4 oz. size. Gold ribbed cap with "A".
CPC on label. Sold in honor of Mr.
McConnell's birthday. OSP 20c. **CMV $50.
MB, $40. BO.**

**MARIONETTE SACHET SPECIAL ISSUE
BOX 1940 ONLY**
(Left) Short issue blue & pink box holds
regular issue marionette powder sachet on left
in 1 1/4 oz. size. Sold for 20c with regular
order. **CMV $25. MB in this box only.**
MARIONETTE SACHET 1938 ONLY
(Right) 1 1/4 oz. ribbed glass bottle with
turquoise plain metal cap or ribbed plastic
turquoise cap. OSP $1. **CMV $25. BO, $28.
MB.**

MARIONETTE TOILET WATER 1940-46
2 oz. gold ribbed cap & gold label. Also came
with plastic caps. OSP $1.04. **CMV $30. BO
mint, $35. MB.**

MARIONETTE SACHET 1938-46
1 1/4 oz. with turquoise plain metal cap or
ribbed turquoise plastic cap. Shown with
regular issue box. OSP $1. **CMV $20. MB,
$15. BO.**

MARIONETTE TOILET WATER 1939-40
2 oz. plastic cap, long front label. OSP 20c.
CMV $45. MB, $35. BO.

MERRIMENT

JOLLY SURPRISE 1955
Pink & blue flip open box holds choice of 4
oz. bottle of Merriment cologne. OSP
$1.75. Or bubble bath. OSP $1.50. With
pink caps. **CMV $55. each MB, $40. BO.**

MISS LOLLYPOP

MISS LOLLYPOP COLOGNE BOOT 1967-69
2 oz. glass boot with gold cap & red tassel.
Red & white box. OSP $2. **CMV $8. MB, BO
with tassel $5.**

MISS LOLLYPOP CREAM SACHET 1967-70
(Left) .66 oz. dark or light yellow glass jar with
white kitten on red, white & pink cap. Kittens
eyes are blue or black, head also turns on
some. OSP $2. **CMV $5. MB, $4. BO.** Also
came with white base. **CMV $7. MB, $6. BO.**
COLOGNE MIST 1967-70
(Right) 3 oz. pink plastic coated bottom with
red band, white hat with red & yellow ribbon.
OSP $3. **CMV $6. MB, $5. BO.**

**MISS LOLLYPOP POWDER MITT 1968-
70**
(Left) Yellow, orange & white plastic mitt
filled with powder. Pink & white box. OSP
$2.50. **CMV $5. MB.**
SOAP & SPONGE 1967-70
(Right) Pink soap & 9" long sponge. Pink &
white box. OSP $2.50. **CMV $12. MB.**

MISS LOLLYPOP LIP POPS 1967-69
(3 on Left) Girls face on handle. Pink
lemonade, cherry, raspberry, peppermint &
cola. OSP $1.75 each. **CMV $3. - $4. MB.**
ROLLETTE 1968-69
(Center) Pink, yellow & white cap. 1/3 oz.
size. OSP $1.50. **CMV $3. MB, $2. BO.**
PERFUMED TALC 1968-70
(Right) 3 1/2 oz. paper container with plastic
shaker top. OSP $1. **CMV $5. MB, $4. CO.**

MOONWIND

MISS LOLLYPOP HAND CREAM 1968
(Left) 2 oz. white plastic tube, white boots & purse, yellow cap. OSP 75c. **CMV $3.**
HAND CREAM 1968
(Right) 2 oz. white plastic tube, black boots & purse, yellow cap. OSP 75c. **CMV $3.**

MISS LOLLYPOP POWDERETTE 1967-68
(Left) 3 1/2 oz. container of perfumed talc, red plume on top is long handled puff. OSP $2.50. **CMV $10. MB.**
PRETTY TOUCH 1969
Yellow, pink, green & orange plastic light switch plate. OSP 29c with purchase of Miss Lollypop items. Hard to find. Sold only 1 campaign. **CMV $9. MB.**

MISS LOLLYPOP ICE CREAM PUFF 1968-70
(Left) 3 1/2 oz. yellow plastic bottom with pink fluff. Holds talc. OSP $3. **CMV $4. BO, $6. MB.**
DOUBLE DIP BUBBLE BATH 1968-70
(Right) 5 oz. orange & white plastic bottle, red cap. OSP $2. **CMV $4. BO, $5. MB.**

PRETTY ME 1968
Box with white plastic tray holds Miss Lollypop perfume rollette & lip pop in choice of peppermint, pink lemonade, cherry, raspberry or cola. OSP $3.25. **CMV $12. MB.**

MOONWIND PERFUMED SOAP 1975-78
3 cakes blue soap. Blue & silver lid slides over gold box. OSP $4. **CMV $6. MB.**

MOONWIND COLOGNE & BATH OIL 1973
4 oz. clear glass bottles, gold caps. Came in Treasure Chest set only. **CMV $3.**

MISS LOLLYPOP LIP POP 1967
(Left) 1st issue pink & white dots, mirror top with face on back. OSP $1.50. **CMV $4. MB, $8. lip pop.**
LIP POP 1968
(Right) Same box came with 2 pink & white dot lip pops, no mirror top. OSP $1.75. **CMV $5. MB.**

MOONWIND FRAGRANCE 1971-78
All are blue trimmed in silver.
COLOGNE MIST 1971-75
(No. 1) 3 oz. blue with silver painted top. OSP $7.50. **CMV $1.**
COLOGNE MIST 1975-80
(No. 2) Blue with flat top, 2.7 oz. size. OSP $8. **CMV 50c.**
PERFUME ROLLETTE 1971-76
(No. 3) 1/3 oz. OSP $4.50. **CMV 50c.**
BEAUTY DUST 1971-76
(No. 4) 6 oz. OSP $10. **CMV $3. - $6. MB.**
PERFUMED POWDER MIST 1972-77
(No. 5) 7 oz. silver or blue caps. OSP $5. **CMV 50c.** Some upside down painted label. **CMV $8.**
PERFUMED SKIN SOFTENER 1972-73
(No. 6) 5 oz. blue glass. OSP $5. **CMV 50c.**
CREAM SACHET 1971-75
(No. 7) .66 oz. OSP $4. **CMV 50c.**
PERFUMED SOAPS 1972-73
(No. 8) 3 bars, blue, in blue box. OSP $6. **CMV $7. MB.**
FOAMING BATH OIL 1972
(Not Shown) 6 oz. OSP $5. **CMV $1.50.**

NEARNESS

NEARNESS BODY POWDER 1956-58
Frosted glass bottle with blue cap & label. Blue & gold box. OSP $1. **CMV $12. MB, $10. BO.**
NEARNESS PERFUMED TALC 1957-61
Blue can & cap. OSP 69c. **CMV can only $5., $7. MB.**
NEARNESS POWDER SACHET 1956-61
1 1/4 oz. blue glass bottle with blue cap & label. OSP $1.50. **CMV $10. MB, $7. BO.** Also came .9 oz. size. **Same CMV.**

NEARNESS TOILET WATER 1956-61
2 oz. bottle with blue cap & see through label on back side. Came in blue & gold box. OSP $2. **CMV $15. MB, $10. BO.**

NEARNESS COLOGNE 1955-61
4 oz. bottle with blue cap & see through label on back side. Came in blue & gold box. OSP $2.50. **CMV $15. MB, $10. BO.**

NEARNESS PERFUME 1955-59
Blue satin draw bag holds clam shell with pearl & 1/2 oz. bottle with blue cap & see through label on back side. OSP $7.50. **CMV in bag $100, $50. BO.**

NEARNESS COLOGNE MIST 1957-59
(Left) 3 oz. blue plastic coated bottle with blue cap, blue & gold box. OSP $2.75. **CMV $20. MB, $15. BO mint.**

NEARNESS COLOGNE MIST 1959-61
(Right) 3 oz. blue plastic coated bottle with pearl on pearl colored cap. Cap will turn gray in sunlight & not considered mint. Blue & gold box. OSP $2.95. **CMV $15. BO mint, $20. MB.**

NEARNESS COLOGNE 1957 ONLY
(Left & Center) 1/2 oz. clear glass. Sold in Gems & Crystals set only. Came with 2 different caps. Available in 4 fragrances. **CMV $7.**

NEARNESS CREAM SACHET 1955-61
(Right) Blue glass bottom, blue metal cap. OSP $1.50. **CMV $5. BO, $8. MB.**

NEARNESS BEAUTY DUST 1959-61
Plastic pearl color lid with lavender rim & turquoise bottom. General issue. OSP $2.95. **CMV $15. MB, $10. CO.** Rare issue came all lavender matching rim & bottom. **CMV $18. MB, $13. CO.**

NEARNESS SEA SHELL NECKLACE 1956 ONLY
Gold finished pendant with pearl on fine chain. Came only in Always Near set. **CMV $25.**

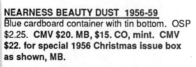

NEARNESS BEAUTY DUST 1956-59
Blue cardboard container with tin bottom. OSP $2.25. **CMV $20. MB, $15. CO, mint. CMV $22.** for special 1956 Christmas issue box as shown, MB.

NEARNESS 1 DRAM PERFUME 1955-59
(Left) 1 dram, clear smooth glass, gold scroll cap. Came in blue felt wrapper. OSP $2.25. **CMV $8. BO.**

TWO PEARLS SET 1956-57
(Right) Blue & gold box with 2 pearls on lid holds Nearness body powder & cream sachet. OSP $2.50. **CMV $40. MB.**

NEARNESS CHARM 1957
Blue box holds Nearness toilet water & can of talc. OSP $2.50. **CMV $40. MB.**

ALWAYS NEAR SET 1956
Blue sea shell box with pink satin lining holds Nearness 2 oz. toilet water, 1 dram perfume & gold sea shell necklace with pearl. OSP $5.95. **CMV $75. MB.**

SEA MIST SET 1958
Blue & gold box with net lining holds Nearness cologne mist & cream sachet. OSP $3.95. **CMV $60. MB.**

NEARNESS GIFT PERFUME COMBO SET 1956
1/2 oz. Nearness perfume on the clam shell in blue satin bag. Came with 1 dram Nearness perfume in blue felt wrapper in white box & outer sleeve. OSP $7.95. **CMV $130. MB.**

CIRCLE OF PEARLS 1957
Blue plastic box with blue plastic cover holds Nearness 2 oz. toilet water, cream sachet & pearl necklace. OSP $6. **CMV $65. MB.**

OCCUR!

OCCUR! POWDER SACHET 1963-67
(Left) 9/10 oz. black glass & cap, painted label. OSP $2.50. **CMV $7. MB, $5. BO.**
OCCUR! CREAM SACHET 1963-75
(Center) .66 oz. black glass & cap. 2 caps: 1 says Occur!, 1 says Occur! Cream Sachet. OSP $3. **CMV 50c.**
OCCUR! CREAM SACHET 1976-78
(Right) .66 oz. clear glass with black & gold lid. OSP $3. **CMV 25c.**

OCCUR! CREAM LOTION 1964-68
(Left) 4 oz. gold cap & painted label. Came in black & gold box. OSP $1.75. **CMV $4. MB, $2. BO.**
OCCUR! 1/2 OZ. COLOGNE 1970-71
(Center Left) 1/2 oz. size with gold cap & painted letters. Came in black & gold box. OSP $1.50. **CMV $1. BO, $2. MB.**
OCCUR! PERFUME OIL 1964-69
(Center Right) 1/2 oz. gold cap & painted label. Came in black & gold box. OSP $5. **CMV $6. MB, $4. BO.**
OCCUR! 2 OZ. COLOGNE 1964-71
(Right) 2 oz. bottle with gold cap & painted label. Came in black & gold box. OSP $2.50. **CMV $1. BO, $2. MB.**

OCCUR! PERFUMED TALC 1964-74
(Left) 2.75 oz. black can & cap, gold painted label. OSP $1. **CMV 50c.**
OCCUR! FOAMING BATH OIL 1966-74
(Center) 6 oz. black plastic bottle with gold cap & painted label. Came in black & gold box. OSP $3.50. **CMV $3. MB, $2. BO.**
OCCUR! COLOGNE MIST 1963-76
(Right) 3 oz. black plastic coated bottle with gold cap & painted label. Came in black & gold box. Older issue was gold bottom under plastic coating. **CMV $3.** Came with & without 3 oz. on front of bottle. **CMV $2.**

OCCUR! SOAP 1965-67
Black & gold box holds 3 yellow bars. OSP $2.25. **CMV $15. MB.**

OCCUR! BEAUTY DUST 1971-75
6 oz. black cardboard, non-refillable. OSP $8.50. **CMV $3. - $4. MB.**
OCCUR! BEAUTY DUST 1963-70
Black plastic box with gold handle on black lid. OSP $5. **CMV $3. - $5. MB.**
OCCUR! PERFUMED SKIN SOFTENER 1964-72
5 oz. black painted over white milk glass or clear glass jar with black & gold lid. OSP $1.75. **CMV $1.** ALso came white milk glass painted black or solid black glass. **CMV $3. each.**
OCCUR! PERFUMED SOAP 1965-68
Black wrapped soap. OSP 49c. **CMV $2.**

OCCUR! PERFUMED BATH OIL 1964-65
6 oz. black plastic bottle with gold cap & painted label. Black & gold box. OSP $2.75. **CMV $2. BO, $4. MB.**

OCCUR! PERFUME OIL FOR THE BATH 1963
(Left) Black & gold box holds 1/2 oz. bottle with gold cap & painted label. OSP $5. **CMV $10. MB, $8. BO.**
OCCUR! COLOGNE MIST 1963-66
(Center & Left) 2 oz. frosted glass with black cap & gold painted label. Came in black & gold box. OSP $3. **CMV $4. BO, $6. MB.** Also came with 4A embossed bottle with black neck label & gold plastic cap. OSP $2.50. **CMV $5. MB, $3. BO.**

OCCUR! SCENTED HAIR SPRAY 1966-70
(Left) 7 oz. black can with black cap. OSP $1.50. **CMV $3.**

PERFUME ROLLETTE 1965-69
(Center Left) .33 oz. gray ribbed carnival glass, gold cap. OSP $2.50. **CMV $3. BO, $4. MB.**

PERFUMED CREAM ROLLETTE 1963-65
(Center Right) .33 oz. 4A embossed bottle with gold cap. OSP $2.50. **CMV $2., MB $3.**

OCCUR! PERFUME MIST 1963-68
(Right) Gold box holds 2 dram black & gold metal case with white cap. OSP $3.75. **CMV $4. MB, $3. BO.**

OCCUR! PRODUCTS NOT SHOWN
PERFUMED TALC 1970s
3.5 oz.
FOAMING BATH OIL
6 oz. plastic.
PERFUMED SKIN SOFTENER
5 oz. plastic jar.
COLOGNE SPRAY
2.7 oz. glass.
CMV 50c each.

OCCUR! FRAGRANCE FORTUNE SET 1964-65
Black & gold box holds Occur! 2 oz. cologne & 1/2 oz. perfume oil. Both have gold caps. OSP $6.95. **CMV $30. MB.**

ORCHARD BLOSSOMS

ORCHARD BLOSSOMS COLOGNE 1941-45
(Left) 6 oz. bubble sided bottle, short front label has tree with flowers on it. OSP $1.50. pink cap. **CMV $30. BO, $40. MB.**

ORCHARD BLOSSOMS COLOGNE 1945-46
(Right) Same as above with long blue & white front label, pink cap. OSP $1.50. **CMV $45. MB, $35. BO.**

OCCUR! DELUXE SET 1965
Black & gold box holds Occur! beauty dust, perfumed skin softener & cologne mist. OSP $13.95. **CMV $35.**

OCCUR! ELEGENCE SET 1964
Black & gold box holds Occur! 4 oz. cream lotion, perfumed talc & 2 oz. cologne. OSP $5.75. **CMV $35. MB.**

OCCUR! SOPHISTICATE SET 1963-64
3 oz. Occur! cologne mist, perfume cream rollette & beauty dust. Black & gold box. OSP $12. 95. **CMV $35. MB.**

PETAL OF BEAUTY 1945-46
Blue & white box holds 6 oz. Orchard Blossoms cologne and blue & white box beauty dust. OSP $2.20. **CMV $100. MB.**

PETAL OF BEAUTY 1943-44
Blue box with pink satin lining holds 6 oz. Orchard Blossoms cologne & blue feather design beauty dust or Apple Blossom beauty dust. OSP $2.20. **CMV $100. MB.**

PATTERNS

PATTERNS 1969
TRAY 1969-70
10" black plastic tray with gold edge when held to light shows purple, red, gray (these are transparent). There is an opaque black one-rare. **CMV red, gray & purple $4. MB, $2. BO.** Reissued in 1975. Black (no light comes through) $7.50.
POWDER SHADOW COMPACT 1969-70
Black & white plastic.
LIPSTICK 1969-70
CREAM SACHET 1969-74
COLOGNE MIST 1969-72
PERFUME ROLLETTE 1969-74
PATTERNS PERFUME GLACE RING 1969-70
gold ring with black set. OSP $6. **CMV MB $6, ring only $3.**
All others CMV $1. each.

PENNSYLVANIA DUTCH

PENNSYLVANIA DUTCH DECANTERS 1973-76
Yellow painted over clear glass with orange fruit and yellow caps. **All items CMV $4. BO, $6. MB.**

HAND & BODY LOTION 1973-76
10 oz. came in Patchwork or Sonnet only. SSP $5.

COLOGNE DECANTER 1973-74
(Salt or pepper shaker) Holds Moonwind, Patchwork or Sonnet. 4 oz. SSP $5.

FOAMING BATH OIL 1973-76
6 oz. SSP $5.

POWDER SACHET SHAKER 1973-75
1.25 oz. SSP $5.

PERFUMED SKIN SOFTENER 1973-76
5 oz. OSP $5.

PERSIAN WOOD

PERSIAN WOOD PERFUME OIL 1964-66
Red & gold box holds 1/2 oz. bottle, white lettering & gold cap. OSP $3.50. **CMV $8. MB, $5. BO.**

PERSIAN WOOD COLOGNE 1961-66
2 oz. clear glass, gold lettering, gold cap. In red & gold box. OSP $1.75. **CMV $6. MB, $4. BO.**

PERSIAN WOOD COLOGNE 1960-63
Red & gold box holds 4 oz. bottle with gold lettering & gold cap. OSP $2.75. **CMV $10. MB, $6. BO.**

PERSIAN WOOD MIST 1959-64
(Left) 3 oz. red plastic coated glass, gold crown cap. Came in red & gold box. OSP $3. **CMV $6. MB, $5. BO.**

COLOGNE MIST 1964-76
(Center) 3 oz. red plastic coated glass, gold crown cap. Came in red & gold box. OSP $7. **CMV $1. - $2. MB.**

PERFUME OIL FOR THE BATH 1963
(Right) 1/2 oz. bottle with gold cap, painted label. Came in red & gold box. OSP $3.50. **CMV $12. MB, $10. BO.**

PERSIAN WOOD TOILET WATER 1959-61
(Left) 2 oz. gold cap, painted label. Came in red & gold box. OSP $2.50. **CMV $6. MB, $4. BO.**

PERSIAN WOOD MIST 1957-59
(Center) 3 oz. red plastic coated glass, smooth gold cap. Came in red & gold box. OSP $3. **CMV $6. BO, $8. MB.**

PERSIAN WOOD MIST 1956-59
(Right) 3 oz. red plastic coated glass, raised gold cap with 4A on top. Came in red & gold box. OSP $3. **CMV $8. MB, $6. BO.**

PERSIAN WOOD POWDER SACHET 1957-66
(Left) 1 1/4 oz. red plstic squeeze bottle, gold cap, red & gold box. OSP $2. **CMV $7. MB, $4. BO.**

LOTION SACHET 1957-61
(Right) Red plastic coated, gold cap. Came in red & gold box. OSP $2. **CMV $4. BO, $7. MB.**

PERSIAN WOOD CREAM LOTION 1961-66
(Left) 4 oz. clear glass, gold lettering, gold cap. Came in red & gold box. OSP $1.25. **CMV $5. MB, $3. BO.**

PERFUMED BATH OIL 960-66
(Center) 6 oz. red plastic bottle with gold cap. Came in red & gold box. OSP $2.25. **CMV $6. MB, $4. BO.**

BODY POWDER 1961-63
(Right) 4 oz. red plastic bottle with gold cap, in red & gold box. OSP $1.95. **CMV $10. MB, $9. BO.**

PERSIAN WOOD COLOGNE 1962-63
(Left) 2 1/2 oz. clear glass, gold cap. Red label on front of flat sided bottle. Came in Refreshing Hours set only. **CMV $10.**

CREAM SACHET 1975-76
(Right) .66 oz. clear glass, red & gold cap. OSP $1.50. **CMV 50c.**

PERSIAN WOOD PERFUMED SKIN SOFTENER 1960-64
(Left & Center) 5 oz. off-white glass bottom with straight sides. Red & gold cap with either curved or straight sides. OSP $3. **CMV $5. MB, $3. BO.**

PERFUMED SKIN SOFTENER 1964-66
(Right) 5 oz. white glass, round bottom, red & gold cap. OSP $3. **CMV $3. BO, $4. MB.**

PERSIAN WOOD PERFUMED TALC 1958-62
(Right) Red & gold box holds red can with brass cap & trim. OSP 79c. **CMV $4. MB, $2. CO, mint.**

PERFUMED TALC 1962-68
(Left) Same as above only with a white or red plastic cap. OSP 79c. **CMV $3. MB, $1. CO.**

PERSIAN WOOD BEAUTY DUST 1957-60
(Left) Red glass bottom with red & gold tin lid. Lid also came in cardboard just like tin lid shown. Same CMV. OSP $3. **CMV $10. mint, $15. MB.**

PERSIAN WOOD BEAUTY DUST 1960-66
(Right) White plastic with red design around gold handle. OSP $3.25. **CMV $8. mint, $12. MB.**

PERSIAN WOOD 4 OZ. COLOGNE 1960-62
Red & gold flip open box holds 4 oz. Persian Wood cologne. OSP $3. **CMV $20. MB.**

PERSIAN WOOD CREAM SACHET 1959-76
(Left to Right) .66 oz. red bottom with smooth gold lid. **CMV $6. BO, $8. MB.** Gold embossed cap with curved sides. **CMV $2. BO, $4. MB.** Same cap with straight sides. **CMV 50c.** Came red paint over clear or milk glass.

PERSIAN WOOD BEAUTY DUST REFILL 1960s
Box holds plain paper refill pack with red powder puff. OSP $2.98. **CMV $6. MB.**

PERSIAN WOOD SET 1964
Red & gold box with white lining holds Persian Wood cream sachet & 1 dram perfume. OSP $4. **CMV $22. MB.**

PERSIAN WOOD PERFUME MIST 1963-67
(Left) 2 drams, red base, white cap, in gold box. OSP $3.25. **CMV $4. - $5. MB.**

SPRAY PERFUME 1957-63
(Right) 2 dram, red metal with gold cap, red & gold box. OSP $3.50. **CMV $7. MB, $5. BO.**

PERSIAN WOOD BEAUTY DUST 1962-63
Red paper sides with gold writing around sides & clear plastic top. Came in Fragrance Magic sets only. **CMV $15. mint.**

PERSIAN WOOD FANCY SET 1957-58
Red & gold box with red lining holds Persian Wood mist & lotion sachet or powder sachet. OSP $5. **CMV $40. MB.**

PINE & ROYAL PINE

PERSIAN WOOD INTRIGUE SET 1963-64
Red & gold box holds Persian Wood mist, cream lotion & perfumed cream rollette. OSP $6.50. **CMV $32.50.**

PERSIAN MAGIC SET 1961-62
Red & gold box holds Persian Wood 2 oz. cologne & cream sachet . OSP $3.50. **CMV $22. MB.**

PERSIAN TREASURE SET 1959-60
Fancy gold box with white satin lining holds Persian Wood mist, 2 oz. toilet water, perfume spray & cream sachet. OSP $10. 75. **CMV $60. MB.**

PERSIAN LEGEND SET 1961-62
Red & gold box with red satin lining holds Persian Wood mist & beauty dust. OSP $6.50. **CMV $40. MB.**

ROYAL PINE BATH SALTS 1954-57
8 oz. clear glass with green lid. Green & brown label. OSP 75c. **CMV $20. - $25. MB.**

ROYAL PINE BATH OIL 1957-59
8 oz. bottle with green cap & pine cones on label in yellow, white & green box. OSP $1.95. **CMV $15. MB, $10. BO.**

PINE BATH SALTS 1953
8 oz. clear glass jar, green lids, painted pine branch. Came in 2 different ways. Both came in 1953 Royal Pine set only. **CMV $30. each mint.**

ROYAL PINE BATH OIL 1963-68
8 oz. green plastic bottle & cap. OSP $2. **CMV $3. MB, $1. BO.**

PINE SOAP 1959
Plain green box with gold printing on lid. 3 green flat edge bars. **CMV $30. MB.**

PINE SOAP 1940 ONLY
Special box holds 3 green bars of Pine soap. OSP 69c. **CMV $45. MB.**

PINE BATH OIL 1942-51
6 oz. flat sided bottle with turquoise cap. OSP 95c. **CMV $22., MB $28.**

PINE BATH OIL 1944-45
(Left) 6 oz. flat sided bottle with green cap & brown label. OSP $1. **CMV $25. MB, $20. BO.**

ROYAL PINE BATH OIL 1955-57
(Center) 6 oz. flat sided bottle, green cap. OSP $1.25. **CMV $20. BO, $25. MB.**

PINE BATH OIL 1955-56
(Right) 2 oz. pink cap. Pink & white curtain label. Came in "That's for Me Set" only. **CMV $15.**

PINE BATH OIL 1955-57
4 oz. bottle with green cap. Came in Pinehurst Set only. **CMV $20.**

PINE SOAP 1940-59
(Top) Green box with pine cone on lid holds 3 green round bars of Pine soap. OSP 69c. **CMV $30. MB.**

ROYAL PINE SOAP 1959-65
(Bottom) Same design box & same design on soap, only edge of soap is flat instead of round. OSP $1.25. **CMV $25. MB.**

ROYAL PINE SET 1954-57
Pine covered box holds 8 oz. jar with green lid of Royal Pine bath salts & green bar of Pine soap. OSP $1.39. **CMV $35. set, $20. BO.**

ROYAL PINE SET 1953
Pine box holds 1 bar of Pine soap & 8 oz. jar with green lid & pine cone & branch painted on bottle. OSP $1.25. **CMV $45.**

BREATH OF PINE SET 1940
Box holds 9 oz. bottle of Pine bath salts & 2 green bars of Pine soap. OSP $1.25. **CMV $60. MB.**

PINE SOAP SUBSTITUTE 1940
3 green bars of pine soap came in brown and green box that was the Royal Pine set box. A letter from Avon stating the regular soap boxes were not available & Royal Pine set box was substituted. Rare, with letter. OSP ?. **CMV $45. MB with letter as shown.**

PINEHURST SET 1955-57
Pine box holds 2 green bars of Pine soap & 4 oz. bottle of Pine bath oil with green cap. OSP $1.75. **CMV $52.50 MB.**

ROYAL PINE SET 1940-43
Pine comes on lid of box, holds 2 green bars of Pine soap & 6 oz. bottle of Pine bath oil with brown label. OSP $1.35. **CMV $55. MB.**

BREATH OF PINE SET 1940-42
Green & white box holds 2 green bars of Pine soap & 9 oz. bottle of Pine bath salts. OSP $1.25. **CMV $55. MB.**

TOWERING PINE SET 1941-42
Pine comes on lid of box, holds Apple
Blossoms body powder, green bar of Pine bath
soap & 6 oz. bottle of Pine bath oil with tulip A
on label. OSP $1.65. **CMV $65. MB.**

ROYAL PINE SET 1943
Beige box with pine cones & crest on lid, holds
6 oz. Royal Pine bath oil with brown label & 2
bars Pine soap. Came in 2 different size
boxes as shown. OSP $1.60. **CMV $60. MB
each set.**

PRETTY PEACH CREAM SACHET 1964-67
Yellow glass jar with peaches on lid. OSP $1.
CMV $7. MB, $5. jar only.
PEACH POMADE 1964-67
Foam peach with green leaf holds pomade
lipstick. OSP $1. **CMV $16, MB $18.**

PRETTY PEACH SOAP 1964-66
Pink box holds 2 peach halves & brown seed
center soap. OSP $1.50. **CMV $24. MB, $15.
soap only mint.**

PRETTY PEACH

**PRETTY PEACH "SODA" COLOGNE MIST
1964-67**
2 oz. pink plastic coated bottle with pink top
with white flowers & blue straws. Came in 2
different silver stands. OSP $2.50. **CMV $8.
each MB, $5. BO mint.**

**FOREIGN PRETTY PEACH EAU DE
COLOGNE 1960s**
(Left) Peach cap & painted label. **CMV $10.**
FOREIGN PRETTY PEACH HAND CREAM
CMV $6.

**PRETTY PEACH CREAM LOTION &
BUBBLE BATH 1964-67**
4 oz. pink plastic bottle with peach on cap,
painted label, pink box. OSP $1.35. **CMV $6.
- $8. MB each.**

PRETTY PEACH COLOGNE 1964-67
2 oz. bottle with peach cap with green leaf &
painted label. Pink box. OSP $1.50. **CMV $7.
MB, $4. BO.**

PRETTY PEACH NECKLACE 1965
Small peach on gold chain. Came in Peach
Delight Set only. **CMV $20. - $25. on card.**
SACHET SAMPLES 1964-67
Box holds 10 peach shaped samples of cream
sachet packets. **CMV $2.50 box of 10.**

PRETTY PEACH TALC PUFF 1965-66
Pink box holds pink & white puff filled with
powder. OSP $1.50. **CMV $6. MB, puff only
$2. mint.**

**PRETTY PEACH SOAP ON A ROPE 1964-
67**
(Left) 5 oz. peach shaped soap on white rope.
OSP $1.35. **CMV $17. MB, $11. soap only.**
PERFUMED TALC 1964-67
(Center) 2 1/2 oz. pink & white paper
container. OSP 79c. **CMV $6., MB $8.**
BEAUTY DUST 1964-67
(Right) Pink & white cardboard box. OSP
$2.50. **CMV $10., MB $14.**

JUST PEACHY SET 1964-65
Pink & white box holds Peach soap on a rope & Peach pomade. OSP $2.35. CMV $42.50 MB.

PEACH SURPRISE SET 1964
Pink & white box holds Pretty Peach 2 oz. cologne with choice of 4 oz. bubble bath or cream lotion. OSP $2.85. CMV $20. MB.

QUAINTANCE

BUTTONS 'N BOWS SONG SHEET 1949
Green song sheet with words to help sell Quaintance products. 4 1/4" wide x 6 1/2" high. CMV $5.

PEACH DELIGHT SET 1965
Box holds Pretty Peach necklace, beauty dust & cologne. OSP $5.95. CMV $55. MB set.

PRETTY PEACH PRINCESS 1965-66
Box holds Pretty Peach talc & cream sachet. OSP $2.25. CMV $20. MB.

QUAINTANCE PERFUME 1950
White box with white lace trim holds 3 dram perfume with plain red cap & green leaf. OSP $4. CMV $125. MB.

PEACH SMOOTH SET 1965
Peach box holds 2 tubes of Pretty Peach hand cream. OSP $1.35. CMV $12. MB, $4. tube only mint.

MISS AVON SET 1964-65
Blue & black plastic case holds Pretty Peach cologne, bubble bath, perfumed talc & 10 Lip Dew samples in a bag. Also talc samples. OSP $7.50. CMV $50. set in blue case, $55. set MB.

QUAINTANCE DIARY PERFUME 1949-56
3 dram glass bottle, painted label, rose flowered cap & green leaf. Box green felt. Diary has white cover with red rose & turquoise design. OSP $4. CMV $150. MB.

PEACHY KLEEN SET 1966-67
Pink box holds pink & white sponge & soap. OSP $2.25. CMV MB $12, soap & sponge only $8.

QUAINTANCE POWDER SACHET 1948-56
9 oz. clear glass, white cap & painted label. Cap same as Bright Night without stars, but came this way. Very rare. CMV $15. BO, $20. MB.

QUAINTANCE DIARY PERFUME AWARD 1949
Given to Representatives in 63rd anniversary campaign for selling 63 pieces of Avon. Green felt cover trimmed in gold, holds 3 dram bottle with rose flowered cap & painted label, green leaf around neck. Not shown in picture. Must have leaf to be mint. 63rd anniversary inscribed inside cover. **CMV $100. MB.**

QUAINTANCE BODY POWDER 1948-56
(Left) 5 oz. red & white paper box, shaker top. OSP 75c. **CMV $16. MB, $12. CO.**

QUAINTANCE PERFUME 1948-50
(Right) 1 dram size with red rose cap, painted label in large or small lettering. Blue & white box. OSP $1.50. **CMV $80. MB, $70. BO.**

QUAINTANCE BATH OIL 1949-56
(Left) 4 oz. clear glass, green painted label. Rose on cap. OSP $1.25. **CMV $20. MB, BO $16. mint.**

QUAINTANCE CREAM LOTION 1949-56
(Right) 4 oz. clear glass, white painted label. Rose cap. OSP 89c. **CMV $14. MB, $12. BO.**

62nd ANNIVERSARY QUAINTANCE COLOGNE 1948 ONLY
1st issued in white lace design box. 4 oz. size. Given to Reps for selling 62 Avon items on 62nd anniversary celebration. **CMV $65. MB.**

QUAINTANCE COLOGNE 1948-56
4 oz. clear glass, green painted label, ribbed corners, rose cap with green leaf. OSP $1.75. **CMV $15. MB, $10. BO.**

QUAINTANCE 2 OZ. COLOGNE 1948-50
2 oz. bottle with rose cap, painted label & ribbed corners. Came in Quaintance Set & Quaintance Bow Knot Set only. **CMV $20.**

QUAINTANCE TOILET WATER 1953-56
2 oz. clear glass, green painted label, ribbed corners, rose cap with green leaf. OSP $1.25. **CMV $20. MB, $15. BO.**

QUAINTANCE COLOGNE 1955-56
2 oz. bottle with blue cap, came in Daintiness Set and Bath Bouquet Set. **CMV $15.** Quaintance cream lotion in same sets. **CMV $12.**

QUAINTANCE CREAM SACHET 1953-56
White square glass jar with red rose on white cap. OSP $1.25. **CMV $12. MB, $10. BO.**

QUAINTANCE SACHET 63RD BIRTHDAY BOX 1949
Regular issue powder sachet came in special issue Avon's 63rd Birthday box. **CMV $15. MB as shown.**

QUAINTANCE BEAUTY DUST 1948-57
Red rose on tin lid, white paper sides & tin bottom, white box. OSP $1.50. **CMV $18. MB, $12. beauty dust only mint.**

DAINTINESS SET 1956
White box with pink & blue ribbon holds 2 oz. bottles of Quaintance cream lotion & cologne with blue caps & blue bar of Quaintance soap. OSP $1.95. **CMV $55. MB.**

QUAINTANCE POWDER SACHET 1948-56
(Left) 9/10 oz. or 1 1/4 oz. clear glass with red cap, painted label. OSP $1.19. **CMV $11. MB, $10. BO.**

QUAINTANCE POWDER SACHET 1948 ONLY
(Right) 9/10 oz. clear glass with red cap & larger painted label. OSP $1.19. **CMV $20. MB, $16. BO.** Also came in 1 1/4 oz. size with large size label. **CMV $20. MB, $16. BO.**

QUAINTANCE

QUAINTANCE SACHET VALENTINE BOX 1952
Short issue box at Valentine time. Holds regular issue powder sachet. OSP $1.19. CMV in this box $19. mint.

QUAINTANCE BATH OIL 1955-56
2 oz. pink cap, pink & white label. Came in That's For Me set only. CMV $15. mint.

DAINTINESS SET 1955
White box with pink & blue ribbons, holds 2 oz. bottles of perfumed deodorant & Quaintance cologne with blue caps & blue bar of Quaintance soap. OSP $1.95. CMV $52. MB.

QUAINTANCE SOAP 1955-56
3 blue bars with embossed bows. OSP $1.59. CMV $40. MB.

BATH BOUQUET SET 1955
White & blue box with red rose on lid holds 2 oz. bottles of Quaintance cream lotion & cologne with blue caps. Blue bar of Quaintance soap. OSP $1.95. CMV $52. MB.

ROSE GAY SET 1954-56
Blue & white box holds Quaintance 4 oz. cream lotion & body powder. OSP $1.95. CMV $55. MB.

GAY BONNET SET 1948
White hat shaped box with black ribbon & red rose around hat lid contains gold lipstick & 1 dram bottle of Quaintance perfume with rose cap. OSP $2.35. CMV $125. MB.

QUAINTANCE ROSE GAY SET 1950-51
Blue & white box with red rose holds Quaintance body powder & 4 oz. cream lotion. OSP $1.85. CMV $50. MB.

LEISURE HOURS SET 1954-55
Blue & yellow fold up box holds 4 oz. Quaintance bath oil & cream lotion. OSP $2.75. CMV $55.

MISS QUAINTANCE SET 1952-53
Blue & white octagonal box holds Quaintance body powder & 4 oz. cream lotion. OSP $1.95. CMV $50. MB.

QUAINTANCE HARMONY SET 1952-53
Box with blue ribbon on clear plastic lid holds 4 oz. Quaintance cream lotion & cologne. OSP $2.75. CMV $45. set MB, 4 oz. cologne with rose cap $20.

QUAINTANCE HARMONY SET 1950-51
White box with blue ribbon over clear plastic lid holds Quaintance 4 oz. cologne & body powder. OSP $2.95. CMV $50. MB.

BEAUTY MUFF SET 1949
(Left) Red, white & blue box with blue ribbon on lid contains white lambswool muff with 1 dram Quaintance perfume with rose cap & gold lipstick. OSP $2.35. CMV $135. MB.

BEAUTY MUFF SET 1950
(Right) Same set & box only came with 1 dram gold scroll top perfume. CMV $65. MB.

QUAINTANCE SET 1948
Blue & white box contains 2 oz. Quaintance cologne & powder sachet. Both have red caps. OSP $2.35. **CMV $55. MB.**

QUAINTANCE BOW KNOT SET 1950
Box holds Quaintance 2 oz. cologne & powder sachet. OSP $2.25. **CMV $50.**

QUAINTANCE HARMONY 1954-55
Blue & white flip open box holds Quaintance cologne & cream lotion.

RAPTURE

RAPTURE FOAMING BATH OIL 1966-72
6 oz. blue plastic bottle & cap. OSP $2.75. **CMV $1.**
PERFUMED BATH OIL 1965-66
6 oz. blue plastic bottle & cap. OSP $2.75. **CMV $2. BO, $3. MB.**
CREAM LOTION 1965-68
4 oz. blue plastic bottle & cap. OSP $1.75. **CMV $2. BO, $3. MB.**

RAPTURE COLOGNE MIST 1966 ONLY
2 oz. medium blue glass, gold trim. OSP $3.
COLOGNE MIST 1966 ONLY
2 oz. dark blue glass, no gold trim. OSP $3.
COLOGNE MIST 1965-66
2 oz. very light, appears almost frosted glass. **CMV each $4. BO, $5. MB.**

RAPTURE PERFUME OIL 1964-69
(Top Left) 1/2 oz. green glass & cap. OSP $5. **CMV $4. - $6. MB.**
RAPTURE COLOGNE 1964-71
(Top Center) 2 oz. blue glass & cap. OSP $2.50. **CMV $1. BO, $2. MB.**
RAPTURE COLOGNE MIST 1964-74
(Top Right & Bottom Two) 3 oz. turquoise plastic coated cap, all have gold letters. OSP $5. **CMV $1. BO, $1.50 MB.** Pictured above with regular issue box on right & special issue 1970 box on left. **Add $1. for 1970 box.**

RAPTURE SCENTED HAIR SPRAY 1966-70
(Left) 7 oz. blue can. OSP $1.50. **CMV $3.**
RAPTURE PERFUMED TALC 1965-72
(Left Center) 2.75 oz. blue can. OSP $1. **CMV $1.**
(Right Center) Foreign Rapture perfume talc is 2.75 oz. blue can, but shorter than U.S. can. **CMV $2.**
RAPTURE BEAUTY DUST 1971-74
(Right) 6 oz. blue & gold cardboard. OSP $4.50. **CMV $5. CO, $7. MB.**

RAPTURE DELUXE SET 1965
Turquoise box contains beauty dust, perfumed skin softener & cologne mist in Rapture. OSP $13.95. **CMV $32.50.**

RAPTURE RHAPSODY SET 1964-65
Rapture powder sachet, 1 dram perfume & 2 oz. cologne sit on blue velvet, trimmed in gold. Rapture mirror in center with 2 doves on mirror. OSP $10.95. **CMV $30. tray, set mint, $40. set MB.**

RAPTURE POWDER SACHET 1964-66
9/10 oz. blue frosted glass with blue lid with 2 white doves. OSP $2.50. **CMV $6. MB, $4. BO.**
CREAM SACHET 1964-75
.66 oz. dark purple glass jar with 2 white doves on purple plastic lid. OSP $3. **CMV 50c.**
RAPTURE PERFUMED SOAP 1966-67
(Inside Left) 3 oz. soap in turquoise wrapper. OSP 49c. **CMV $4.**

RAPTURE PERFUMED SKIN SOFTENER 1964-73
5 oz. with blue & gold lid. Came blue painted over clear glass. CMV $1. ALso came blue painted over white milk glass. OSP $3.50. CMV $2.

RAPTURE BEAUTY DUST 1965-68
Blue box holds 3 blue bars with 2 doves embossed. OSP $2. CMV $17.50 MB.

RAPTURE SOAP 1965-68
Blue box holds 3 blue bars with 2 doves embossed. OSP $2. CMV $17.50 MB.

RAPTURE 1/2 OZ. COLOGNE 1969-72
1/2 oz. green cap. OSP $1.50. CMV $1. BO, $2. MB.

RAPTURE PERFUMED CREAM ROLLETTE 1964-65
Gold cap, embossed 4A design on 1/3 oz. bottle. OSP $2.50. CMV $3.

RAPTURE PERFUMED ROLLETTE 1965-69
1/3 oz. blue ribbed glass, gold cap. OSP $2.50. CMV $4. BO, $5. MB.

REGENCE

REGENCE PERFUME 1966-69
1 oz. frosted glass bottle & stopper, trimmed in gold, green & white box. Gold neck tag. OSP $30. CMV $20. BO, $30. MB.

REGENCE PERFUME 1966-69
1/2 oz. frosted glass with gold plastic cap. Bottle trimmed in gold, green & white box. Gold neck tag. OSP $15. CMV $15. BO, $25. MB.

REGENCE CREAM SACHET 1968
.66 oz. clear glass painted gree. Green & gold tone cap & base. Sides are smooth, no design. CMV $4. BO, $6. MB.

REGENCE HAND MIRROR 1966
Green & gold metal 4 1/2" long. Came in Regence gift set. CMV $10. MB, $7. mirror only.

REGENCE FRAGRANCE SAMPLE 1967-71
Foil packet. CMV $1. box of 10.

REGENCE 1/2 OZ. COLOGNE 1970-71
(Left) 1/2 oz. clear glass bottle with gold cap. OSP $1.75. CMV $2. MB, $1. BO.

PERFUME OIL 1968-69
(Inside Left) 1/2 oz. gold cap. Came with either clear bottom label or gold neck tag label. OSP $6. CMV $4. BO, $6. MB.

COLOGNE 1967-69
(Center) 2 oz. gold cap. OSP $3. CMV $2. MB, $1. BO.

COLOGNE SILK 1968-70
(Inside Right) 3 oz. gold cap, frosted glass bottle. OSP $4.50. CMV $2. MB, $1. BO.

SKIN-SO-SOFT 1968-70
(Right) 6 oz. gold cap. OSP $5. CMV $2. MB, $1. BO.

REGENCE 4 OZ. COLOGNE 1969-71
4 oz. gold cap. OSP $6. CMV $2.

FOAMING BATH OIL 1969-72
6 oz. light plastic bottle with gold cap. OSP $4. CMV $1.

COLOGNE MIST REFILL 1966-71
3 oz. green plastic coated. OSP $4. CMV $1. BO, $2. MB.

REGENCE CREAM SACHET 1966-67
(Left) Green painted glass with green paper band. Green & gold cap, gold base. OSP $3. CMV $2. - $3. MB.

CREAM SACHET 1968-75
(Right) Solid green glass, green plastic cap. OSP $3. CMV $1. Both also came green painted over clear or milk glass. Same CMV.

REGENCE COLOGNE MIST 1966-71
(Left) 3 oz. green & gold plastic. Base is gold on older ones and green on newer ones. OSP $6. **CMV gold base $3, green base $2. MB, $1. BO.**

HAIR SPRAY 1968-71
(Center) 7 oz. green & gold with green cap. OSP $1.50. **CMV $3.**

REGENCE BEAUTY DUST 1966-73
(Right) Green & gold plastic bottom, clear plastic lid with gold crown. OSP $6. Paper side older, **CMV $8. MB.** Plastic side newer, **CMV $5. MB, $2. less each for no box.**

REGENCE GIFT SET 1966
Green box holds cream sachet, cologne mist, green & gold hand mirror. OSP $12.50. **CMV $37.50.**

REGENCE PERFUME ROLLETTE 1967-68
.33 oz. ribbed glass, smooth gold cap. OSP $3. **CMV $2. MB, $1.50. BO.**

PERFUME ROLLETTE 1969-73
.33 oz. ribbed glass & green cap. OSP $3. **CMV $1. BO, $1.50 MB.**

PERFUMED GLACE 1967-70
(Right) Green & gold box holds green & gold glace compact. OSP $5.50. **CMV $8. MB, $5. compact only.**

REGENCE PERFUME SKIN SOFTENER 1968-71
(Left) 5 oz. ribbed glass, small silver edged cap. Gold center & multi color cap. OSP $4. **CMV $2.**

REGENCE PERFUMED SKIN SOFTENER 1971-74
(Center) 5 oz. ribbed glass, large silver edged, gold center & multi-color green cap. OSP $4. **CMV $1.**

REGENCE PERFUMED SKIN SOFTENER 1967-68
(Right) 5 oz. green ribbed glass, small silver edge cap with gold center & plain green cap. $4. **CMV $3. - $4. MB.**

REGENCE TALC 1968-72
(Left) 3 1/2 oz. green paper box. OSP $1.25. **CMV $1.**

REGENCE PERFUMED POWDER MIST 1967-72
(Right) 7 oz. greencan with gold cap, painted label. OSP $4. **CMV $1, with paper label $3.**

ROSE GERANIUM

ROSE GERANIUM BATH OIL 1957-58
8 oz. bottle with red cap. OSP $1.95. **CMV $15. MB, $10. BO.**

ROSE GERANIUM BATH OIL 1943-50
6 oz. flat sided bottle has Tulip A label, pink cap. OSP 95c. **CMV $20. BO, $25. MB.**

ROSE GERANIUM SOAP 1966-67
Flowered box holds 4 flower shaped soaps. OSP $2.25. **CMV $18. MB.**

ROSE GERANIUM LIQUID SOAP FRAGRANCE 1942 ONLY
(Left) 6 oz. flat sided bottle came in Rainbow Wings and Bath Bouquet Set only. **CMV $45. MB.**

ROSE GERANIUM BATH OIL 1943-48
(Right) 6 oz. flat sided bottle, pink cap. OSP 95c. **CMV $20. BO, $25. MB.**

PERFUMED SOAP 1982
(Left) 3 oz. bar. SSP $1.27. CMV $1.
ROSES ROSES PERFUMED SOAP BAR 1976
(Right) 3 oz. bar wrapped in red paper. Short issue. OSP $1.25. CMV $2.

ROSE GERANIUM AFTER BATH FRESHENER 1964-68
8 oz. glass bottle with rose colored cap, red flowered box. OSP $2.50. CMV $2. BO, $3. MB.
PERFUMED BATH OIL 1964-67
8 oz. frosted plastic bottle with rose colored cap. Red flowered box. OSP $2.50. CMV $1.
PERFUMED TALC 1964-66
3 1/2 oz. rose covered paper container with plastic shaker top. OSP 89c. CMV $4. MB, $3. CO. ALso came with upside down label. CMV $8.
PERFUMED SOAP 1964-66
3 oz. bar with rose design wrapping. OSP 39c. CMV $3.

GLOW OF ROSES PERFUMED CANDLE 1972-73
4 1/2" high, pink frosted glass. SSP $6. CMV $5. BO, $6. MB.
SCENT OF ROSES DECANTER 1972-73
6 oz. red glass jar with gold lid, filled with Cologne Gelee. SSP $5. CMV $3.
DEW OF ROSES PERFUMED SKIN SOFTENER 1972-73
5 oz. frosted pink glass jar with gold lid. SSP $2. CMV $2.
SCENT OF ROSES COLOGNE GELEE 1972-76
3 oz. clear or tinted glass jar, gold lid. SSP $2. CMV 75c.

SILK & HONEY MILK BATH 1970-71
6 oz. gold plastic milk can bottle with flowers around neck. OSP $5. CMV $4.

ROSES ROSES

SILK & HONEY PERFUME SOAP 1970-76
3 oz. gold and yellow wrapper. OSP $1.25. CMV $1.50.
SILK & HONEY BANK 1969
Yellow plastic Beehive Bank. CMV $15.

ROSES PERFUME TALC 1974-77
3.5 oz. pink and gray cardboard. OSP $1. CMV 25c.
TOUCH OF ROSES SOAP 1976-78
3 oz. pink soap, pink and gray wrapper. OSP $1. CMV $1.
ROSES ROSES SOAP 1974-75
3 oz. pink soap, pink wrapper with floral band. OSP $1. CMV $1.50.
PERFUMED SKIN SOFTENER 1973-76
5 oz. pink plastic with pink and gold metal lid. OSP $3. CMV 25c.
SACHET OF ROSES CREAM SACHET 1975-78
.33 oz. clear glass with pink metal lid. OSP $3. CMV 25c.

MIST OF ROSES COLOGNE MIST 1972-77
3 oz. pink plastic coated bottle, gold cap. OSP $7. CMV $1.
TOUCH OF ROSES PERFUMED SOAP 1972-77
Pink box holds 3 pink flowered soaps. OSP $5. CMV $5. MB.
ROSES CREAM SACHET 1972-75
.66 oz. pink glass jar with pink rose on gold lid. Also came in clear glass. OSP $3. CMV 50c.
All other Roses products CMV 25c.

SILK & HONEY BATH FOAM 1969-74
CREAMY LOTION 1969-74
CREAMY MASQUE 1969-74
SOFTALC 1969-71
PERFUMED POWDER MIST 1970-76
All plastic bottles & tin cans CMV 25c each.
BATH GELEE 1969-70
4 oz. gold frosted glass jar with gold beehive lid and gold spoon. OSP $6. CMV $7. MB, $5. BO with spoon.

SMALL WORLD

SMALL WORLD PRODUCTS 1970-73
(Back row left to right)
COLOGNE (SPLASHU) 1970-72
2 oz., 4 1/2" high. OSP $3.50. **CMV $6.**
BUBBLE BATH (BUBBLY-O-BATH) 1970-71
5" high, 5 oz. green plastic bottle. OSP $3.50.
CMV $8., $10. MB.
PERFUMED TALC 1971-73
3 1/2 oz. blue paper container. OSP $1.25.
CMV $4.
(Front row left to right)
LOVE CAKES SOAP 1970-73
3 pink heart shaped bars in blue box. OSP $2.
CMV $9. MB.
ROLLETTE 1971-72
3" high, .33 oz. Indian design. OSP $1.75.
CMV $3.
DEMI STICK 1970-73
3" high with pink cap. OSP $1.50. **CMV $2.**
PIN PAL PERFUME GLACE 1970-71
Black hair, white and red body. OSP $2.50.
CMV $5., $7. MB.
NON-TEAR SHAMPOO (POOLU) 1970-71
5 1/2" high, red bottle, black hair. OSP $3.50.
CMV $6.
COLOGNE MIST (HEIDI) 1970-71
3 oz. 5" high, purple bottle, yellow hair. OSP
$5. **CMV $6.**

(Add $2. each item MB)

SMALL WORLD PRODUCTS 1970-73
(Back row left to right)
CREAM LOTION (WENDY) 1971-72
5 oz, 5" high cowgirl plastic bottle. OSP $5.
CMV $6., $8. MB.
BUBBLE BATH (BRITISH MISS) 1971-72
4 1/2" high, 3 oz. pink plastic bottle. OSP $5.
CMV $6., $8. MB.
COLOGNE MIST (GIGI) 1971-72
5" high, 5 oz. blue plastic coated bottle with
white collar and blue & red hat. OSP $3.50.
CMV $6., $8. MB.
NON-TEAR SHAMPOO (SENORITA) 1971-72
5" high, 5 oz. orange plastic bottle with pink
flower in hair on cap. OSP $3.50. **CMV $10.
BO, $12. MB.**
(Front row left to right)
CREAM SACHET 1971-72
.66 oz. white jar with pink and white lid. OSP
$2.50. **CMV $3. MB, $2. BO.**
LIPKINS 1970-73
3" high with pink, yellow and orange caps in
Dutch Chocolate, Tropical Fruit or French Mint.
OSP $1.75. **CMV $3. each MB, $2. BO.**
LOVE DOVE CREAM SACHET 1970-73
White jar and dove lid. OSP $3. **CMV $4., $5.
MB.**

SMALL WORLD COLOGNE SAMPLE - Canada 1974
1/8 oz. clear glass, white cap. Used by Avon
Reps. as sample in Canada. **CMV $3.**

SMALL WORLD SUCKER 1970
Sent to representatives at introduction of Small
World. Red and yellow wrapper says "Avon
Watch for the Small World". **CMV $25. mint.**
SMALL WORLD PERFUME GLACE 1971-72
Blue and white polka-dots. OSP $2.50. **CMV
$5., $6. MB.**
SMALL WORLD GLACE WATCH 1971
Orange with striped band. OSP $3. **CMV $6.,
$8. MB.**

SOMEWHERE

ALL CONTAINERS PRICED EMPTY
See front of book for Grading Examples on
Mint Condition

SOMEWHERE PERFUME 1961-63
1 oz. pink jewel cap, jewels in glass around
bottom of bottle. Has 4 butterflies on lid. OSP
$20. **CMV $80. MB, $50. BO.**

SOMEWHERE PERFUMED SKIN SOFTENER 1964-66
5 oz. pink glass jar with pink and gold lid. OSP
$3.25. **CMV $2.**
SOMEWHERE PERFUMED SOAP 1965
3 oz. pink soap with pink & white wrapper.
OSP 39c. **CMV $4. mint.**

SOMEWHERE PERFUMED OIL FOR THE BATH 1963
1/2 oz. clear glass, white lettering, pink cap.
OSP $4. **CMV $7. BO, $10. MB.**
SOMEWHERE PERFUMED OIL 1964-66
1/2 oz. clear glass, white lettering, pink cap.
OSP $4. **CMV $5. BO, $7. MB.**

SOMEWHERE BATH OIL 1962-66
6 oz. pink plastic bottle and cap. OSP $2.50.
CMV $2. BO, $3. MB.
SOMEWHERE COLOGNE MIST 1961-66
3 oz. pink plastic coated glass, pink jeweled lid.
OSP $4. **CMV $3. BO, $5. MB.**

SOMEWHERE CREAM LOTION 1963-66
4 oz. pink lid without jewels. OSP $1.50. **CMV**
$3., $5. MB.
SOMEWHERE COLOGNE 1961-66
2 oz. pink jeweled lid. OSP $2. **CMV $3, $5.**
MB.

SOMEWHERE TALC 1962-66
2 3/4 oz. pink can and lid. OSP 89c. **CMV $3.,**
$5. MB.
SOMEWHERE 2 DRAM PERFUME MIST
1964-66
White lid, pink bottom, gold band. OSP $3.25.
CMV $9. MB, $7. Mist only.

SOMEWHERE BEAUTY DUST 1967-70
White plastic with green around bottom. Gold
handle. OSP $4. **CMV $10. MB, $6. CO.**
PERFUME TALC 1968
3 1/2 oz. green cardboard with gold trim.
Came with Fluff Puff set. **CMV $2.**

SOMEWHERE DUSTING POWDER 1961-66
Pink plastic bottom, clear plastic top with pink
jeweled crown. OSP $4. **CMV $10. MB, $6.**

PERFUME MIST AWARD 1961
Given to each representative sending in an
order during the 75th Anniversary Campaign.
This was also the introduction to a new
fragrance - Somewhere. **CMV $15. MB.**

UNFORGETTABLE SET 1962-63
Pink, yellow and blue box holds Somewhere
Cologne Mist, Cream Sachet and Beauty Dust.
OSP $10. 95. **CMV $45. MB.**

SOMEWHERE POWDER SACHET 1962-66
1 1/4 oz. pink glass bottom, pink jeweled lid.
OSP $2. **CMV $6. MB, $4. BO.**
SOMEWHERE CREAM SACHET 1962-66
Pink glass and pink jeweled lid. OSP $2.
CMV $1., $3. MB. Some came pink paint on
milk glass. **Same CMV.**

SOMEWHERE POWDER SACHET 1967
ONLY
(Left) 9/10 oz. white glass bottom, white and
gold cap with green ribbon. Issued during
bottle strike in 1967. Bottom is same as
Wishing Powder Sachet. OSP $2. **CMV $15. -**
$20. MB.
SOMEWHERE POWDER SACHET 1966-68
9/10 oz. white glass, green label, white lid with
gold band. Hard to find. OSP 42. **CMV $12.**
MB, $10. BO.

SOMEWHERE PRODUCTS 1966-67
(Left to Right)
CREAM SACHET 1966-75
White glass trimmed in green and gold. .66 oz.
OSP $3. **CMV 50c.**
SKIN SOFTENER 1966-72
Green and gold lid, 5 oz. glass jar. Came in
green paint over clear glass. **CMV $1,** or
green paint over white milk glass. **CMV $1.**
OSP $3.50.
PERFUME OIL 1966-69
1/2 oz. green label, gold cap. OSP $4. **CMV**
$4., $6. MB.
COLOGNE 1966-71
2 oz. gold cap. OSP $2.50. **CMV $1.**
COLOGNE MIST 1966-76
3 oz. green plastic coated, gold cap, green
label. OSP $7. **CMV $1.**

SOMEWHERE
(Green and White design)

CREAM SACHET 1976
Gold and green lid. OSP $1. CMV 50c.

DEMI STICK 1975-76
OSP $1. CMV 50C.

COLOGNE 1970-71
1/2 oz. gold cap. OSP $1. CMV $2. MB, $1. BO.

CREAM LOTION 1967-68
4 oz. gold cap. OSP $1.50. CMV $3. BO, $4. MB.

SOMEWHERE TALC 1973-76
3.5 oz. green cardboard, round container. OSP $2. CMV $1.

SOMEWHERE SOAP 1966-68
Green and white box holds 3 bars. OSP $2. CMV $15. MB.

SOMEWHERE SOAP 1962-66
Pink box holds 3 bars with embossed name. OSP $1.75. CMV $22. MB.

SOMEWHERE SOAP 1968-69
3 white bars in green box. OSP $3. CMV $13. MB.

SOMEWHERE FOAMING BATH OIL 1966-72
6 oz. green plastic bottle with gold cap. OSP $3.50. CMV $1. BO.

SOMEWHERE PERFUME MIST 1966-68
2 dram, white cap, green bottom. OSP $3.25. CMV $4. MB, $2. BO.

DREAMS OF SOMEWHERE SET 1964
Box holds 2 dram bottle of Somewhere Perfume Mist, 6 oz. Beauty Dust and 4 oz. bottle of Cream Lotion. OSP $9.29. CMV $04. MB.

SOMEWHERE SCENTED HAIR SPRAY 1966-71
7 oz. green can. OSP $1.50. CMV $3.

SOMEWHERE SOAP 1966-67
Single bar in green wrapper. OSP 49c. CMV $4.

SOMEWHERE TALC 1966-72
2 3/4 oz. green and white can, green cap. OSP $1. CMV $1.

DREAM CASTLE SET 1964
Pink and white box holds 2 oz. bottle of Somewhere Cologne and Cream Sachet. OSP $4. CMV $30. MB.

SONNET

SONNET PRODUCTS 1973-78
(White and gold design)

PERFUMED POWDER MIST
7 oz. metal can, white cap.

PERFUMED TALC
3.5 oz. cardboard with plastic top and bottom. Rare upside down label. CMV $5.

CREAM SACHET
.66 oz. jar.

BEAUTY DUST
6 oz. plastic puff. OSP $10. CMV $2., $5. MB.

PERFUMED SKIN SOFTENER
5 oz. plastic jar.

PERFUMED ROLLETTE
.33 oz. bottle.

COLOGNE MIST
3 oz. spray bottle. OSP $8. 1st issue 1973. Issued with no gold ring around neck. CMV $2. 1973-78 issued with gold ring around neck. CMV 50c.

FOAMING BATH OIL 1973-74
6 oz. white plastic bottle, gold cap. CMV 50c all products not priced.

SONNET POWDER SACHET 1975-78
1.25 oz. white and gold cardboard. OSP $2.
CMV 50c.
SONNET PERFUMED SOAP 1976-78
3 oz. white bar with gold and white wrapper.
OSP $1. **CMV $1.**
SONNET PERFUMED SOAP 1974-75
3 oz. white with multi-colored center. OSP $1.
CMV $1.
SONNET PERFUMED DEMI STICK 1974-78
White and gold. OSP $1. **CMV 25c.**

SONNET BODY POWDER 1941-43
Flat sifter top, scroll box. **CMV $22. MB, CO
$18. mint.**
**SONNET PERFUME POWDER MIST (double
stamped label) 1973-77**
Regular issue can came out with double stamp
label on entire can. Rare. **CMV $5.**

FRAGRANCE MIST SONNET 1940-42
Blue and gold box holds 2 oz. Sonnet Toilet
Water, gold cap and label and Spray atomizer.
Also came in other fragrances. See Fragrance
Mist Sets of 1940s. OSP $1.35. **CMV $50.
MB, $35. BO mint.**

SONNET SET 1941-42
Satin lined lavender box holds 2 oz. Sonnet
Toilet Water with gold top atomizer & Sonnet
Body Powder. OSP $2. **CMV $70. MB.**

**SONNET COLOGNE & SONNET SKIN SO
SOFT BATH OIL 1973**
4 oz. clear glass bottles, cap is gold. Came in
Treasure Chest set only. **CMV $3. each.**

BLUE BIRD SET 1943-44
Blue and white box, blue satin lining holds
feather design face powder, cardboard or
plastic lipstick and Sonnet or Apple Blossom
Body Powder. OSP $2.25. **CMV $75.**

SONNET TOILET WATER 1941 ONLY
2 oz. purple cap and label. 2 different labels.
One has yellow dress on box and label and the
other has green dress on box and label. OSP
20c. **CMV $30. BO, $40. MB each.**

SONNET PERFUMED SOAP 1974-77
3 oz., three pink oblong shaped bar soap, in
gold and white box. OSP $4. **CMV $5. MB.**
SONNET PERFUMED SOAP 1972-74
3 oz. three pink round shaped bars of soap, in
gold and white box. OSP $3. **CMV $6. MB.**

SONNET TOILET WATER 1941-46
2 oz. gold ribbed cap and gold front label.
OSP $1.04. **CMV $30. BO mint, $35. MB.**
SONNET BODY POWDER 1941-43
Special issue box, angel on box, blue and
white paper container with plastic shaker top.
OSP 65c. **CMV $25. MB as shown, $18. CO.**

STRAWBERRY

**STRAWBERRY PORCELAIN NAPKIN RINGS
& SOAP SET 1978-79**
Box holds 2 porcelain napkin rings and 1 red
strawberry shaped soap. Porcelain made in
Brazil. SSP $10. **CMV $10. MB set.**

SWAN LAKE

STRAWBERRY BATH GELEE 1971-72
4 oz. red strawberry base and gold cap and spoon. OSP $7. CMV $4., $6. MB.
STRAWBERRY GUEST SOAP 1971-72
Red box holds 3 strawberry soaps. OSP $3. CMV $7. MB.
STRAWBERRY BATH FOAM 1971-72
4 oz. red glass and top, 6" high. OSP $4. CMV $4., $5. MB.

STRAWBERRY PORCELAIN DEMI CUP CANDLETTE 1979-80
Box holds 4" saucer and 2 1/4" high cup. Strawberry design. Made in Brazil for Avon 1978 on bottom of each. SSP $7. CMV $7. MB.

SWAN LAKE BATH OIL 1947-49
6 oz. flat sided bottle, pink cap, painted label. OSP $1.25. CMV $55., $65. MB.
SWAN LAKE COLOGNE 1947-50
4 oz. pink cap, painted label. OSP $1.35. CMV $45. BO, $55. MB.

BIG BERRY STRAWBERRY 1973-74
10 oz. red plastic with green cap top. Holds Bath Foam. SSP $4. CMV $2., $3. MB.
BERRY NICE STRAWBERRY COMPACT 1979-80
Small red and green plastic holds lip gloss. SSP $3.49. CMV $2.50 MB.
STRAWBERRY FAIR SHOWER SOAP 1979-80
Red strawberry soap on a green rope. SSP $3.49. CMV $3.50 MB.

STRAWBERRY PORCELAIN SUGAR SHAKER & TALC 1979
Box holds white porcelain shaker and 3.5 oz. box of strawberry perfumed talc. Made in Brazil. Avon 1978 on bottom of shaker. SSP $12. CMV $10. MB set. Early orders and demos had 1978 on bottom of sugar shaker and regular issue had only "Avon" and no date on bottom. Talc only CMV $2., shaker only CMV $8. no date, CMV $10. 1978 date. Talc also came with upside down label from factory by mistake. CMV $5. upside down label on talc.

SWAN LAKE 3 PIECE SET 1947-50
Blue and white box holds 9 oz. blue boxes of Swan Lake Bath Salts, Body Powder and 4 oz. cologne with white cap. OSP $3. CMV $120. MB.

STAWBERRIES & CREAM BATH FOAM 1970
4 oz. white milk, red cap and design, or orange cap and design. OSP $3.50. CMV for red cap $6, orange cap $4.
STRAWBERRY FAIR SOAP 1969-70
Red soap in yellow plastic basket with green grass, wrapped in cellophane and bow. OSP $3. CMV $7. - $10. MB.

SWAN LAKE 2 PIECE SET 1947-49
Blue and white box holds 6 oz. Swan Lake Bath Oil and 9 oz. blue box of Swan Lake Body Powder. OSP $2. CMV $100. MB.

SWAN LAKE BODY POWDER 1947-49
9 oz. blue, pink and white paper box. Came with swan or ballerina on side. OSP 85c. CMV $30., $35. MB. Also came 4 1/2 oz. size in sets. CMV $30. mint.
SWAN LAKE BATH SALTS 1947-49
9 oz. blue, pink and white paper box. OSP 85c. CMV $30., $35. MB.

TO A WILD ROSE

TO A WILD ROSE PERFUME 1955-59
Pink & white box holds 1/2 oz. white glass bottle with pink cap & painted label. OSP $5. CMV $35. BO, $70. MB.

TO A WILD ROSE TOILET WATER 1956-62
(Left) 2 oz. white glass, pink cap, has paper flower band around base. OSP $1.50. CMV $10. BO, $12. MB.
PERFUME OIL FOR THE BATH 1963
(Right) 1/2 oz. white glass, pink cap, pink & white box. OSP $1.50. CMV $10. MB, $8. BO.
TOILET WATER 1956
(Not Shown) 1/2 oz. size. Same size & design as perfumed oil shown above. White glass with pink cap & lettering. Came in Special Date Set, rare. CMV $27. mint.

TO A WILD ROSE PERFUME 1950-56
(Left) Pink flowers on pink & blue box. 3 dram bottle with blue cap & flower around neck. OSP $4.50. CMV $110. MB, BO with tag $75.
SPRAY PERFUME 1960-63
(Right) Red, white & gold box holds pink & white metal spray perfume with pink flowers. OSP $2.95. CMV $11. MB, spray only $7.

TO A WILD ROSE COLOGNE 1957
(Left) 2 oz. white glass with paper label, pink cap. Came in Trilogy Set only. CMV $16. mint.
LOTION 1957
(Right) 2 oz. white glass with paper label & pink cap. Came in Trilogy Set only. CMV $16. mint.

TO A WILD ROSE 2 OZ. COLOGNE 1961-68
(Left & Center) 2 oz. white glass, pink letters & cap. Came with & without painted flowers around base. OSP $1.50. CMV $3.
SPRAY PERFUME REFILL 1960-63
(Right) Box holds small metal refill. CMV $4. MB, $2. refill only.

TO A WILD ROSE CREAM LOTION 1965-68
(Left) 4 oz. painted label, white glass, pink cap. OSP $1.25. CMV $4. BO, $5. MB.
CREAM LOTION 1956-65
(Right) 4 oz. white glass, pink cap, paper label. OSP $1.25. CMV $5. BO, $7. MB.

TO A WILD ROSE COLOGNE 1970-71
(Left) 1/2 oz. white glass with pink cap & letters. OSP $1.75. CMV $2. MB, $1. BO.
PERFUMED TALC 1962-72
(Center) 2 3/4 oz. white & pink can with pink cap. OSP $1. CMV $1.
TALC 1954-55
(Right) Blue can & cap with pink flowers. OSP 49c. CMV $8. CO, $10. MB.

TO A WILD ROSE COLOGNE 1955-63
4 oz. white glass bottle, pink cap, has flowered paper border around base. OSP $2.50. CMV $10. BO, $12. MB.
BODY POWDER 1950-55
5 oz. blue paper container, 2 different bottoms. One is refillable from the bottom. OSP 85c. CMV $15. - $20. MB. Some issued as shown with To A Wild Rose Body Powder on side & some only say Avon Body Powder.

TO A WILD ROSE BODY POWDER 1955-59
(Left) 4 oz. white glass & cap with rose on lid, paper label around bottom, pink letters. OSP $1. **CMV $10. BO, $13. MB.**
BODY POWDER 1961-63
(Center) 4 oz. white hard plastic bottle, white lid with roses. OSP $1.79. Also came 3 oz. size & with short issue pink cap. **CMV $12. pink cap.** CMV $8. BO, $10. MB.
BODY POWDER 1955-59
(Right) 4 oz. white glass & cap with rose on lid, paper label. OSP $1. **CMV $10. BO, $13. MB.**

TO A WILD ROSE 4 OZ. COLOGNE 1960-61
Pink, green & white Christmas box holds 4 oz. white glass bottle with pink cap & neck ribbon. No flower band around base, but also came with a paper flower band around base as shown. OSP $2.50. **CMV $25. in box pictured.**

TO A WILD ROSE 4 OZ. COLOGNE 1960-61
Pink & white box holds 4 oz. white glass bottle, pink cap, painted label, pink silk ribbon on neck. OSP $2.50. **CMV $15. BO with ribbon mint, $17. MB.** Came with and without painted flowers around base.

TO A WILD ROSE CREAM SACHET 1950-55
(Left) Blue cap with pink flowers, white glass, 3 cornered shape. OSP $1.25. **CMV $10. MB, $8. BO.**
(Center) Same shaped jar as one on right only has blue lid as on the left jar. Lid will not interchange with jar on right. Also came with white lid, label on bottom with no zip code, is older. Rare. **CMV $9. BO, $11. MB.**
CREAM SACHET 1955-72
(Right) White glass, white lid with painted rose. OSP $1.25. **CMV $1. MB.**

TO A WILD ROSE COLOGNE MIST 1958-59
3 oz. white plastic coated over clear glass, pink cap. Came with or without embossed rose on lid. OSP $2.50. **CMV $17. BO, $22. MB.**
TO A WILD ROSE SOAP 1966-67
3 oz. white embossed soap in pink & green wrapper. OSP 49c. **CMV $3.**

TO A WILD ROSE BATH OIL 1956-59
4 oz. white glass bottle with pink cap. OSP $1.35. **CMV $12. MB, $10. BO.** 2 oz. white glass bottle with pink cap, same label came in Trilogy set only. **CMV $15.**

TO A WILD ROSE TALC 1956-62
(Left) White can with pink flowers & cap. OSP 69c. **CMV $5. - $7. MB.** Add $4. for 1959 Christmas box shown.
FOAMING BATH OIL 1966-68
(Right) 6 oz. white plastic bottle with pink cap. OSP $2.50. **CMV $1. BO, $2. MB.**

TO A WILD ROSE BEAUTY DUST 1964-70
White plastic trimmed in pink. OSP $3.25. **CMV $4. - $6. MB.**
PERFUMED SKIN SOFTENER 1959-70
5 oz. white glass, pink & white lid. OSP $3.50. **CMV $2.**

TO A WILD ROSE BEAUTY DUST 1950--55
Blue can with flowers on lid. OSP $1.75. **CMV $15. CO, $20. MB.**

TO A WILD ROSE PERFUMED BATH OIL 1959-61
8 oz. white plastic bottle with pink cap. OSP $2.25. **CMV $3. BO, $5. MB.**
PERFUMED BATH OIL 1961-66
(Not Shown) Same only 6 oz. size. **CMV $3. MB, $2. BO.**

TO A WILD ROSE COLOGNE MIST 1959-75
(Left) 3 oz. white plastic coated with pink flower on cap. OSP $5. **CMV $1. - $2. MB.**
COLOGNE MIST 1976
(Not Shown) 3 oz. white bottle, pink letters, pink cap, no flower. OSP $7. **CMV 50c.**
PERFUMED MIST 1964-68
(Right) 2 dram, pink & white, gold band. OSP $3. **CMV $4. MB, $2. mist only.**

TO A WILD ROSE POWDER SACHET 1955-67
White glass, white lid with painted rose. Paper band around bottom with roses. Came in 9 oz. & 1.25 oz. OSP $1.25. **CMV $7. BM, $6. BO.**
PERFUME OIL 1964-68
1/2 oz. white glass, pink letters & cap. OSP $3.50. **CMV $6. BO, $8. MB.**

TO A WILD ROSE BATH OIL 1953-55
4 oz. bottle with blue cap, with or without embossed roses. Blue label. OSP $1.25. **CMV $20. MB, $17. BO.**

TO A WILD ROSE TALC 1969
2.75 oz. pink & white can, pink cap. Came in 1969 Perfumed Pair set only. **CMV $2.**
BATH OIL 1955-56
2 oz. pink cap & label. Came in "That's Me Set" only. **CMV $15. mint.**

TO A WILD ROSE BEAUTY DUST 1962-63
(Left) Pink & green flowers, clear platic top, cardboard. Came in Fragrance Magic Sets only. **CMV $16. mint.**
BEAUTY DUST 1955-59
(Right) Pink ball on top, trimmed in pink, tin lid & bottom. Sides cardboard. OSP $1.75. **CMV $12. - $16. MB.**

TO A WILD ROSE SACHET 1953-55
1 1/4 oz. blue cap with embossed flower on top. Blue box. **CMV $15. MB, $12. BO mint.**

TO A WILD ROSE COLOGNE OR CREAM LOTION 1954
2 oz. clear glass with blue caps. Came in Bath Bouquet Set. **CMV $17.50 each mint.**

TO A WILD ROSE SCENTED HAIR SPRAY 1966-69
7 oz. pink & white can, pink cap. OSP $1.50. **CMV $3.**
PERFUMED POWDER MIST 1968-73
7oz. pink & white can, 2 different labels. **CMV paper label $4, painted label $2.** OSP $3.50 each.

TO A WILD ROSE TOILET WATER 1950-55
(Left) 2 oz. blue cap, with or without embossed roses. Three cornered bottle. OSP $1.50. **CMV $20. MB, $17. BO.**
CREAM LOTION 1953-55
(Right) 4 oz. blue cap & label, with or without embossed roses. OSP 89c. **CMV $15. BO, $17. MB.**

BATH BOUQUET SET 1955
White & pink box holds To A Wild Rose 2 oz. cologne & cream lotion with white caps & 1 bar of soap. OSP $1.95 **CMV $55. MB.**

MISS COED SET 1954
Blue box holds three 2 oz. bottles of To A Wild Rose cologne, cream lotion & bath oil. All have white caps. OSP $2.35. **CMV $75. set, $17.50 each bottle.**

TO A WILD ROSE COLOGNE 1950-55
4 oz. clear glass, blue cap, blue label. OSP $2. CMV $20. MB, $16. BO.

POWDER SACHET 1953-55
1 1/4 oz. blue smooth top cap, blue label, clear glass. OSP $1.25. CMV $12. - $15. MB.

CREAM SACHET 1975-76
.66 oz. clear glass jar, red & gold lid. OSP $3. CMV 50c.

TO A WILD ROSE COLOGNE, BATH OIL, CREAM LOTION 1954
2 oz. clear glass with white cap, blue label. Came in Miss Coed Set only. CMV $17.50 each.

TO A WILD ROSE COLOGNE OR CREAM LOTION 1955
2 oz. clear glass with white caps. Came in bath bouquet Set. CMV $15. each mint.

TO A WILD ROSE BATH OIL & COLOGNE 1956
Both 2 oz. bottles with white caps. Came in 1956 Bath Bouquet Set only. CMV $15. each mint.

TO A WILD ROSE SOAP 1969-73
Floral box holds 3 white bars. OSP $3. CMV $7. MB.

TO A WILD ROSE SOAP 1952-56
White box holds 3 white bars. OSP $1.50. CMV $26.50

TO A WILD ROSE SOAP 1954
Blue box of 3 bars. CMV $30. MB.

TO A WILD ROSE SOAP 1957-68
Pink & white box holds 3 bars in 2 different size boxes. OSP $1.59. CMV large box $25. MB, small box $17.50 MB.

BATH BOUQUET SET 1956
White & pink box holds To A Wild Rose cologne & bath oil with white caps & 1 bar of soap. OSP $2.25. CMV $55. MB. Also came with 2 bath oils as substitutes.

BATH BOUQUET SET 1954
Pink & blue box. To A Wild Rose 2 oz. cologne & cream lotion with blue caps & white soap. OSP $1.95. CMV $55. MB. One box has sleeve top and one with a lift off lid. Came with and without flowers on bottom of box.

SWEETHEART SET 1956
White & pink box holds To A Wild Rose beauty dust & 4 oz. cologne. OSP $3.95. CMV $45. MB.

ROSES ADRIFT SET 1957
Pink & white box holds To A Wild Rose beauty dust, cream sachet & cologne. OSP $4.95. CMV $50. MB.

SPRAY OF ROSES SET 1961
White & pink box with pink satin lining holds To A Wild Rose beauty dust & cologne mist. OSP $5.90. CMV $30. MB.

TO A WILD ROSE

TO A WILD ROSE SPECIAL DATE SET 1956
Pink & gold box holds black lipstick, powder pak & 1/2 oz. of To A Wild Rose Toilet Water. OSP $2.50. **CMV $45. MB.**

HOLIDAY ROSES SET 1963-64
Box holds To A Wild Rose beauty dust, splash cologne, cream lotion, with paper label. Same set in 1964 with painted label. OSP $6.50. **CMV $37. each set MB.**

ADORABLE SET 1955-56
Pink & white box with pink flowers on top holds To A Wild Rose body powder & cream sachet. OSP $2.25. **CMV $32.50 MB.**

ADORABLE SET 1956
Pink & white box with pink ribbon on lid holds To A Wild Rose body powder & cream sachet. OSP $2.25. **CMV $32.50 MB.**
A SPRAY OF ROSES SET 1958
Pink & white box holds To A Wild Rose cologne mist & cream sachet. OSP $3.95. **CMV $37. MB.**

LOVELY AS A ROSE SET 1961
Pink & white box holds 2 oz. To A Wild Rose cologne & cream sachet. OSP $3.50. **CMV $20. MB.**

WILD ROSES SET 1953
To A Wild Rose body powder with cream sachet on top. Pink ribbon around set. OSP $1.95. **CMV $37.50 MB.**

SWEETHEARTS SET 1955
Pink & white box holds To A Wild Rose beauty dust with pink ribbon & 4 oz. cologne. OSP $3.95. **CMV $55. MB.**

WILD ROSES SET 1964
Multi-pink flowered box holds 2 oz. bottle of To A Wild Rose cologne & cream sachet. OSP $3.50. **CMV $25. MB.**

PETAL OF BEAUTY SET 1953
Pink box holds blue & pink satin bag, all blue bag, or all pink bag with To A Wild Rose 4 oz. cologne & beauty dust with 5/8 dram perfume, "Small Square Bottle" with ribbon tied around it. Inside beauty dust. OSP $5.25. **CMV MB $75. Bag & contents only $55.** 1950-52 set sold without 5/8 dram perfume. **CMV $65. MB, $50. no box, in bag.**

TRILOGY SET 1957
Box holds 3 To A Wild Rose 2 oz. bottles of bath oil, cream lotion & cologne. OSP $2.95. **CMV $60. MB.**

TO A WILD ROSE SET 1950-52
Blue & pink box holds To A Wild Rose body powder & 4 oz. cologne. OSP $2.85. **CMV $60. MB.**

ROSE PETALS SET 1953-54
Two clear glass bottles, blue caps, holds bath oil & cream lotion. OSP $2.15. **CMV $57.50 MB.**

TOPAZE PERFUME 1935 ONLY
1/4 oz. gold cap, gold & white label & box. Introducing Topaze for the 50th wedding anniversary of Mr. and Mrs. D. H. McConnell. OSP 20c. **CMV BO $50., $70. MB.**

PETAL OF BEAUTY 1954-55
Blue & pink box with blue ribbon around outside holds 4 oz. cologne & beauty dust. OSP $3.75. **CMV $62.50 MB.**

TOPAZE
See Stockholders Gift section for 1960 Topaze Treasure Set.

TOPAZE PERFUME OIL 1963-69
(Left) 1/2 oz. gold cap & painted label. OSP $4. **CMV $4., MB $6.**
PERFUME OIL FOR THE BATH 1963
(Center) 1/2 oz. gold cap, painted label. OSP $4. **CMV $40. BO, $45. MB.**
1/2 OZ. COLOGNE 1970-71
(Right) Gold cap & painted label. OSP $1.50. **CMV $2. MB, $1.50 BO.**

TOPAZE 4 OZ. COLOGNE 1959-63
(Left) Gold cap. OSP $3. **CMV $8. in plain yellow box, $4. BO.**
2 OZ. COLOGNE 1960-71
(Right) Gold cap, painted label. OSP $2. **CMV $1., MB $2.**

ANNIVERSARY SPECIAL SET 1956
Pink & white box holds 2 cans of To A Wild Rose talc. OSP $1.10. **CMV $20. MB.**

TOPAZE PERFUME 1959-63
1 oz. amber glass & amber jeweled glass stopper. Bottle cut like a gem. In yellow & white box. OSP $20. **CMV $135. MB, $85. BO.**

PINK BELLS SET 1955
Pink box holds 2 blue cans of To A Wild Rose talc. OSP $1. **CMV $22.50 MB.**

TOPAZE PERFUME MIST 1964-68
(Left) 2 dram yellow bottle, white top with gold band, box gold. OSP $3.25. **CMV $2. - $4. MB.**
SPRAY PERFUME 1959-63
(Right) Yellow box holds 2 dram metal spray perfume, gold top & yellow bottom. OSP $3.75. **CMV $7. - $12. MB.**

TOPAZE 4 OZ. GIFT COLOGNE 1959-61
Gold cap, clear glass in yellow & gold satin lined box. OSP $3.75. **CMV $17. MB as shown.**

TOPAZE BEAUTY DUST 1960-70
(Left) Yellow plastic bottom, white lid with yellow jewel. OSP $4. **CMV $3. - $5. MB.**
PERFUMED SKIN SOFTENER 1964-72
(Right) 5 oz. yellow painted over white milk glass or clear glass, gold & white lid. OSP $3.50. **CMV $2. MB, $1. BO.**

TOPAZE TREASURE SET 1960
Box holds 2 oz. cologne and beauty dust. OSP $5.95. **CMV $40.**

TOPAZE SOAP COLUMN 1965-66
Holds 3 yellow bars. OSP $1.75. **CMV $25. MB.**

TOPAZE PERFUME ROLLETTE 1965-69
.33 oz. ribbed carnival glass, gold cap. OSP $2. **CMV $2. BO, $3. MB.**
SCENTED HAIR SPRAY 1966-70
7 oz. yellow can. OSP $1.50. **CMV $3.**

TOPAZE BATH OIL 1961-66
(Left) 6 oz. yellow plastic bottle & cap. OSP $2.50. **CMV $1.**
FOAMING BATH OIL 1966-73
(Center) 6 oz. yellow plastic bottle and cap. OSP $2.75. **CMV $1.**
BODY POWDER 1961-63
(Right) 4 oz. yellow plastic bottle & cap. OSP $2.25. **CMV $4. - $6. MB.**

GOLDEN TOPAZE 1960-61
Gold box with plastic cover holds Topaze Cream Sachet, Cologne Mist and Beauty Dust. OSP $9.95. **CMV $40. MB.**

CREAM LOTION 1959-67
(Left) 4 oz. clear glass, yellow cap. OSP $1.50. **CMV $2.** ALso came with yellow cap with jewel, rare. **CMV $8.**
TOPAZE COLOGNE MIST 1959-68
(Right) 3 oz. yellow plastic coated, yellow jewel on lid, in round yellow box. OSP $7. **CMV $3. in round box.** 1969-76 issue came in square box. Same bottle. **CMV $1.**

TOPAZE POWDER SACHET 1959-67
Both 9/10 oz. yellow glass, yellow caps. OSP $2. common issue with large cap. **CMV $6. MB, $5. BO. CMV small cap $6. BO, $7. MB.**

TOPAZE PERFUMED TALC 1961-62
(Left) 2 1/4 or 2 3/4 oz. yellow round can & cap. OSP $1. **CMV $5., $7. MB.**

TOPAZE SOAP 1961-64
Yellow box holds 2 bars of Topaze soap. OSP $1.50. **CMV $22. MB.**

TOPAZE SETTING SET 1964
Yellow box holds 2 oz. bottle of Topaze Cologne and Powder Sachet. OSP $4. **CMV $25. MB.**

TOPAZE TEMPLE OF LOVE 1960-61
Yellow and gold. Holds yellow and white plastic holder. Came with .75 oz. Topaze Cream Sachet. OSP 75c. **CMV MB $20., $10. holder only. $6. for .75 oz. Cream Sachet only.**
CREAM SACHET 1960-75
.66 oz. yellow paint on clear or milk glass, yellow cap. OSP $3. **CMV 25c.**

TOPAZE JEWEL SET 1961
Gold box holds Topaze Cologne Mist and Cream Lotion. OSP $4.95. **CMV $30. MB.**

TOPAZE ELEGANCE 1963
Gold and white box holds Topaze Beauty Dust, 4 oz. Creme Lotion, and 2 oz. Cologne. OSP $7.95. **CMV $35. MB.**

GOLDEN GEM SET 1961
Gold box holds 2 oz. Topaze Cologne and Cream Sachet in .75 oz. size. OSP $4. **CMV $25. MB.**

TOPAZE PRINCESS SET 1964
Gold box holds Topaze 3 oz. Cologne Mist and 4 oz. Cream Lotion. OSP $5.95. **CMV $25. MB.**

UNFORGETTABLE

UNFORGETTABLE PERFUME OIL 1965-69
(Left) Clear glass, gold cap, no neck trim.
(Center Left) Clear glass, gold cap, cut out gold neck trim.
(Center Right) Clear glass, gold cap, solid gold neck trim, scalloped edge.
(Right) Solid gold neck trim with smooth edge.
OSP $5. **CMV $7. MB, $6. BO each.**

UNFORGETTABLE BEAUTY DUST 1965-70
Pink plastic trimmed in gold. OSP $5. **CMV $3. - $6. MB.**
SKIN SOFTENER 1965-73
5 oz. pink painted over clear or milk glass, pink & gold lid. OSP $3.50. **CMV $1.**

UNFORGETTABLE COLOGNE 1970-71
(Left) 1/2 oz. with gold cap. OSP $1.75. **CMV $2. MB, $1.50 BO.**
PERFUMED TALC 1966-74
(Right) 2 3/4 oz. pink can & cap. OSP $1. **CMV $1.**

UNFORGETTABLE SOAP 1965-68
Orange box holds 3 orange soaps with gold centers. OSP $2.25. **CMV $20. MB.**

UNFORGETTABLE POWDER SACHET 1966-68
All are .9 oz.
(Left) Pink glass, gold pattern printing & gold cap. No neck trim.
POWDER SACHET 1965 ONLY
(Center Left) Pink glass, gold lettering, cap & trim. Neck trim has cut out pattern.
(Center Right) no trim
POWDER SACHET 1965 ONLY
(Right) 9 oz. pink glass, gold lettering, cap & trim. No holes in trim. OSP $2.50 each. CMV $6., MB. $8. each.

UNFORGETTABLE COLOGNE MIST 1965-76
(Left & Center) 3 oz. pink plastic coated, gold cap. Two different gold trims around neck. OSP $5. CMV 50c with holes in gold trim, $4. on solid gold neck trim.
CREAM SACHET 1965-75
Pink painted over clear or milk glass bottom with gold plastic cap & gold trim. OSP $2.50. CMV 50c.

UNFORGETTABLE CREAM LOTION 1966-68
(Left) 4 oz. orange plastic bottle with gold cap. OSP $1.75. CMV $2. - $3. MB.
FOAMING BATH OIL 1966-72
(Right) 6 oz. orange plastic bottle with gold cap. OSP $3. CMV $2. BO, $3. MB.

UNFORGETTABLE SCENTED HAIR SPRAY 1966-71
(Left) 7 oz. orange & gold cn. OSP $1.50. CMV $3.
BEAUTY DUST 1971-73
(Center Left) Orange & gold 6 oz. cardboard box. OSP $4.50. CMV $3. mint, $5. MB.
PERFUMED POWDER MIST 1968-72
(Center Right & Right) 7 oz. orange & gold can, 2 different labels painted on paper. OSP $3.75. CMV $1. - $3. paper.

UNFORGETTABLE PERFUMED SOAP 1965
(Left) 3 oz. pink & gold wrapper. OSP 49c. CMV $4.
CREAM SACHET SAMPLE 1965-74
(Center Left) Pink, gold plastic. CMV box of 10, $1.50.
FRAGRANCE SAMPLE 1965-76
(Center Right) Box holds 10 samples in pink foil. CMV 50c box.
POWDER SACHET SAMPLE 1966-68
CMV 50c per box.

UNFORGETTABLE COLOGNE 1966-71
(Left) 2 oz. gold cap, painted label. OSP $2.50. CMV $2.
PERFUME MIST 1964-68
(Right) 2 dram, rose colored bottom, white cap, gold trim, all metal. OSP $3.25. CMV $2. - $4. MB.

UNFORGETTABLE DELUXE SET 1965
Gold & white box holds beauty dust, cream sachet & cologne mist. OSP $12.95. CMV $32.50 MB.

UNFORGETTABLE HEIRLOOM 1965-66
Gold & white tray holds 1 2/ oz pink & gold cardboard perfumed talc. CMV $15. 9/10 oz. powder sachet, gold cap & 1/2 oz. perfume oil with gold cap. OSP $10.95. For set CMV $30. - $40. MB.

VIOLET BOUQUET

VIOLET BOUQUET REPRESENTATIVE GIFT 1945
Avon's 59th Anniversary gift to each representative. Violet colored net ribbon around white cap. 16 oz. crackle glass bottle. CMV $150. mint, $175. MB.

VIOLET BOUQUET COLOGNE 1946-49
6 oz. bottle. Came in different color caps.
OSP $1. CMV $80. MB, $70. BO.

WHITE MOIRE

WHITE MOIRE SOAP 1946-49
Blue & white box, white bow tie soap. OSP
$1.22. CMV $50. MB.

WHITE MOIRE SACHET 1946
White cap & small plain paper label. CMV $20.
BO, $25. MB.

WHITE MOIRE BODY POWDER 1945-49
(Left) 5 oz. or 4 1/2 oz. size, blue & white
paper container with plastic sifter top, came in
blue & white box. OSP 65c. CMV $30. MB,
$25. CO mint.

WHITE MOIRE SACHET 60th ANNIVER-SARY BOX 1946
1 1/4 oz. regular issue bottle, white cap. Came
in special issue blue & white box with white
ribbon and blue & silver tag saying "Avon
Diamond Anniversary 60th Year". OSP $1.15.
CMV $30. MB as shown.

WHITE MOIRE POWDER SACHET 1948-49
(Left) 1 1/4 oz. clear glass, blue and white
label, blue cap. OSP $1.15. CMV $20. MB,
$15. BO.
POWDER SACHET 1946-47
(Right) 1 1/4 oz. clear glass, white or blue
plastic cap. OSP $1.15. CMV $15. BO, $20.
MB. Both bottles pictured have same label.

WHITE MOIRE SET 1945-49
Blue & white box with white silk bow on lid
contains 6 oz. White Moire cologne with white
cap. Blue & white label. Also 5 oz. White
Moire body powder, blue & white cardboard.
OSP $2.50. CMV $115. MB.

WISHING

WISHING COLOGNE 1947
4 oz. bottle with gold cap, painted label.
Same bottle as Golden Promise cologne.
Came in fancy open front & top box. Given
to Avon Representatives for calling on 61
customers during 61st Anniversary
Campaign in campaign 9 - 1947. CMV $85.
BO, $110. MB.

WISHING BATH OIL 1964-66
6 oz. white plastic bottle, gold lettering,
white box. OSP $2.25. CMV $10. MB, $7.
BO.

WISHING BEAUTY DUST 1963-67
4 oz. white plastic trimmed in gold. OSP
$2.95. CMV $8. - $10. MB.
PERFUMED SKIN SOFTENER 1964-69
5 oz. white glass jar with gold & white lid.
OSP $3. CMV $4. MB, $2.50 jar only.

WISHING TOILET WATER 1952
(Left) 2 oz. white cap. Same as Flowertime bottle. OSP $1.25. CMV $25. BO, $30. MB.
TOILET WATER 1947-49
(Right) 2 oz. white cap. OSP $1.25. CMV $35. MB, $30. BO. Also came in gold 61st Anniversary box. CMV $40. MB.

WISHING COLOGNE MIST 1963-70
(Left) 2 1/2 oz. white plastic coated, gold trim. Gold wishbone on neck, white box. OSP $2.95. CMV $3. BO, $5. MB.
BUBBLE BATH 1963-66
(Center) 4 oz. white plastic bottle & cap, white box. OSP $1.35. CMV $7. MB, $5. BO.
WISHING CREAM LOTION 1963-67
(Right) 4 oz. white plastic bottle & cap. White box. OSP $1.35. CMV $6. MB, $5. BO.

WISHING POWDER SACHET 1964-68
(Back Two) 9/10 oz. white glass bottom. Bottle on right has white plastic cap, bottle on left has yellow plastic cap, not faded. Both have wishbone in center of cap. White box. OSP $1.75. CMV yellow cap $10., white cap $6., add $2. MB each.
WISHING CREAM SACHET 1963-70
(Front Two) White glass bottom with white plastic cap, gold wishbone in center of cap. Also came with Wishing written on lid. CMV $2. with wishbone, $25. with Wishing lettering. OSP $1.75.

WISHING PERFUME OIL 1964-67
(Left) 1/2 oz. clear glass, white cap, gold lettering with small gold wishbone on gold string. White box. OSP $3.50. CMV $8. BO, $10. MB.
WISHING COLOGNE 1963-67
(Right) 2 oz. clear glass, white cap, gold lettering with gold wishbone on neck, white box. OSP $1.75. CMV $7. MB, $4. BO.

WISHING SCENTED HAIR SPRAY 1966-67
7 oz. white can with gold lettering, white cap. OSP $1.50. CMV $10.
PERFUMED SOAP 1965-66
3 oz. white soap with white & gold wrapper. OSP 39c. CMV $5. mint.

WISHING PERFUME MIST 1965-67
2 dram, white metal, gold trim, white box. OSP $3. CMV $6.
PERFUMED TALC 1963-66
2.75 oz. white can, gold lettering. OSP 79c. CMV $4.

SECRET WISH SET 1963 65
White box holds Wishing perfumed talc & 4 oz. cream lotion. OSP $2.10. CMV $20. MB.

WISHING NECKLACE 1964-65
22K gold wishbone necklace came in Charm of Wishing set only. CMV $25. in small pink & white box, $17. necklace only.

New Wishing Duette

WISHING DUETTE 1964-65
White, gold & pink box holds Wishing cream rollette & cream sachet. OSP $3.50. CMV $20. MB.

WISHING SET 1963 ONLY
White & gold box holds Wishing 2 oz. cologne & cream sachet. OSP $3.10. CMV $25. MB.

CHARM OF WISHING SET 1964-65
Gold & white box holds Wishing beauty dust, cologne mist & 22K gold plated Wishbone necklace on 9" chain. OSP $8.50. **CMV $62.50 MB.**

WISHING PERFUMED PAIR 1964
White box holds Wishing perfumed talc & bar of soap in white wrapper. OSP $3.50. **CMV $19. MB.**

KIDDIE COLOGNE 1954-55
2 oz. bottle of Young Hearts Cologne has pink cap with white foam dog head on cap, in yellow, white and blue box. OSP $1.25. **CMV $50. MB, $25. BO. Add $15. for foam head on BO mint.**

YOUNG HEARTS BUBBLE BATH 1954-55
White foam dog head on pink cap, in yellow, white & blue box. OSP $1.10. **CMV $25. BO. Add $15. for foam head on BO mint. $50. MB.**

WISH COME TRUE SET 1963-64
White & gold box holds Wishing bubble bath & 2 oz. cologne with wishbone on neck. OSP $3.10. **CMV $26. MB.**

YOUNG HEARTS

YOUNG HEARTS TALC 1952-53
1 2/3 oz. cardboard talc. Came in sets only. **CMV $20.**

YOUNG HEARTS COLOGNE 1952-54
2 oz. cologne with pink cap and painted label. OSP $1.25. **CMV $30. BO mint.**

YOUNG HEARTS BUBBLE BATH 1952-54
2 oz. pink cap and painted label. OSP $1.25. **CMV $30. BO mint.**

YOUNG HEARTS KIDDIE BUBBLE BATH 1952-54
2 oz. bottle with pink cap and white foam cat head on cap. Blue and white box, painted label. OSP $1.10. **CMV $50. MB with foam head. $30. BO. Add $10. for foam head.**

YOUNG HEARTS KIDDIE COLOGNE 1952-53
2 oz. bottle with white foam cat head over pink cap, painted label. Blue and white box. OSP $1.25. **CMV $50. MB with cat head. $30. BO. Add $10. for foam head.**

WISHING DATE SET 1965
White & gold box holds Wishing perfume skin softener, perfume rollette & white vinyl covered Wishing date book. OSP $6. **CMV $32.50 MB.**

WISHING SOAP 1963-66
White box holds 3 white Wishbone embossed soaps. OSP $1.35. **CMV $25. MB.**

YOUNG HEARTS 1952-54
1 dram perfume, pink cap and painted label. Came in sets only. **CMV $60.** I/2 oz. Toilet Water with pink cap and painted label. Came in sets only. **CMV $30.** 1 oz. Cologne with pink cap. Came in sets only. **CMV $30.**

YOUNG HEARTS TALC 1954-55
Pink and white metal can.
COLOGNE
Pink cap.
BUBBLE BATH
Pink cap. All 3 came in sets only.

FOR YOUNG HEARTS SET BOTTLES 1945-46
Each are 2 oz. frosted glass with pink caps. In Cotillion Toilet Water, Cream Lotion and Bubble Bath. **CMV $20. each.**

YOUNG HEARTS CREAM LOTION 1954
Bottle has pink cap, in pink and white heart shaped box. OSP 50c. **CMV $25. MB, $20. BO.**

YOUNG HEARTS CREAM LOTION 1952-53
2 oz. pink cap. Came in sets only. **CMV $20. mint.**

YOUNG HEARTS POLISH REMOVER 1952-53
2 oz. pink cap. Came in "N Everything Nice set only. **CMV $20. mint.**

YOUNG HEARTS SACHET 1945-46
One pink lace net with pink ribbons on each end. Came in For Young Hearts set only. **CMV $25. MB.**

YOUNG HEARTS SACHET 1945-46
Box holds two pink lace net sachets with pink ribbons on each end and flower in the middle. Refills for the Young Hearts set. **CMV $40. MB.**

YOUNG HEARTS BEAUTY DUST 1954-55
Blue, white and yellow paper box. OSP $1.19. **CMV $20., $25. MB.**

RAIN DROPS SET 1954-55
Red umbrella hand bag holds Young Hearts Cologne, Pomade and Cream Lotion. OSP $3.25. **CMV $90. set MB.**

RAIN DROPS 1952
Red umbrella bag holds 1 oz. Young Hearts Cologne, Perfume and Cream Lotion. All have pink caps. OSP $2.95. **CMV $125. MB.**

RAIN DROPS 1953
Red umbrella hand bag holds Young Hearts Cologne, Pomade and Cream Lotion. Pink caps. OSP $2.95. **CMV $95. set MB.**

HONEY BUN SET 1953
Blue and pink round box holds 2 1/2 oz. Young Hearts Toilet Water with pink cap and gold Pomade Lipstick. OSP $1.19. **CMV $50. MB.**

HONEY BUN SET 1954-55
Young Hearts Cologne and gold lipstick in
white, blue and yellow box. OSP $1.19. **CMV
$50. MB.**

YOUNG HEARTS SET 1953
Blue and white box holds Young Hearts
Cologne, Bubble Bath and Talc. OSP $1.75.
CMV $100. MB.

LITTLE DOLL SET 1954-55
Plastic doll with blond hair. Blue dress is a
zipper handbag containing Young Hearts
Cream Lotion, Cologne and Gold Pomade.
OSP $2.95. **CMV $115. set MB.**

HONEY BUN SET 1954
Blue, white and yellow box holds Young Hearts
Toilet Water, and gold Pomade Lipstick. OSP
$1.19. **CMV $50. MB.**

FOR YOUNG HEARTS SET 1945-46
Pink box holds three 2 oz. frosted glass bottles
of Cotillion Toilet Water, Cream Lotion and
Bubble Bath. All have pink caps. Pink net
sachet in top box. OSP $3.75. **CMV $110. set
MB, or $22.50 each bottle, $20. for net
sachet.**

YOUNG HEARTS SET 1954-55
Cologne, Talc, and Bubble Bath with pink caps
and pink hearts on label, in pink and white box.
OSP $1.95. **CMV $85. MB.**

MISS FLUFFY PUFF SET 1954-55
Young Hearts Beauty Dust and Cologne in
blue and pink. Pink cap in pink and white box.
OSP $2.35. **CMV $60. MB.**

NEAT & SWEET SET 1954-55
Young Hearts Cologne and Cream Lotion with
pink heart shaped soap. Pink caps in yellow,
white and blue box. 1955 set came with green
and gold spray atomizer. OSP $2.50. **CMV
$85. MB, $95. for atomizer set.**

HONEY BUN SET 1952
Pink and white 8 sided box holds Young
Hearts Toilet Water and gold Pomade Lipstick.
OSP $1.19. **CMV $50. MB.**

'N EVERYTHING NICE SET 1952
Box holds Young Hearts Cream Lotion, pink
cap. Polish Remover, pink cap. Nail Polish,
white cap. Emery board and orange stick.
OSP $1.50. **CMV $60. MB.**

YOUNG HEARTS SET 1952
Blue, white and pink box holds Young Hearts Cologne, Talc and Bubble Bath. OSP $1.50. **CMV $85. MB.**

'N EVERYTHING NICE SET 1953
Box holds Young Hearts Cream Lotion, Polish Remover with pink caps and Nail Polish, white cap, Emery Board and Orange Stick. OSP $1.65. **CMV $65. MB. Top different from back of lid.**

MEN'S AFTER SHAVES & COLOGNES

AFTER SHOWER FOR MEN 1959-60
8 oz. gold cap with gold foil on neck & gold neck cord with Stage Coach on bottom. OSP $2.50. **CMV with foil top & tag, $30. mint, $40. MB.**

VIGORATE AFTER SHAVE 1959-60
8 oz. clear glass with white cap. Bottle indented on bottom with carriage. Box is black with red ribbon, gold bottom, plastic white insert on top with gold carriage. OSP $2.50. **CMV $20. BO mint, $35. MB.**

DELUXE AFTER SHAVE "WOOD TOP" 1961-63
6 oz. Some have gold letters on bottle, some have gold paper labels. Came in Deluxe Electric Pre-Shave Lotion, Deluxe After Shave Lotion, After Shave Lotion Spicy, Electric Pre-Shave Lotion Spicy. OSP $1.79. **CMV each $25. MB, $20. BO mint.** 4 different fragrances.

AFTER SHAVING LOTION 1932-36
4 oz. black caps. Two different yellow paper labels. OSP 37c. **CMV $30. BO mint each, $40. MB.**

COLOGNE FOR MEN 1946-49
6 oz. maroon cap. Shield on paper label. OSP $1.50. **CMV $35.80. In 2 different maroon boxes, $50.**

LOVER BOY AFTER SHAVE 1980
3 oz. clear glass. Red letters & cap. Red box. SSP $3.49. **CMV $3. MB.**

FOREIGN 4A AFTER SHAVE
(Left) 4 oz. foreign 4A on left with Invigorate. **CMV $18. MB, $25.**

4A AFTER SHAVE 1964-66
(Right) 6 oz. 4A painted on clear glass, black cap with gold mirror on top. OSP $2. **CMV $15. BO, $18. MB.**

4A AFTER SHAVE LOTION SAMPLE 1964-66
Box holds 10 packet samples. **CMV $3. box, mint.**

AFTER SHAVES MISC. 1965-66
2 oz. with 4A on black caps. Came in Island Lime, Blue Blazer, Leather, Tribute, Spicy, Bay Rum, Original, 4A After Shaves, Leather All Purpose Cologne & After Shower Cologne. Came in Bureau Organizer, Fragrance Wardrobe & After Shave Selection sets only. **CMV each $8. MB, 10 different $5. BO. Add $3. for Blue Blazer.**

GENTLEMEN'S SELECTION 1970
2 oz. each with gold caps. Came in COlogne in Oland, Tribute, Excalibur, Leather, Wild Country & Windjammer. OSP $1.75 each. **CMV $2. BO, $3. MB.**

DEODORANT FOR MEN 1948-49
2 oz. maroon cap & label. OSP 59c. **CMV $10.**
COLOGNE FOR MEN 1948 ONLY
2 oz. size, maroon cap. Came in 1948 Pleasure Cast set only. **CMV $15.**

GENTLEMEN'S CHOICE 1969-70
Red & silver box holds 2 oz. embossed bottles with silver, gold & black caps. Came in Excalibur, Wild Country, Tribute, Leather & Windjammer cologne. OSP $1.75 each. **CMV $2. each with black caps, $4. BO, $6. MB.**

COLOGNE ACCENT FOR MEN 1979-80
(Left) .5 oz. clear glass. Blue cap, blue & silver box. SSP $1.25. **CMV $1. MB.**
GIFT COLOGNE FOR MEN 1978-79
(Center) 2 oz. clear glass, black cap. Holds Everest, CLint, Wild Country or Deep Woods cologne. SSP $2. **CMV $1. MB.COLOGNE**
MINIATURE FOR MEN 1978-79
(Right) 5 oz. clear glass, brown cap. Holds Wild Country, Clint, Everest or Trazarra. SSP $1. **CMV $1. MB.**

AFTER SHAVING LOTION SAMPLE 1936-40
(Left) Maroon cap. CPC on back label. **CMV $35. mint.**
AFTER SHAVE LOTION SAMPLE 1940-49
(Center) 1/2 oz. maroon cap. **CMV $35.**
HAIR TONIC SAMPLE 1939
(Right) 1/4 oz. maroon cap. **CMV $40. - $45. MB.**
HAIR LOTION SAMPLE 1940s
(Not Pictured) Same as 1/4 oz. Hair Tonic. **Same CMV.**

AFTER SHAVE 1975-79
(Left) 5 oz. clear glass, brown cap. Came in Deep Woods, Everest, Oland, Tai Winds, Wild Country & Clint. Different labels, same bottles. OSP $3. **CMV $1. each.** Issued in 1981-82 in 4 oz. size. Same shape in Wild Country, Weekend, Trazarra & Clint. SSP $4. **CMV $1.**
GIFT COLOGNE FOR MEN 1974-75
(Center) 2 oz. clear glass with gold cap. Came in Wild Country, Deep Woods, Oland or Tai Winds. OSP $2. **CMV $1. MB.**
GIFT COLOGNE FOR MEN 1975-76
(Right) 2 oz. clear glass, gold cap. Choice of Wild Country, Tai Winds, Deep Woods or Oland. OSP $2. **CMV $1.**

AFTER SHAVING LOTION 1936-49
4 oz. maroon cap, maroon & cream colored box. OSP 37c. **CMV $30. MB, $22. BO.**

EAGLE ORGANIZER BOTTLE 1972
(Left) 3 oz. clear glass, eagle embossed, gold cap. Came in set only in Deep Woods & Tai Winds. **CMV $3. each.**

GIFT COLOGNE FOR MEN 1976
(Right) 2 oz. came in Deep Woods, Tai Winds, Wild Country, Everest or Oland. SSP $2. **CMV $1. MB, 50c BO.**

CJ GIFT EDITION COLOGNE 1982-83
.5 oz. mini cologne. Clear glass, gray cap, Christmas box. SSP $1.45. **CMV $1. MB.**

MEN'S ITEMS, MISC.

CREAM HAIR LOTION 1948-49
4 oz. maroon cap. OSP 59c. **CMV $20., $25. MB.**

SERVICE KIT AFTER SHAVE BOTTLE 1951-52
4 oz. clear plastic with red cap. **CMV $12.**

COLOGNE SPRAY FOR MEN 1970-72
4 oz. silver can with red cap in Leather, brown cap in Wild Country, and tan cap in Oland. This can leaked & most boxes were ruined. OSP $5. **CMV $3. each MB, $2. CO.**

STYPTIC CREAM 1936-49
Maroon & ivory tube. OSP 17c. **CMV $8., $15. MB.**

SHAVING STICK 1936-49
Avon on maroon base on Soap Stick. Maroon box. OSP 39c. **CMV $10., $17. MB.**

GIFT COLOGNE FOR MEN 1980
(Left) .5 oz. black cap, clear glass. Choice of Trazarra, Wild Country, Clint, Weekend, Light Musk, Cool Sage, Brisk Spice or Crisp Lime. SSP $1.50. **CMV $1. MB.**

COLOGNE MINIATURE FOR MEN 1977-78
(Right) 5 oz. smoked glass, black cap. Came in Clint, Everest or Wild Country. SSP 88c. **CMV $1.**

COUNTRY CHRISTMAS COLOGNE 1982
(Left) 2 oz. ribbed, clear glass, green cap & box. Came in Country Christmas set only in men's cologne. **CMV $2. MB.**

COLOGNES FOR MEN 1979-82
(Right) 3 oz. clear glass bottle. Gold caps. Choice of Brisk Spice, Cool Sage, Light Musk or Crisp Lime. Came in box. SSP $3. **CMV $1. each MB.**

HAIR TONIC EAU DE QUININE 1936-38
For normal, dry or oily hair. 6 oz. turquoise cap. OSP 78c. **CMV $15.** Also came in 16 oz. size, **$25. BO, $30. MB.**

TALC FOR MEN 1943-46
Maroon & ivory colored cardboard. One on left also came with black octagonal cap as shown and also with maroon or black round cap. One on right was smooth top. You punched holes in it. OSP 37c. **CMV $35. each mint.**

HAIR TONIC 1938-39
(Left) 6 oz. clear glass, maroon cap and label. OSP 52c. **CMV $30. BO mint, $40. MB.**
HAIR LOTION 1940-49
(Right) 6 oz. maroon cap & box. OSP 69c. **CMV $40. MB, $30. BO mint.** Some labels say "formerly Hair Tonic".

SHAVING BOWL 1953-56
Wood Shaving Bowl, green label. No center handle. OSP $1.25. **CMV $30., $40. MB.**
SHAVING BOWL 1949-53
Wood Shaving Bowl, green label with red center handle. OSP $1.10. **CMV $35., $45. MB.**

TALC FOR MEN 1929 ONLY
(Left) Green can. OSP 25c. **CMV $55. mint.**
TALC FOR MEN 1930-36
(Right) Greenish yellow can, black cap. OSP 35c. **CMV $45. mint.**

STICK DEODORANT FOR MEN 1959-61
2 3/4 oz. black & red plastic container. Came with two different caps, 1 flat, 1 indented. OSP $1. **CMV $12. each, $15. MB.**

ORIGINAL AFTER SHAVE SPRAY 1965-66
5 1/2 oz. green can with red cap. OSP $1.50. **CMV $3. CO, $7. MB.**
TALC FOR MEN 1949-58
2 5/8 oz. green can, red cap. OSP 69c. **CMV $5., $7. MB.** Also came in 2.6 oz. size.

SHAVING STICK 1934-36
(Left) Nickel metal container. OSP 36c. **CMV $50. MB, $40. mint only.**
SHAVING STICK 1929-33
(Right) Green metal can. CPC on lid. OSP 35c. **CMV $50. CO mint, $60. MB.**

LATHER & BRUSHLESS SHAVING CREAM 1949-59
Green tubes, flat red caps, used in 1949-56. Tall red caps used 1957-59. OSP 49c. **CMV $10. each MB, $8. tube only mint.**

KWICK FOAMING SHAVE CREAM 1955-57
10 oz. green & white can, pointed red cap. OSP 98c. **CMV $4., $7. MB.**
SAME CAN 1957-58
With flat red top, red cap. **CMV same.**

165

SHAVING STICK 1949-57
Green & red box holds Shaving Soap Stick with red plastic base. OSP 59c. **CMV $12.50 MB, $4. stick only.**
STYPTIC CREAM 1949-57
1/3 oz. green tube with red cap. OSP 39c. **CMV $10., MB $15.**

SHAVING CREAM SAMPLE 1949-58
1/4 oz. green tubes of lather & brushless shaving cream, red caps. **CMV $5. each mint.** Also came in 1/2 oz. size sample tubes. **CMV $8. each mint.**

COLOGNE FOR MEN 1949-58
All three sizes have red caps & silver labels, 6 oz. size. 1949-57 OSP $1.50. **CMV $15. MB.** 4 oz. size 1952-57 came in sets only. Also with green label. **CMV $9.** 2 oz. size 1949-58 OSP 69c. **CMV $6.**

ORIGINAL SOAP ON A ROPE 1966-68
White bar with embossed carriage. OSP $1.75. **CMV $25. MB, $17.50 soap only mint.**
ORIGINAL AFTER SHAVE 1965-69
4 oz. green label, red cap & red & green box. OSP $1.25. **CMV $4. BO, $6. MB.**

CREAM HAIR DRESS 1949-57
2 1/4 oz. green tube & box. Came with flat or tail red cap. OSP 49c. **CMV $15. MB.**

COLOGNE FOR MEN SAMPLE 1949-58
1/2 oz. red cap, silver label. **CMV $25.**
AFTER SHAVING LOTION SAMPLE 1949-58
1/2 oz. red cap, green label. **CMV $5.**

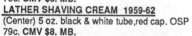

BRUSHLESS SHAVING CREAM 1959-62
(Left) 5 oz. black & white tube, red cap. OSP 79c. **CMV $5. MB.**
LATHER SHAVING CREAM 1959-62
(Center) 5 oz. black & white tube, red cap. OSP 79c. **CMV $8. MB.**
KWICK FOAMING SHAVE CREAM 1958-62
(Right) 6 oz. black & white can, red cap. OSP 79c. **CMV $5.**

DEODORANT FOR MEN SAMPLE 1949-58
1/2 oz. bottle with red cap, green label. **CMV $25. mint.**

DEODORANT FOR MEN 1954-57
4 oz. red cap & green label. Came in sets only. **CMV $9. MB, $7. BO.**
DEODORANT FOR MEN 1949-58
2 oz. red cap & green label. OSP 63c. **CMV $6., $8. MB.**

COLOGNE FOR MEN 1952-57
4 oz. clear glass bottle with red cap. Label is green & red. **CMV $9.**

AFTER SHAVE LOTION 1949-58
4 oz. bottle with silver label & red cap. OSP 69c. **CMV $6. BO, $9. MB.**
AFTER SHAVE 2 OZ. 1957
Silver label. Came in Good Cheer set only. **CMV $8.**

FIRST CLASS MALE 1953-56
6 oz. cologne for men, box red & white. OSP $1.50. CMV $25. MB as shown.

TRIUMPH 1957
Special issue box holds 6 oz. cologne for men. Silver label, red cap. OSP $1.19. CMV $25. MB.

KING FOR A DAY 1957
Box holds 4 oz. bottle of Electric Pre-Shave Lotion or choice of cologne for men, or 4 oz. deodorant for men. All had red caps. OSP 89c. CMV $22.50. MB.
ELECTRIC PRE-SHAVE LOTION 1957-58
4 oz. red cap, silver label. OSP 89c. CMV $9., $10. MB.

HAIR LOTION 1949-58
4 oz. silver label & red cap. OSP 59c. CMV $7. BO, $12. MB.
CREAM HAIR LOTION 1949-58
4 oz. bottle, silver label, red cap. OSP 59c. CMV $7. BO, $12. MB.
AFTER SHAVE LOTION 1953-54
4 oz. silver label, red cap, as above. CMV $15.

HAIR LOTION 1 OZ. 1953-54
1 oz. bottle with red cap & green label. CMV $20. BO, $25. MB.
CREAM HAIR LOTION 1 OZ. 1953-54
1 oz. bottle with red cap, green label. CMV $10. BO, $25. MB in trial size box.
LIQUID SHAMPOO 1953-54
1 oz. bottle with red cap & green label. CMV $22. BO, $27. MB.

COLOGNE FOR MEN 1953-54
4 oz. green label, red cap. Came in Before & After set only. CMV $15.

ELECTRIC PRE-SHAVE LOTION 1959-62
4 oz. red cap, black & white label. OSP 89c. CMV $12. MB, $8. BO.
AFTER SHAVING LOTION PLASTIC 1960-62
3 1/2 oz. white plastic bottle with red cap. Came in Overnighter Set only. CMV $4. 2 oz. After Shave, red plastic & cap as above came in 1959 Lamplighter Set. CMV $4.
SPRAY DEODORANT FOR MEN 1959-62
2 3/4 oz. white plastic bottle with red cap. OSP 89c. CMV $5. MB, $3. BO. 1 1/2 oz. size in white plastic, red cap, came only in 1959 Lamplighters Set. CMV $5.

ROYAL ORDER 1957 ONLY
Red & green box holds 6 oz. cologne for men. Silver label. OSP $1.50. CMV $25. MB.

AFTER SHAVE LOTION SAMPLE 1958-62
(Left) 1/2 oz. red cap, black & white label. CMV $8.
AFTER SHAVE LOTION 1958
(Center) 2 oz. red cap. Came in sets only. CMV $6.
AFTER SHAVE LOTION 1958-62
(Right) 4 oz. red cap, black & white label. OSP 89c. CMV $4.

COLOGNE FOR MEN 1958-59
4 oz. black glass, red cap. OSP $1.25. CMV $15. MB, $12. BO.
AFTER SHOWER SAMPLE 1959-62
1/2 oz. black glass, red cap. CMV $6.
AFTER SHOWER FOR MEN 1959-62
4 oz. black glass, red or gold cap. OSP $1.25. CMV $12.

COLOGNE FOR MEN 1958
2 oz. red cap, black & white label. Came in Happy Hours Set only. **CMV $7. BO.**
DEODORANT FOR MEN 1958-62
2 oz. red cap. OSP 69c. **CMV $8. MB, $6. BO.**

VIGORATE AFTER SHAVE 1960-62
4 oz. frosted glass bottle, gold or red caps. 2 different painted labels. OSP $1.25. **CMV $10., $15. MB.**

DELUXE STICK DEODORANT NORMAL 1962-63
2 1/2 oz. brown & gold plastic bottle. OSP $1.35. **CMV $8.**
STICK DEODORANT FOR MEN A SPICY FRAGRANCE 1961-62
2 3/4 oz. brown & gold plastic holder. OSP $1.35. **CMV $9., $11. MB.**

AFTER SHOWER FOR MEN 1959-60
2 oz. black plastic bottle with red cap. OSP $1.25. **CMV $4.**
AFTER SHAVE 1959-60
2 oz. red plastic bottle & cap. Came in 1959 Lamplighter Set. **CMV $4.**

AFTER SHAVE FOR DRY & SENSITIVE SKIN 1960-61
2 oz. white plastic bottle with red cap. OSP 89c. **CMV $7. BO, $10. MB.** Also came in 2 3/4 oz.
CREAM HAIR LOTION 1960-61
2 oz. white plastic bottle with red cap. Came in 1 st Prize Set only. **CMV $7. BO.** Also came in 2 3/4 oz. size. **$10. MB.**

CREAM HAIR LOTION 1962-65
4 oz. white plastic bottle, red cap. OSP 89c. **CMV $10. MB, $7. BO.**
LIQUID HAIR LOTION 1962-65
4 oz. clear glass bottle, red cap. OSP 89c. **CMV $12. MB, $8. BO.**
HAIR TRAINER 1962-65
4 oz. white plstic bottle, red cap. OSP 89c. **CMV $10. MB, $7. BO.**

STAGE COACH EMBOSSED BOTTLES 1960-61
2 oz. size. Red or white caps. Came in First Prize Set only in After Shower for Men. Vigorate, Deodorant for Men, After Shave Lotion, Electric Pre-Shave Lotion, Liquid Hair Lotion. **CMV each $18. MB, $10. BO.**
1961 ONLY
4 oz. size with white cap came in Spice After Shave Lotion. OSP $1.25. **CMV $10. BO, $14. MB.**
1960-61
8 oz. size with gold metal cap, came in Spice After Shave Lotion. After Shave Lotion, Vigorate & After Shower for Men. OSP $2.50. **CMV each $17., with indented gold cap $25. MB.**

DELUXE TALC FOR MEN 1962-63
4 oz. brown can. OSP $1.35. **CMV $8., $10. MB.**
DELUXE FOAM SHAVE CREAM 1962-63
6 oz. brown can & cap. Regular or mentholated. OSP $1.35. **CMV $8., $10. MB.**

AFTER SHAVE LOTION SPICY 1962-65
ELECTRIC PRE-SHAVE LOTION SPICY
AFTER SHOWER COLOGNE FOR MEN
ORIGINAL AFTER SHAVE LOTION
VIGORATE AFTER SHAVE LOTION
Each bottle is 4 oz. size with red caps. OSP each 89c. **CMV each $7. BO, $10. MB.**

DELUXE AFTER SHAVE AFTER SHOWER SPRAY 1962-63
(Left) 5 1/2 oz. brown can, gold cap. OSP $1.98. **CMV $8., $10. MB.**
AFTER SHOWER POWDER SPICY 1961 ONLY
(Center) 4 oz. brown can. OSP $1.35. **CMV $12., $14. MB.**
AFTER SHAVE AFTER SHOWER SPRAY LOTION - A SPICY FRAGRANCE 1961-62
(Right) 5 1/2 oz. brown can, gold cap. OSP $1.79. **CMV $12. mint, $14. MB.**

TALC FOR MEN SPICY 1962-65
3 oz. white can, red cap. OSP 89c. **CMV $7.** Also came in 3.1 oz. size.
ROLL ON DEODORANT FOR MEN 1960-63
1 3/4 oz. white plastic with red cap. OSP 89c. **CMV $5. MB, $4. BO.**

BODY POWDER FOR MEN 1967-68
6 oz. maroon cardboard box. OSP $4. **CMV $8. MB, $12.50.**

VIGORATE AFTER SHAVE AFTER SHOWER SPRAY 1963-65
ORIGINAL AFTER SHAVE AFTER SHOWER SPRAY SPICY 1963-65
AFTER SHAVE AFTER SHOWER SPRAY SPICY 1963-65
AFTER SHOWER COLOGNE SPRAY 1963-65
5 1/2 oz. each. White can with red caps. OSP Spicy & Original, $1.50 each, cologne & Vigorate, $1.75 each. **CMV $3. each, $5. MB.**

STAND UP HAIR STICK 1962-65
1 1/2 oz. white plastic, red cap. OSP 89c. **CMV $4. MB, $3. BO.**
ROLL ON DEODORANT FOR MEN 1963-66
1 3/4 oz. glass bottle, red cap. OSP 89c. **CMV $4. MB, $3. BO.**
SPRAY DEODORANT FOR MEN 1962-66
2 3/4 oz. white plastic bottle, red cap. Came in gentle, normal or plain. OSP 89c. **CMV $3. MB, $2. BO.**
LIQUID DEODORANT FOR MEN - GENTLE OR PLAIN 1962-65
4 oz. & 2 oz. clear glass bottle, red cap. OSP 79c. **CMV 2 oz. $6., 4 oz. $7.**

LIQUID HAIR LOTION 1966-70
(Bottles) 4 oz. clear glass bottle with white cap. OSP 89c. **CMV $2.** 1970-71 bottle is white, red cap, 6 oz. plastic. **CMV $1.**
HAIR DRESS 1966-71
(Tubes) 4 oz. tube in Cream Clear & Clear for Extra Control. OSP 98c. **CMV $1.** Also came in 3 oz. tube. **CMV $1. each.**

MEN'S SQUEEZE BOTTLE 1963-64
2 oz. white plastic bottles with red caps & letters. Came in Vigorate, Spicy & Original After Shave Lotions, Electric Pre-Shave Lotion, Spicy Liquid Hair Lotion, Hair Trainer, Cream Hair Lotion, After Shower Cologne for Men, Liquid Deodorant for Men, gentle or Plain. Came only in 1964 Christmas Trio Set & 1965 Jolly Holly Day Set. **CMV $3. each.**

AFTER SHAVE FOR DRY OR SENSITIVE SKIN SPICY 2 OZ. 1962-65
LATHER SHAVE CREAM SPICY 4 OZ. 1962-65
All three white tubes with red caps. OSP each 89c. **CMV $3., $6. each MB.**
LATHER SHAVE CREAM 1962-63
4 oz. tube, red cap. OSP 89c. **CMV $4. mint, $6. MB.**

CREAM HAIR LOTION 1958-62
4 oz. white plastic bottle, red cap. OSP 89c. **CMV $4., $6. MB.**
HAIR LOTION 1958-62
4 oz. clear glass, red cap, black & white label. OSP 79c. **CMV $14. MB, $10. BO.** Glass bottle on right also came in Deer Head box on left.

AFTER SHOWER COLOGNE SPRAY 1962
5.5 oz. white can & cap. OSP $1.75. **CMV $7.**
FOAM SHAVE CREAM SPICY 1962-65
6 oz. white can, red cap. Came in regular or
mentholated. OSP 89c. **CMV $6. MB, $4. BO.**
Came with tall or flat red caps as shown.

ELECTRIC PRE-SHAVE LOTION 1966-72
(Left) 4 oz. white cap. OSP $1.50. **CMV $1.**

HAIR GUARD & HAND GUARD 1958 ONLY
Both 2 oz. bottles with red caps. Came in
Avon Guard set only. **CMV hand guard $16.,
hair guard $20.**

FOAMY BATH FOR CLEANER HIDES 1957
(Left) 2 oz. red cap, cow hide on label. Came
in Trading Post set only. **CMV $20.**
**HAIR TRAINER FOR TRAINING WILD HAIR
1957**
(Right) 2 oz. red cap, cow hide on label.
Came in Trading Post set only. **CMV $20.**

SKIN CONDITONER FOR MEN 1969-73
(Center) 5 oz. black glass, red lid and red &
black label. OSP $2.50. **CMV $2.50 MB.**
**ALL PURPOSE SKIN CONDITIONER FOR
MEN 1966-68**
(Right) 5 oz. black glass, tan lid, gold label.
OSP $2.50. **CMV $5. MB.**

CREAM HAIR LOTION 1966-69
4 oz. white plastic bottle with red cap and red
label. Regular issue OSP 98c. **CMV $1.** Very
short issue sold 1966 only with red cap and red
label with black border. **CMV $2.**

BATH OIL 1969-72
(Left) 4 oz. black glass bottle, red cap. OSP
$2.50. **CMV $2.**
AFTER SHAVE SOOTHER 1969-72
(Center) 4 oz. frosted glass bottle with red
cap. OSP $2.50. **CMV $2.**
**PROTECTIVE HAND CREAM FOR MEN
1969-72**
(Right) 3 oz. black plastic tube with red cap.
OSP $1.50. **CMV $1.**

AFTER SHOWER FOAM FOR MEN 1965-67
(Left) 4 oz. silver can, black & red cap. Came
in silver box. OSP $2.50. **CMV $4. BO, $6.
MB.**
BATH OIL FOR MEN 1965-67
(Right) 4 oz. silver paint over clear glass, red
cap & red Avon plastic tag on gold neck cord.
Came in silver box. OSP $2.50. **CMV $5. -
$7. MB.**

TALC FOR MEN 1959 ONLY
(Left) Black & white can, red cap. OSP 69c.
CMV $12. MB, $10. can only, mint.
**AFTER SHOWER POWDER FOR MEN 1959-
62**
(Right) 3 oz. black & white can, red cap. OSP
89c. **CMV $6. - $7. MB.**

HAIR TRAINER BOXES 1958-61
(Left to Right) 4 oz. red plastic bottle with 1958 box on left, 1962 box center, 1960-61 on right. 1959 box came with boxer on front of box. CMV add $5. for each box mint, $1. BO.

HAIR TRAINER 1957-58
(Left) 6 oz. clear glass bottle with white or blue cap. Came in 1957 Hair Trainer Set. OSP 79c. CMV $20.
HAND GUARD & HAIR GUARD 1951-52
(Right) 2 oz. clear glass with blue cap; hair guard has red cap. Label is red, white & black. Came in Changing of the Guard set only. CMV $20. each.

HAND GUARD & HAIR GUARD 1954-57
2 oz. red cap on Hair Guard. 2 oz. green cap on Hand Guard. Both came in Back Field set & Touchdown set. Hair Guard also came in Pigskin Parade set. CMV $18. each.
CREAM HAIR LOTION 1955
2 oz. clear glass, red cap. Came in Space Scout set only. Rare. CMV $25.

BAY RUM

All Men's Product lines 1975 or newer are no longer collectable because of little or no interest and mass production. Only soaps & sets in this catagory are collectable after 1975.

ANTI-PERSPIRANT DEODORANT FOR MEN 1971-74
(Left) 4 oz. red, white & black can. OSP $1.50. CMV 25c. With upside down label, CMV $8.
LIQUID DEODORANT FOR MEN 1966-70
(Inside Left) 2 oz. red cap. OSP 79c. CMV $2.
STICK DEODORANT FOR MEN 1968-70
(Inside Right) 2.25. oz. red, white & black plastic. OSP $1.25. CMV $1.
DEODORANT SOAP DRY - FOREIGN CMV $3.

TODAY'S MAN SHAVE CREAM 1975-76
(Left) 5 oz. white with red & black design, black cap. OSP $2. CMV 50c.
TODAY'S MAN HAND CONDITIONER 1975-76
(Center) 5 oz. white plastic tube with black & red design, black cap. OSP $1.69. CMV 50c.
TODAY'S MAN AFTER SHAVE FACE CONDITIONER 1975-76
(Right) 5 oz. white with red & black, black cap. OSP $2.50. CMV 50c.

BAY RUM GIFT SET 1964
Green box holds 4 oz. Bay Rum after shave with black cap & green 4 oz. paper Bay Rum talc for men. OSP $2.50. CMV $35. MB.

BAY RUM SOAP 1964-65
Green box holds 2 Bay Rum shaped soaps. OSP $1.25. CMV $27.50, MB.

HAIR TRAINER LIQUID 1958-74
(Left) 4 oz. red plastic bottle, white cap. OSP 89c. CMV $1.
ATTENTION CREAM HAIR DRESS 1959-62
(Center) 4 oz. red & white tube, red cap. OSP 89c. CMV $8. MB, $10.
STAND UP HAIR STICK 1958-65
(Right) Red & white container with white cap. OSP 69c. CMV $3. - $7. MB.

BAY RUM 1936-49
4 oz. maroon cap. 2 different labels. Both bottles have indented shoulders. Also came in 8 & 16 oz. size. OSP 52c. **CMV $22. BO, $30. MB each.**

BAY RUM AFTER SHAVE 1964-65
(Left) 4 oz. clear glass, black cap. OSP $1.25. CMV $8.50 BO, $12.50. MB.
BAY RUM JUG 1962-65
(Center) 8 oz. white painted bottom, green top over clear glass, black cap. Bay Rum after shave. OSP $2.50. **CMV $6. BO, $10. MB.**
BAY RUM TALC 1964-65
(Right) 4 oz. green paper container. OSP $1.25. **CMV $10.**

BLACK SUEDE

BLEND 7

BLEND 7 PRODUCTS 1973-74
SOAP ON A ROPE 1973-76
5 oz. yellow with black cord. SSP $2. **CMV $4. MB.**
All other products 25c each.

BLUE BLAZER AFTER SHAVE 1964-68
6 oz. blue glass with red square cap over small red cap. Horses on labels, came in gold or silver & with or without lines across horses. Some labels have 6 oz. at bottom of horse label. OSP $2.50. **CMV $15. mB., $12. BO.**
BLUE BLAZER SOAP ON A ROPE 1964-68
Blue soap on white rope. OSP $1.75. **CMV $20. MB, $10. soap only mint.**

BLACK SUEDE PRODUCTS 1980-84
Basic Color is tan & black.
GIFT SOAP & CASE 1980 ONLY
Black plastic soap case & soap. SSP $5. **CMV $5. MB.**
SOAP BAR ONLY
SSP $1.50. **CMV $1. mint.**
SOAP ON A ROPE
SSP $3. **CMV $3. MB.**
All other products 25c each.

BLUE BLAZER

BLUE BLAZER FOAM SHAVE CREAM 1964-65
(Not Shown) 6 oz. blue can, red cap. OSP $1.25. **CMV $10. MB, $7. CO.**
AFTER SHAVE SPRAY 1964-65
(Left) Blue 6 oz. can, red cap. OSP $1.95. **CMV $10. MB, $7. CO.**
TALC 1964-65
(Center) 3 1/2 oz. blue paper box. OSP $1.25. **CMV $12. MB, $9. CO.**
HAIR DRESS 1964-67
(Right) 4 oz. blue tube, red cap. OSP $1.25. **CMV $8. MB, $6. TO.**

BLUE BLAZER 1 SET 1964-65
Blue & red box holds 6 oz. Blue Blazer after shave lotion & Blue Blazer soap on a rope. OSP $3.45. **CMV $50. MB.**

BLUE BLAZER DELUXE SET 1965
Blue & red box holds 6 oz. Blue Blazer after shave, Blue Blazer spray deodorant & silver Blue Blazer emblem tie tac. OSP $5.50. **CMV $67.50 MB.**

BLUE BLAZER SOAP & SPONGE SET 1966-67
Red & blue box holds bar of blue soap and red & blue sponge. OSP $2.50. **CMV $22.50 MB.**

BLUE BLAZER II SET 1964-65
Blue & red box holds Blue Blazer talc & spray deodorant. OSP $2.50. **CMV $25.**

BLUE BLAZER SPRAY DEODORANT 1964-67
2.75 oz. blue plastic bottles, red caps. One bottle has lines on horse design & 1 plain. The plain one is hardest to find. OSP $1.25 each. **CMV $8. Different label on right. CMV $7. with 2.75 oz. on front side.**

BLUE BLAZER TIE TAC 1964
Silver Blue Blazer emblem tie tac. Came in Blue Blazer Deluxe Set only. In blue & red box. **CMV $22. MB, $10. pin only.**

BRAVO

BRAVO AFTER SHAVE TOWELETTES 1969-72
Pink & black box holds 100 sample packets. **CMV $10. MB or 10c per sample.**

BRAVO AFTER SHAVE SAMPLE 1969-72
Box of 10 samples. **CMV $1.50 MB.**
BRAVO TALC 1969-72
3.5 oz. pink & black paper container. OSP $1.25. **CMV $1.50.**

BRAVO AFTER SHAVE 1969
(Left) 4 oz. bottle with black cap, pink label. OSP $2. **CMV $4. MB, $2. BO.**
BRAVO AFTER SHAVE 1970-72
(Right) 4 oz. black cap, pink label with black border around label. OSP $2. **CMV $2. MB, $1. BO.**

SANTA'S HELPER 1970
Green box holds 4 oz. Bravo After Shave. Box came with foam stick on decorations. OSP $1.98. **CMV $8. MB only.**

CLINT

CLINT AFTER SHAVE 1977-79
(Left) 5 oz. glass bottle, brown cap. OSP $5. **CMV $1.50.**
CLINT SHOWER SOAP 1977-78
(Center) Soap on green or white rope. OSP $5. **CMV $3.50. MB.**
CLINT COLOGNE 1976-79
(Right) 5 oz. bottle with Clint painted on front. OSP $7.50. **CMV 75c.** Also came in 4 oz. size, same design.

CLINT TRAVEL KIT 1977
Comes empty, gray, maroon & green bag.
OSP $14. CMV $6. MB.
CLINT SOAP 1977-78
3 oz. soap. OSP $1.25. CMV $1.50.
All other Clint products CMV 25c.

CLINT GIFT SET 1977-78
(Left) Gray & green box with outer sleeve.
Came with Clint soap on a rope & 5 oz. Clint
cologne. OSP $12.50. CMV $10. MB.
CLINT TRAVEL SET 1977
(Right) Cardboard 1.5 oz. talc & 3 oz. Clint in
plastic bottle with maroon cap. OSP $3.50.
CMV $3.50 MB.

DEEP WOODS

DEEP WOODS PRODUCTS 1972-79
AFTER SHAVE 1976-79
(Left) 5 oz. brown cap. OSP $3. CMV 50c.
SHOWER SOAP ON A ROPE 1972-75
(Center) OSP $2. CMV $6. MB.
SHOWER SOAP ON A ROPE 1976-79
(Right) OSP $3. CMV $3. MB.
DEEP WOODS SOAP BAR 1977-78
(Top) Brown wrapped soap, 3 oz. bar. OSP
$1.25. CMV $1. mint.
All other products CMV 50c.

EVEREST

EVEREST SOAP ON A ROPE 1975-79
(Left) Blue soap, white rope. OSP $3. CMV
$3. MB.
EVEREST SOAP BAR 1977-79
(Top) Blue wrapped 3 oz. bar. SSP $1.25.
CMV $1. mint.
All other Everest products CMV 50c.

ISLAND LIME

ISLAND LIME AREOSOL DEODORANT 1966-67
(Left) 4 oz. green & yellow checked can &
green cap. OSP $1.50. CMV $3. CO, $5. MB.
ISLAND LIME AFTER SHAVE 1969-73
(Center & Left) 6 oz. green frosted glass &
green cap with yellow letters. OSP $4. CMV
$1.50. 1973-74 issue has gold cap, green
letters. OSP $4. CMV $4. MB, $2. BO.

ISLAND LIME SPRAY TALC 1974-76
(Left) 7 oz. green & yellow with dark green
cap. OSP $2. CMV 50c.
ISLAND LIME AFTER SHAVE 1966-69
(Right) First issue 6 oz. dark yellow basket
weave. CMV $12. MB, $9. BO. 1967 issue
has light yellow weave on clear. CMV $10.
1968 issue has light green weave. CMV $10.
All 66 to 68 are clear glass bottles. 1969 issue
is green glass bottle & low issue. CMV $20.
MB, $14. BO. OSP each $3. All have green &
yellow caps. Add $3. each MB. Came with
small or large flowers on caps.

ISLAND LIME SOAP 1966-68
Green soap on a rope. OSP $2. CMV $22.
MB. Two different weave designs on soap.

EXCALIBUR

EXCALIBUR COLOGNE FOREIGN & AMERICAN 1969-73
Smaller foreign Excalibur on left. CMV $12.
American on right. 6 oz. gold cap. Bottom of
bottle appears to have rocks in glass. OSP $5.
CMV $5. MB, $2. BO. American rare issue
came with sword pointing to right side low end
of rocks. CMV $15. mint.

EXCALIBUR SOAP ON A ROPE 1969-71
(Left) Blue soap on a rope. OSP $2.50. CMV
$10. MB.
EXCALIBUR SPRAY TALC 1970-72
(Right) 7 oz. black can & cap. OSP $3. CMV
$1.

LEATHER

LEATHER SOAP 1966
One bar in brown & red box. OSP $1.75.
CMV $18. MB.

ALL PURPOSE COLOGNE LEATHER 1966
(Left) 4 oz. black cap, red label. Came in
Fox Hunt set only. CMV $10.
AFTER SHAVE LOTION LEATHER 1968
(Right) 3 oz. red cap, clear glass. Came in
Boots & Saddle set only. CMV $5.

LEATHER AEROSOL DEODORANT 1966-67
(Left) 4 oz. tan & red can with black cap.
OSP $1.50. CMV $5. MB - $3. can only.
LEATHER SPRAY TALC 1969-72
(Right) 7 oz. tan & red can, black cap. OSP
$3. CMV $2.

OLAND

OLAND GIFT SET 1970
Brown and silver box holds bar of Oland soap,
31/2 oz. Oland talc & 6 oz. Oland cologne.
OSP $8. CMV $15.

OLAND COLOGNE 1970-77
6 oz. embossed bottle with brown cap. OSP
$6.50. CMV $2.
OLAND SOAP ON A ROAP 1970-77
Tan bar of soap on green rope with plastic "O".
OSP $4. CMV $7 MB with plain rope (no
"O"). CMV $5. MB.
OLAND SPRAY TALC 1970-77
7 oz. brown spray can with brown cap. OSP
$3. CMV $1.

OLAND SPRAY TALC 1970-72
(Left) 7oz. can with O on brown cap. Painted
label on can is upside down. Can was filled &
sold by Avon by mistake. OSP $3. CMV $5.

OLAND AFTER SHAVE & COLOGNE 1970
3 1/2 oz. clear glass with gold cap. Came in
Master Organizer only. CMV $5. each.

SPICY

SPICY AFTER SHAVE 1967-74
4 oz. clear glass, black cap, CMV 50c. 4 oz.
amber glass with black cap. OSP $1.50. CMV
$2. MB

SPICY SOAP SET 1965-66
Five brown bars. OSP $2. CMV $22.50 MB

COLOGNE PLUS SPICY 1965-67
2 oz.. gold ribbed cap. OSP $2.50. CMV $20.
in box. Bottle only $17.50.
AFTER SHAVE LOTION 1965-67
4 oz. tan cap. OSP 98c. CMV $7.

TALC FOR MEN - SPICY 1967-74
3 1/2 oz. brown & white container. OSP 98c.
CMV **$1.** Upside down label **CMV $5.**
AFTER SHAVE SPRAY - SPICY 1965-67
5 1/2 oz. Bamboo style can, gold cap. OSP
$1.50. **CMV $6.**

**AFTER SHAVE FOR DRY OR SENSITIVE
SKIN - SPICY 1967-75**
2 oz. black, brown & white tube, brown or white
cap. OSP 98c. One has all white letters.
CMV $1. One has black over print on white
letters. Hard to find. **CMV $3.**

SPICY AFTER SHAVE SAMPLES 1961
Plastic sample tubes of Spicy After Shave
Lotion. Full box of 30. Same samples also
came in Cream Hair Dress. Rich Moisture
Cream & Dew Kiss. **CMV 25c each sample
or $7. for full box of 30 mint.** Comes in 2
different boxes.

TALC FOR MEN - SPICY 1965-67
3 1/2 oz. Bamboo style box. OSP 89c. **CMV
$5. MB - $3. CO.**
AFTER SHAVE SPRAY - SPICY 1965-67
5/12 oz. Bamboo style can, tan cap. OSP
$1.50. **CMV $5. MB - $3. CO.**

**AFTER SHAVE FOR DRY OR SENSITIVE
SKIN - SPICY 1965-67**
2 oz. tan & white tube, tan cap. OSP 89c.
CMV $4. mint. Upside down label on right is
rare. **CMV $8. mint.**

**SPICE AFTER SHAVE LOTION SAMPLES
1961**
Small white envelope holds 2 plastic samples.
CMV $3.

OATMEAL SOAP - SPICY 1967-76
(Left) Large bath size & 3 oz. size in brown &
white wrapper. OSP 60c. **CMV $2.**
OATMEAL SOAP - SPICY 1965-67
(Right) Brown & white wrapping. OSP 49c.
CMV $7

FORE N AFTER SPICY 1966
Spicy box holds 4 oz. Electric Pre-Shave
Lotion Spicy & 4 oz. After Shave Lotion Spicy.
White caps on both & wood grained paper
label. OSP $1.96. **CMV $22. MB.**
**ELECTRIC PRE-SHAVE & AFTER SHAVE
LOTIONS - SPICY 1966**
4 oz. white caps & wood grained paper labels.
Came in Fore N After Set only. **CMV $9. each.**

SPICY THREE 1965
Brown box holds 2 bars of Spicy Oatmeal
Soap & Spicy Talc for Men. OSP $1.85. **CMV
$22.50 MB.**

TWICE SPICE 1967
Brown striped box holds 4 oz. Spicy After Shave Lotion & Spicy Talc for Men. OSP $2.23. **CMV $15. MB.**

FIRST EDITION SPICY 1965
Book type box holds 4 oz. Spicy After Shave Lotion & Spicy Talc for Men. OSP $1.69. **CMV $22.50 MB.**

OVERNIGHTER 1965-66
Brown vinyl zippered bag holds Spicy Talc, 4 oz. Spicy After Shave Lotion & bar of Spicy Oatmeal soap for men. OSP $7.50. **CMV $22.50 MB.**

SPORTS RALLY

SPORTS RALLY BRACING LOTION 1966-68
4 oz. glass bottle with blue cap. OSP $1.50. **CMV $4. MB, $2. BO.**
BRACING TOWELETTE 1966-68
Blue & white box holds 12 packets. OSP $1.25. **CMV $5. MB.**
SPORTS RALLY SOAP ON A ROPE 1966-68
4 oz. soap on white rope. OSP $1.50. **CMV $12., $15. MB.**
AEROSOL DEODORANT 1966-68
4 oz. red, white & blue can, white cap. OSP $1.25. **CMV $3. MB, $2. BO.**

CHRISTMAS WREATH 1965
Gold box holds two 4 oz. bottles of Spicy After Shave Lotion with tan caps. OSP $1.95. **CMV $20. MB.**

SPICY TREASURES 1968
Brown chest type box holds 4 oz. Spicy After Shave Lotion & 3 1/2 oz. Talc for Men. OSP $2.23. **CMV $15. MB.**

HOLIDAY SPICE 1965
Brown & white box holds Spicy Talc for Men & 4 oz. Spicy After Shave Lotion. OSP $1.85. **CMV $22.50 MB.**

SPICE 'O' LIFE SET 1966 ONLY
Box holds Spicy Talc for Men & 4 oz. After Shave Lotion. Came out at Fathers Day. OSP $1.96. **CMV $22.50 MB.**

SPORTS RALLY HAIR DRESS 1966-68
4 oz. red & white tube, red cap. OSP $1. **CMV $2., $4. MB.**
SPORTS RALLY ALL PURPOSE TALC 1966-68
3 1/2 oz. blue & white cardboard container. OSP $1. **CMV $2., $4. MB.**
SPORTS RALLY CLEAR SKIN SOAP 1966-68
2 bars with blue band around them. OSP $1. **CMV $4. ea. bar, $10. set.**
SPORTS RALLY CLEAR SKIN LOTION 1966-68
4 oz. white plastic bottle, red cap. OSP $1.25. **CMV $2. MB, $1. BO.**

SPORTS RALLY BRACING TOWELETTE 1966-68
Contains 50 Towellettes in foil packets. **CMV $10. MB.**

TAI WINDS

TAI WINDS COLOGNE 1971-79
5 oz. green glass, blue-green cap & yellow ribbon. OSP $6.50. **CMV 50c.**
SPRAY TALC 1971-76
7 oz. blue-green & yellow can. OSP $4. **CMV $1.**
AFTER SHAVE 1971-75
5 oz. clear glass, blue-green cap, yellow ribbon. OSP $5. **CMV $1.50. MB.**
SOAP ON A ROPE 1972-79
Yellow soap on rope. OSP $4. **CMV $5. MB.**

TAI WINDS GIFT SET 1971-72
5 oz. green glass bottle with green cap. Yellow bands, 5 oz. embossed soap. SSP $7. **CMV $15. MB.**

TRIBUTE

TRIBUTE AFTER SHAVE SAMPLES 1963-68
Box holds 30 foil samples. **CMV $5. MB.**

TRIBUTE COLOGNE FOR MEN 1964-66
4 oz. blue & silver top, cap & neck tag. OSP $2.50. **CMV with tag $10., $12. MB.**
TRIBUTE ALL PURPOSE COLOGNE 1967-68
4 oz. blue & silver top, cap & neck tag. OSP $3. **CMV with tag $10., $12. MB.** Later issues had no tags. **CMV $4. BO, $6. MB.**

TRIBUTE AEROSOL DEODORANT 1963-67
3 oz. blue & silver can & cap. OSP $1.75. **CMV $6. MB, $4. CO.** 4 oz. size same can, 1967 only. OSP $1.50. **CMV $6. MB, $4. CO.**
TRIBUTE CREAM HAIR DRESS 1963-66
4 oz. blue & silver tube & cap. OSP $1.75. **CMV $8. MB.**
TRIBUTE FOAM SHAVE CREAM 1963-66
6 oz. blue & silver can & cap. Came in regular & mentholated. OSP $1.75. **CMV $6. MB.**

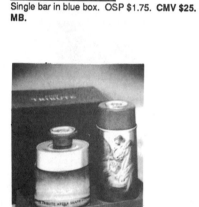

TRIBUTE SOAP 1966-67
Blue & silver box holds 2 white bars with blue & silver centers. OSP $1.75. **CMV $20. MB.**
TRIBUTE SOAP 1963-66
Single bar in blue box. OSP $1.75. **CMV $25. MB.**

TRIBUTE SHAVE SET 1964-65
Blue box holds 6 oz. After Shave Lotion & can of Foam Shave Cream. OSP $4.25. **CMV $35. MB.**

TRIBUTE AFTER SHAVE LOTION 1963-68
(Left) 6 oz. silver & blue cap. OSP $2.50. **CMV $6. mint.**
TRIBUTE AFTER SHAVE 1968-72
(Right) 4 oz. blue label, blue & silver cap. Same bottle also reads After Shave Lotion on label. OSP $2.25. **CMV $2.50 mint.**

TRIBUTE TALC 1963-66
4 oz. blue & silver can, blue cap. OSP $1.75.
CMV $6. mint.
TRIBUTE AFTER SHAVE AFTER SHOWER SPRAY 1963-66
5 1/2 oz. blue & silver can & cap. OSP $2.50.
CMV $6. mint.

TRIBUTE GIFT SET NO. 2 1963-64
Blue & silver box holds 6 oz. Tribute After Shave Lotion, Talc & Aerosol Deodorant. OSP $6.50. CMV $35. MB.

WILD COUNTRY

WILD COUNTRY PRODUCTS 1976-80
All products for this design period 25c.
Soap $1. Belt Buckle $3.

TRIBUTE SPRAY TALC 1969-72
7 oz. blue can. OSP $3. CMV $1. Upside down label, rare. CMV $10.
TRIBUTE SHAMPOO 1964-66
Blue & silver tube. OSP $1.75. CMV $5.
TRIBUTE ELECTRIC PRE-SHAVE LOTION 1963-66
4 oz. blue & silver cap. OSP $1.75. CMV $8.
MB, $5. BO.

WILD COUNTRY TRAVEL SET 1977
Box holds 1.5 oz. talc and 3 oz. after shave in plastic bottle with brown cap. OSP $3.50.
CMV $3.50 MB.
WILD COUNTRY GIFT SOAP 1977-78
Metal container holds 5 oz. bar of white Wild Country soap. SSP $3. CMV $3. MB. Also came with label printed upside down on bottom of can. CMV $8.

WILD COUNTRY HAND CREAM 1973-74
3 oz. brown & white plastic tube with brown cap. SSP $1.75. CMV $1.75.
WILD COUNTRY DEODORANT 1975-77
4 oz. brown & white, white cap. OSP $1. CMV 75c. With upside down label, $8.

TRIBUTE GIFT SET NO. 1 1963-64
Blue & silver box holds Tribute Talc, Foam Shave Cream & After Shave After Shower Spray. OSP $6. CMV $35. MB.

WILD COUNTRY SOAP ON A ROPE 1967-76
Ivory colored bar with bulls head in center. Round. OSP $4. CMV $4, $5. MB.
FOAM SHAVE CREAM 1970-73
11 oz. brown can. OSP $1.75. CMV $1.
SPRAY TALC 1969-77
7 oz. brown can. OSP $4. CMV $2. With special upside down label, CMV $5.
AFTER SHAVE 1971-76
4 oz. silver label & black cap. OSP $4.50.
CMV $1.
TALC 1971-74-78
3 1/2 oz. brown shaker top container. OSP $1.50. CMV 50c. Reissued in 1978.
COLOGNE
6 oz. bottle with silver cap & label. OSP $4.
CMV $2.50.
ALL PURPOSE COLOGNE 1968-80
6 oz. silver cap & label. OSP $6.50. CMV $1.
SOAP ON A ROPE 1976-78
Not shown, squared side, not round. OSP $4.
CMV $4. MB.

WILD COUNTRY SADDLE KIT 1970-71
Brown & white cowhide kit holds Wild Country 6 oz. cologne, Foam Shave Cream & Spray Talc. OSP $16. CMV $12. MB.

WILD COUNTRY COLOGNE SAMPLES 1970
Box of 10 sample packets. **CMV 50c box.**

WILD COUNTRY BODY POWDER 1967-68
6 oz. brown & white cardboard box. OSP $4. **CMV $8. mint, $12. MB.**
WILD COUNTRY COLOGNE SPRAY 1969-70
2 1/2 oz. white coated plastic bottle with silver cap. OSP $4. **CMV $4. MB, $2.50 BO.**

WILD COUNTRY ROLL ON DEODORANT 1978
2 oz. white & brown plastic bottle. SSP 99c. **CMV 50c.**
WILD COUNTRY PENDANT 1978
Silver & ivory bull head. Neck chain for men. Avon on back. SSP $8.99. **CMV $4. MB.**

WINDJAMMER

CANADIAN WINDJAMMER SOAP ON A ROPE 1973
CMV $12. MB.
WINDJAMMER SPRAY TALC 1968
7 oz. blue can. OSP $2.50. **CMV $3.** Also came in 4 oz. size. **CMV $4.**
WINDJAMMER RUB DOWN COOLER 1969-72
10 oz. plastic bottle, blue & gold cap. Lettering gold. Also came with blue lettering. OSP $3. **CMV $1., $2.50 MB.**

WINDJAMMER COLOGNE 1968-69
(Left) 5 oz. blue glass bottle & cap with ring. Painted label. OSP $4. **CMV $8. MB, $5. BO.**
WINDJAMMER COLOGNE 1969-72
(Right) 5 oz. blue glass & cap with blue paper label. OSP $4. **CMV $2. BO, $3.50 MB.**

WINDJAMMER TOWELETTES 1968-69
Blue & white box holds 10 packets. **CMV $2.50 MB.**

COLOGNES - MISC.

All Colognes 1975 or newer have little value to collectors. If they are not pictured in this book, we suggest you do not collect them. No new colognes will be added to this book 1984 or newer.

REFRESHING COLOGNE 1940-41
4 oz. bottle with turquoise cap and label. Turquoise box. OSP 52c. **CMV $35. MB, $30. BO.**

INHALANT COLOGNE 1936-40
4 oz. bottle with turquoise cap and label. Turquoise and white box. OSP 52c. **CMV $35. MB, $30. BO.**

HEADACHE COLOGNE 1931-36
4 oz. ribbed glass bottle with dark blue cap & silver label. OSP 75c. **CMV $50. BO, $60. MB.**

BE MY VALENTINE MINI COLOGNE 1984
His & Her's cologne in 2 separate 1/2 heart boxes. .5 oz. clear glass, red cap on hers, black on his, choice of Odyssey, Foxfire, Timeless, Candid, Ariane, Tasha, Pavi Elle & Soft Musk for her & Rugger Musk for Men, Black Suede, Wild Country for him. SSP $1.75 each. **CMV $1. each.**

GOLD CAP ROCKER COLOGNE 1967-68
1/2 oz. gold round cap. Came in Brocade, Regence, Unforgettable, Rapture, Occur!, Somewhere, Topaze, Cotillion, Here's My Heart, To A Wild Rose, Persian Wood and Wishing. OAP $1.25. **CMV $3. each BO, $4. MB.**

FLAT TOP ROCKER COLOGNE 1959-62
1/2 oz. flat plastic cap. Came in Persian Wood, Here's My Heart, Cotillion, To A Wild Rose, Topaze, Somewhere, Regence, Bright Night and Nearness. OSP $1. each. **CMV $4. BO, $6. MB. Add $1. for Nearness and Bright Night.**

DEMI COLOGNE 1973-75
1/2 oz. clear glass, gold cap. Came in Imperial Garden, Patchwork, Sonnet, Moonwind, RosesRoses, Field Flowers, Bird of paradise, Charisma, Unforgettable, Topaze, Occur!, Here's My Heart. SSP $1. **CMV $1. MB.**

FAN ROCKER 1962-63
1/2 oz. cologne, gold cap with neck cord. Came in To A Wild Rose, Here's My Heart, Persian Wood, Cotillion, Somewhere, Topaze. OSP $1. **CMV $3. BO, $4. BO with cord, $6. MB.**

COLOGNE MINIATURE FOR MEN 1977-78
(Left) 1/2 oz. Came in Clint, Everest or Wild Country. Smoked glass, gray cap. SSP 88c. **CMV $1. MB.**

CHRISTMAS CANDLE COLOGNE DECANTER 1977
(Center) 1 oz. green glass. Came in Charisma, Sweet Honesty, Topaze or Moonwind. SSP $1.29. **CMV $1.50. BO, $2. MB.**

FRAGRANCE FACETTES 1977
(Right) 1/2 oz. colognes. Came in Moonwind, Charisma, Topaze, Occur, Unforgettable, Here My Heart, Cotillion, Sweet Honesty, Sonnet or Bird of Paradise, with gold cap. SSP $1. **CMV $1. MB.**

COLOGNE 1975-77
2 oz. clear glass with gold cap. Name of cologne on side in gold. Came in Moonwind, Charisma, Topaze, Sonnet. OSP $4. **CMV 50c.**

DEMI-COLOGNE 1975-76
Pepper Mill Shape. 1/2 oz. clear glass with gold cap. Holds Sonnet, Moonwind, Charisma, Patchwork, Somewhere, Topaze, Occur!, Cotillion. OSP $2. **CMV $1.**

BATH CLASSIC 1962-63
1 1/2 oz. clear glass with gold design & gold cap. Came in Bath Classic Set only. Came in Somewhere, Cotillion, Topaze, Here's My Heart, Persian Wood, & To A Wild Rose. **CMV $10. BO mint.**

POWDER BOX COLOGNE 1956
1/16 oz. Came in Beauty Dust only with ribbons attached. In Cotillion, Forever Spring, Golden Promise, To A Wild Rose & Quaintance. **CMV $11. BO, $13. mint with ribbon.**

FRAGRANCE COLOGNES 1956
(Left) 3 dram bottle with white painted label and cap. Came in Fragrance Rainbow set only in Nearness, Cotillion, Bright Night & To Wild Rose. **CMV $15. mint.**

BEAUTY DUST COLOGNE 1953-55
(Right) 5/8 dram bottle with no label & flat white or round white cap. Came in Beauty Dust at Christmas only. Each had a silk neck ribbon with gold edge. Quaintance, blue ribbon; To A Wild Rose, pink ribbon; Forever Spring, purple ribbon; Cotillion, pink ribbon; Nearness, pink ribbon; Elegante, red ribbon. **CMV with ribbon $12., $8. BO.**

DAZZLING PERFUME 1969-75
(Left) 1/8 oz. gold cap. Came in Unforgettable, Rapture, Occur!, Somewhere, Topaze, Cotillion, Here's My Heart, To A Wild Rose, Charisma, Brocade, Regence, Bird of Paradise, Elusive & Moonwind. OSP $3. CMV $1. - $2. MB.

MINUETTE COLOGNE 1969-70
(Inside Left) 1/2 oz. gold cap. Elusive, Charisma, Brocade, Regence, Unforgettable, Rapture, Somewhere, Topaze, Occur!, Cotillion. OSP $1.50. CMV $1. - $2. MB.

FRAGRANCES FLING COLOGNE 1968-69
(Inside Right) 1/2 oz. gold cap. Came in Charisma, Brocade, Regence, Occur!, Unforgettable, Rapture, Somewhere, Topaze, Cotillion, Here's My Heart, To A Wild Rose, Wishing, Persian Wood. OSP $4. CMV $2. - $4. MB.

1/2 OZ. COLOGNE 1953-55
(Left) 1/2 oz. size with white cap & painted label. Came in Cupids Bow, Fragrance Tie Ins, Fragrance Rainbow & Special Date Set only. Came in Forever Spring, Cotillion, Quaintance & To A Wild Rose, Bright Night. CMV $10. each mint.

REFRESHING HOURS COLOGNE 1962-63
(Right) 2 1/2 oz. gold cap, front side of bottle is flat, trimmed in gold. Came in Somewhere, Topaze, Cotillion, Here's My Heart, Persian Wood, To A Wild Rose Cologne. Came in Refreshing Hours Set only. CMV $8. mint.

COLOGNE RIVIERA 1968
(Left) 4 oz. silver cap & silver on bottle. Unscrew bottom of bottle & reverse metal to make stand for bottle. Came in Brocade & Regence. OSP $6. CMV $5. BO, $7. MB.

COLOGNE CLASSIC 1967-68
(Center) 4 oz. spiral bottle with gold cap, came in Here's My Heart, To A Wild Rose, Somewhere, Topaze, Cotillion, Unforgettable, Rapture, Occur!. OSP $3. CMV $3. BO, $5. MB.

GIFT COLOGNE 1969
(Right) 4 oz. gold cap. Came in Topaze, To A Wild Rose, Somewhere, Here's My HEart, Cotillion & Rapture. OSP $4. CMV $3. BO, $5. MB.

COIN FAN BOTTLES 1958
1/2 oz. clear glass with turquoise caps. Box pink & gold. Came either cologne or lotion sachet, choice of To A Wild Rose, Cotillion, Nearness, Forever Spring, Bright Night, Elegante, Here's My Heart & Persian Wood. Came in Wishing Coin Set only. CMV $3. BO each, $8. MB.

1/2 OZ. GEMS IN CRYSTAL COLOGNES 1957 ONLY
1/2 oz. bottle in 2 different shapes. Both came with pointed & flat top plastic caps. Each came in To A Wild Rose, Cotillion, Bright Night, Nearness. Each has matching tops and labels. All came in Gems in Crystal Set only. CMV $15. flat top, $18. pointed cap.

COLOGNE PETITE 1976-79
(Left) 1/2 oz. Came in Charisma, Moonwind, Topaze, Here's My Heart, Unforgettable, Sweet Honesty, Cotillion, Occur!, Persian Wood, Regence, Rapture and Brocade. Gold cap. SSP 99c. CMV 50c.

ULTRA COLOGNE 1977-78
(Center and right) .33 oz. Came in Unspoken, Emprise, Ariane, Timeless, Candid. Came with silver or gold caps. SSP $1.50. CMV 50c MB.

COLOGNE 1/2 OZ. 1977-78
.5 oz. Came in Field Flowers, Honeysuckle, Hawaiian White Ginger, Apple Blossom, Raining Violets, Roses Roses, Lily of the Valley. Different fragrances came with different colored caps. OSP $2. CMV $1. each, $1.50 MB.

COLOGNE SILK 1966-70
3 oz. frosted glass bottle, gold cap, colored neck labels. Came in Here's My Heart, To A Wild Rose, Somewhere, Topaze, Cotillion, Unforgettable, Rapture, Occur!. OSP $3.50. CMV $2. BO, $3. MB.

BUD VASE COLOGNE 1968-69
4 oz. gold neck trim, colored paper label in Here's My Heart, To A Wild Rose, Somewhere, Topaze, Cotillion, Unforgettable, Rapture, Occur!. OSP $4. CMV $2. BO, $3. MB.

MINUETTE COLOGNE 1970-71
5 oz. clear glass cologne bottle with gold cap. Came in Bird of Paradise, Elusive, Charisma, Brocade, Regence, Unforgettable, Rapture, Occur!, Somewhere, Topaze, To A Wild Rose, Cotillion, and Here's My Heart. OSP $1.50. **CMV $2. BO, $3. MB.**

COLOGNE 1/2 OZ. 1966
Has embossed leaves in glass, gold cap. Came in Unforgettable, Rapture, Occur!, Somewhere, Topaze, Cotillion, Here's My Heart, To A Wild Rose or Wishing. Came in red and gold box in Renaissance Trio only. **CMV $5. MB, $3. BO.**

SILKEN SCENTS COLOGNE 1980-82
1.7 oz. clear glass. Sold with Silken Scents Scarf Set. **CMV $1. MB.**

CLASSIC FRAGRANCE NOTE 1983
.5 oz. clear glass, black cap. Cologne in choice of Moonwind, Charisma, Topaze, Occur!, Sweet Honesty, Wild Jasmine, Willow, Tea Garden or Amber Mist. SSP $1.80. **CMV $1. MB.**

1/2 OZ. HEART SHAPED COLOGNE 1964-66
Left is gold band on plastic cap. Came in Unforgettable, Rapture, Occur!, Cotillion, Somewhere, Topaze, Here's My Heart, Persian Wood, To A Wild Rose, and Wishing. OSP $1.25. **CMV $5. MB, $3. BO.**
HEART SHAPED EAU DE COLOGNE (Foreign)
(Right) No gold band around plastic cap. **CMV $8.**

ULTRA COLOGNE .33 OZ. 1978-79
.33 oz. clear glass. Came in gold & silver caps in Timeless, Ariane, Tempo, Candid, Emprise, Unspoken. Each comes with different color bands on caps & different boxes. SSP $1.50. **CMV $1. MB.**

ANNIVERSARY COLOGNE PETITE 1979
(Left) .5 oz. clear glass, gold cap, special box. Comes in Regence, Persian Wood, Rapture or Brocade. SSP $1.25. **CMV $1. MB.**
COLOGNE CLASSIQUE 1979-80
(Center) .5 oz. clear glass, gold cap. Comes 11 fragrances. SSP $1.25. **CMV $1. MB.**
PURSE CONCENTRE 1979-80
(Right) .33 oz. octagonal shaped bottle. Different color stripe on cap for 9 different fragrances. SSP $1.50. **CMV $1. MB.**

ULTRA FRAGRANCE JEWELS 1982
(Left) .33 oz. clear glass jewel shaped bottle, gold cap. SSP $3. **CMV $1. MB.**
VINTAGE FRAGRANCE COLLECTION COLOGNE 1982
(Center) Pineapple shaped bottle, gold cap. Red & green box. Choice of .5 oz. cologne in Cotillion, Here's My Heart, Regence, Persian Wood, Brocade or Rapture. SSP $2. **CMV $1. MB.**
COUNTRY CHRISTMAS COLOGNE 1982
(Right) .33 oz. clear glass. Choice of Foxfire, Odyssey, Timeless, Tasha, Candid, Ariane. In Christmas box, came in set only. **CMV $1. MB.**

CRYSTAL DROP COLOGNE 1980
(Left) Red Xmas box, .5 oz. clear glass, gold top. Choice of Moonwind, Charisma, Topaze, Occur!, Sweet Honesty, Zany, Sportif or Country Breeze. SSP $1.10. **CMV $1. MB.**
ULTRA COLOGNE .33 OZ. 1980-81
(Right) .33 oz. clear glass, gold or silver caps. Choice of Tempo, Candid, Timeless, Ariane, Emprise, Unspoken, Tasha & Foxfire. SSP $2. **CMV $1. MB.**

SNOW FLAKE COLOGNE 1957-58
1/8 oz. round white caps. Came in Beauty Dust only in Cotillion, Forever Spring, To A Wild Rose, Nearness, Elegante, & Bright Night. No labels on bottles. **CMV $9. each.** Flat top bottle came in all Beauty Dust at Christmas 1963. **CMV $8. each.**

FRAGRANCE FACETS 1973
.5 oz. gold cap. Came in Brocade & all fragrances. OSP $1.50. **CMV $1.50 MB.**

COLOGNE MIST, SPRAYS - MISC.

All Cologne mist & Sprays 1975 or newer have little collector value. If they are not pictured in this book, we suggest you do not collect them. No new cologne mist or sprays will be added & all others 1975 or newer have been dropped from this book.

COLOGNE & COLOGNE MIST SPECIAL ISSUE BOXES
Each was sold with choice of fragrance on a short selling period.
COLOGNE 1968
(Left) **CMV $2. box.**
COLOGNE 1969
(Inside Left) **CMV $2. box.**
COLOGNE MIST 1974
(Inside Right) **CMV $1. box.**
COLOGNE MIST 1971
(Right) **CMV $1. box.**
Continued on next page

COLOGNE GEMS 1966-69
1 oz. clear glass with flat plastic top. Came in Cotillion, Rapture, Unforgettable, Somewhere, Occur!, Topaze, Here's My Heart & To A Wild Rose. OSP $1.75. **CMV $2. BO, $4. MB.**

COLOGNE STICK 1952-56
Turquoise plastic cologne stick came in Golden Promise, Cotillion, Quaintance, Forever Spring & To A Wild Rose. 1956 only Nearness & Bright Night came in white plastic of same design. OSP $1.50. **CMV each $10.**

COLOGNE STICK 1956-58
White plastic with colored caps. Came in Nearness, Bright Night, OSP $1.50; Cotillion, Quaintance, To A Wild Rose, Forever Spring, OSP $1.25. Came in blue, white & gold pape ornament at Christmas only. **CMV in ornament $20., stick only $6.**

COLOGNE STICK 1956-58
White plastic with colored cap. Gold, white & red paper ornament package. Christmas only in 1957-58. Came in Nearness, Elegante, Bright Night, To A Wild Rose, Forever Spring, Cotillion. OSP $1.25. **CMV stick only $6., MB $20.**

ULTRA SHIMMER COLOGNE DECANTER 1981
(Left) .75 oz. octagonal shape clear glass, gold cap. Choice of Timeless, Foxfire, Tasha, Odyssey. In gold box dated 1981. SSP $4. **CMV $1. MB.**
CLASSIC MINIATURE COLOGNE 1981-82
(Inside Left) Small .33 oz. clear glass, gold cap. Choice of Tasha, Foxfire, Odyssey, Candid, Timeless, Unspoken, Ariane, Emprise. In gold box dates 1981. SSP $1.30. **CMV $1. MB.**
FLUTED PETITE COLOGNE 1981-82
(Inside Right) .5 oz. clear glass, gold cap, 4" tall. Choice of Moonwind, Topaze, Charisma, Occur!, Sweet Honesty, Zany or Country Breeze. SSP $1.25. **CMV $1. MB.**
CHRISTMAS CHARMER COLOGNE 1981
(Right) .33 oz. clear glass, red cap. Came with Country Charmer Candlestick. Zany or Charisma. **CMV $1. BO.**

COLOGNE STICKS CHRISTMAS PACKAGING 1953-54
(Left) Green & red on white cardboard, pink ribbon on top. **CMV $20. MB.**
COLOGNE STICK CHRISTMAS PACKAGING 1952 ONLY
(Right) Red & white candy striped cardboard, red ribbon top. **CMV $20. MB.**

CRYSTAL GLORY 1962-64
(Left) Does not say Spray Essence on cap. Plastic gold top & base. 1 oz. refillable bottle. Came in Topaze, Somewhere, Cotillion, Here's My Heart, Persian Wood, To A Wild Rose. OSP $4.50 - $5. **CMV $4. BO, $6. MB.**

CRYSTAL GLORY SPRAY ESSENCE 1962-64
Gold top & base. Same fragrances as above. OSP $4.50 - $5. **CMV $4. BO, $6. MB.**

SILVER TOP CRYSTAL GLORY SPRAY ESSENCE 1962
Metal on top & base is silver instead of gold. Rare. Same fragrances as above. OSP $4.50 - $5. **CMV $20.**

CRYSTAL GLORY REFILL 1962-64
(Right) 1 oz. spray bottle fits inside Crystal Glory bottle. Came in all fragrances above. OSP $2. **CMV $2. MB.**

COLOGNE MIST 1969-70
(Left) 2 oz. gold cap, frosted glass. Came in Charisma, Brocade, Elusive & Regence. OSP $4.25. **CMV $1.**

SPRAY ESSENCE 1969-71
(Right) 1 1/4 oz. gold cap, ribbed glass. Came in Charisma, Brocade, Regence. OSP $4.50. **CMV $1.**

COLOGNE MIST SPECIAL ISSUE BOXES
Each came in choice of fragrance & was sold for a short period.
COLOGNE MIST 1975
(Left)
COLOGNE MIST 1975
(Inside Left)
COLOGNE MIST 1976
(Inside Right)
ULTRA COLOGNE SPRAY 1978
(Right)
Add $1. to CMV of each bottle for each box shown.

SPRAY ESSENCE 1959-66
(Left) 1 oz. black plastic coated, gold & blue lid. Came in Cotillion, To A Wild Rose, Bright Night, Nearness. OSP $3. Persian Wood, Here's My Heart. OSP $3.25. Somewhere 1962-66. OSP $3.50. Rapture, Occur! 1965-66. OSP $4. **CMV $2. BO, $5. MB.**

ESSENCE DE FLEURS 1957-59
(Right) 1 oz. black plastic coated, gold & blue lid. Came in Nearness, Elegante, To A Wild Rose, Cotillion, Bright Night & Forever Spring. OSP $3. **CMV $4. BO, $7. MB.**

COLOGNE MIST 1968-72
(Left) 2 oz. gold cap, gold & white band. Came in Here's My Heart, Topaze, To A Wild Rose, Somewhere, Cotillion, Occur!, Roses Roses & Unforgettable. OSP $2.50. **CMV $1.**

COLOGNE MIST 1963-66
(Right) Embossed bottles with gold plastic caps, came with black & gold paper label and green & gold cloth type label and green & white paper label. Held 2 oz. of Occur!, Somewhere, Topaze, Cotillion, Persian Wood, Here's My Heart & To A Wild Rose. OSP $2.50. **CMV $3. each MB, $2. BO.**

CHRISTMAS BOX 1965
Special issue box used by Avon at Xmas 1965 for several different products. **Add $4. to value of product for this short issue box.**

COLOGNE MIST 1966-68
(Left) 2 oz. gold cap with 4A design on cap. Came in Here's My Heart, To A Wild Rose, Somewhere, Topaze, Cotillion, Unforgettable, Rapture, Occur!. OSP $3. **CMV $1. BO, $2. MB each.**

SPRAY ESSENCE 1966-67
(Right) 1 1/4 oz. palstic coated glass with gold cap. Came in Here's My Heart, To A Wild Rose, Wishing, Somewhere, Topaze, Cotillion, Rapture, Unforgettable, Occur! OSP $3. **CMV $1. BO, $2. MB.**

SPRAY ESSENCE 1967-70
1 1/4 oz. All had gold caps. Eight different fragrances with 8 different colored bands around neck. Unforgettable, Rapture, Occur!. OSP $4. Somewhere, Topaze, Cotillion. OSP $3.75. Here's My Heart, To A Wild Rose. OSP $3.50. **CMV $2. BO, $3. MB.**

PURSE SPRAY ESSENCE 1970-76
(Left) 1/4 oz. glass bottle with gold cap in Elusive, Charisma, Brocade, Regence, Unforgettable, Rapture, Occur!, Somewhere, Topaze, Cotillion, Bird of Paradise & Hana Gasa. OSP $3.50. **CMV $1. MB.**
COLOGNE MIST 1971-75
(Right) 2 oz. silver top. Came in Bird of Paradise, Hana Gasa, Elusive, Charisma, Brocade & Regence. OSP $4.25. **CMV $1.**

DECORATOR COLOGNE MIST 1972
4 oz. plastic coated bottle in color to match fragrance. Long gold cap with top matching fragrance color. Came in Moonwind (deep blue), Charisma (crimson red), Bird of Paradise (pale blue) & Field Flowers (spring green). SSP $5. **CMV $2. BO, $3. MB.**

CREAM SACHET CHRISTMAS BOX 1958
Special issue box came with choice of cream sachet in To A Wild Rose, Cotillion, Forever Spring, Nearness, Bright Night, Elegante. OSP $1.50 each. See jar in each fragrance line and add $5. for this box.

CREAM SACHETS - MISC.

Cream sachets 1975 or newer have been dropped from this book & no new ones will be added due to little collector interest.

CREAM SACHET BOXES
Special short issue boxes came with cream sachets in several fragrances. Left to Right: 1956,1964,1958,1954. **CMV** see bottle in each fragrance line and add $5. each for these boxes.

CREAM SACHET JARS 1973-75
Clear ribbed glass jar with colored border on lid & colored flower to match fragrance. .66 oz. came in Gardenia, Violet, & Carnation. SSP $1.25. **CMV $1 each.**

CREAM SACHET DECOR 1960
Ribbed clear plastic with removable bottom sold for 50c at Xmas with purchase of cream sachet in Bright Night, Nearness, Cotillion, To A Wild Rose, Persian, Wood & Here's My Heart. **CMV $8.** holder only $12. MB.

CREAM SACHET 1958
.3 oz. white glass jar. Turquoise flower lid. Came in 1958 Wishing Trio set., Pink & gold box. **CMV $5.** jar only - $10. MB

CREAM SACHET CHRISTMAS BOX 1957
Special issue at Christmas. Pink & white, came in choice of Cotillion, Forever Spring, Bright Night, To A Wild Rose, Elegante cream sachet. OSP $1.50. See bottle in each fragrance line and add $6. for this box.

CREAM SACHET 1957
(Left) White jar with green, yellow or pink lid. Came in Cotillion, To A Wild Rose, Bright Night & Nearness. Came in Rainbow Set. **CMV $8.**
CREAM SACHET PETITES 1956
(Right) Plastic cream sachet came in Cotillion, Bright Night, Nearness, To A Wild Rose. Came in Cream Sachet Petites Sets only. 4 different colors. **CMV $10. each MB**

MAGNOLIA CREAM SACHET 1974-76
(Left) .66oz. clear embossed glass with white lid and pink & yellow on flower. OSP $1.25 **CMV $1.**
MAGNOLIA DEMI STICK 1974-77
(Inside Left) .19 oz. white with floral colored center. OSP $1.25. **CMV $1.**
HYACINTH DEMI STICK 1974-77
(Right) .19 oz. white with pink flowers. OSP $1.25. **CMV $1.**

SENTIMENTS CREAM SACHET 1969
1/2 oz. clear glass jar, gold lid, 4A design on lid. Came in Scentiments Set only in Unforgettable, Rapture, Occur!, Somewhere, Topaze or Cotillion. **CMV $4. BO.**

POWDER SACHETS, - MISC

POWDER SACHET 1936-38
1 1/4 or 2 oz. ribbed glass with turquoise cap & label. Came in Ariel 1936-38, Cotillion 1937-38, Marionette 1938 only, Jardin D'Amour 1936-38 or Jardin Sachet. OSP each $1.04. All prices are mint only. **CMV $20. each BO. $25. MB**

POWDER SACHET 1939-48
1 1/4 oz. glass bottle with turquoise cap & label. Came in Jardin D'Amour 1939-40, Ariel 1939-42, Cotillion 1939-46, Garden of Love, turquoise or black cap 1940-46, Attention 1942-48, Marionette 1939-46. OSP $1.04 each. **CMV $10 each BO $15. MB**

TURN-OF-CENTURY POWDER SACHET SHAKER 1973-75
(left) 1.25oz. clear glass with solid gold cap. Came in Roses Roses, Charisma, Unforgettable. OSP $4.50. **CMV $3.50 MB - $2. BO**
POWDER SACHET SHAKER 1972-73
(right) 3 1/2" high, 1.25 oz. white glass jar with gold cap. Came in Moonwild. OSP $5.; Bird of Paradise, Unforgettable, Field Flowers. SSP $3. **CMV $3. BO - $5. MB.**

POWDER SACHET 1969-70
(Left) 1 1/2 oz. Painted red over clear glass, red neck bow with silver lid. Comes in Cotillion, Charisma, Unforgettable & To A Wild Rose. OSP $4.50. **CMV $6. in MB - $5. BO**
POWDER SACHET 1970-71
(Right) Crystal-like glass bottle holds 1 1/4 oz. of powder sachet in Elusive, Charisma, Unforgettable, & Topaze. OSP $4. **CMV $3. BO - $4. MB.**

POWDER SACHET 1944-45
1 1/4 oz. pink paper sachet boxes. Came in Attention, Garden of Love, Cotillion, Marionette. Pink plastic flower on lid. OSP $1.15 each. **CMV $15. each - $20. MB**

POWDER SACHET 1930-32
(left) Clear glass bottle with brass cap & silver & blue label. Came in Ariel and Jardin D'Amour. OSP $1.04. **CMV $60. mint.**
POWDER SACHET 1934-36
(right) 1 1/4 oz. ribbed glass bottle with dark blue cap & silver & blue label. Came in Jardin D'Amour & Ariel. OSP 78c. **CMV $28. each mint - $33. MB**

CROWN TOP POWDER SACHET 1965-66
.9 oz. frosted bottle with gold cap. Came in Perfume Pillowette Set in Rapture, Wishing, Occur, Lavender, Somewhere, Topaze, Cotillion, Here's My Heart, To A Wild Rose. **CMV $6. BO - $8. MB**

POWDER SACHET CHRISTMAS BOX 1952 only
Special issue red & green box for all powder sachets at Christmas. Came in Cotillion, Golden Promise, Quaintance & Flowertime. See bottle in each fragrance line & add $5. for this box.

POWDER SACHET CHRISTMAS BOX 1958
Special issue pink & white box came with powder sachet in choice of To A Wild Rose, Cotillion, Forever Spring, Nearness, Bright Night, Elegante. OSP $1.50 each. See jars in each fragrance line for CMV & add $5. for this box.

POWDER SACHET CHRISTMAS BOX 1963
(Left) Short issue box came in 6 fragrances at Christmas. Add $4. to CMV of bottle for this box.
POWDER SACHET CHRISTMAS BOX 1965
(Right(High top boot design box was short issue. Came in 8 fragrances. Add $4. to CMV of bottle for this box.

POWDER SACHET CHRISTMAS BOX 1956
Special issue Christmas box came with choice of 6 fragrances. Add $5. to CMV of bottle for this box.

PERFUMED TALC CHRISTMAS BOX 1958
Special issue Christmas box for perfumed talc in choice of To A Wild Rose, Cotillion, Nearness & Forever Spring. OSP 69c each. Check fragrance line for MB CMV on talc & add $5. for this box.

VALENTINE GIFT SACHET 1952
Short issue box in red & white. Came in Flowertime, Golden Promise, Cotillion & Quaintance. Cotillion came in same design, different shaped box. Add$7. CMV to price of each bottle for this box.

PERFUMED TALCS - MISC.
All Talcs 1960 or newer have little value to collectors. If it is not in this book, we suggest you don't collect it unless you know it is old.

PERFUMED TALC SPECIAL ISSUE CHRISTMAS BOXES
(Left to Right) 1966 Christmas, 1967 Christmas, 1969 Christmas, 1970 Christmas. Each came in choice of talc. Add $2. each box to CMV of the talc it holds, MB.

POWDER SACHET CHRISTMAS BOX 1957
Pyramid shaped box in pink, green, blue & white. Came in To A Wild Rose, Forever Spring, Cotillion, Nearness, Bright Night & Elegante powder sachet. Short issue - RARE. OSP $1.50 each. See bottle in each fragrance line & add $6. for this box mint.

PERFUMED TALC CHRISTMAS BOX 1959
Short issue box in choice of 6 fragrances of talcs. Add $4. CMV for this box to price of talc, MB.

FLORAL PERFUMED TALC 1959-60
Lavender & white can. Matching box. OSP 69c. CMV $5. CO, $7. MB.

TOILET WATERS - MISC.

TOILET WATER 1940 ONLY
(Left) 2 oz. plastic caps, blue & gold label with tulip. Came in Cotillion, Vernafleur, Lily of the Valley, White Rose, Lilac, Trailing Arbutus, Marionette, Lilac Vegetal. OSP 78c. **CMV $35. BO mint, $40. MB.**

TOILET WATER 1940-46
(Center) 2 oz. gold ribbed cap & gold label. Also came with plastic caps. Came in Cotillion, Jasmine, Marionette, Lilac, Lily of the Valley, Trailing Arbutus, Apple Blossom, Sonnet & Attention. OSP $1.04. **CMV $30. BO mint, $35. MB.**

TOILET WATER 1935-40
(Right) 2 oz. gold cap with A on top of cap. Blue & gold tulip label. CPC on back of label. Came in same as 1st toilet water on left. OSP 78c. **CMV $35. BO mint, $40. MB.**

TOILET WATER 1933-34
2 oz. ribbed bottle came in Trailing Arbutus, Vernafleur, Lily of the Valley, White Rose, Lilac Vegetal. Black or blue cap. OSP 75c. **CMV $50. BO mint, $60. MB.**

7 DRAM TULIP PERFUME 1934-39
Glass stoppered bottle, gold label with tulip. Came in Jardin D'Amour, Bolero, Cotillion, Ariel, Narcissus, Rose, Lily of the Valley, Trailing Arbutus, Gardenia, Sweet Pea, Marionette, Topaze, Courtship, Lucy Hays. OSP $2. **CMV $125. MB, $100. BO.**

PERFUMES - MISC.
All must be in new mint condition for CMV

1/4 OZ. TULIP PERFUME 1934-39
Glass stopper, gold label with tulip. Came in Lucy Hays, Topaze, Jardin D'Amour, Bolero, Cotillion, Ariel, Narcissus, Rose, Lily of the Valley, Trailing Arbutus, Gardenia, Sweet Pea, Marionette, Courtship. OSP $1.04. **CMV $75. BO, $90. MB.**

GIFT ATOMIZER PERFUME 1931-34
1 oz. red glass bottle with screw on metal top & white squeeze bulb. Came in Atomizer Set No. 6 only. Does not say Avon or CPC. Also comes in green glass. **CMV $85.**

7 DRAM TULIP PERFUME 1934-39
Glass stopper, gold label with tulip. Came in Lucy Hays, Topaze, Jardin D'Amour, Bolero, Cotillion, Ariel, Narcissus, Rose, Lily of the Valley, Trailing Arbutus, Gardenia, Sweet Pea, Marionette, Courtship. OSP $2.60. **CMV $125. MB, $100. mint.**

1/8 OZ. PERFUME OR 1 DRAM 1946-50
Gold box, gold label. Some have metal gold caps. Came in Crimson Carnation, Lily of the Valley, Gardenia, Cotillion, Golden Promise, Garden of Love, Ballad, Quaintance, Flowertime. OSP $1. **CMV $20., Crimson Carnation $30. Add $5. each MB.** Also came in Gold Box set of 1947-49.

1/8 OZ. PERFUME 1940-42
(Left) 1 dram or 1/8 oz. gold cap & label. Came in Cotillion, ballad, Gardenia, Garden of Love, Apple Blossom, Marionette, Trailing Arbutus, Lily of the Valley, Sweet Pea. **CMV $25. BO mint, $35. MB.**

1/8 OZ. PERFUME 1940-44
(Right) Gold metal or plastic caps & gold label. Came in Garden of Love, Gardenia, Marionette, Sweet Pea, Lily of the Valley, Trailing Arbutus, Ballad, Courtship, Apple Blossom, Cotillion. OSP 75c. **CMV $25. BO mint, $30. MB**

RIBBED PERFUME 1933-36

(Left) 1/2 oz. ribbed glass bottle with black octagonal cap & gold label. Came in Gold Box set in Bolero, 391, Gardenia, Ariel, Vernafleur. **CMV $45. mint.**

PERFUMES 1933-36

(Right) Small six sided bottles with silver label & black caps. Came in Ariel, Bolero, Gardenia, Trailing Arbutus, 391, Vernafleur. Came in Little Folks set & Handkerchief set. **CMV $45. mint.**

FLORAL PERFUMES 1944-45

3 dram gold cap & labels. Came in yellow feather design box in Ttrailing Arbutus, Cotillion, Gardenia, Sweet Pea, Lily of the Valley, Marionette. 2 different boxes. OSP $1.65. **CMV $60. BO mint with tag, $90. MB.**

2 DRAM TULIP PERFUME 1934-39

1/4 oz. or 2 drams, gold cap & label with tulip. CPC on back of label & Avon on bottom of bottle. Came with 2 different labels as shown. Came in Jardin D'Amour, Bolero, Cotillion, Ariel, Narcissus, Rose, Lily of the Valley, Trailing Arbutus, Gardenia, Sweet Pea, Marionette, Courtship, Lucy Hays, Topaze. OSP 78c. **CMV $65. MB, $55. BO mint.**

VALENTINE'S DAY PERFUME 1941

1/8 oz. clear glass bottle with gold cap with Ballad perfume. Box red & white. Came in several fragrances. **CMV $75. MB.**

BOUQUET PERFUMES 1940-44

3 dram, glass stopper, box is gold base & orange lid. Came in Garden of Love, Apple Blossom, Marionette, Courtship, Cotillion. Gold neck tag. OSP $2.50 each. **CMV $100. BO mint, $135. MB.**

PERFUME 1946-50

(Left) 1/8 oz. clear glass, gold cap, painted label. Available in Crimson Carnation, Lily of the Valley, Gardenia, Cotillion, Golden Promise, Garden of Love, Ballad, Quaintance, Flowertime. OSP $1. **CMV $20. BO, $25. MB.**

5/8 DRAM PERFUME 1954 ONLY

(Right) Came in 1954 House of Charms set only. Blue caps, pink, blue & white label. Came in Cotillion, Quaintance, To A Wild Rose, Golden Promise, Lily of the Valley. Rare. **CMV $22. each.**

PERFUME 1937-46

1/8 oz. bottle on right has flower on label with 3 branches on each side. Came in sets only in Gardenia, Cotillion, Narcissus, Trailing Arbutus, Sweet Pea. **CMV $15. each.** White, blue, red, green or yellow plastic caps. 2 dram size or 1/4 oz. on left came in 1939-40 Gold Box sets & Little Folks sets in same fragrances and caps. **CMV $25. each.**

FLORAL PERFUMES 1946-47

Blue & white box holds 3 dram bottle with plastic cap. Came in Crimson Carnation, Gardenia, Lily of the Valley. OSP $3.75. **CMV $75. MB, $50. BO. Crimson Carnation, CMV $100. MB, $60. BO.**

ONE DRAM GIFT PERFUME 1958
1 oz. smooth clear glass bottle, cap either smooth or embossed. Box is blue, white & gold. Choice of Elegante, Nearness, Bright night, Forever Spring, To A Wild Rose or Cotillion. OSP $2. **CMV $20. MB as shown, $5. BO.**

1/8 OZ. PERFUME 1946-53
(Left) Flower on label, plastic cap. Came in Trailing Arbutus, Cotillion, Crimson Carnation, Quaintance, Lily of the Valley, Sweet Pea. Came in Fair Lady, Your Charms & Hair Ribbons sets. **CMV each $15. Crimson Carnation & Sweet Pea, CMV $25. mint.** Same label came out on 5/8 dram size "smaller bottle" but has no size on label. **Same CMV.**

1/8 OZ. PERFUMES 1941-45
(Right) 1/8 oz. 2 different flat gold caps & also plastic caps. White paper label. Came in Courtship, Sweet Pea, Lily of the Valley, Trailing Arbutus, Marionette, American Ideal, Apple Blossom, Cotillion, Ballad, Gardenia, Garden of Love. OSP $1. **CMV $30. mint BO, $40. MB.**

FLORAL PERFUMES 1944 ONLY
3 dram gold cap & label. Came in yellow feather design box in Trailing Arbutus, Gardenia, Sweet pea, Lily of the Valley, Cotillion. OSP $2.50. **CMV $90. MB, BO $60. mint.**

FLORAL PEFUME 1940-42
3/8 oz. gold cap & label in gold speckled box. Came in Sweet pea, Gardenia, Trailing Arbutus, Lily of the Valley. OSP $1.50. **CMV $50. BO mint, $80. MB.**

PERFUMES 1950
5/8 dram each. Quaintance, Cotillion, Golden Promise, Luscious. Green, blue, pink & yellow caps. Came in Avon Blossoms set. **CMV $12. each mint.**

PERFUMES FOR SIZE COMPARISON ONLY
(Left to Right) 2 dram or 1/4 oz., 1/8 oz. or 1 dram, 5/8 dram, 5/8 dram.

PERFUMES 5/8 DRAM 1951-53
Bottle with pink, yellow, green or blue caps came in Cotillion, Quaintance, Forever Spring, Golden Promise, Luscious, Lily of the Valley. Came in 1952-53 House of Charm, 1951 Always Sweet Set & Sweet As Honey Beehive Set. **CMV $12. each, mint.**

1/8 OZ. PERFUME 1946 ONLY
(Left) 1/8 oz. plastic cap. Came in Gardenia, Cotillion, Garden of Love, Lily of the Valley, Trailing Arbutus, Sweet Pea. OSP 75c. **CMV $25. BO, $30. MB each mint.**

1/8 OZ. PERFUME 1941-46
(Right) 1/8 oz. size, white paper label, gold metal caps & plastic caps. Came in Gardenia, Sweet Pea, Courtship, Apple Blossom, Cotillion, Trailing Arbutus, Lily of the Valley, Garden of Love, Marionette. OSP 75c. **CMV $25. BO, $30. MB.**

391 PERFUME 1931-33
(Left) Silver & blue box holds 1 oz. glass stopper. Blue ribbon on neck. OSP $2.60. **CMV $125. BO, $150. MB.**

391 PERFUME FLACONETTE 1931-33
(Center) Small embossed bottle with glass stopper with long dabber. Brass cap with 391 on it. OSP $1.30. **CMV $85. BO, $95. MB.**

391 PERFUME 1933-36
(Right) 1/2 oz. ribbed glass bottle with black octagonal cap. Came in Gold Box set. **CMV $45. mint.**

BOUQUET PERFUMES 1945-47
Blue, pink & white box holds 3 dram glass stoppered bottle with gold neck tag. Came in Cotillion, Courtship, Garden of Love. OSP $3. CMV $125. MB, $100. BO.

1 OZ. HEART PERFUME 1963-71
Gold box, 4A insignia on glass stopper. Gold neck tag. Came in Unforgettable & Occur!, Somewhere, Topaze, Cotillion, Here's My Heart, Persian Wood, Rapture, To A Wild Rose. OSP $17.50. CMV $25. BO, $45. MB.

PERFUMES "1 DRAM" 1955-59
Clear smooth glass, gold scroll cap with felt like wrapper. Nearness, gray; Bright Night, black; Elegante, maroon; To A Wild Rose, pink; Forever Spring, green; Cotillion, gold. Simulated grain leather, Luscious, 1st issue 1950 tan; Here's My Heart, blue. OSP $2.25. CMV $10. each in wrapper mint, $5. BO, $12. MB.

BOUQUET PERFUMES 1944 ONLY
Blue & pink box holds 3 dram perfume, glass stopper. Came in Marionette, Cotillion, Garden of Love. Gold neck tags. OSP $3. CMV $140. MB, $100. BO with tag.

ROCKER PERFUME 1959-63
White box holds 1 oz. bottle with flat glass stopper with 4A on top. Gold cord criscrossed bottle with white tag label. Came in Here's My Heart, Persian Wood, To A Wild Rose, Bright Night, Nearness. OSP $15. Cotillion, OSP $20. CMV BO with tag $25.

PERFUME 1953-54
Green and pink fold out box holds 1 dram ribbed glass bottle with gold scroll cap. Came in To A Wild Rose, Cotillion, Forever Spring, Quaintance, Golden Promise, Luscious, Ballad. OSP $1.75. CMV $25. MB as shown.

CHRISTMAS PERFUME 1955
1 dram, gold cap in red, white, blue and gold Christmas box. Came in To A Wild Rose, Cotillion, Forever Spring, Golden Promise, Luscious and Quaintance. OSP $1.75. CMV $25. MB.

VALENTINE PERFUMES 1953
1 dram perfume came in To A Wild Rose, Forever Spring. OSP $1.75. Cotillion, Golden Promise, Quaintance, OSP $1.50. CMV $25. MB as shown.

PERFUMES "1 DRAM" 1950-55
Ribbed bottles with gold caps came in Cotillion, Quaintance, Ballad, Golden Promise, Gardenia, Lily of the Valley, Forever Spring and To A Wild Rose. OSP $1.50. CMV $12. MB, $8. BO.

WITH LOVE PERFUMES 1951-52
(Left) Pink heart box opens to 1 dram ribbed bottle and cap in Lily of the Valley, To A Wild Rose, Luscious, Quaintance, Golden Promise, Cotillion, Ballad, Flowertime, Gardenia. OSP $1.75. CMV $25. MB as shown.

CHRISTMAS BELL PERFUME 1951
(Right) Gold bell box holds 1 dram, ribbed bottle and cap in Forever Spring, To A Wild Rose, Luscious, Cotillion, Flowertime, Quaintance, Golden Promise, Ballad, Gardenia and Lily of the Valley. OSP $1.60. CMV $25. MB as shown.

PERFUME HALF OUNCE 1971
1/2 oz. bottle with clear plastic top in a pink and gold box. Came in Somewhere, Topaze, Cotillion, Unforgettable, Rapture, Occur!, Regence, Brocade, Charisma, Elusive. OSP $12. CMV $16. MB, as shown, $6. BO.

ONE DRAM PERFUME GOLD BOX 1964-65
(Center) 4A embossed gold box. Ribbed bottle, gold cap. Came in Somewhere, Topaze, Cotillion, Here's My Heart, Persian Wood, Occur!, To A Wild Rose, Wishing, Rapture and Unforgettable. On left, same bottle sold in regular issue box. 1962-66. OSP $2.25. CMV $6. MB in gold box. 1965 Christmas special issue box on right. CMV $7. MB, CMV regular issue box $2. BO, $3. MB.

TOP STYLE CHRISTMAS PERFUME 1959-60
Sold only at Christmas time in box shown. Came in all regular fragrances of Top Style perfume. OSP $2.50. CMV $15. MB in this box only.

PERFUME FLACON 1966-67
(Left) 1 dram, gold ribbed cap, ribbed glass. Came in Here's My Heart, Wishing, To A Wild Rose, Somewhere, Topaze, Cotillion, Unforgettable, Regence, Rapture, Occur!. OSP $2.50. CMV $2. BO, $4. MB.
TOP STYLE PERFUME 1959-62
(Right) Shown with general issue box. 1 dram size, gold cap. Came in Topaze, Persian Wood, Here's My Heart, To A Wild Rose, Cotillion, Bright Night and Nearness. OSP $2.50. CMV $3. BO, $5. MB.

GOLDEN GIFT PERFUME 1961
Blue, gold and green box holds 1 dram top style perfume. Came in Cotillion, To A Wild Rose, Nearness, Bright Night, Somewhere, Here's My Heart, Persian Wood, Topaze. OSP $2.25. CMV $13. MB.

PERFUME ROLLETTES 1965-69
.33 oz. glass bottles available in Somewhere, Topaze, Cotillion, Here's My Heart, To A Wild Rose, Wishing, Regence, Occur!, Rapture, Unforgettable, Brocade and Persian Wood. Issued in carnival glass or clear ribbed glass. OSP $1.75. CMV clear, $2. MB, $1. BO; CMV carnival $4. BO, MB $6. Box pictured is 1966 Christmas box. Add $2. extra for this box.

PERFUME CREME ROLLETTE 1963-65
4A embossed bottles with gold caps. Came in Here's My Heart, Persian Wood, To A Wild Rose, Cotillion, Somewhere, Topaze and Wishing, Occur! and Rapture. OSP $2.50. CMV $3. MB, rollette only $2. mint.

1/2 OZ. PERFUME 1969-72
(Left) Pink box holds jewel like clear glass bottle 4" high. Comes in Elusive, Charisma, Brocade, Regence, Unforgettable, Rapture, Occur!, Somewhere, Topaze, Cotillion. OSP $12.50. CMV $13. MB, $6. BO.
PERFUME 1966-69
(Right) 1/2 oz. gold cap, metal leaves around base. White and gold box. Came in Unforgettable, Rapture, Occur!, Somewhere, Topaze, Cotillion, Here's My Heart, To A Wild Rose, Wishing. OSP $10. CMV $18. MB, $10. BO.

PERFUME "1 DRAM" 1951-53
Vertical ribbed bottle and ribbed gold cap with scroll on cap. Came in Cotillion, Golden Promise, Quaintance, To A Wild Rose, Forever Spring. OSP $1.75. CMV $8. MB, $5. BO mint.

PERFUME OILS

PERFUME PENDANT 1972-75
Gold with 2 simulated half pearls, 32" chain.
Came in Sonnet or Moonwind perfume. OSP
$10. **CMV $10. MB, Pendant only $5.**

PERFUME OIL 1969-73
(Left) 1/2 oz. gold caps. Came in Elusive,
Rapture, Hana Gasa, Charisma, Brocade,
Moonwind, Regence, and Bird of Paradise,
Unforgettable and Occur!. OSP $5. **CMV $2.,
$3. MB.**
BULLET PERFUME OIL 1965
(Right) 5/8 dram, gold top. Came in Wishing,
Somewhere, Occur!, Rapture, To A Wild Rose,
Topaze, Unforgettable, Here's My Heart,
Cotillion. Came in Fragrance Ornaments Set
only. **CMV $8. with holder, $4. BO.**

**PERFUME OIL PETITES (PIN CUSHION)
1966**
5/8 dram, clear bottle, gold cap and label.
Came in Pin Cushion Set only. Came in
Somewhere, Wishing, Occur!, Rapture,
Topaze, To A Wild Rose, Here's My Heart,
Unforgettable, Cotillion. **CMV $5. each mint.**

JEWEL PERFUME OIL 1964-65
(Left) 5/8 dram, gold cap. Perfume Oil came
in Jewel Collection only. Came in Cotillion,
Topaze, Persian Wood, Here's My Heart, To A
Wild Rose. **CMV $6. each mint.**
FOREIGN JEWEL EAU DE COLOGNE
(Right) 1/2 oz. gold cap. **CMV $20.**

**GOLDEN MOMENTS PENDANT PERFUME
1971-72**
Antiqued brass pendant on 32" gold chain.
Holds 1/8 oz. perfume in Moonwind, OSP $15.
Bird of Paradise, Elusive, Charisma, OSP $14.
**CMV pendant on chain only $10. mint, $16.
MB.**
PERFUME PENDANT 1970
Gold pendant with ruby teardrop, holds 1 dram
liquid perfume. Comes in Charisma, Elusive,
Brocade and Regence. OSP $14. **CMV $15.
MB, $10. pendant only mint.**

**SCENTIMENT PERFUME ROLLETTE 1973-
74**
(Left) .33 oz. white base with blue bird and
pink flowers, gold trim and cap. Holds
Moonwind, Patchwork, Sonnet. SSP $2.50.
CMV $3. BO, $4. MB.
**SCENTIMENT PURSE SPRAY ESSENCE
1974**
(Right) .25 oz. blue plastic coated bottom,
white and pink bird design on paper label with
gold cap. Came in Field Flowers, Bird of
Paradise or Charisma. SSP $3. **CMV $4. BO,
$6. MB.**

AVON BOTTLES -
MISC., ETC.

HEART STRINGS PERFUME FLACON 1986
.18 oz. gold cap. OSP $4. **CMV $2. MB.**
ULTRA PERFUME 1984
Gold box holds .6 oz. perfume, glass stopper.
OSP $4. **CMV $2. MB.**

LIQUID POWDER 1930-36
4 oz. ribbed glass bottle with dark blue cap,
silver and blue label. OSP $1. **CMV $40. MB,
$35. BO.**
LOTUS CREAM 1930
4 oz. ribbed glass. OSP 75c. Rare with
flowered label. **CMV $50. BO, $60. MB.**

Misc. Avon Bottles are very high production items and most collectors are no longer interested in them unless they are very old, "1950s or older". We have removed all plastic bottles and most bottles back to the 50s or newer from this book. They have little or no value to most collectors. The Skin So Soft section has been dropped. Sets from this section will be found in sets of the 1960s, soaps in Soap Section for women. Some SSS glass bottles are in this section. All plastic SSS bottles have been dropped from this book because of no value to collectors.

ANTISEPTIC MOUTHWASH 1955-59
(Left) 7 oz. white cap. Label says antiseptic only. OSP 59c. CMV $7. BO, $10. MB.
ANTISEPTIC MOUTHWASH 1959-68
(Right) 7 oz. white cap. OSp 59c. CMV $6. MB, $5. BO.

HAIR TONIC EAU DE QUININE FOR OILY HAIR 1931-36
1 pint size. Silver metal cap. (For dry hair, same price and date). OSP $1.75. CMV $45. MB, $40. BO.
HAIR TONIC EAU DE QUININE 1931-36
6 oz. ribbed glass bottle with dark blue cap with silver and blue label. Came in Tonic for Dry Hair and for Oily Hair. OSP 90c. CMV $40. MB, $35. BO.

ANTISEPTIC 1932-36
(Left) Metal cap, green label. 6 oz. size. OSP 36c. CMV $35. MB, $30. BO. Also came in 12 oz. size with same label. OSP 62c. CMV $40. MB, $35. BO.
ANTISEPTIC 1936-40
(Right) 6 oz. metal cap. Turquoise box and label. OSP 36c. CMV $35. MB, $30. mint BO.

ANTISEPTIC 1940-50
6 oz. clear glass bottle with turquoise cap. Early issue had metal cap. Also came in 12 oz. size. OSP 62c, OSP 36c. CMV 6 oz. size $12. BO. OSP MB., 12 oz. size, $16. BO, $20. MB. Add $5. for CPC label.
ANTISEPTIC ONLY 1946
6 oz. round bottle, black cap. 2 different labels. Rare. OSP 39c. CMV $45. MB, $40. BO.

ASTRINGENT 1936-54
2 oz. and 4 oz. size with turquoise caps. OSP 78c. CMV MB $15. BO $12.50 each mint. Add $5. for CPC label.

ASTRINGENT 1930-36
Came in 2 and 4 oz. size as pictured on right for size comparison. Both are ribbed glass bottles with dark blue caps and silver and blue labels. OSP 75c for 4 oz., 40c for 2 oz. CMV $40. MB, $35. BO. mint each size.

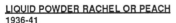

LIQUID POWDER RACHEL OR PEACH 1936-41
4 oz. green cap, clear glass. OSP $1.04. CMV $20. MB, $15. BO. Add $5. for CPC label on box.

COCONUT OIL SHAMPOO 1951-55
6 oz. bottle with turquoise cap and label. OSP 59c. CMV $17. MB, $12. BO.

PRE-SHAMPOO OIL 1936-38
2 oz. bottle with turquoise cap and label. OSP 52c. CMV $22. MB, $18. BO. Add $5. for CPC label on bottle in box.

SKIN FESHENER 1954-65
4 oz. bottle with green cap and label. OSP 89c. CMV $1. each. 1965 bottle has For Dry Skin and For Normal Skin added to label. CMV $1. BO, $2. MB.

ASTRINGENT 1954-65
4 oz. bottle with green cap & label. OSP 89c. CMV $2. MB, $1. BO.

ASTRINGENT FRESHENER FOR OILY SKIN 1965
Same 4 oz. bottle as 1954-65 Astringent only name is changed. OSP $1.25. CMV $1. BO, $2. MB.

SKIN FRESHENER 1954-58
2 oz. bottle with turquoise cap and label. Came in Beautiful You Set, A Thing of Beauty Set, For Your Beauty Set and Happy Traveler Set with white cap. CMV $1.

BRILLIANTINE 1931-36
2 oz. ribbed glass bottle with dark blue cap and silver and blue label. OSP 52c. CMV $45. MB, $40. BO.

COCONUT OIL SHAMPOO 1951-55
1 pint bottle with black pouring or flat black cap. OSP $1.19. CMV $22.50 BO, $27.50 MB.

LIQUID COCONUT OIL SHAMPOO 1956-57
1 pint with green label and double pouring cap. OSP $1.59. CMV $18. BO, $22. MB.

SKIN FRESHENER 1930-36
2 or 4 oz. ribbed glass, blue or black cap. OSP 75c. 2 oz. size came in sets only. CMV $40. BO, $45. MB each.

LOTUS CREAM 1936-44
4 oz. clear glass, green cap. OSP 52c. CMV $17. MB, $12. BO. Add $5. for CPC label on bottle in box. Came with 2 different labels and 2 different boxes.

SKIN FESHENER 1955
Rare 2 oz. glass bottle with embossed flowers around neck. Turquoise cap. Came in 1955 Happy Traveler Set only. CMV $12. mint.

LOTUS CREAM 1930-36
(Left) 4 oz. ribbed glass bottle, blue cap. OSP 75c. CMV $40. MB, $35. BO.

BATH SALTS 1929-30
10 oz. bottle with metal lid, silver & blue label. Ribbed glass sides. OSP 75c - **CMV $60 BO, $75. MB.**

BATH SALTS SAMPLE 1933-37
Ribbed glass bottle with blue cap. Came in Ariel, Vernafleur. **CMV $60.** Pine and Jasmine **CMV $55. each.**

BATH SALTS 1936
8 1/2 9 oz. glass jars with turquoise lids from 1936-44, small paper label. 9 oz. jars from 1943-53 came in Ariel, 1936-44, Pine 1936-44 then 46-53, Vernafleur 1936-44, Attention 1936-44, and Jasmine 1936-44 then 46-48. See Attention Fragrance for regular issue box. OSP .63c **CMV $20. BO $30. MB.**

BATH SALTS 1954-57
8 oz. bottle with turquoise cap and label. Came in Jasmine and Pine. OSP 89c each. **CMV $15. MB, $10. BO.**

BATH SALTS 1931-33
(Right) 10 oz. ribbed glass bottle with blue lid, silver label. 2 different labels. OSP 75c, **CMV $60. MB, $40. BO.**
BATH SALTS 1933-37
(Left) 8 1/2 oz. ribbed glass jar with dark blue cap. Came in Ariel & Vernafleur from 1933-37, Pine & Jasmine from 1935-37. OSP 63c each, **CMV $60. MB, $40. BO.**

BATH SALTS 1943-45
5 oz. and white paper containers Came in Attention, Jasmine, Pine, and Vernafleur. OSP 69c each. **CMV $25. each mint, $30. MB.**

CREME HAIR RINSE 1953-55
6 oz. clear glass bottle with green cap and label. OSP 89c, **CMV $4. MB $2. BO**
CREME LOTION SHAMPOO 1954-56
6 oz. bottle with turquoise cap, painted label. 1956 label has 4A design. OSP $1., **CMV $4. MB, $2. BO.**

CREME LOTION SHAMPOO 1956 only
6 oz. clear glass, green cap. OSP $1., **CMV $3. MB, $2 BO.**
LIQUID COCONUT OIL SHAMPOO 1956-57
6 oz. clear bottle with green cap, painted label. OSP 79c, **CMV $3. MB, $2. BO.**
CREME HAIR RINSE 1956
6 oz. bottle with white cap and painted label with 4A design. OSP 89c, **CMV $3 MB, $2. BO.**

SKIN FRESHENER 1936-54
(Left to Right) 2 and 4 oz. bottles. Both 4 oz. bottles in center have 2 different labels. Turquoise caps. OSP 78c, **CMV $10. MB, $5. BO.**

LIQUID SHAMPOO 1937-50
6 oz. turquoise cap. Indented top of bottle. OSP 59c. MCV $20. MB, $15. BO. Add $5. for CPC label on bottle in box.

WITCH HAZEL 1923
16 oz. bottle with cork stopper. OSP $1.20. CMV $75. BO, $100. MB.

LIQUID SHAMPOO 1943-45
6 oz. round shoulder bottle, black cap. This bottle is rare with round shoulders. OSP 50c. CMV $30. BO, $35. MB.

SOAPLESS SHAMPOO 1946-49
6 oz. turquoise cap. OSP 59c. CMV $20. BO, $25. MB. Also came in 16 oz. round size with same label. 1946-49. OSP $1.19. CMV $20. BO, $25. MB.

PRE-SHAMPOO OIL 1931-36
2 oz. ribbed glass bottle with dark blue cap, silver and blue label. OSp 52c. CMV $40. MB, $35. BO.

BRILLIANTINE 1936-54
2 oz. green cap and label, 3 different labels. OSp 59c. CMV $20. MB, $15. BO. Add $5. for CPC label.

LIQUID SHAMPOO 1930-36
(Left) 1 pint size, metal cap. OSP $1.02. CMV $35. BO, $40. MB.

LIQUID SHAMPOO 1931-36
(Right) 6 oz. ribbed glass bottle with dark blue cap and silver and blue label. OSP 75c. CMV $40. MB, $35.. BO.

LIQUID SHAMPOO 1937-50
1 pint size with raised pouring or flat metal or black cap. OSp $1.19. CMV $20. BO, $25. MB. 1937-39 has CPC label $30.

SKIN SO SOFT 1966-67
(Left) 1 oz. gold cap with painted leaf. Came in set of three only. Unforgettable, Rapture, Occur!, Somewhere, Topaze, Cotillion, Here's My Heart, To A Wild Rose, Wishing. CMV $3. MB, $2. BO.

SKIN SO SOFT 1969
(Center) 1 oz. gold cap & paper label. Came in Unforgetttable, Rapture, Occur!, Somewhere, Topaze, Cotillion, To A Wild Rose & Here's My Heart. OSp $1.50. CMV $4. MB, $3. BO.

SKIN SO SOFT SCENTED BATH OIL 1969-70
(Right) 2 oz. clear glass bottom, clear plastic top. This top is the same as the clear Just II. Came in Charisma, Brocade, Rapture, Unforgettable, Occur!, Here's My Heart, Cotillion, To A Wild Rose & Regence. OSP $2.50. CMV $4. MB, $3. BO.

ROSE WATER, GLYCERINE & BENZOIN 1926
(Left) 4 oz. ribbed bottle with cork stopper, front and neck label. OSP 50c. CMV $60. BO, $75. MB. See CPC bottles for different label.

ROSE WATER, GLYCERINE & BENZOIN 1930-36
(Right) 4 oz. ribbed glass bottle, blue cap. OSp 75c. CMV $40. BO, $45. MB. Regular issue box in center. Add $5. for 1935 special issue Christmas box shown on right.

NAIL CLIPPER 1960s
Avon on nail clippers. We have no information on this. Rare. CMV $5.5

WAVE SET 1936-44
4 oz. bottle with turquoise cap and label. OSP 52c. CMV $20. MB, $15. BO. Add $5. for CPC label on bottle in box.

FOUNDATION LOTION 1950-51
2 oz. bottle with turquoise cap. OSP 59c, Formerly called Finishing Lotion. CMV $20. MB, $15. BO.

LEG MAKE-UP 1943-49
4 oz. clear glass with turquoise cap on left. 2 different bottles as shown. OSP 69c. CMV $20. MB, $15. Bo each.

DEODORANT 1931-36
2 oz. ribbed glass bottle with silver label and dark blue cap. OSP 50c. CMV $40. MB, $35. BO.

BATH OILS - MISC. 1965
Came in Bath Bouquet Set only. 2 oz., gold cap and label. Came in Rapture, Occurl, Somewhere, Topaze, Cotillion, Here's My Heart, To A Wild Rose and Wishing. CMV $3 each.

FINISHING LOTION 1938-50
2 oz. clear glass bottle 52c. CMV $17. MB, $12. BO. Add $5. for CPC label on bottle in box.

ROSE WATER, GLYCERINE & BENZOIN 1936-44
4 oz. bottle with turquoise cap. OSP 52c. CMV $17. MB, $12. BO. Add $5 for CPC label on bottle in box.

WITCH HAZEL 1936-48
4 oz. green cap and label. Also came with black cap. OSP 37c. CMV $15. BO, $20. MB. Add $5 for CPC label on bottle in box. (Also came in 8 and 16 oz. size).

DEODORANT 1936-48
(Left) 2 oz. turquoise cap and label. OSP 52.c. CMV $20. MB, $14. BO. Add $5. for CPC label on bottle in box. 1946-48 came with black applicator with sponge end. CMV $25. MB, $20. BO.

LIQUID DEODORANT 1944-45
(right) 2 oz. turquoise cap with applicator. OSP 59c. CMV $20. BO, $25. MB.

WAVE SET 1930-36
4 oz. ribbed glass bottle with dark blue cap, and silver and blue label. OSP 52c. CMV $40. MB, $35. MB.

WITCH HAZEL 1930-36
4 oz ribbed glass bottle with dark blue plastic cap, green label. OSP 50c. CMV $45. MB, $40. BO. Also came in 8 and 16 oz. size.

STICK DEODORANT 1961-62
1 3/4 oz. white cap, green glass jar with painted label. OSP 89c. **CMV $5., $7. MB.**
STICK DEODORANT 1956-61
Green cap and label on clear glass jar, 2 different caps. Older has 4A design on top and newer one has "New" spelled on lid. OSP 79c. **CMV $6., $7. MB each.**

TOILET WATER, CREAM, LOTION & BUBBLE BATH 1945
All are 2 oz size, frosted glass and pink caps. Came in 1945 Young Hearts Set. **CMV $20. each.** Toilet Water is in Cotillion fragrance.

NAIL POLISH 1936-37
Clear glass with turquoise cap. CPC label. OSP 37c. **CMV $15. BO - $20. MB.**

DOUBLE DARE NAIL POLISH 1946-47
1 oz. black cap, red paper label. OSP 43c. **CMV $8. BO, $10. MB.**

CUTICLE SOFTENER 1936-39
1.2 oz. bottle with turquoise cap. CPC on label. **CMV $15. BO, $20. MB.**
OILY POLISH REMOVER 1955-62
2 oz. white cap and label. OSP 49c. **CMV $4.**

NAIL POLISH 1931-36
Ribbed glass bottle with black octaginal cap. Gray and blue box. OSP 50c. **CMV $30. MB.**
POLISH REMOVER & CUTICLE SOFTENER 1931-36
Both 1/2 oz. ribbed glass, black 8 sided caps. Silver labels. OSP 50c. **CMV $25. each BO, $30. MB.**

OILY POLISH REMOVER 1946-50
2 oz. bottle with turquoise cap. OSP 43c. **CMV $15. MB, $10. BO.**
OILY POLISH REMOVER 1950-53
2 oz. white cap. OSP 49c. **CMV $6. BO, $10. MB.**

NAIL POLISH 1950-54
1/2 oz. bottle with white cap and gold line through label. Came in nail polish, cuticle softener, cling-tite, oily polish remover, clear nail polish and double coat. OSP 39c. to 49c. **CMV $1. each.**

NAIL POLISH 1954-58
With 4A design on label, came in long last nail polish, cuticle softener, silvery base, top coat, oily polish remover. OSP 39c. to 59c. **CMV $1. each.**

NAIL POLISH 1938-50
1/2 oz. and 1/4 oz bottle came in polish remover, cream polish, cuticle softener, cuticle oil, oily polish remover, nail polish base and top coat. 1946-50 same bottles and labels with black caps. Also came in double coat, nail polish and cling-tite. OSP 29c. to 43c. **CMV $1. BO, $3. MB.**

HAND LOTION 1943-50
4 oz. clear glass, turquoise cap. OSP 59c. **CMV $7. MB, $3. BO.**

FASHION FILM 1954-58
(Left) 1 oz. white cap. OSP 95c. **CMV $4. BO.**
FASHION FILM 1951-54
(Center) 1 oz. white cap. OSP 75c. **CMV $5. BO.**
FASHION FILM 1958-61
(Right) 1 oz. pink cap. OSP $1.10. **CMV $4. BO. Add $1. each for each box.**

CREAM LOTION 1951
2 oz. bottle with blue cap. Came in 1951 Always Sweet Set. **CMV $18.**
CREAM LOTION 1950-51
2 oz. clear glass with turquoise cap, label has red, yellow and blue streamers. Came in 1951 Always Sweet Set and 1950 Jolly Surprise. **CMV $12.**

BUBBLE BATH 1948-51
4 oz. bottle with blue cap. Round blue and pink box with top of bottle sticking through lid. OSP $1.29. **CMV $25. MB, $15. BO.**
BUBBLE BATH 1951-58
Same bottle as above in a square box of same design. OSP $1.29. **CMV $20. MB, $15. BO.**

INSECT REPELLENT 1959-65
2 oz. bottle with red and white caps. OSP 59c. **CMV $5. MB, $3. BO.**

BUBBLE BATH 1944-48
Blue and white box with pink ribbon holds 8 oz. bottle with blue cap and label. OSP $2.25. **CMV $45. MB, $35. BO mint.**

BEAUTIFUL JOURNEY BOTTLES 1957
1 oz. clear glass bottles came in Beautiful Journey Set only. Pink caps. Came in hand lotion, skin freshener, deep clean, deodorant and Cotillion cologne. **CMV $5. each.**

CREAM LOTION 1942-49
6 oz. pink cap, back side of bottle is flat. Flowered box shown sold in 1942 only. OSP 79c. **CMV $30. MB, $20. BO.**

LIQUID TWIN-TONE 1944-45
2 oz. bottles. OSP 89c. **CMV $15. BO, $20. MB.**
EYE AND THROAT OIL 1967
1 oz. gold cap. Issued during glass strike in 1967 only. Short issue. OSP $2.50. **CMV $3. BO, $4. MB.**

LIQUID ROUGE 1954-59
(Right) 1/8 oz. gold embossed cap. OSP 69c. **CMV $7. MB, $5. BO.**
LIQUID ROUGE 1959-66
(Left) 1/4 oz. smooth brass cap, 2 different labels. OSP 89c. **CMV $4. MB, $3. BO.**

CREAM LOTION BOX 1942-43
Box shown sold 1942-43 only. 6 oz. flat sided bottle with pink cap sold 1942-49. OSP 49c, as pictured. **CMV $30. MB as shown, $20. BO mint.**

SUN CREAM 1943-48
4 oz. clear glass, turquoise cap. OSP 85c.
CMV $10. MB, $5. BO.

POLISH REMOVER 1936-40
(Left) Has Good Housekeeping seal on turquoise and gold label. Black cap. OSP 50c.
CMV $15. BO, $20. MB.
POLISH REMOVER 1936-39
(Right) 1/2 oz. bottle, turquoise cap. CPC on label. OSP 31c. **CMV $15. BO, $20. MB.**

SUN LOTIN 1954
2 oz. bottle, white cap. Came in camping kit set only. **CMV $22.**
SUN FOAM 1955-57
Peach colored can and cap. OSP $1.35. **CMV $5. MB, $3. CO.**
HAND LOTION 1954-58
4 oz. green cap and label. OSP 59c. **CMV $1. BO, $2. MB.**

HAND LOTION & PUMP 1963-64
8 oz. gold stripes on bottle, gold and white pump. Also came without gold neck band. OSP $2.50. **CMV $3. MB, $1. BO.**
LOTION LOVELY 1964-65
8 oz. gold painted label. Came in Wishing, Here's My Heart, Persian Wood, To A Wild Rose. OSP $3. Somewhere, Topaze, Cotillion. OSP $3.50. Occur!, Rapture. OSP $4. **CMV $3. MB, $1. BO.**

SUN LOTION 1949-58
4 oz. bottle with white cap. Montreal label to 1954. **CMV $11.** Pasadena label 1954-58. OSP $1. **CMV $10. BO, $12. MB.**

HAND LOTION 1950 ONLY
4 oz. clear glass, turquoise cap and label. OSP 59c. **CMV $7. BO, $10. MB.**
HAND LOTION 1950
4 oz. pink cap. Same bottle as Cotillion of that period. This was a substitute bottle. Rare. OSp 59c. **CMV $10. MB, $7. BO.**

HAND LOTION 1948
(Left) 2 oz. glass bottle with blue cap. Came in 1948 Hair Ribbons Set. **CMV $5.**
HAND LOTION ROSE WATER, GLYCERINE & BENZOIN LOTION 1942 ONLY
(Right) 6 oz. flat sided bottle. Came in sets only. **CMV $20. mint.**

HAND LOTION 1951-54
4 oz. pink or white plastic cap, blue and pink label. OSP 59c. **CMV $10. MB, $5. BO.**

COLOR PERFECT HAIR COLOR 1971-72
2 oz. brown glass with white cap. **CMV $1.50.**
HAIR COLOR COLORANT 1969
2 oz. brown glass with white cap. has 4A on cap. **CMV $3.**
EAU DE COOL 1972-75
6 oz. light blue glass, silver cap. OSP $5. **CMV $1.**

PROPER BALANCE VITAMINS 1979-81
3 different bottles, 60 and 100 size. Proper balance for the whole family. Womens Vitality, Dieters Support. **CMV $5. each MB.**

VITAMINS SAMPLES 1979-81
3 different vitamins on sample cards. **CMV $1. each.**

ULTRA SHEER LIQUID FOUNDATION 1966-67
1 oz. gold top, embossed bottle. OSP $2.25. **CMV $1.**
ULTRA SHEER NATURAL VEIL 1968-74
1 oz. embossed bottle, same as Liquid Foundation only named changed. OSP $2.25. **CMV 50c.**
EYE & THROAT OIL 1965-72
1 oz. gold cap, painted label. OSP $2.50. **CMV $1.**

VITAMIN SAMPLE DEMO 1979-81
CMV $10. MB.

VITA MIGHTS FOR KIDS 1980-81
Vitamins for kids, bottle of 100 tablets. **CMV $7. MB.**

SKIN SO SOFT 1970
(Left) Clear glass container holds 2 oz. Skin-So-Soft, gold cap. Comes in Bird of Paradise, Elusive, Charisma, Brocade, Unforgettable, Field Flowers, Occur!, Rapture & To A Wild Rose. OSp $2.50. **CMV $2.**
SKIN SO SOFT "2 OZ." 1971-72
(Right) 2 oz. 7 layer glass bottle with gold cap. 4 1/2" high. Came in Bird of Paradise, Elusive, Charisma, Brocade, To A Wild Rose. OSP $2.50. **CMV $2. BO, $3. MB.**

DEW KISS DECANTER 1973
(Left) 4 oz. clear glass with gold cap. SSP $3. **CMV $1.**
DEW KISS DECANTER 1974
(Center) 4 oz. clear glass with gold cap. SSP $2.50. **CMV $1.**
DEW KISS 1960-66
(Right) 1 1/2 oz. pink lid, gold string with pink and gold tag, with 4A design. OSP $1.25. **CMV $2. MB, $1. BO.**

BEAUTY DUST, POWDERS, TALC - MISC.

All Powders past 1975 are not pictured and have little or no value to collectors.

DUSTING POWDER 1945-48
6 oz. blue and white cardboard with ladies face on lid. Also contained Apple Blossom Beauty Dust. OSP $1.35. **CMV $25.**
DUSTING POWDER 1936-49
13 oz. turquoise and beige can with "A" on top. 1st (1936-39) issue has CPC on bottom. **CMV $30.** 1940-49 Avon Products label only. OSP $1.39. **CMV $20., $25. MB.** There are at least 3 different varieties of the 1936-49 metal dusting powder. One has a deeply indented bottom, shining silver, with CPC on it, another has a slightly indented dull silver bottom, no CPC on it.

DUSTING POWDER 1930-34
(Left) 8 oz. blue and silver square can. OSP $1.35. **CMV $40. MB, $30. CO mint.** Gold can, blue letters came in sets only. **CMV $50. mint.**
DUSTING POWDER 1926-29
(Right) Gold metal can with black stripes. Came in Daphne, Vernafleur, Trailing Arbutus, California Rose, Baby Powder and Super Rite Talcum. OSP $1. **CMV $50. MB, $40. CO.**

BEAUTY DUST CHRISTMAS BOX 1944
Special issue Christmas box. Holds feather design paper container of beauty dust. OSP $1.10. **CMV $27. MB as shown, beauty dust only mint, $22.**

DUSTING POWDER 1943-46
13 oz. paper box, turquoise and ivory. OSP $1.39. **CMV $35. MB, $30. BO mint.**

BEAUTY DUST REFILL 1965
White outer box holds colorful inner box with plain beauty dust refill. Came in choice of Persian Wood, Cotillion, To A Wild Rose, Somewhere, Topaze, Occurl, Here's My Heart, and Rapture. OSP $2.98. **CMV $7. as shown MB.**

DUSTING POWDER 1935-36
13 oz. metal gold colored can. Came in Bath Ensemble Set only. **CMV $35. mint.**
DUSTING POWDER 1935-36
Same as gold can only general issue was silver and blue can. OSP $1.20. **CMV $30. CO mint, $40. MB.**

DUSTING POWDER CHRISTMAS BOX 1940-41
Special issue blue and white Christmas box holds regular issue metal can of dusting powder. OSP $1. **CMV $35. MB as shown.**

FACE POWDER 1930-36
Silver and blue paper box came in Ariel and Vernafleur. OSP 78c. **CMV $16. MB, $12. CO mint.**

DUSTING POWDER CHRISTMAS BOX 1943
Outer box special issue for Christmas. Holds square cardboard beauty dust. **CMV $50. MB as shown.**

DUSTING POWDER 1943-44
Turquoise and white paper box. OSP $1.39. **CMV $35., $40. MB.**

(Left to Right)
BEAUTY DUST 1942-48
6 oz. blue feather design cardboard. Came in Avon Beauty Dust and Apple Blossom. OSP $1.19. **CMV $22., $25. MB.**
FACE POWDER 1942-48
1 3/4 oz. blue feather design cardboard. OSP 89c. **CMV $8. mint, $12. MB.**
HEAVENLIGHT FACE POWDER 1946--48
2 1/2 oz. same feather design paper box. OSP 89c. **CMV $8., $12. MB.**
ROUGE 1942-49
Blue feather design, paper container on right. OSP 55c. **CMV $5., $7. MB.**
FEATHER DESIGN LIPSTICK 1942-46
Blue plastic top and bottom with cardboard sides. Also came with red plastic top and bottom. OSP 59c. **CMV $5., $8. MB.**

DUSTING POWDER REFILL 1930-36
Gray box holds plain paper wrapped box of powder. OSP 59c. **CMV $25. MB.**

DUSTING POWDER MOTHERS DAY BOX 1941
Special issue lavender box with white lace holds regular issue dusting powder. Sold during Mothers Day. OSP $1. **CMV $35. MB as shown.**

DUSTING POWDER REFILL 1936-49
Round cardboard container. Came in Jasmine or Avon dusting powder. OSP 89c. **CMV $15. MB. Add $5. for CPC label.**

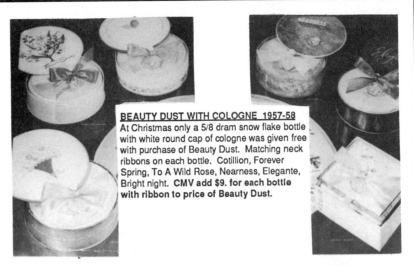

BEAUTY DUST WITH COLOGNE 1957-58
At Christmas only a 5/8 dram snow flake bottle with white round cap of cologne was given free with purchase of Beauty Dust. Matching neck ribbons on each bottle. Cotillion, Forever Spring, To A Wild Rose, Nearness, Elegante, Bright night. **CMV add $9. for each bottle with ribbon to price of Beauty Dust.**

BEAUTY DUST DEMO 1966-68
White box, came in choice of beauty dust refill and different fragrance empty container. Both came boxed. Used by Reps C10, 1966. **CMV $11. MB.**

BEAUTY DUST WITH COLOGNE 1956
At Christmas only a 5/8 dram bottle with white falt cap and neck ribbon came in Beauty Dust. Elegante with red ribbon, nearness, lavender ribbon, Cotillion, and To A Wild Rose, pink ribbons, Forever Spring, purple ribbon, Quaintance, blue ribbon. Each ribbon has gold edge. **Add $12. to each Beauty Dust if bottle has ribbon.**

FACE POWDER 1936-39
3" diameter, turquoise and cream container, cardboard. Came in Cotillion, Ariel or Vernafleur fragrance. Choice of natural, rose, peach, Rachel No. 1, Rachel No. 2, orchre, orchre-rose and suntan shades. OSP 78c. **CMV $10. MB, $6. CO.**

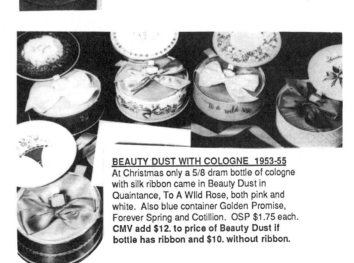

BEAUTY DUST WITH COLOGNE 1953-55
At Christmas only a 5/8 dram bottle of cologne with silk ribbon came in Beauty Dust in Quaintance, To A Wild Rose, both pink and white. Also blue container Golden Promise, Forever Spring and Cotillion. OSP $1.75 each. **CMV add $12. to price of Beauty Dust if bottle has ribbon and $10. without ribbon.**

SHEER MIST FACE POWDER 1955-57
Turquoise cardboard with white and pink flowers and gold 4A design on lid. OSP $1.10. **CMV $4., $5. MB.**

SHEER MIST FACE POWDER 1958-59
2 1/2 oz. white cardboard box with pink rose on lid and pink rim around edge. OSp $1.10. **CMV $1. BO, $3. MB.**
FACE POWDER 1960-63
Same design as Sheer Mist only has plastic lid, no pink rim. OSP $1.25. **CMV $1., $1.50. MB.**
FASHION FINISH FACE POWDER 1963-67
1 1/2 oz. white plastic box. OSP $2.25. **CMV 50c.**

ELITE FOOT POWDER 1943-46
Maroon and cream colored paper box. 2.75 oz. Black screw off octagonal cap. OSP 43c. **CMV $25. mint.**
ELITE FOOT POWDER 1943-46
2.75 oz maroon and white victory paper box. Flat punch out top with paper lift off lid. OSP 43c. **CMV $25. mint.**

ELITE POWDER 1943-46
Turquoise and white paper boxes in family size. OSP $1.19. **CMV $30.** Regular size OSP 43c. **CMV $20.** Three different caps, plastic cap, punch out top and punch out top with paper top and bottom cover. **Same CMV.**

ELITE POWDER 1931-36
Silver and blue can with blue cap is general issue in regular size on right. OSP 37c. **CMV $25.** Family size 1 ln. can on left. OSP $1.04. **CMV $30. Add $5. MB.**
ELITE POWDER 1934-35
Same design and shape cans. Came in sets only in gold and blue cans. **CMV small size $35. Large family size $35. Add $5. each MB.**

TOOTH POWDER 1936-49
Box holds 2 1/4 oz. turquoise and white can. Silver slide open cap. OSP 49c. **CMV $10., $15. MB.**

ELITE POWDER 1936-48
Large family size on left, turquoise and white can. OSP $1.19. **CMV $25., $30. MB.**
ELITE POWDER 1936-54
2.9 oz. or 3 oz. size on right, turquoise and white can, 2 different boxes. OSP 43c. **CMV $10. CO, $12. MB. Add $3. for CPC label.**

SMOKERS TOOTH POWDER 1932-36
Green cap OSP 51c. **CMV $35. MB, $25. CO.**

HEAVENLIGHT FACE POWDER 1944
General issue feather design paper box. Shown in 1944 pink design box. 2 1/2 oz. contents. Powder only sold in 1944-48. **CMV $12. MB as shown. Powder box only $8.**

TALCUM POWDER 1930-32
Silver and blue can came in regular and family size. OSP 50c. **CMV $35., $40. MB.** 1 lb. family size OSP $1. **CMV $35., $45. MB.**

SMOKERS TOOTH POWDER SAMPLES
(Left) 1936-40 small 1/4 oz. turquoise and white can. CPC label, turquoise sifter cap. **CMV $35. mint.**
(Right) 1940-49 Same can only has chrome lift off cap. **CMV $30. mint.**
(Center) Same can, has small chrome cap. **CMV $30.**

TOOTH POWDER 1930-36
(Left) Green metal can. OSP 35c. **CMV $30. MB, $25. CO mint.**
TOOTH POWDER 1936-50
(Right) Turquoise and white metal can, silver cap. OSP 36c. **CMV $14. MB, $10. CO.**

SMOKER'S TOOTH POWDER 1944-46
Turquoise and white paper container. Plastic cap. OSP 57c. **CMV $23. mint.**

(Left to Right)
SMOKERS TOOTH POWDER 1936-49
Metal cap, 3 1/2 oz. turquoise and white can. OSP 36c. **CMV $16., $18. MB.**
SMOKERS TOOTH POWDER 1950-54
3 1/2 oz. turquoise and white can, turquoise tilt cap. OSP 57c. **CMV $14., $16. MB.**
SMOKERS TOOTH POWDER 1946-50
3 1/2 oz. turquoise and white can, turquoise plastic cap. OSP 57c. **CMV $14., $16. MB.**

AMMONIATED TOOTH POWDER 1949 ONLY
3 oz. turquoise can and tilt cap. This can with this style cap was a very short issue. OSP 49c. **CMV $15. MB, $13. CO mint.**

TOOTH POWDER 1943-46
Flat metal top, paper side container. 3 oz. size. Turquoise and white. OSP 39c. **CMV $25. MB, $20. CO mint.**

ELITE POWDER 1943-46
2.75 oz. or 3 oz. paper box. OSP 43c. **CMV $18. mint.**
TOOTH POWDER 1943-46
3 oz. paper box. OSP 39c. **CMV $20. mint.**
SMOKERS TOOTH POWDER 1943-46
3 1/2 oz. paper box with metal top and bottom. OSP 59c. **CMV $20. mint.** All are turquoise and white.

AMMONIATED TOOTH POWDER 1949-55
3 oz. turquoise and white can with turquoise lid. OSP 49c. **CMV $10. $13. MB.**

AQUA DENT 1958-66
7 oz. green color can with white cap. OSP
79c. CMV $1., $2. MB.

TALC FOR MEN 1936-49
Maroon and cream colored can with maroon
cap. OSP 37c. CMV $15. MB, $12. CO.
SMOKERS TOOTH POWDER 1938-49
Maroon and cream colored can. Came in
Men's Sets only. CMV $16. mint.

BEAUTY DUST 1960-61
3 oz. white plastic bottle, has paper label or
painted label, turquoise cap. This came in
Modern Simplicity Set only. Came in Cotillion,
To A Wild Rose and Here's My Heart. CMV
$5.

**SMOKERS TOOTH POWDER "PAPER"
1943-46**
(Left) Maroon and cream paper sides, tin top
and bottom. OSP 36c. CMV $20. mint, $25.
MB.
TALC FOR MEN "PAPER" 1943-46
(Right) Maroon and cream paper container.
metal screw on cap in black or maroon. OSP
37c. CMV $20. mint.

ANTISEPTIC POWDER 1956-62
(Left) 3 oz. gray and white can, red cap. OSP
59c. CMV $2.
ANTISEPTIC POWDER 1962-64
(Right) 3 oz. gray and white can, red cap.
OSP 69c. CMV $1.50.
ANTISEPTIC POWDER 1965-68
Same as 1962-64 can only 2 3/4 oz. size.
OSP 69c. CMV $1.

**POWDER PUFF COMPACT REFILLS 1960-
70s**
2 different puffs and package for compacts.
CMV $3. each mint.

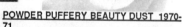

**POWDER PUFFERY BEAUTY DUST 1970-
71**
5 oz. white plastic base with pink puff in
Charisma, Brocade, Cotillion and To A Wild
Rose. OSP $5. CMV $3. MB.

POWDER PAK PUFFS REFILL 1940s
Envelope holds 2 compact puff refills. CMV
$5. mint.
POWDER PUFF REFILLS 1960s
Envelope holds 2 puff refills. CMV $3.

SACHET PILLOWS 1963
Green and white holder contains powder
sachet pillow. Came 6 to a pack. OSP 50c.
CMV for set of 6, $5. mint.

BATH BOUQUET TALC 1965
1 1/2 oz. green paper box. Came in Bath
Bouquet Set only in all fragrances of that set.
CMV $4. mint.

**HEAVY DUTY POWDERED HAND
CLEANSER 1973-76**
10 oz. blue, white, pink and black cardboard
with plastic top and bottom. OSP $2.25. CMV
$1.

COMPACTS & LIPSTICKS - MISC.

Compacts & Lipsticks 1975 or newer have been dropped from this book due to mass production & little collector interest. Only the very decorative items & items in the kids lines will be included in in the future.

DUSTING POWDER PUFF 1940s-50s
Envelope holds Avon puff. Rare. **CMV $10.**

TRIM TONE COSMETIC STOCKING 1940s
Beige with gold band, box turquoise. OSP $1.50. **CMV $25. MB.**

FAN COMPACT 1931-33
Silver and blue compact. OSP $2. **CMV $30. BO, $40. MB.**

MASCARA COMPACT 1933-36
Blue and silver metal compact. OSP $1.04. **CMV $30. BO, $35. MB.**

COMPACT 1930-32
Silver metal compact in single size. OSP $1.35, double size. OSP $1.85. **CMV $30. each, $40. MB.**

TRIPLE COMPACT 1931-33
Blue and silver compact. Avon on lid. OSP $1.30. **CMV $35. , $40. MB.**

SINGLE ROUGE COMPACT 1930-36
Blue and silver metal compact. OSP 52c. **CMV $20., $25. MB.**
EYE LASH CREAM 1930-33
Blue compact with mirror, same as above rouge compacts. OSP $1. **CMV $20. - $25. MB.**

DOUBLE COMPACT 1934-36
Blue and silver compact and puffs. OSP $1.75. **CMV $30. BO, $35. MB.**

DRESSING TABLE ROUGE 1930-36
Silver and blue paper box. OSP 47c. **CMV $12. BO, $16. MB.**
LIIPSTICK 1932-36
Blue and silver metal tube. OSP 52c. **CMV $20., $25. MB.**

NAIL WHITE & NAIL CUTICLE CREAM 1937-39
Both turquoise and white small metal cans. Came in Manicure Set only. **CMV $7. BO.**
COMPACT 1932-33
Octaganal shaped blue and gold. Avon lid shown closed and open. Came in 1932-33 Vanity Set only. **CMV $30. BO.**

NAIL WHITE & NAIL CREME 1931-36
Both small silver and blue or gold and blue cans. Came in Manicure Sets only. **CMV $8. BO.**

209

COMPACT REFILLS 1931-36
Avon on small and large size, blue and silver puff and refill cake. Came in gray box. **CMV $4. each.**

CREME ROUGE COMPACT 1930-36
Blue metal compact as above. OSP 75c. **CMV $20. , $25. MB.**

FACE POWDER SAMPLE 1936-42
Cream colored metal can. Came in Vernafleur, Ariel in 5 shades. **CMV $5. CPC label $2. MB.**

DRESSING TABLE ROUGE 1936-42
Turquoise and gold cardboard with turquoise and white box. Came in 5 shades. OSP 47c. **CMV $5., $8. MB.** Add $2. for CPC label.

POWDER ROUGE REFILL 1936-42
Turquoise and white box. Refill fits double compacts. OSP. 52c. **CMV $6. MB.**

CREME ROUGE COMPACT 1936-42
Turquoise and gold metal case. OSP 78c. **CMV $7., $9. MB.**

SINGLE ROUGE COMPACT 1936-42
Turquoise and gold metal case. OSP 52c. **CMV $7., $9. MB.**

(Left to right back row)
COMPACT DELUXE & LIPSTICK DELUXE 1960-66
Silver and gold. OSP Compact $3.50. **CMV $5., $6. MB.** OSP Lipstick $1.35. **CMV $3., $4. MB.**

ENCORE COMPACT & LIPSTICK 1971-73
Green ribbed plastic, gold 4A design on top. OSP Compact $3.50. **CMV $2.** OSP Lipstick $1.35. **CMV $1., $2. MB.**

SIMPLICITY LIPSTICK 1971-73
(Front) Pink plastic gold design. OSP $2.75. **CMV $1., $2. MB.**

MASCARA 1949-52
Gold metal case. OSP $1. **CMV $8. MB. $5. case only.**

LIPSTICK PLASTIC 1942-46
Blue feather design plastic lipstick. OSP 52c. **CMV $8. MB. lipstick only $4.**

RING FLING 1969
Plastic tube of lipstick with beaded ring to match. White top lipstick, white and black beads. Lime green top, lime green and green beads. Blue top, dark blue and light blue beads. Pink top, dark pink and light pink beads. Yellow top, red and orange beads. OSP $3.49. **CMV $6. with rings. MB.**

SWING FLING COMPACT 1969
.5 oz. dark pink with colored design. OSP $2. **CMV $2.50, $4. MB.**

ENAMEL FLING 1969
.5 oz. clear glass, white cap. OSP $1. **CMV $1., $1.50 MB.**

FESTIVE FANCY LIPSTICK & COMPACT 1968
(Top Left) Green plastic with white flowers. OSP compact $3. **CMV $2.** Lipstick OSP $1.75. **CMV $1.**

LIPSTICK A-LA-MODE 1971-72
(Top Right) White plastic, top holds glace, bottom lipstick. OSP $4.50. **CMV $1.**

FASHION LIPSTICK & COMPACT 1967-73
(Lower Left) Brown plastic with gold trim. OSP lipstick $1.35. **CMV 50c.** OSP compact $2.25. **CMV 75c.**

ENCORE COMPACT & LIPSTICK 1968-71
(Lower Right) Gray with gold trim. OSP lipstick $1.25. **CMV 75c.** OSP compact $2. **CMV $1.50.**

CAPTIVATORS COMPACT & LIPSTICK 1969
Leapord, Zebra, and tiger design plastic compacts. OSP $3.50. **CMV $4., $5. MB each.** Matching lipsticks, OSP $1.75. **CMV $2., $3. MB.**

LIP DEW 1969-78
Gold and white case. CMV 50c.
LIP MAKER 1970-71
Pink and red. CMV 50c.
QUICK COVER 1968-73
Tan and brown case. CMV 50c.
HIDE N' LITE 1970-74
White with green and gray stripes CMV 50c.
SUN SAFE STICK 1973 Only
Gold, tan and white. CMV 50c.

DELUXE LIPSTICK 1970-71
Carved ivory design. OSP $2. CMV $3., $5. MB.
LIPSTICK REFILLABLE 1965-67
Gold metal case. Held Encore Lipstick. OSP $2. CMV $3., $4. MB.
ULTRA SHEER 1966-74
White plastic. OSP $1. CMV $1., $2. MB.
FASHION LIPSTICK 1960-61
White and pink plastic. OSP 98c. CMV $2., $3. MB.
FASHION LIPSTICK 1967-72
Tortoiseshell case. OSP $1. CMV $1., $2. MB.
FASHION CASE CAMEO LIPSTICK 1964-66
White plastic with cameo on lid. OSP 98c. CMV $3., $4. MB.

MASCARA COMPACT 1936-41
Turquoise and gold. OSP $1.04. CMV $12., $15. MB.
LIPSTICK 1936-41
Turquoise and gold. OSP 52c. CMV $8. BO $10 MB.

ABOUT TOWN LIPSTICK 1974-78
Brown and gold. CMV 50c.
RING FLING LIPSTICK 1969
Plastic top, white, black, lime green, blue, pink or yellow. CMV 50c.
ULTRA SHEER LIPSTICK 1966-74
White plastic. CMV 50c.
ENCORE LIPSTICK 1972-73
Clear plastic. CMV 50c.
WINDSOR LIPSTICK 1973-78
Dark blue plastic. CMV 50c.
ENCORE LIPSTICK 1968-71
Gray and gold plastic. CMV 50c.

CHAP STICK 1943-45
Olive green metal case. Lipstick Anti Chap and Sunburn Protective Hot Climate. Avon Products, Inc., New York on label. Given to G.I.'s in World War II in first aid kit. CMV $25. BO.

1980 Lip Balms
DIPLOMA 1980
Short issue. Came in autograph hound stuffed animal. CMV 50c.
SMOOTH DAYS AHEAD 1981
1981 Calendar. SSP 69c. CMV 50c.
Candy Cane
Came in red or green. CMV 50c.

MAKE A FACE POMETTES 1982
Came in set only. Orange, blue & black. CMV $1 each.

CHAP CHECK 1956-59
(Left) Small white plastic tube, red cap. OSP 25c. CMV $3. BO.
CHAP CHECK 1960-73
(Center) Is same color as above only longer tube. OSP 39c. CMV $1.
CHAP CHECK 1951-55
(Right) Small turquoise and white plastic tube. 1/10 oz. size. OSP 25c. CMV $4. BO.

SUNNY LIP GLEAMER 1973-74
Clear pink top, white plastic tube. CMV 50c.
COLOR MAGIC 1973-74
White case with colorful butterfly. CMV 50c.
LOOKING PRETTY MIRRORED LIPSTICK 1973-75
Green plastic. CMV 50c.
POP TOP LIPSTICK 1973-73
Turquoise plastic, gold design. CMV 50c.
POP TOP LIPSTICK 1973-75
Brown plastic, gold design. CMV 50c.

COLOR CREME MOISTURE LIPSTICK 1981-82
Blue and silver, clear plastic cap. CMV 50c.
BAZOOKA LIP BALM 1982
Red, white, and blue. Red cap. CMV 50c.
JELLY BEAN LIP BALM 1982
Red cap, Jelly bean design. CMV 50c.

FLOWER PRINT COMPACT & LIPSTICK 1967
4 compacts with matching lipsticks. Designs are Sunflower, Daisy, Poppy, and Carnation. Compacts OSP $2.50. **CMV $3., $5. MB.** Lipsticks OSP $1.50. **CMV $2., $3. MB.** Also came in flower print nail polish. See Misc. Bottles.

JEWELED LIPSTICK 1954
Gold Christmas box holds gold lipstick with jewel on top. OSP $1.75. **CMV $15. MB.**
JEWELED LIPSTICK 1954-56
Gold lipstick with white jewel on top. OSP $1.75. **CMV lipstick only $5., $8. MB.**

EMPRESS LIPSTICK 1970-71
Green, blue and gold lipstick. OSP $3. **CMV $2., $3. MB.**
EMPRESS COMPACT 1970-71
Green, blue and gold compact. OSP $7.50. **CMV $4., $5. MB.**

JEWELED LIPSTICK 1968-69
Gold lipstick with simulated diamond. OSP $6. **CMV $5., $6. MB.**
JEWELED COMPACT 1968-69
Gold powder compact with simulated diamonds. OSP $10. **CMV $12. MB.** Compact only $8.50.

COMPACT & LIPSTICK DELUXE 1967-69
Gold compacts. OSP $5.50 each. **CMV $6., $8. MB.** Gold lipstick OSP $2. **CMV $3., $5. MB.**

SLICK TINT FOR LIPS 1983-84
Rose & silver color. SSP $1.50. **CMV 50c.**
SANTA CLAUS LIP BALM 1983
Red, white, blue. SSP $1. **CMV $1.**

PETIT POINT LIPSTICK 1970
Black, pink and green floral lipstick and box. **CMV $3. MB.**
ABOUT TOWN TRIAL OFFER LIPSTICK 1979
Box came with Candid lipstick. Made in Spain on label. OSP 79c. **CMV $1. MB.**

(Left to Right)
SMOOTH DAYS AHEAD LIP BALM 1979-80
White, blue and red calendar on side **CMV 50c.**
FESTIVE FANCY DEMI LIPSTICK 1968
Green and gold matching box. **CMV $1., $1.50 MB.**
LIPSTICK 1960's
Black and white. **CMV $1., $2. MB.**
TOP STYLE LIPSTICK 1958-61
Brass. **CMV $4., $5. MB.**

(Left to Right)
DELUXE LIPSTICK 1948-58
Gold metal case. OSP 95c. **CMV $3., $5. MB.**
FASHION LIPSTICK 1962-63
Black metal case. OSP 89c. **CMV $3., $4. MB.**
ENCORE LIPSTICK 1967-68
Gold and white plastic. OSP $1. **CMV $1.50. MB.**
GADABOUTS 1968-69
Black and white or yellow and white plastic. OSP 99c. **CMV $1.50 each MB.**
FASHION CASE LIPSTICK 1957-60
White metal. OSP 89c. **CMV $3., $4. MB.**
ULTRA SHEER LIPSTICK 1968
White plastic, gold base. OSP 99c. **CMV $1.**

COOL MILLION LIP BALM 1982
Green & white. SSP $1.40. **CMV $1.**
WEATHER BARRIER LIP BALM 1982
SSP $1. **CMV $1.**
BEARING GIFTS LIP BALM
Red & green. **CMV $1.**

FLAVOR SAVERS LIP GLOSS 1979-80
All in different colors. Strawberry, lime, chocolate, cherry, orange, and grape. SSP $1. **CMV 50c.**

FRUIT STIX PERFUMED DEMI STICK 1975
.19 oz. available in apple, (pink and red) lemon (yellow and gold) or strawberry (pink and red) OSP $1., **CMV $1.50 MB.**

ROUGE PUFFS REFILLS 1940's
(Left) Avon package holds 3 small turquoise rouge double compact puffs. **CMV $3. BO.**
POWDER COMPACT PUFFS REFILLS 1940's
(Right) Avon package holds 2 turquoise puff refills. **CMV $3. BO.**

NAIL WHITE PENCIL 1941-48
White plastic pencil in turquoise box. OSP 29c. Avon on pencil. **CMV $2.** pencil only $5. **MB.**

FACE POWDER COMPACT 1943-44
Feather design cardboard compact with mirror inside. 3 1/2 " across. **CMV $20., $25. MB.**

MASCARA 1943-49
Blue and white feather design paper box. OSP 69c. **CMV $14. BO $17. MB.**
FACE POWDER SAMPLE 1942-49
Blue and white feather design, metal case or paper box in 1943-46. **CMV $4. BO.**
HEAVENLIGHT COMPACT 1943-45
Blue plastic or metal with white feather, came in rouge or face powder. Rouge is smaller. OSP 59c. **CMV $8., $10. MB.**
EYE SHADOW 1945-49
Blue plastic compact with white feather. Same as 1943 Rouge feather compact above. OSP 79c. **CMV $7., $9. MB.**

COMPACTS 1936-42
Single compact. OSP $1.25. Double compact. OSP $1.75. Both turquoise and gold metal. **CMV $15., $20. MB.**

CPC EYEBROW PENCILS 1916-20
Metal tubes. OSP 30c. **CMV $15. each, $25. MB.**
LIPSTICK REFILL 1944
Foil wrapped lipstick in plastic case, for metal or paper case. Came in green and white box. 2 different boxes. Some are white top, green bottom as shown or reversed. **CMV $10. MB**

MASCARA COMPACT 1941-48
Gold metal, bamboo design. Sold 1942-43 then 1946-48. OSP $1.19. **CMV $12., $15. BO.**
BAMBOO LIPSTICK 1941-48
Gold metal bamboo design. OSP 79c. **CMV $6., $8. MB.**
BAMBOO SINGLE ROUGE COMPACT 1941-48
Gold metal bamboo design. OSP 79c. **CMV $7., $9. MB.**
BAMBOO CREME ROUGE COMPACT 1941-48
Gold metal bamboo design. OSP 69c. **CMV $7., $9. MB.**

BAMBOO COMPACT 1941-49
Gold metal, bamboo design. OSP $2.35 for double size. $1.75 for single size in same design. Sold 1942-43 then 1946-49. **CMV $15. BO $20. MB.**

VIOLET NUTRI CREAM 1930-34
(Left) White jar, metal lid, silver & blue label. 2 & 4 oz. size. OSP 78c. on 4 oz., & 52c. for 2 oz.. CMV **$40. MB. $35. jar only.**
CLEANSING CREAM 1930-34
(Right) 4 oz. white glass ribbed jar with aluminum lid. Silver & blue label. OSP $1. CMV **$35. jar only - $40. MB.**

ROSE COLD CREAM 1930-34
(Left) 2 & 4 oz. white glass ribbed jars with aluminum lids. Silver & blue labels. OSP 2 oz. 52c., 4 oz. 78c. CMV **$40. MB - $30 jar only.**
BLEACH CREAM 1932-33
(Right) 3 oz. frosted glass jas, metal lid, silver & blue label. OSP 78c. CMV **$50. - $55. MB.**

CREAM JARS - MISC. 1933-36
Ribbed white glass jar with blue metal caps. Following came in 2 & 4 oz. size. Rose Cold Cream, Violet Nutri Cream; 4 oz. size only in Cleansing Cream; 2 oz. size only in Bleach Cream, Vanishing Cream, Tissue Cream. OSP 78c. on 4 oz. & 52c. on 2 oz. size. CMV **$30. $35. MB.**

CREAM JARS - MISC. 1936-55
This style bottle was sold from 1935-55. Came in Tissue Cream, Rose Cold Cream, Special Formula Cream, Foundation Cream, Violet Protective Cream, All Purpose Cream, Bleach Cream, Cleansing Cream, Night Cream, Violet Nutri Cream, Complexion Cream, Super Rich Cream, 1947 Special Dry Skin Cream, 1948 Facial Mask Cream. White glass jars came in small, medium, and large size with turquoise metal caps. Paper caps were used 1943-46. OSP 52c. to 89c. CMV **$4. each.** Add $3. each for turquoise paper caps. CMV with CPC labels on jar or box 1936-39 **$8. jar only. $12. CPC label on box.**
ANTISEPTIC CREAM 1954-55
3 1/2 oz. large size jar only. OSP 89c. CMV **$4., $5. MB.**

CREAM DEODORANT 1954-59
White glass jar, turquoise lid. OSP 49c. CMV **$4. BO. $2.50 jar only.**

ROSE COLD CREAM BOX 1939
2 oz. white glass jar, turquoise lid in special short issue design box. CPC on box. OSP 10c. CMV **$20. MB as shown.**

CREAM DEODORANT 1939 Only
White glass jar, turquoise lid. OSP 37c. This is Rare. CMV **$16. MB $12. jar only, mint.**

ROSE COLD CREAM SPECIAL ISSUE BOX 1942
Special issue blue & pink rosebud box holds regular issue large size jar of Rose Cold Cream. OSP 49c. CMV **$17.50 MB.**

TISSUE CREAM 1930-34
(Left) Ribbed white glass, metal lid, silver & blue label. 2 oz. size. OSP 75c. CMV **$35., $40. MB.**
VANISHING CREAM 1931
(Right) 2 oz size white glass jar with aluminum lid. Silver & blue label. OSP 52c. CMV **$40 BO. $35. jar only.**

ROSE COLD CREAM SPECIAL ISSUE BOX 1941
Special issue rose color box with girls face on side. Came with regular issue middle size jar of Rose Cold Cream for 10c. with regular orderCMV **$20. MB as shown.**

ROSE COLD CREAM BOX 1940
1 3/4 oz. jar if Rose Cold Cream came in special issue box for Reps to use as demonstrator only. Cost Reps 10c. **CMV $20. MB as shown.**

COLOR PICK-UP CREAM 1946
7/8 oz. white glass jar, turquoise lid. OSP 89c. **CMV $15. BO. $18. MB.**

COLOR PICK-UP CREAM 1946-47
Painted over twin tone lid. 1 7/8 oz. white glass jar with green lid. OSP 89c. **CMV $12. $15. MB.**

COLOR PICK-UP LIQUID 1946-50
(Left) 1 oz. clear glass bottle with turquoise cap. OSP 89c. **CMV $8. - $11. MB.**
COLOR PICK-UP CREAM 1946-54
(Right) 17/8 oz. white glass jar with turquoise lid. OSP 89c. **CMV $6. - $10. MB.** Also came in 1 oz. jar. Same lid & jar.

TWIN TONE MAKE-UP 1943-46
(Left) 1 7/8 oz. white jar, turquoise paper lid & metal lid. OSP 89c. **CMV metal lid $9. - paper lid $12.**
TWIN TONE MAKE-UP 1943-46
(Right) 7/8 oz. white glass jar, turquoise paper lid. OSP 89c. **CMV $10 - $14. MB.**

HAND CREAM 1945 Only
3 1/2 oz. clear glasss jar, turquoise lid. Rare **CMV $25. - $30. MB.**

RICH MOISTURE CREAM 1957-60
In 3 1/2 & 2 oz. turquoise jars with 4A on white lids. OSP 2 oz. $1.50 -3 oz. $2.50. **CMV $2. MB. $1. jar only.**
RICH MOISTURE CREAM 1954-57
Turquoise jar & cap in 2 oz & 3 1/2 oz. size. OSP $1.50 for 2 oz. - $2.50 for 3 1/2 oz. jar came with 2 different size neck & caps **CMV $3 each size MB $2. jar only.**

CREAM CAKE 1955-57
(Left) Avon in center of pink lid, white glass bottom. OSP 95c. **CMV $3 - $4. MB.**
CREAM CAKE 1948-55
(Right) Dove on top of pink lid. white glass bottom. OSP 95c. **CMV $4 - $5. MB.**

CREAM SHAMPOO 1953
4 oz. jar very short issue. RARE. OSP $1., **CMV $15. MB - $10. jar only.**

RICH MOISTURE CREAM 1961-72
(Left) 2 oz. & 3 1/2 oz. turquoise glass jar with 4A on white lid. OSP 3 1/2 oz. $2.50 2 oz. $1.50. **CMV 25c. each.** On 1972 jar the 4A design was dropped.
HORMONE CREAM 1961-65
(Right) 2 oz. turquoise glass jar with 4A on white lid. Same as Rich Moisture Cream jar. OSP $2. **CMV $1. MB. 50c. jar only.**

RICH MOISTURE CREAM 1954
(Left) 1 1/2 & 3 1/2 oz. turquoise glass jars with turquoise plastic lids. OSP $1.50. **CMV $3 - $4. MB.**
CREAM FOUNDATION 1963-66
(Right) 1 oz. white glass jar with white plastic lid with gold center. OSP $1.35. **CMV $1.**

STRAWBERRY COOLER 1956
Frosted glass jar with strawberry on white lid.
OSP $1.50 **CMV $2. - $3. MB.**

NAIL BEAUTY 1954-57
1 oz white jar with white lid. OSP 59c. **CMV $3 - $4. MB.**

CREAM DEODORANT 1936-54
1 oz. white glass jar, turquoise lid. OSP 39c.
CMV $7. jar only. $10. MB. Add $4. for CPC label.

AVON CREAMS 1954-61
(Left to Center) White glass jar with green lid & label. Came in : Hormone Cream, Super Rich Cream, Cleansing Cream & Antiseptic Cream in large & small jars. OSP 89c. **CMV $2. each.**
STAY FAIR NIGHT CREAM 1967-69
(Right) 2 1/4 oz. light blue base, blue and white lid. OSP $2. **CMV $1.**

VITA MOIST CREAM 1959-61
2 oz. yellow glass jar with white smooth cap.
OSP $3. **CMV $1.50.**
VITA MOIST CREAM 1961-68
1 oz. yellow glass jar with white smooth cap.
OSP $1.75. **CMV $1.50.**
SUPER RICH CREAM 1965-69
2 1/4, pink glass bottom, white & pink cap.
OSP $3. **CMV 75c.**
SUPER RICH CREAM 1969-74
2 1/4 oz. blue glass jar with white & blue cap.
OSP $3. **CMV 25c.**

NAIL & CUTICLE CREAM 1940-50
(Left) 1 oz. white glass jar, turquoise lid. OSP 43c. **CMV $5. - $8 MB.**
NAIL BEAUTY 1951-54
(Right) 1 oz. white glass jar, white lid. OSP 49c. **CMV $4 - $5. MB.**

FRENCH FROSTING 1957-63
(Left) 1 oz. clear glass jar with pink plastic lid with gold center. OSP $1.25. **CMV $2. jar only.**
COVER PERFECT 1969-76
(Right) 2 oz. clear glass jar with white, pink and brown striped lid. OSP $2. **CMV 50c. - $1. MB.**

HAIR CONDITIONER 1967-71
6 oz. white jar, pink metal cap. OSP $250.
CMV $1.

COLOR PICK UP CREAM 1955-57
(Left) White glass jar with pink lid. OSP 95c.
CMV $6. each MB, $4. jar only.
WHITE VELVET CREAM 1961-65
(Inside Left) 3 1/2 oz. white glass jar with 4A on turquoise lid. OSP $1.25. **CMV $1. - $2. MB.**
POLISH REMOVER PADS 1963-66
(Inside Right) White glass jar with red lid, holds 20 pads. OSP 98c. **CMV $2. - $3. MB.**
ANTISEPTIC CREAM 1954-58
(Right) 3 1/2 oz. white glass jar with gray lid.
OSP $1. **CMV $2. - $3. MB.**

VITA MOIST CREAM 1961-69
2 1/4 oz. yellow glass jar with white smooth cap.
VITA MOIST CREAM 1969-72
2.25 oz. yellow glass jar with ribbed white cap.
CREAM SUPREME 1961-69
2 1/4 oz. pink glass jar with white cap with gold design around edge.
CREAM SUPREME 1969-72
2 1/4 oz. pink glass jar with pink 4A on white ribbed cap. **CMV 50c.**

SKIN-SO-SOFT VANITY JAR 1973-74
(Left) 5 oz. clear glass with antiqued gold lid.
CREAM SACHET VANITY JAR 1973-75
(Center) 1 oz. clear glass with antiqued silver lid. Holds Field Flowers, Charisma or Topaze.
RICH MOISTURE CREAM VANITY JAR 1973
(Right) 5 oz. clear glass with antiqued silver lid. SSP $2.50. **CMV $2. each.**

HORMONE CREAM 1965-76
(Left) 2.25 oz. white glass jar with gold tip on white lid. OSP $1.50. **CMV 25c.**
EYE CREAM 1960-74
(Right) White glass jar with an eye on metal lid. OSP $1.50. **CMV 25c.**

MAKE-UP SETTING PADS 1970
Pink frosted jar, white cap. Has 45 pads per box. OSP $2.75. **CMV $1.**

COLOR CAKE 1961-65
(Top) 2 oz. white cap & pink base. OSP $1.95. **CMV $1. - $2. MB.**
CAKE MAKE-UP 1947-54
(Bottom) 1 3/4 oz. pink base, white cap. OSP $1. **CMV $3. - $4. MB.**

AVON NET HAIR SPRAY 1954-57
Green & white, white caps. Came in 5 oz. size. OSP $1.25, 11oz. size, $2. **CMV $4. MB, $2. each CO.**

SPRAY CANS - MISC.

All Spray Cans 1960 & newer are mass produced & have little value to most collectors. We have dropped most spray cans 1960 or newer for this reason. All Avon spray cans not pictured in this book 1960 or newer would not have a value over 25c each. We suggest you do not collect them unless they are very old. New spray cans will not be added to this book in the future.

AVON NET HAIR SPRAY 1957-58
White & pink spray can came in 5 & 11 oz. sizes. OSP $1.25. & $2. **CMV $5. each.**
AVON NET FOR FINE HAIR 1958-60
5 oz. blue & white can & cap. OSP $1.25. **CMV $2.**
AVON NET REGULAR 1959-64
5 oz. pink & white can & cap. OSP $1.25. **CMV $2.**
LATHER FOAM SHAMPOO 1956
Green cap & can, short issue. OSP $1.29. **CMV $3. mint.**

KLEAN AIR 1956-58
(Left) 12 oz. blue & white spray can with white cap. Mint scented. OSP $1.89. **CMV $5. mint.** Also came 3 oz. pink & white. Same shape can. **CMV $3.**

SMOOTH-FLO TOOTHPASTE 1959-61
(Left) 5 1/2 oz. white, red & gray metal can, red cap. OSP 89c. **CMV $2.**
MOTH PROOFER 1956-60
(Right) 12 oz. red & white spray can, white cap. OSP $1.89. **CMV $2.**
MOTH PROOFER 1968-72
11 oz. red & white spray can with white cap. OSP 1.89. **CMV $1.**

TUBES - MISC.

Tubes 1965 or newer have been dropped from this book due to mass production & little or no interest to most Avon collectors. Only fancy decorated or cute kids type tubes are considered collectable after 1965. All other tubes not pictured in this book unless they are very old should not be collected for future value.

TO - means Tube Only

MENTHOL WITCH HAZEL 1914
OSP 25c. CMV $45. MB, $40. TO mint.
WITCH HAZEL CREAM 1914
Small & large tube. OSP 25c & 50c. CMV
$45. MB, $40. TO mint.

WITCH HAZEL CREAM 1904
OSP 2 oz. tube 25c, 6 oz. tube 50c. CMV $50.
MB, $45. TO mint.
ALMOND CREAM BALM 1904
OSP 2 oz. tube 25c, 6 oz. tube 50c. CMV $50.
MB, $45. TO mint.

WITCH HAZEL CREAM 1908
2 & 6 oz. size tubes. OSP 25c & 50c. CMV
$50. each MB, $40. TO mint.
ALMOND CREAM BALM 1908
2 & 6 oz. size tubes OSP 25c & 50c. CMV
$50. each MB, $40. TO.

WITCHHAZEL CREAM 1923
Large & small green tube. OSP 30c & 59c.
CMV $40. MB, $35. TO mint.

MENTHOL WITCH HAZEL CREAM 1909
2 oz. tube, 1sr issue. OSP 25c. CMV $45.,
$50. MB.

**BAYBERRY SHAVING CREAM SAMPLE
1925**
Small sample tube in sample box. Comes with
instruction sheet. CMV $70. MB.
MENTHOL WITCH HAZEL CREAM 1923
Green tube. OSP 33c. CMV $35. MB, TO
mint, $30.

**AMBER CREAM SHAMPOO OR AMBER
GEL 1948-50**
Turquoise & white tube with blue cap. OSP
59c. CMV $8. MB, $4. TO.
CREME SHAMPOO 1955-60
Green and white tube, CMV $10. MB, $6. TO.

CREME SHAMPOO WITH LANOLIN 1960-62
Green & white box holds yellow tube with
turquoise cap. OSP 69c. CMV $6. MB.
WITCH HAZEL CREAM SAMPLE 1925
Green tube, says on back "Not for sale
Sample". CMV $45. MB, $40. TO mint.

MENTHOL WITCH HAZEL CREAM 1930-36
Green & black tube. OSP 50c. CMV $20. MB,
$15. TO mint.
WITCH HAZEL CREAM 1930-36
Green & black tube OSP 75c. CMV $20. MB,
$15. TO mint.

ALMOND CREAM BALM 1910
Tube came in 2 sizes. OSP 25c & 50c. CMV
$45. MB, $40. TO mint.
COLD CREAM TUBE 1923
Large & small tube. OSP 23c & 45c. CMV
$30. TO mint, $40. MB.

SEN-DEN-TAL 1936-42
(Left) Turquoise & white tube. OSP 36c.
CMV $20. MB, TO mint $15.
SEN-DEN-TAL 1933-36
(Right) Green tube of tooth paste. OSP 35c.
CMV $25. MB, $20. TO mint.

WITCH HAZEL CREAM 1936-44
Turquoise & white tube OSP 52c. CMV $15.
MB, TO mint $12.
MENTHOL WITCH HAZEL CREAM 1936-44
Maroon & ivory colored tube. OSP 37c. CMV
$20. MB, TO mint $15.

TAKE ALONG HAND CREAM 1980
1 oz. tube in Vita Moist red design, or Rich
Moisture blue design. SSP 88c. CMV 50c
each.
CREME SHAMPOO 1959
2.4 oz. yellow tube & turquoise cap. Yellow &
blue box. OSP 69c. CMV $5. MB, $3. TO.

BAYBERRY SHAVING CREAM 1923
Green tube, came in Gentlemens Shaving Set.
CMV $35. mint, $40. MB.
STYPTIC PENCIL 1923
White pencil. OSP 10c. CMV $10. ,$15. MB.
BRUSHLESS SHAVING CREAM 1936-49
Maroon & ivory tube. OSP 41c. CMV $20.
MB, $15. TO mint.

CREME SHAMPOO 1949-58
(Top) Green tube with blue or white cap. OSP
59c. CMV mint TO $5., $8. MB.
CREME SHAMPOO 1954-5
(Bottom) Green tube with white cap. OSP 59c.
CMV $8., MB, mint TO $6.

BAYBERRY SHAVING CREAM 1930-36
Green tube. OSP 35c. CMV $25. MB, $20.
TO mint.
BRUSHLESS SHAVING CREAM 1935-36
Green & black tube, OSP 51c. CMV $25. MB,
$20. TO mint.

SEN-DEN-TAL 1921-33
Yellow tube. OSP 47c. **CMV $35. MB, $30 TO mint.** Also came in small sample tube. **CMV $35. mint.**

DENTAL CREAM NO. 2 1932-36
Green tube. OSP 35c. **CMV $25. MB.**

DENTAL CREAM 1915-33
OSP 23c. 1915-23 tube was pink, 1923-33 tube was light blue. **CMV pink tube mint $40., blue tube mint $35. Add $5. for box.**

BAYBERRY SHAVE CREAM 1923
Green tube. OSP 33c. **CMV $40. MB, $35. TO mint.**

SHAMPOO CREAM 1923
Yellow tube. OSP 48c. **CMV $40 MB, $35. TO mint.**

SHAVING CREAM 1936-49
Maroon & ivory tube. OSP 36c. **CMV $20. MB, TO mint $15.**

HAIR DRESS 1931-36
(Left) Silver tube. OSP 37c. **CMV $25. MB, $20. TO mint.**

HAIR DRESS 1936-49
(Center) Maroon & ivory colored tube. OSP 37c. **CMV $20. MB, TO mint $15.**

CREAM HAIR DRESS 1962-65
(Right) 4 oz. white tube. Red cap. Stage coach on tube. OSP 89c. **CMV $4., $6. MB.**

STYPTIC PENCIL 1925
White stick in CPC box. Came in Humidor Set box in French and English. **CMV $25. MB.**

HAND CREAM NEW YEAR BOX 1943
Regular issue tube of hand cream. Came in special short issue Flower designed box. **RARE. OSP 15c. CMV $17. MB as shown.**

DENTAL CREAM 1912
Metal tube, paper label. OSP 25c. **CMV $50. mint, $75. MB.**

ALMOND CREAM BALM 1908
Metal tube. OSP 50c. **CMV $45. mint, $55. MB.**

HAND CREAM 1938
10c with each order, Feb. 1938 bells on box. **CMV $17.50 MB as shown.**

HAND CREAM CHRISTMAS BOX 1934
(Left) Green & red box, short issue, holds silver tube of hand cream. OSP 10c with regular order. **CMV $18. MB as shown.**

HAND CREAM 1934
(Right) Regular issue, gray box holds silver tube of hand cream. OSP 52c. **CMV $12., TO mint $15. MB.**

67th ANNIVERSARY HAND CREAM DUO 1953
Box holds two 2 1/2 oz. tubes of hand cream. OSP $1.10. **CMV $20. MB.**

HAND CREAM INTRODUCTORY 1934-36
Blue & silver tube. OSP 52c. **CMV $25. MB as shown, $20. TO mint.**

HAND CREAM SPECIAL ISSUE BOX 1941
Special issue flowered box holds regular issue tube of hand cream. Sold for 10c with regular order. **CMV $15. MB as shown.**

HAND CREAM DUO 1953
Box holds 2 tubes 2 1/2 oz. size of hand cream. Turquoise & white. OSP $1.18. **CMV $18.50 MB.**

HAND CREAM CHRISTMAS BOX 1935
Silver tube of hand cream came in special issue Christmas box for 10c with regular order. **CMV $17.50 MB as shown.** Same box came with Tulip 'A' tube of Hand Cream on right in 1936. **CMV $15. MB.**

TOOTHBRUSH 1940s - 50s
Turquoise and white box with Tulip A holds 1 Avon tooth brush. OSP 50c. **CMV $3.50 MB.**
TOOTHPASTE 1935-36
Red, white and green tube. OSP 23c. **CMV $17.50 MB as shown, tube only mint $12.**

HAIR BEAUTY 1956
Blue box holds two 2 oz. tubes of creme shampoo. OSP $1.29. **CMV $17.50 MB.**

HAND CREAM SPECIAL ISSUE BOX 1939
Short issue box came with regular issue, tube of hand cream for 10c with regular order. **CMV $17.50 MB as shown.**

HAND CREAM SPECIAL ISSUE BOX 1940
Special issue box is rose and white color. Has hand and flower on box with tulip A in flower. Sold for 10c. Holds regular issue hand cream tube. **CMV $16. MB as shown.**

CARE DEEPLY HAND CEAM 1974
2 tubes 4 oz. in pink, blue, orange & purple box. OSP $2. **CMV $3. MB.**

MERRY CHRISTMAS HAND CREAM DUO 1953 ONLY
2 turquoise & white metal tubes of hand cream in Merry Christmas box. OSP $1.10. **CMV $20. MB.**

FOR BEAUTIFUL HANDS 1956 ONLY
Blue flowered box holds 2 tubes of 2 3/4 oz. hand cream. OSP $1.10. **CMV $16. MB.**

FOR BEAUTIFUL HANDS 1954
2 1/2 oz. turquoise and white tubes with hand cream, turquoise caps. One tube with "Lanolin added" other regular issue. Box bouquet red roses. OSP $1.10. **CMV $17. MB.** In 1955 same box came with 2 tubes of hand cream like in the 1954 Merry Christmas Hand Cream, Duo. **CMV $17. MB.**

HAND CREAM SPECIAL ISSUE BOX 1942
Special issue box with flower design holds regular issue tube of hand cream. OSP 10c. **CMV $16. MB as shown.**

DOUBLY YOURS 1954
Rose box holds 2 tubes of Avon Hand Cream. OSP $1.18. **CMV $17. MB.**

CHRISTMAS TREASURE BOX 1960 ONLY
Red and green box holds turquoise tube of hand cream. OSP 69c. **CMV $7. MB as shown. Tube only $2. mint.**

HAND CREAM CHRISTMAS PACKAGING 1964
Special Christmas boxes in pink, blue and white, came with choice of green tube of 3 oz. hand cream, 4 oz. white plastic bottle of hand loiton, pink and white 3 3/4 oz. tube of moisturized hand cream and 2 1/4 oz. turquoise and white tube of Silicone Glove. OSP 79c or 2 for $1.29. **CMV $3. each MB.**

CLEANSING CREAM SAMPLE 1936
(Left) 1/4 oz. tube, black or turquoise cap. **CMV $6., CPC label add $4.**
CLEANSING CREAM 1957
(Right) 2 1/2 oz. white tube with gray band, turquoise lettering. OSP 59c. **CMV $3., $4. MB.**

MERRY CHRISTMAS TWIN FAVORITES 1956 ONLY
Green & red box holds 2 tubes of hand cream. OSP $1.18. **CMV $18. MB.**

ROSEMINT FACIAL MASK 1962-71
3 oz. pink and white tube. OSP $1. **CMV $1.50. MB.**

MERRY CHRISTMAS HAND CREAM DUO 1954
Red & white box holds two green tubes of Avon Hand Cream. OSP $1.10. **CMV $17. MB.**

HAND CREAM 1955-62
(Left) Turquoise tube and cap. Flat cap sold 1955-57 2 1/2 oz. tube. Tall cap sold 1957-62 2.65 oz. OSP 59c. **CMV $3. flat cap MB, TO $2. flat cap mint $1. less on tall cap tubes.**
HAND CREAM 1937-54
(Right) 2 1/2 oz. turquoise and white tube. OSP 52c. **CMV $8. MB, TO mint $4.**

MOISTURIZED HAND CREAM CHRISTMAS BOX 1963 ONLY
3 3/4 oz. pink and white tube pictured with special issue Christmas box. OSP 89c. **CMV $3. MB TO sold 1957-67, CMV TO $1.**
SILICONE GLOVE CHRISTMAS BOX 1963 ONLY
(Right) 2 1/4 oz. turquoise and white tube in special issue CHristmas box. OSP 79c. **CMV $3. MB, TO sold 1960-69, CMV TO $1.**

MERRY CHRISTMAS GIFT BOXES 1958-59
Special issue gift box came with choice of Moisturized Hand Cream, pink and white tube. OSP 79c. Avon Hand Cream, turquoise tube. OSP 59c. Silicone Formula Hand Cream, white tube. OSP 98c. **CMV $10. MB as shown each.**

HAND CREAM FOR MEN DOUBLE PAK 1966-68
Box holds 2 black & orange tubes. OSP $2.50. **CMV tubes $2. each set, $8. MB.**

HAND CREAM WITH LANOLIN 1954
2 1/2 oz. tube. OSP 59c. **CMV $12. MB, $10. TO mint.**
SPECIAL FORMULAS CREAM 1940-43
Turquoise & white tube. OSP 78c. **CMV $12. MB TO mint $9.**

HAND CREAM 1963-69
3 oz. turquoise tube, white caps (top) tube older, (bottom) newer. Two different labels. (1963-69) $1. and (1970-73) **CMV 50c.**

FALL BAZAAR GIFT BOX 1955
Special issue Christmas box holds 2 turquoise tubes of hand cream. OSP 89c. **CMV $17. MB.**

PORE CREAM 1936-39
(Left) Turquoise & white tube. OSP 78c.
CMV $20. MB, $15. TO mint.
PORE CREAM 1930-36
(Right) Silver & blue tube. OSP 78c. CMV
$25. MB, $20. TO mint.

FLUFFY CLEANSING CREAM 1947
LIQUEFYING CLEANSING CREAM 1947
Both tubes are pink 2 1/4 oz. Came in 1947
Cleansing Cream Demo Kit only. Was never
sold to public. Very rare. **CMV $20. each.**

NIGHT CREAM 1948
SPECIAL DRY SKIN CREAM 1948
Both tubes are blue 2 1/4 oz. size. Came in
1948 Skin Care Demo Kit. Was never sold to
public. Very rare. **CMV each $20. mint full.**

TOOTH PASTE SPECIAL ISSUE BOX 1938
Short issue box holds regular issue tooth
paste. Cost 10c with regular order. CMV
$17.50 MB as shown.

TOOTH PASTE SPECIAL ISSUE BOX 1937
Regular issue tooth paste came in special
issue box for 10c with regular order. **CMV**
$17.50 MB as shown.

AMMONIATED TOOTHPASTE 1949-55
Green & white tube. OSP 49c. CMV $8. MB,
$5. TO mint.
DENTAL CREAM 1936-44
Turquoise & white tube. OSP 26c. **CMV $10.**
MB, $7. TO mint.

DEPILATORY 1931-34
Silver tube. OSP 75c. CMV $17.50 MB, $12.
TO mint.
DENTAL CREAM 1948-53
Red cap, red, white & blue tube. OSP 43c.
CMV $6. MB TO mint $4.

TOOTHPASTE 1940
Special Box, OSP 10c with good order from
Rep. in Sept. 1940. **CMV $18. MB as shown.**

TOOTHPASTE SPECIAL BOX 1939
OSP 10c with order October 1939. CMV $18.
MB as shown.

DENTAL CREAM 1933-36
(Left) Green tube. OSP 25c. **CMV $20. MB, $15. TO mint.**
TOOTHPASTE NO. 2 1936-48
(Center) Turquoise and white tube. OSP 23c. **CMV TO $10. mint, $15. MB.**
TOOTHPASTE 1936-48
(Right) Turquoise and white tube. OSP 23c. **CMV $12. MB, TO mint $7.**

SMOKERS TOOTHPASTE 1957-67
Red & white & grey tube. White cap. OSP 50c. **CMV $2.50 MB, $1. TO mint.**
DENTAL CREAM WITH AVONOL 1957-63
Red, white & gray tube, white cap. OSP 50c. **CMV $3. MB, TO $1.**

CLEARLY GENTLE BABY "BEAR" PRODUCTS 1983
Each item has bear in blanket design.
BABY BATH
1 oz. tube.
BABY CREAM
1 oz. tube.
BABY OIL
1 oz. plastic bottle. SSP $1.30 each. **CMV $1. each.**

CHLOROPHYL TOOTHPASTE 1953-56
Green & white tube, green cap. OSP 49c. **CMV $8. MB, TO mint $5.**
TOOTHPASTE 1953-56
Blue & white tube, white cap. OSP 49c. **CMV $8. MB, TO mint $5.** Also came in 3/4 oz. sample tube. **CMV $5. mint.**

SMOKERS TOOTHPASTE 1964-67
5 oz. white tube, blue cap. OSP 79c. **CMV $1.50. MB.**
PREMIUM TOOTHPASTE 1964-66
5 oz. white tube, red cap. OSP 89c. **CMV $1.50 MB.**
CREAM DEODORANT 1964-67
OSP 69c. **CMV $1.50, $2. MB.**

RABBIT LIP BALM AND HAND CREAM 1983
Both have pink caps and rabbit on side. Hand cream is 1.5 oz. tube. No box. SSP $2. for pair. **CMV $1. each.**

SILICONE FORMULA CREAM 1957-61
White tube, small turquoise cap. OSP 98c. **CMV $2. MB, TO $1.**
MOISTURIZED HAND CREAM 1957-67
Pink & white tube, small white cap. OSP 79c. **CMV $2. MB, TO $1.**

SMOKERS TOOTHPASTE 1941-50
Maroon & cream colored tube. OSP 39c. **CMV $18. MB, $15. TO mint.**

ANTISEPTIC CREAM 1957-60
1 3/4 oz. tube white & gray & red with red cap. OSP 69c. **CMV $1. - $2. MB.**

STARS & STRIPES TO GO AFTER TAN MOISTURIZER 1982 ONLY
1 oz. bottle, red cap. No box. SSP $1.30. **CMV $1.**
SUNTAN LOTION
Factor 4 in 1 oz. tube, red cap, no box. SSP $1.30.

CLOWNING AROUND BODY SOAP 1982
1.5 oz. tubes in red, yellow or blue. SSP $1.25 each. **CMV 50c each.**

SEASONAL SMOOTHERS HAND CREAM 1982
1.5 oz. tubes in blue, red or green. SSP $1. **CMV 50c each.**

SANTA'S HELPER HAND CREAM & LIP BALM 1980
Lip balm is green, red & white. Care Deeply hand cream is red, white & green. 1.5 oz. tube. Sold together with no box. SSP $2.50. **CMV $2. mint set.**

HOT STUFF 1981-82
Tanarifics Tanning lotions. 3.75 oz. Yellow tube. SSP $2. **CMV 50c.**

COOL IT 1981-82
Tanarifics Tanning Lotion 3.75 oz. blue tube. SSP $2. **CMV 50c.**

SAMPLES & DEMON-STRATOR KITS

DELIVERY BAGS
(Left) 1929 black leatherette. **CMV $30.** (Middle) 1948 black leatherette front opening lays flat. **CMV $20.** (Right) 1942 black leatherette. **CMV $20.**

CPC SALES MANAGERS DEMO BAG 1913
Leather bound straw bag used by early day Avon ladies to show their products. Measures 14" wide, 4" deep. 10" high. Does not say CPC on case. **CMV $75. mint.** Also came with CPC Products label on inside lid. Same design case only size is 17" x 11 1/4" x 4" deep. **CMV $100.**

DREXYL DRAGON DECORATING BODY SOAP 1981
3 different color dragon design tubes. Red, blue, or yellow. SSP $3. each. **CMV 50c.**

FRUIT FOR ALL HAND CREAM & LIP BALM 1981
Lip balm & 1.5 oz. mathcing tube of hand cream in strawberry, grape or orange. SSP $2. set each. **CMV $2. each set.**

DEMO BAG 1937
Simulated ostrich leather holds Avon sales catalog & room for 4 demo packages. Used by Avon Reps. **CMV $35. bag only mint.**

DELIVERY BAG 1941-43
Black imitation leather waterproof bag used by Reps to deliver Avon products. Base of bag measures 15 1/2" long, 7" wide. 10" high and has a 21 inch zipper. Cost a Rep $1.49. **CMV $15. mint.**

DELIVERY BAG PRIZE 1944
Black waterproof bag, zipper top, metal buttons on bottom to set on. Given to Reps for placing order of $150. or more. Used to deliver Avon products. **CMV $15. mint.**

DELIVERY BAG 1950s
Black leatherette. **CMV $17. mint.**

SALES BAG 1953
Black bag used by Avon reps in early 50s.
CMV $22. mint.

DELIVERY BAG 1970s
White, blue & green design used by Avon
ladies. **CMV $6.**

DELIVERY BAG 1976
(Left) Blue brocade bag used by Avon Reps to
make delivery of Avon products. **CMV $3.**
BEAUTY SHOWCASE DEMO BAG 1976
(Right) Used by Avon Reps to carry Avon
demonstration products. Matching blue
brocade. **CMV $3.**

BEAUTY SHOWCASE BAG 1960s (early)
(Right) Two tones blue with black trim. Used
by Reps. **CMV $6.**
BEAUTY SHOWCASE BAG 1960s (late)
(Left) Two toned blue & blue trim. Used by
Reps. **CMV $5.**

DELIVERY BAG 1960s
Used by Avon Reps. **CMV $25.**

HAND CARE DEMONSTRATOR KIT 1953
Box holds 2 bottles of nail polish, 1 tube of
hand cream, jar of nail beauty. **CMV $40. MB.**

DELIVERY BAG 1960s
Two toned blue, silver 4A emblem under
handle. **CMV $6.**

BEAUTY SHOWCASE BAG 1970s
Blue & green vinyl came with blue plastic
holder for samples. **CMV $10. for both or $5.
each.**

REPRESENTATIVES DEMO BAG 1970
White background with bright colored flowers.
Silver 4A emblem under handle. **CMV $6.
mint.**

COLORWORKS SHOULDER BAG 1977
Given to customers who bought all 5
Colorworks products. Sold to Reps for $2.50
as a demo. Tan canvas bag with red, yellow
and green strap. Measures 8 1/2" x 10". **CMV
$3.**

**REPRESENTATIVE DEMONSTRATOR KIT
1948**
Black leather kit. **CMV $90. mint.**

REPRESENTATIVE DEMO KIT 1940
Box holds jard of cleansing cream, night cream, foundation cream & bottle of skin freshener. OSP $1. **CMV $50. MB.**

SHAMPOO DEMO KIT 1947
Box holds 2 bottles of soapless & liquid shampoo. For Reps only. **CMV $50. mint.**

SKIN CARE DEMONSTRATOR 1956
Plastic case holds plastic bottle of Deep Clean Cleansing Cream, 1 oz. glass bottle of Skin Freshener, 2 white jars of Rich Moisture & Hormone Cream & plastic spoon.. **CMV $37.50 MB.**

DEMONSTRATOR KIT 1942 ONLY
Box holds jar of cream deodorant & a bar of Lemonol soap. **CMV $45. MB.**

PACK UP YOUR SKIN TROUBLES DEMONSTRATOR KIT 1953
Cardboard carrying case holds jars of cleansing cream & tissue cream & 4 oz. bottle of astringent. **CMV $50. MB.**

DEMONSTRATOR KIT 1946
Box holds tube of toothpaste & hand cream & bottle of antiseptic. **CMV $45.**

MAKE-UP TRIO DEMO KIT 1936
Brown box holds 1 3/4 oz. box of Ariel Suntan Face Powder, turquoise & gold rouge compact in Crusader red & matching lipstick in Crusader red. Came with fold out display card. **CMV $60. MB.**

BEAUTY SHOWCASE DEMO BAG 1980-81
Used by Reps to show Avon products. **CMV $5.**

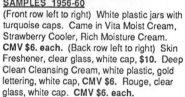

BEAUTY COUNSELOR DEMO KIT SAMPLES 1956-60
(Front row left to right) White plastic jars with turquoise caps. Came in Vita Moist Cream, Strawberry Cooler, Rich Moisture Cream. **CMV $6. each.** (Back row left to right) Skin Freshener, clear glass, white cap, **$10.** Deep Clean Cleansing Cream, white plastic, gold lettering, white cap, **CMV $6.** Rouge, clear glass, white cap. **CMV $6. each.**

HAND LOTION & HAND CREAM DEMO KIT 1948
Demo box holds tubes of hand cream & 4 oz. bottle of hand lotion. Not sold. Used by Reps to sell products. **CMV $30. MB.**

SKIN CARE DEMO KIT 1952
Flip open display box holds 1 jar each of Cleansing Cream and Night Cream and a bottle of skin freshener. Used by Reps to show products. **CMV $35. MB.**

DEMONSTRATOR KIT 1949
Demo box holds tubes of hand cream and creme shampoo and jar of perfumed deodorant. Used by Reps to show products. **CMV $35. MB.**

SKIN CARE DEMO KIT 1948
Demo box holds blue 2 1/4 oz. tube of Fluffy Cleansing Cream, 4 oz. bottle of Skin Freshener & tube of Special Dry Skin Cream. Not sold to public. Used by Reps as demonstrator. **CMV $55. MB.**

FACIAL DEMO KIT 1940s
Green lid box with pink base holds white glass jars of cleansing cream, night cream, foundation cream & 4 oz. bottle of skin freshener. All have turquoise caps. Used by Reps to demonstrate facial products. **CMV $45. MB.**

CLEANSING CREAM DEMONSTRATOR KIT 1951
Demo box holds 2 white glass jars with turquoise lids of Cleansing Creams & 1 jar of Night Cream. Used by Reps to show products. **CMV $25. MB.** Comes in 2 different boxes.

CLEANSING CREAM DEMO KIT 1947
Box with lady's face on lid holds tube of liquifying & fluffy cleansing cream. Pink tubes, 2 1/4 oz. each. Tubes were never sold to public. For Reps only. **CMV Rare $45. MB.**

DENTAL DEMO KIT 1949
Box holds tube of Ammoniated toothpaste and can of Ammoniated tooth powder. Not sold to public. Used by Reps to show products. **CMV $40. MB.**

CLEANSING CREAM DEMONSTRATOR KIT 1942
Box holds jar & 3 sample tubes of cleansing cream. **CMV $35. MB.**

FACIAL DEMONSTRATOR KIT 1942
Box holds 3 tubes of night cream, jar of night cream, foundation cream & 4 oz. bottle of skin freshener. OSP 69c. **CMV $50. MB.**

CLEANSING CREAM SAMPLE SET 1940s
Box holds 10 turquoise 1/4 oz. sample tubes of cleansing cream. Also came with 2 stacks of Your Skin Can Be Beautiful pamphlets. **CMV $35. MB.**

HAND CREAM SAMPLES 1938
Box of 24 1/4 oz. turquoise & white tubes. **CMV $3. each tube, mint complete $100.**
CLEANSING CREAM SAMPLES 1938
Same box as hand cream samples. Box of 24 1/4 oz. tubes. **CMV $3. each tube mint, complete set $100.**

PERFUME DEMO KIT 1940-41
Green & gold box holds three 1 dram bottles with colored caps. Perfume samples set used by Representatives. Came in Marionette, Garden of Love, Coitllion & Gardenia. OSP 30c. CMV $67.50 MB.

BIRTHDAY CAKE 1951
Blue & white box holds foam cake with five 1 dram ribbed perfumes. To A Wild Rose, Golden Promise, Cotillion, Quaintance & Flowertime. This was a demonstrator kit, for Reps. CMV $90. cake & bottles only mint, $125. MB.

PERFUME SAMPLES 1947-50
Small sample tubes with glass vials of perfume inside. Gardenia, Lily of the Valley, Crimson Carnation, Luscious, Garden of Love, Ballad, Quaintance & Golden Promise. CMV $20. each with vials. Here's My Heart, FLower-time, Quaintance & Cotillion came in pink or blue tubes. CMV $15. each mint.

76th ANNIVERSARY CELEBRATION DEMO KIT 1962
Pink cardboard box holds 2 oz. Cotillion cologne, Cotillion cream sachet, 2 oz. perfumed deodorant, 6 oz. Rosiest Spray Sachet, Silver Notes Eye Shadow & Hi Light Shampoo. CMV $30.

PERFUME SAMPLE 1964
Small 1/8 oz. bottle came in Occurl, Some-where, Cotillion, Topaze, Here's My Heart, Persian Wood, To A WIld Rose. CMV $8. each.

PERFUME SAMPLE 1932
Very small glass vial with cork stopper in envelope. Came in Gardenia, Jardin D'Amour, Bolero, Cotillion, Ariel, Narcissus, Rose, Lily of the Valley, Sweet Pea, Trailing Arbutus. CPC on package. CMV $18. each in envelope mint.

GARDEN OF LOVE PERFUME SAMPLE 1940
Small bottle with metal cap in sample envelope. Also came in Ballad, Trailing Arbutus, Cotillion, Gardenia, Merriment, Sweet Pea, Courtship, Lily of the Valley, Jardin D'Amour. CMV $18. each in envelope only. Add $2. for CPC on envelope.

PERFECT BALANCE MANAGER'S DEMO KIT 1974
Contained Tissue-Off cleansing cream, Toning Freshener, night cream, Wash-Off cleansing lotion, Toning astringent, night time moistur-izer. CMV $20. MB.

MANAGERS DEMO KIT 1965
White box holds eye & face make-up. CMV $55. MB.

PRIMA NATURA PRODUCTS INTRODUC-TION DEMO KIT FOR MANAGERS ONLY 1970
White Avon embossed box holds Creme of Soap, Night Veil Concentrate, Toning Freshener, Moisturizing Freshener. CMV $25.

MAKE-UP DEMO CASE 1979
Large tan vinyl case. **CMV $5. MB.**

77th ANNIVERSARY DEMO SET 1963
Demo kit for Avon Reps on 77th Anniversary.
Top of box has rose in left corner & says
"Celebrating Avon's 77th Anniversary." Box
holds 2 oz. cologne mist with 4A's embossed
on side, jar of cream foundation, 4 oz. skin-so-
soft & petti pat compact. **CMV $35. MB.**

**FASHION MAKEUP GROUP COLLECTION
1977**
Demo kit used by Reps to sell Fashion Makeup
products. Box is black & gold with white base.
Outside sleeve. Cost Rep $5.47. **CMV $5.50
MB complete.**

**ENVIRA MAKE-UP DEMO KIT & PRODUCTS
1979-80**
Pink lid box with outer sleeve & white plastic
inner base holds 1 each of Envira Products
which are also sold separate: Conditioning
Make-up, Pure Color Blush, Gentle Eye Color,
Pure Color Lipstick, Soft Eye Definer,
Conditioning Mascara. **CMV complete set in
demo box, mint, $7.50.**
SAMPLES CONDITIONING MAKE-UP
Box of 10.
SAMPLES OF PURE COLOR BLUSH
Box of 10. **CMV 25c. All products listed
each.**

MOISTURE SECRET KIT 1980
Outer sleeve holds white and pink plastic case.
4 small pink plastic containers of creams. SSP
$3.50. **CMV $3.50. MB.**

CANDID MANAGERS DISPLAY 1976
Orange plastic display for Avon managers to
display new Candid products. Base holds 7
Candid lipsticks, 6 eye colors, 2 mascaras, 3
cheek colors & three 1 1/2 oz. bottles of
makeup. **CMV complete full set MB $45.,
empty items 25c each, base only $15.**

FRESH LOOK MAKE-UP DEMO KIT 1979
Used by Reps only. Peach color box. **CMV
$5. MB.**

REP'S DEMO & ORDER CASE 1970
Blue plastic snap shut case. Has order pad &
fragrance samples & color brochures. **CMV
$10. mint.**

COLORWORKS DEMO KIT 1977
Silver & white box with outer sleeve holds Oil
Free Liquid Makeup, Oil Free Cheekblush,
Supershine Lip Gloss, Lasting Eye Shadow &
Lashes, Lashes Mascara. Used by Reps to
sell new Colorworks prooducts. Rep cost
$4.50. **CMV $5. MB complete.**

SAMPLE & DEMONSTRATOR KITS

TIME CONTROL DEMO KIT 1980
Black & pink box & sleeve has small white hour glass & .75 oz. plastic bottles of Time Control. Plus 6 more bottles in box. Used by Reps as demo kit. CMV $8. MB.

MOISTURE SECRET SKIN CARE KIT 1978
White & pink plastic kit holds pink plastic tubes of Moisture Secret Enriched Creme gel Cleanser, Enriched Freshener & Enriched Daytime Moisturizer. All with PMB and pink plastic jar of Enriched Night Concentre. All are trial size. Came with outer sleeve over kit. SSP $2.50. CMV $4. MB.

CANDID MAKEUP DEMO KIT 1977
For Reps only. Box lid Candid is in different position than regular set sold. Came with outer sleeve and says (Not for Resale) on back side. Box holds 5 items. Makeup, lip color, eye color, cheek color, mascara with lash builders. CMV $10. MB with outer sleeve only. Sold to public for $10.95. Same CMV.

ACCOLADE DEMO KIT 1982
Carmel color plastic case holds Accolade products for Avon managers. CMV $20. mint.

FACE POWDER DEMO PALETTE 1940s
Green palette holds 5 Tulip "A" metal samples in Ariel & Vernafleur. CMV $32. mint.

BEAUTY FLUID SAMPLE KIT 1980
Given to President's Club member Reps. Box has outer sleeve. Silver & brown box & sleeve. Holds 3 oz. bottle of beauty fluid & pack of tissues. CMV $12. MB.

MAKING EYES DISPLAY 1976
Plastic base used by managers to display new turquoise color eye makeup products. Base holds 12 powder eye shadows, 5 dream eye shadows, 2 eye shadow wands, 3 mascaras, 3 brow & liner pencils. CMV $25. MB as shown full. Products 25c each empty. CMV base only $5.

REPRESENTATIVE DEMO CASE 1936
Black case with metal mirror in lid. Handle is on opposite side of lid opening. Inner shelf is dark blue & lifts out of case. Storage area under shelf. Case came complete with 1936 sales catalog, 1/4 oz. glass stopper perfume in Cotillion, metal cap 1/4 oz. perfume in Gardenia, blue & silver lipstick & rouge compact, silver box of face powder, ribbed glass bottle of skin freshener (2 oz.), astringent 92 oz.), Lotus Cream (4 oz.), Rosewater Glycerin & Benzoin (4 oz.). All with black caps. 2 oz. jars of vanishing cream & tissue cream & 4 oz. jars of cleansing cream. CMV $700. MB complete set.

GIFT DISPLAY ENSEMBLE DEMO 1943
A special hand carrying box used by Reps at Christmas time to show Christmas sales items & sets. To determine price of this kit, look up each set & get their price, then add $25. for this demo box.

GIFT DISPLAY ENSEMBLE DEMO 1942
A special hand carrying box used by Reps at Christmas time. Came with several sets to show customers. To determine price of this kit, look up each set & get price. Then add $25. for the demo box.

DEMO KIT - CHRISTMAS 1941
For Representatives only. **CMV complete $350.**

FACE POWDER DEMONSTRATOR PALETTE 1957
Turquoise board holds 10 samples with clear plastic tops. **CMV $10.**

FACE POWDER DEMONSTRATOR PALETTE 1942
Board holds 8 paper box samples. **CMV $15. mint.**

REPRESENTATIVE DEMO CASE 1930s
Black case held sets & demo products & catalog. No price established. **Case only $75. mint.**

FACE POWDER DEMONSTRATOR PALETTE 1938
Board holds 5 samples in Ariel & Vernafleur. **CMV $20. mint.**

HEAVENLIGHT FACE POWDER SAMPLE PALETTE 1946
Each pink sample has Heavenlight written across each top. **CMV $15.**

BEAUTY COUNSELOR DEMO KIT 1959-60
Black shoulder bag with outside pocket holds removable turquoise & white plastic inner case with Avon & 4A design on lid containing 3 white plastic jars with turquoise lids holding .46 oz. of Rich Moisture Cream, Vita Moist Cream & Strawberry Cooler, 1 oz. glass bottle sample of Skin Freshener, 1 1/4 oz. white plastic sample bottle Deep Clean Cleansing Cream, 17 sample bottles of Liquid Powder, 5 liquid rouge samples in small bottles, 45 gold metal lipstick samples & 16 plastic shaker powder samples. **CMV $200. complete.**

FACE POWDER DEMONSTRATOR PALETTES
HEAVENLIGHT 1946-49
(Left) Blue board holds 9 feather design samples. **CMV $15.**
FACE POWDER PALETTE 1949-54
(Right) Turquoise board holds 8 to 10 samples. **CMV $10.**
FACE POWDER PALETTE 1954-55
(Bottom) Turquoise board holds 10 samples. **CMV $10.**

FACE POWDER DEMONSTRATOR PALETTE 1940
Board holds 8 metal samples. **CMV $20. mint.**

FACE POWDER DEMONSTRATOR PALETTE 1940
Board holds 6 metal samples in Ariel, Cotillion & Vernafleur. **CMV $20.**

**FACE POWDER PALETTE DEMONSTRA-
TOR 1950s**
Board holds 10 sample powders. Came in
pink envelope. Used by Reps. Same palette
came in different envelopes. **CMV $10. with
envelopes.**

**FACE POWDER DEMONSTRATOR
PALETTE 1939**
Board holds 6 different face powder samples
with tulip A on lid in Cotillion, Ariel or
Vernafleur. **CMV $20. mint.**

**HEAVENLIGHT FACE POWDER SAMPLE
1940s**
Blue metal case, white feather on lid. **CMV $2.
mint.**

FACE POWDER SAMPLES 1949-55
(Left) Green metal samples. **CMV $1. each
mint.**
FACE POWDER SAMPLE 1930-36
(Right) Small silver can, came in Ariel or
Vernafleur. **CMV $2. mint.**

FACE POWDER SAMPLE SET 1942
Box holds 30 metal face powder samples.
OSP 50c. **CMV $45. set MB, $1. each
sample.** Also came with CPC Avon label.
CMV $65. set MB.

**HEAVENLIGHT FACE POWDER SAMPLES
1946-49**
Box holds 30 feather design samples. OSP
50c. **CMV $35. MB.** Samples came both in
cardboard & tin.

FACE POWDER SAMPLE BOX 1940s
Light green box holds 30 plain blue face
powder samples. Avon on back. **CMV $25.
box complete mint.**

LIPSTICK SAMPLES
(Left) 1947 red box holds 30 brass samples.
Also came 2 boxes in a plain carton from Avon.
CMV $30. CMV $60. box of 2 sets.
(Right) 1951 white plastic tray holds 30 brass
lipstick samples. **CMV $25.**

LIPSTICK DEMONSTRATOR 1952
Box holds 4 full size gold embossed lipsticks &
1 refill. Used early to mid-50s. **CMV $30. MB.**

LIPSTICK DEMONSTRATOR 1940
Box holds 30 metal lipstick samples, with
cards. **CMV $35. MB with all 30 cards.**

NEW CUSTOMER KIT 1936-40
Turquoise box holds 30 turquoise metal lipstick
samples with 30 sample cards. **CMV $45. set
MB with all cards.**

FACE POWDER SAMPLES 1942
Box holds 30 blue feather design samples.
CMV $42. MB.

CREAM CAKE SAMPLES 1949-55
Holds 6 shades of cream cake. **CMV $8. mint.**

FACE POWDER SAMPLES 1940-50s
Avon envelope holds 10 sample packets of
face powder. **CMV $3. mint.**

FACE POWDER DEMO SAMPLES 1949-50
Pink & white feather box holds 50 demo
packets of face powder. Used by Reps.
Packets are different. Was not sold to public.
CMV $15. MB.

DEMONSTRATOR KIT 1940
Box with gold Avon seal on lid holds lipstick
sample box, face powder palette, box of face
powder & 30 cotton puffs. **CMV complete set
$75. MB.**

LIPSTICK DEMONSTRATOR CASE 1942
Box holds 30 turquoise plastic or metal
samples or 30 brass bamboo samples. **CMV
$40. MB.** Lady's face on top of box.

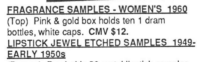

FRAGRANCE SAMPLES - WOMEN'S 1960
(Top) Pink & gold box holds ten 1 dram
bottles, white caps. **CMV $12.**
**LIPSTICK JEWEL ETCHED SAMPLES 1949-
EARLY 1950s**
(Bottom) Box holds 30 metal lipstick samples.
CMV $30.

COLORSTICK PENCIL SAMPLER 1977
Plastic base with sleeve lid holds color chart &
5 Colorstick pencils & brown plastic 2 hole
pencil sharpener, marked Avon. Used by
Reps to sell Colorstick products. **CMV $2. MB
complete.**

COLOGNE DEMONSTRATOR SET 1956
1 dram bottles of To A Wild Rose, Forever
Spring, Bright Night, Nearness, Elegante &
Cotillion. All different color caps, in pink & gold
box. **CMV $15. MB.** Also came out in Canada
in all white caps. **CMV $15. MB.**

BATH FRESHENER SAMPLES 1968
Colored caps, 7 samples. **CMV $6. MB.** 14
samples, white caps. **CMV $7. MB.**

FRAGRANCE COLOGNE SAMPLES 1965
Pink & gold box holds 10 cologne samples with
white caps. **CMV $7. MB.**

SAMPLES & DEMONSTRATOR KITS

LIPSTICK PACKS 1950s
Two different packs of 10 brass lipsticks. **CMV** $6. complete pack or 50 sample pack, brass. **CMV $15.** complete.

COLOGNE DEMONSTRATOR SET EARLY 1950s
1 dram bottles of Cotillion, Quaintance, Forever Spring, Golden Promise & To A Wild Rose. In green & gold box. Came in 5 & 6 bottle sets. **CMV $17. MB.**

NOSE GAY LIPSTICK DEMO KIT 1960
White foam, pink ribbon & flowers. Holds 4 white lipsticks. Came only in plum, orange, peach & cherry blossom. Made up like flower bouquet. **CMV $65.** mint.

LIPSTICK SAMPLE 1940
Gold metal case on display card. Came in 2 different size & style cards as shown. **CMV $1.** on card, lipstick only 25c.

LIPSTICK SAMPLE 1938
Same card as 1940 card only came with turquoise metal lipstick sample. **CMV $1.** on card, mint.

CUSTOM CONDITIONER 1971-72
(Left) 3/4 oz. bottle with white cap. Used in Avon beauty shops for professional use only. **CMV $10.**

NEW DIMENSION EXTRA & REGULAR 1971-72
(Right) 3/4 oz. glass bottle. Used in Avon beauty shops for professional use only. Top of bottle must be broken to use contents. **CMV $10.**

EYE SHADOW DEMONSTRATOR CARD 1960
Six gold metal eye shadow tubes. **CMV $2.** mint.

CLEAR 'N' COVER SAMPLE 1960s
(Left) **CMV $1.**
LUMINOUS CREAM EYE SHADOW 1960
(Right) **CMV $1.**

LIPSTICK DEMONSTRATOR 1961
A demonstrator piece sold to representatives for $1.35. Black plastic base with clear lucite dome. Came with silver deluxe lipstick with 4A on top (wrong lipstick shown in case). **CMV $22. MB.**

LIPSTICK DEMONSTRATOR KIT 1949
Black flannel roll-up kit holds 10 gold full size lipsticks. **CMV $30.** mint.

LIPSTICK DEMO 1978
Demo card holds turtle shell lipstick. **CMV $2.** mint on card.

LIPSTICK DEMONSTRATOR 1953
Green leatherette zippered case holds 5 gold lipsticks. **CMV $27.50 mint.**

FOUNDATION MAKEUP DUO 1977
(Left) Box holds 7 Even-Tone foundation tubes with white caps. Marked not for resale on back. **CMV $2. MB.**

COLORCREME MOISTURE LIPSTICKS DEMO SET 1978
(Right) Fruit basket design box holds 15 small white plastic sample lipsticks & 1 full size lipstick in silver & blue tube. Box came with outer sleeve. **CMV $2. MB.**

HARMONY ROUGE SAMPLES 1956
(Left) 5 sample bottles. **CMV $15.**

COLOGNE SAMPLES 1950
(Right) Green box holds 6 samples, colored lids. **CMV $12. MB.**

COLOGNE SAMPLES 1968
(Bottom) Green box with woven design holds 7 samples, all have yellow caps. **CMV $5. MB.**

MEN'S AFTER SHAVE SAMPLES
Two on left are 1960s. Box red & silver, bottles have red caps. **CMV $10. MB.** Two on right are late 60s & early 70s. Box is red woven design & black, bottles have red caps. Came with 2 different outer sleeves as shown on top. **CMV $6. each MB.**

TRIBUTE AFTER SHAVE SAMPLES 1963
(Left) Box of 10. **CMV $5.**

OCCUR! CREAM SACHET SAMPLES 1965
(Center) Box of 30. **CMV each $5.**

CREAM HAIR DRESS SAMPLES 1961
(Right) Box of 30 tubes. **CMV $5. MB, each tube 25c.**

LIPSTICK SAMPLES 1960s-70s
(Top Left) Turquoise plastic box holds 40 white plastic lipstick samples. **CMV 10c each sample or $5. MB complete.**

LIQUID POWDER SAMPLES 1967
(Top Right) Box of 12 samples, clear plastic top. **CMV $5. MB.**

POWDER SAMPLES 1958
(Bottom) 14 samples, square container. **CMV $7. MB.**

FOUNDATION DEMONSTRATOR 1960s
Clear glass bottles with white plastic lids. (Top to bottom) 6 bottle set, 12 bottle set; 10 bottles set. Front row 8 bottle set. **CMV all sets $5. MB.**

TISSUE DEMONSTRATOR 1949
Small packet of Avon tissues for demonstrations. **CMV $12. mint.**

FRAGRANCE DEMO KIT 1978-83
Plastic demo kit holds 6 sample bottles of Avon fragrance. **CMV $2.**

NAIL POLISH DEMONSTRATOR 1957
Six 1/2 dram bottles with white caps. **CMV $20. MB.**

FOUNDATION MAKEUP DEMO 1973
Box holds 7 bottles with white caps. Used by Reps only. **CMV $3. MB.**

FACIAL TISSUE SAMPLES 1937-44
Beige & green paper wrapper. **CMV $10. mint.**

SAMPLES & DEMONSTRATOR KITS

EYE SHADOW TRY-ONS 1964
Demo paper container with 50 match samples, double sided. **CMV $6. mint.** Eye shadow Try-Ons also came with 15 match samples. **CMV $5. mint.**

FLAVOR BUDS TOOTHPASTE SAMPLE 1950s
Red & white box with foil tear off samples. **CMV $7. MB.**

VERSATILITIES MAKEUP DEMO KIT 1982
Gray box with sleeve & black box lid holds black & gray lipstick & Versatilities nail polish & eye makeup. Used by reps for demo. **CMV $5. MB.**

POWDER SACHET PACKETS 1950s
Came in all fragrances, 10 in an envelope. **CMV $1. each or $7. for packet of 10 mint.**

NEW BEAUTY FOR EYES DEMO 1960
Cardboard card opens up with 6 brass lipstick samples, brass eye shadow stick, eyebrow penil & curl 'n' color. Used by Reps. **CMV $4. mint.**

COORDINATES MAKEUP DEMONSTRATOR 1983
Plastic display case used by Avon reps to show makeup products. Size 11" x 16". Red & white lip stick sample tubes, nail enamel fan demo, eye shadow, blush colors. Avon rep cost $20. **CMV $20. MB.**

BEAUTY EXPERIENCE DEMOS 1985
(Left) 6" gray plastic double mirrors. Gray box & felt bag. **CMV $4. MB.**
BEAUTY MAKE-UP DEMOS KIT
(Right) Came in gray box. **CMV $5. MB.**

HOLIDAY SURPRISE GIFT CARDS DEMO 1983
Green folder holds 6 miniature cards with small vial for fragrance on each. Sold to customers in sets of 3 cards. Demo card. **CMV $2.50, regular issue set of 3 cards CMV $1.**

FILM STRIP DEMO KITS 1970s
Used at sales meetings by managers to show & tell about new products & training programs. Kits contain 2 film strips & casette tapes. Many different kinds. **CMV $5. each.**

FACIAL TISSUES DEMO 1940s
Plain box of Avon Tissue used as demo for reps. **CMV $20. mint.**

FRAGRANCE SAMPLER 1984
Gold box holds 7 one inch vials of fragrance, 4 womens & 3 mens. **CMV $4. MB.**

FACE POWDER SAMPLE 1941
(Left) 1 metal face powder sample of Tulip "A" design on round card. Silverback says "Avon Products 1 dollar." **CMV $6. mint.**

FACE POWDER SAMPLE MASTERPIECE 1941
(Right) Blue card holds Tulip "A" metal samples of Rose & Ochre Rose. **CMV $7. mint.**

FACE POWDER SAMPLES 1930-36
Plain box of 30 silver & blue metal samples. With CPC card inside. **CMV $30. MB.**

BABY BOOK 1920
(Left) **CMV $50.**

CATALOG CPC 1898
(Center) 62 page sales catalog. Only has illustrations, not pictures of products. Book is dated 1898. **CMV $175.**

CATALOG CPC 1897
(Right) 62 page sales catalog. Book is dated 1897. **CMV $175.**

CPC MAIL ORDER CATALOG 1916-18
(Left) 4 1/2" x 6" gray cover 40 page booklet sent to customers in areas where CPC Reps did not call. Rare. **CMV $150.**

CPC CATALOG 1898
(Right) 5" x &' size blue cover and 64 pages in blue paper. Used by CPC Reps to sell products. Eureka Trade Mark on back cover. Very rare. **CMV $175.**

PAPER ITEMS - SALES CATALOGS

CPC CALLING CARD 1896
(Left) Has list of products on back side and CPC Co., 126 Chambers St., New York on front. **CMV $25.**

CPC SALES CATALOG 1896
(Right) Small 30 page booklet on products. Contains no pictures. Rare. **CMV $75.**

INSTRUCTIONAL MANUAL 1912
(Left) Used by CPC Slaes Managers. **CMV $50.**

CATALOG CPC 1912
(Center) 64 page sales catalog used by Reps. **CMV $150.**

WOMEN BEAUTIFUL BOOKLET 1909
(Right) Small booklet on massage cream. **CMV $35.**

CATALOGS CPC
1900 CPC Catalog shown on top left, top right 1898, bottom right 1908 and bottom left is 1915. Each one shows the item sold during that period by CPC and gives prices. 1915 was the last small catalog printed. 1916 they went to the large black hard bound color books. For comparison of size, the 1896 is 4 1/2" wide and 6 5/8" high. **CMV $150.**

CPC SALES CATALOG 1916-29
On bottom is black hard bound CPC Sales Catalog with 32 to 40 color pages. Book is 10 1/2" x 16" in size. The hard bound book was first issued in 1916 in the big size and last used in 1921. Gold lettering on front. 1922-1929 the black catalog is soft cover and 34 pages in color. 10" x 14 1/2" in size. These catalogs are usually not dated and very hard to find. **CMV** range from **$25.** in very bad condition to **$150** for a mint, new condition catalog. Each year a new book was issued.

CATALOGS - AVON 1930-57
1930-36 10" x 7" dark blue, silver Avon on cover. **CMV $20.** to **$30 depending on condition.**
1936-48 7 1/4" x 10 1/2" size, green cover, gold tulip A. **CMV $20 . to $30.**
1948-54 7 1/4" x 10 1/2" green cover, Avon in gold letters. **CMV $10. to $15.**
Bottom row left to right.
1954 A special gold cover catalog for Honor Presidents Award Reps. **CMV $20 each.**
1954-57 General issue was green cover 7 1/2" x 10 1/2", gold Avon and 4A design. **CMV $10.**
1956 Honor Award - Red cover catalog gold Avon and 4A design. **CMV $15.** Each of these catalogs was made to install or remove pages. The dates given reflect the years that each cover was issued. Each catalog was changed each year on the inner pages.

OUTLOOKS 1905-74
Outlooks were first printed in 1905 and given only to sales Reps. of CPC and Avon. They were to show new items coming out and also show awards they could win. The Outlook was discontinued in 1974 and the name was changed to "Avon Calling". Outlooks were given for each sales campaign during the year. CMV 1905 to 1930, $5. to $15.; 1930 to 1939, $2 to $5.; 1940 to 1949 $1. to $5.; 1950 to 1959, $1 to $4.; 1960 to 1965, $1. to $3.; 1960 to 1969, 50c. to $1.; 1970 to 1976 10c. to 25c. each.

POCKET CATALOG 1937
A small fold out leaflet brochure left with the customer to buy Avon products. CMV $25 mint.

CPC LADY INTRODUCTION CARD 1930's
3 1/2" x 5 1/4" card used by Reps. to introduce themselves to customers. $2.

CHRISTMAS AVON CATALOGS
Starting in the early 1930's thru 1956, Avon printed a special Christmas Sales Catalog showing many gifts never sold at any other time. These catalogs are rare and hard to find. CMV 1930's, $40. each. 1940's $35. each. 1950's $15. each.

CHRISTMAS CATALOG 1967
In upper right part of picture is special hard bound edition. CMV $8. mint.

SALES BROCHURES 1920's 30's
Fold out sales brochures given to customers by CPC and Avon Representatives. Each one shows all items sold in regular sales catalog. These are rare and in color. Left to right 1926, CMV $40.; 1929, CMV $35.; 1931-36, CMV $30. A 1933 brochure is laid out on bottom to see all the products offered.

CPC CALENDAR 1910
9" wide, 12 5/16" high. Printed in 6 colors. Given to all customers with order of 75c. or more. CMV $125. mint.

CPC CALENDAR 1909
Given only to best CPC customers. CMV $125. mint.

CALENDAR 1967
Avon Calling calendar. CMV $8. mint.

CALENDAR - AVON 1979-80
Large Avon calendar given to customers by Avon Reps. Came in big envelope each year. CMV $1. each mint in envelope.

ORDER BOOK 1981
(Bottom) Green & white CMV 50c.
ORDER BOOK 1982
(Top) Pink & white CMV 50c.

CPC INTRO BOOKLET 1928
(Left) 30 page booklet used by Reps to start selling Avon. **CMV $30. mint.**
CPC ORDER BOOKLET 1922
(Right) Used by Reps. to keep records of their orders. **CMV $25 mint.**

ORDER BOOK CPC AVON 1930
(Left) **CMV $15. mint.**
CUSTOMER LIST BOOKLET 1930
(Center) 8 pages. **CMV $5. mint.**
CPC CUSTOMER LIST BOOKLET 1928
(Right) 12 pages. **CMV $8. mint.**

ORDER BOOK CPC 1926
Order book used by Reps. shown with CPC envelope and announcement of new headquarters address in New York. **CMV $25 as shown.**

ORDER BOOKS (Left to right)
1933, 37, 42 Far right 1939 green order book cover. **CMV $15. each mint.**

ORDER BOOK COVER 1940
Dark green cover for order book imprinted with tulip "A" and name of representative. Given for sales during 1940 Founders Campaign. **CMV in envelope $20. - book only $15 mint.**

ORDER BOOK 1960's 70's
Misc. Avon Order Books used by Reps. **CMV 50c. each.**

ORDER BOOKS
(Left to right) 1920's CPC on cover (white cover). **CMV $20.**
1930's Tulip A design (white cover) **CMV $15.**
1940's Script A design (blue cover). **CMV $10.**
1950's 4A design (green cover). **CMV $5.**
1960's 4A design (white cover). **CMV $2.**
All must be in new condition for CMV given.

ADDRESS BOOK 1930's - 40's
(Left) Green leather, gold A design. **CMV $10.**
HONOR AWARD BOOK COVER 1956
(Center) Red plastic, gold design. **CMV $7.50.**

BUSINESS INTRO BOOK 1935
(Left) 20 page booklet on how to be a Avon Lady. Used by Reps. **CMV $5.**
BUSINESS INTRO BOOK 1931
(Right) 17 page booklet on how to be an Avon lady. Used by Reps. **CMV $5.**

AVON FACIAL TISSUE 1937-44
Turquoise & white paper box. Rare OSP 50c. **CMV $20 mint.**

ORDER BOOK 1960
(Left) **CMV $2.**
CALL TAG PADS 1958
(Right) Pad of tear off sheets left by Avon lady. **CMV $3. pad.**

FACIAL TISSUES 1932-36
Box of 160 tissues. OSP 50c. **CMV $30. mint.**

CLEANSING TISSUE 1930-32
Wrapped in cellophane. Package of 135 sheets. OSP 50c. CMV $15. mint.

CALOPAD SANITARY NAPKIN 1926
Cardboard box holds 12 napkins. OSP 50c. CMV $75. MB. Extremely Rare.

The 500 Club Certificate

CPC FIVE HUNDRED CLUB CERTIFICATE 1930's
Sent to a representative when she completes $500. worth of net business. CMV $25. mint.

BEAUTY SERVICE BOOK 1935
30 page booklet showing how to apply Avon cosmetics. Used by Reps. Came in Avon CPC envelope. CMV $10 mint with envelope.

CPC BOOKLET
(Left) Cover says "Introducing You To The CPC". CMV $30.

GREAT OAK BOOKLET 1945
(Right) 20 page, blue cover. Given to Reps. in 1945. Written by D.H. McConnell, founder of CPC in 1903. Came with letter from Russel Rooks who became President of Avon. Rare. CMV $50. with letter.

EARLY 1930's CPC AVON FIVE HUNDRED CLUB
Certificate given to representatives for selling $500 worth of Avon products. CMV $20. each, mint.

50TH ANNIVERSARY GOLD QUILL PEN & LETTER 1936
Sent to representatives to announce the 50th year celebration. The circle stands for the "Avon Family Circle", the feather and quill indicated the opportunities to "Feather Your Nests". Comes complete with attached 50th anniversary letter. It folds in center. Did not come separate. CMV complete as pictured $50. mint.

PAVING THE WAY 1937
Booklet used by the Reps. in 1930's to help train them for better sales. Tulip A on cover. CMV $8.

McCONNELL LETTER BOOK 1930
174 pages of letters from Managers to D. H. McConnell, Avon Founder. Rare. No price established.

CPC SALES REP CONTRACT 1930's
Used to sign up CPC Reps. for sales in early 1930's. Came in CPC Avon business envelope. Shown also with Customer List booklet & booklet "Now You are in Business for Yourself." CMV $25 complete as shown.

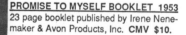

PROMISE TO MYSELF BOOKLET 1953
23 page booklet published by Irene Nenemaker & Avon Products, Inc. CMV $10.

BEAUTY SERVICE BOOKLET 1934
24 page beauty tip book. **CMV $10.**

MANAGERS INFORMATION BOOKLET 1945
8 1/4" x 9" - 18 page booklet for managers to show new Avon Reps. for general information on Avon products. The cover of this booklet is the same artwork Avon Products used to make the 1977 National Asociation of Avon Clubs plate advertised in C26-77 Avon Calling. **CMV $15.**

HOW TO CONDUCT GOOD SALES MEETINGS BOOKLET 1948
Black leatherette spiral bound. Booklet used by Avon managers. **CMV $10.**

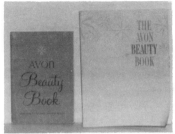

BEAUTY BOOK 1964
(Left) 128 page book used by Reps on beauty counciling. **CMV $4.**
BEAUTY BOOK 1967
(Right) 140 page book used by Reps. on beauty counciling. **CMV $4.**

ROSE STAMPS 1961
Page of 75 rose stamps for Avon Rep use in C-2-1961. Stamps say " Avons 75th Year". **CMV $20.**

BUSINESS CARD - AVON 1968
CMV $3. BO.

AD DISPLAYS 1950's
Magazine advertising on hardbacks. **CMV $15 each.**

NOTEBOOK COVERS -MANAGERS 1960's
3 different blue plastic binders used by Avon Managers. One is Avon Beauty Notes, Group Meetings and Avon on 3rd one. Small one is red. **CMV $3. each.**

WEST GERMAN BRANCH OPENING CARD 1950's
Card introducing the starting of Avon operations in Hamburg, Germany. **CMV $10 mint.**

CHRISTMAS CARD 1950's
(Left) **CMV $1. each.**
COASTER FROM AVON 1970
(Right) Different varieties. **CMV $1 each.**

CHILDREN'S COLOR BOOKS 1960's - 70's
Small World, Mickey Mouse, Peanuts, I Wish I Could. **CMV $2. each.**

IVORY COAST AFRICA 1ST ISSUE AVON CATALOG 1978
47 page catalog given to each Avon manager in U.S. with letter from Avon Products announcing expansion into Africa. **CMV $7.**

MANAGERS SALES MEETING NOTEBOOK 1962
Campaign 15,16,17,18 sales meeting plans. Red and white Christmas tree. **CMV $25.**

BEAUTY BOOK 1963
CMV $2.

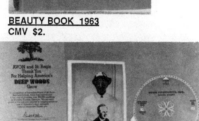

DEEP WOODS ST. REGIS CARD 1972
(Left) Special thank you card for Avon Reps from St. Regis Paper Co. **CMV $1.**

DAVE'S WAITING PICTURE 1970's
(Center) Picture of David Mitchell, Chairman of Avon Products. No Price established.

SALES CHART 1960's
(Right) Green & white paper. **CMV $2.**

CHRISTMAS CARD - CANADA 1959
Avon Christmas card given to customers by Reps. in Canada. **CMV $3.**

MOTHER'S DAY CARD 1976
Given to customers in Mother's day orders 1976 by Avon reps. **CMV $1.**

CALENDAR 1966
Quarterly calendar for Sept., Oct., Nov., Dec. showing Avon for the 1966 Christmas selling season. **CMV $5.**

NOTECARDS 1978
Box of blank Avon note cards. **CMV $4. MB.**

NAPKIN "SWEET DREAMS" 1978
(Left) White napkin with moon & sunrise scene. **CMV $1.**

NAPKIN "GETTING BETTER EVERY DAY" 1979
(Right) For President's club members. White napkin, red letters. **CMV $1.**

NAPKIN "GROUND BREAKING CEREMONY" 1978
(Bottom) Red napkin from Pasadena branch ground breaking ceremony. **CMV $1.**

GREETING CARDS FROM AVON

FATHER'S DAY CARD 1977
(Left) Red & white card. **CMV $1.**

SEYMOUR KENT CARD 1977
(Center) Red card, came with white lace handkerchief made by Desco. **CMV $1.**

FATHER'S DAY CARD 1969
(Right) Straight 8 on front. **CMV $1.**

GREETING CARDS - AVON 1970's
Many different cards used by Avon managers & Reps for different occasions. **CMV about 50c. each.**

AUTO HANDBOOK 1970s
Red plastic 2 ring instruction manual for
employees of Avon with company leased cars.
CMV $5.

CATALOG - HONG KONG 1978
Avon sales catalog from Hong Kong. **CMV $6.**

LETTER FROM CPC 1896
On CPC letterhead. Letter to CPC managers.
CMV $45.

CPC INK BLOTTER 1912
Used by Reps in early 1900s. **CMV $35.**

**CPC INSTRUCTIONAL
MANUAL 1920**
14 page booklet used to
train early day Avon Reps.
Tells them how and what
to do to be a sales lady for
CPC. No pictures. **CMV
$25.**

CPC D. H. McCONNELL LETTER 1900s
On CPC letterhead. Hand written by D. H.
McConnell, founder of Avon to his factory
workers. **CMV for any hand written D. H.
McConnell letter dated 1890s to 1930s
would be $25. to $50. depending on buyer.**
Note that most later years McConnell's
signature is rubber stamped and not hand
written.

SALES MANAGERS CONTRACT 1913
Paper agreement for Avon ladies in early
1900s. Signed by D. H. McConnell, founder of
Avon. **CMV $25.**

**CPC CHRISTMAS GREETING CARD
EARLY 1900s**
1c post card sent out at Christmas time. 126
Chambers Street, New York is the return
address. **CMV $25.**

DEPOT MANAGERS CONTRACT CPC 1909
Paper agreeement between CPC and sales lady. CMV $40. mint.

LETTER FROM AVON 1936
Misc. letters from Avon may vary in price depending on the year. Any letters personally signed by D. H. McConnell, founder of Avon in his own handwriting should be worth at least $25. Letter shown is a copy. CMV $15. mint.

RING SIZE PAPER 1979
Blue and white paper Avon ring sizer issued before plastic sizers were delivered. Very short issue to Avon reps, issued C25-79. Sizes 3 to 9. CMV $1. mint.

TEAM LEADER ORGANIZER 1979
10 1/2" x 12" size light brown binder organizer. came in white box. Team Leader Organizer on front of binder. CMV $2. MB.

BIRTHDAY CARD - AVON 1975
Birthday cards made only for Avon & sent to reps on their birthday. Avon on back & inside. This type of card has been used for years. CMV $1. each.

PLAN BOOKS FOR MANAGERS 1973
CMV $5.

NAPKINS - AVON 1970s-80s
President's Club "Getting Better Every Day"; United Way "We're Going To Make You Feel Beautiful". 1978 Ground Breaking Ceremony, Pasadena, California, April 13, 1978. CMV 50c each.

PLACE MATS 1971
Four Seasons - Robert Woods signed plastic place mats for Avon. Had choice of one of the four when you bought certain products. CMV $3. each.

HERITAGE ALMANAC 1975
1975 calendar given to District Managers only. Duplicate of 1929 calendar, each page shows different outlook. Limited edition, 2,678 given. CMV $25.

MANAGERS INTRODUCTION BOOK 1972
Turquoise binder holds 25 glossy pages. Managers use to get new Avon ladies to sell Avon. CMV $5.

CARDS FROM AVON 1970s
Sent to representatives. CMV $2. each. Many different ones.

SHAVING PADS 1900's
2 different-(Left) with lady and (Right) with Joe Jefferson. **CMV $60. each.**

GEORGE WASHINGTON REPRESENTA-TIVE GIFT LETTER 1976
Folder (on left) and a copy of a letter George Washington wrote from Mt. Vernon. Given at sales meeting in February. **CMV $5.**

DESIGNERS COLLECTION CHRISTMAS CARDS 1971
Box of 25 Avon Christmas cards, all the same design. Came in 36 different designs. No. 1 shown. OSP $4. to $10. per box. Back of each card marked Avon Products, Inc. & gives the card number. **CMV each card 50c. to $1.**
DESIGNER COLLECTION CHRISTMAS CARD SAMPLE SET 1971
Box of 36 different Avon Christmas cards used by Avon Reps. for sales. Short issue. **CMV $35. complete set.**

LOVE NOTES 1981
4 different notes with envelopes 3 1/4" x 4 3/4". Given free to customers with purchase for 1 campaign only. **CMV $1 set.**

ACTIVE WOMEN'S COOKBOOK 1980
80 page cookbook from Avon. **CMV $5.**

CIRCLE OF EXCELLENCE ITEMS 1973
Given to managers on C of E trip to Bermuda. White plastic airline ticket holder; menu, program of events, airline menu. Honor Roll Booklet, blue & gold booklet listing all of C of E managers for 1973. **CMV $5. each.**

BEAUTY CALENDAR 1981
Given to customers by Avon representatives. Comes in 2 different envelopes. **CMV $1.**

ORDER BOOKS 1957
2 different-1 has green Christmas tree on cover & the other has blue cover with tube of new dental cream. **CMV $5 each.**

SHAVING PADS 1908
(Left) Girl holding flowers on cover. **CMV $60. mint.**
SHAVING PADS 1915
(Right) Lady with big flower on hat on cover. **CMV $60.**

TRAINING PORTFOLIO'S 1985
Both gray plastic-1 for District Managers. **CMV $5.** 1 for Division Managers. **CMV $10.**

BOOK COVERS 1980
Plastic book covers from Avon. Used by Managers. **CMV $3. each.**

ONE TO ONE AVON AD PLAQUE 1980
Ad on hardboard given to Avon managers.
Self-standing. **CMV $10.**

ENGINE EARS COLOR TOY 1982
Pop out Easter train from Avon. 12" long. Must
be mint. **CMV $1 mint.**

SHIPPING BOXES
Single carton item boxes for mailing new
products to Avon Reps. Boxes shown are
1941. This type of box has been used since
the 1930's to 1960's. **CMV add $5. for CPC
box & $3. for Avon box above cost of
product inside.**

**DESIGNERS COLLECTIONS CHRISTMAS
CARD CATALOGUE DEMONSTRATOR
1971**
Large spiral bound picture album holds 1 each
of 36 different Christmas cards sold by Avon in
1971. **CMV $75. complete, mint with all 36
cards, album only, no cards, $45.** Never
sold to public.

VALENTINE FUN KIT 1982
Package of red & white heart gift wrap paper, 1
gift card & 4 gum stickers. Given to Avon
customers free. **CMV $1. mint package.**

**MRS. CLAUS' KITCHEN SURPRISE
CALENDAR 1983**
8" x 12" folded 12" x 15" open. Six different
fragrance on calendar. **SSP $5. CMV $3.**

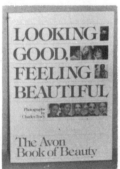

**LOOKING GOOD, FEELING BEAUTIFUL
BOOK 1981-82**
Book of beauty by Avon Products. 95 pages,
small booklet. SSP 75c. **CMV 75c.**

CALENDAR OF ROSES 1983
Hard bound green cover. Comes with outer
sleeve. 7" x 9" size. SSP $3. **CMV $2. mint.**

CHRISTMAS SURPRISE CALENDAR 1982
Paper foldout, blue cover. SSP $4. **CMV $1.**

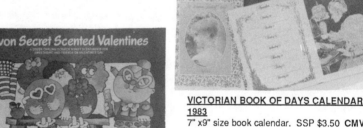

**VICTORIAN BOOK OF DAYS CALENDAR
1983**
7" x 9" size book calendar. SSP $3.50 **CMV
$2.50 MB.**

CALENDAR BEAUTIFUL STYLE 1982
Features women's designs from the past.
Comes in Avon envelope. **CMV $1 mint.**

SECRET SCENTED VALENTINES 1984
12 cutout cards, 2 of each of 6 different
designs. Must be all together to be mint. SSP
$3. **CMV $2 mint.**

GOODY-VILLE PUZZLE 1983
9 1/2 x 12" scratch & sniff puzzle. Comes in blue cardboard envelope. SSP $5. CMV $1 mint.

CHILDHOOD MOMENTS CALENDAR 1983
Comes in envelope on left. CMV 50c.

ADVERTISING

Avon and magazine advertising began in March, 1906, but was rather short lived with only a few California Perfume ads appearing in Good Housekeeping magazine. For the next thirty years the company relied on their representatives and the worth of their products to spread their name and gain new customers.

By 1936 a dramatic change took place in the company's attitude and in April of that year a national advertising campaign was begun. Once again the ever popular Good House-keeping was used as their advertising vehicle. The first advertisements were black & white and not very impressive in comparison to their competitor's full color, full page layouts.. Public response was good enough, however, to continue the series and in 1938 Avon ads began to appear in the Christian Science Monitor as well as Good Housekeeping. The following year Women's Home Companion was added and so on until by the end of the 1940's Avon ads were appearing in 15 of the nations leading publications.

Along the way, color ads and full page ads, as well as some two page ads were introduced. To date Avon ads have appeared in over 40 different magazines and in 1975 found their way into some metropolitan newspapers.

We do not know how many Avon collectors have already begun to collect the ads, but the number is certain to grow in existance. Not only do they reflect the company's public appearance, but they also picture many of Avon's now collectable products.

To date Avon has produced over 500 different magazine advertisements; a spectacular number by any standard. Of these, many were published in as many as 12 magazines at the same time while others were produced for a specific marlket and appeared in only one publication making them quite naturally difficult to obtain. Other factors involved in valuing ads are the content, number of products shown and their collectability and naturally, age. Other considerations are size, 1/2 or full page and if it is in color or black and white.

The prices shown are mainly in relation to age and degree of difficulty to find. The other factors mentioned will cause this price to fluctuate and the value shown should be considered only as a broad guide and by no means a definate price. This "Avon Advertis-ing" section was prepared by Dalene Thomas.

MARCH 1937
CMV $4.

This is "Roses"
The new odor—the most delicate, and yet the most fragrant and lasting Per-fume made. "Roses" is also exclusive—nothing else like it anywhere. Made of the finest imported French Roses, put up in beautiful glass bottles—price 40 cents per ounce. Try it and get acquainted with the famous

C. P. Toilet Specialties
A line of over 50 different high grade articles used by women of refinement in almost every town in the United States. Sold only by local representatives, never in stores.
Write for name of local representative and the C.P. Book which illustrates and describes the complete line, with many suggestions on Beauty and Health.
A few profitable agencies open for good representatives.

California Perfume Co.
San Francisco   New York   Kansas City

GOOD HOUSEKEEPING ONLY MARCH 1906
CMV $25.

Shop at home
THE AVON WAY

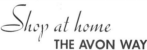

GOOD HOUSEKEEPING ONLY APRIL 1936
CMV $5.

249

Women love these new Avon Cosmetics and

Imagine! You can select the newest, the finest, the most beautifully packaged cosmetics in the world *without stirring from your home*. Glamorous make-up in all its intriguing new forms . . . scientifically formulated creams and lotions for the loving care of your complexion . . . a wide and wonderful variety of fragrance for you to spray on, splash on, dust on, cream on—you choose these with the help of your Avon Representative.

"AVON CALLING" means a pleasant face-to-face chat with your friendly Avon Representative who brings exciting beauty news to your home.

AVON COSMETICS FOR ALL THE FAMILY ARE BROUGHT TO YOUR HOME BY YOUR AVON REPRESENTATIVE

. . . men enjoy good grooming with Avon

Look at these new grooming products for men! Handsome, aren't they? And their performance is first-rate. As for the scent, it's nice and crisp. A complete selection for shaving, for protection, for after-shower use . . . together with excellent hair dressings. Men who care about the impression they make, enjoy using Avon.

AVON
RADIO CITY, NEW YORK

Your Avon Representative is delighted to call at your home. Welcome her and enjoy selecting cosmetics and toiletries the Avon way.

AVON COSMETICS FOR ALL THE FAMILY ARE BROUGHT TO YOUR HOME BY YOUR AVON REPRESENTATIVE

JANUARY 1960
CMV $3.

Think how great it would be to find Avon gifts under your tree!

How can you feel sophisticated, romantic, feminine, modern —whenever you wish? Wear an Avon fragrance. Avon has colorful fragrance gifts to hang on a tree, to tuck in a tote, to sit prettily on a dressing table. In one fascinating fragrance form after another! An Avon Representative also brings soothing bath oils, festive lipsticks, exciting makeup—designed in a gay holiday spirit to please everyone you know. Avon gifts are always a joy to give, a joy to receive.

AVON cosmetics
ROCHELLE PLAZA, NEW YORK

Wear Avon's 12 ways of fragrance for the 12 days of Christmas!

NOVEMBER 1967
CMV $3.

AVON'S NEW BLUE BLAZER FINDS A YOUNG MAN'S SPIRIT!

Blue Blazer. Avon's new line of grooming for men with a carefree new look with style! From the crisp, clean scent to the handsome case, new Blue Blazer matches a jaunty outlook. When the Avon Representative calls be sure to talk about Avon's Blue Blazer grooming aids. Only your Avon Representative brings new Blue Blazer right to your home.

AVON CALLING with Blue Blazer, newest additions to Avon's fine products for men.

AVON FOR MEN
RADIO CITY, NEW YORK

OCTOBER 1962
CMV $3.50

250

Elizabeth Schuller, Red Cross Clubmobile Group Captain, was among the first Red Cross workers to land in Normandy where she showed great courage and initiative, and exerted effort beyond the call of duty.

A tribute to the Red Cros

This Avon Medallion of Honor has been created in recognition of the work women are doing in the service of humanity. This award to Miss Schuller is the first of a series to be presented to women of outstanding achievement, who have been chosen by the following committee of prominent women:

Miss Pennie Hurst, *famous novelist*
Miss Gladys Swarthout, *Metropolitan Opera star*
Miss C. Mildred Thompson, *Dean of Vassar College*

For outstanding service to the Red Cross and to America by materially aiding morale on the battlefield, Avon presents the Medallion of Honor for Women of Achievement to Miss Elizabeth Schuller of Montclair, N. J.

Miss Schuller's devotion to duty is typical of the unstinting contribution that thousands of Red Cross workers, here and abroad, are making to alleviate the suffering of others. On all fronts the Red Cross is first to bring comfort to fighting men and prisoners, and cheer to distressed civilians. Our efforts at home must not slacken. Give liberally NOW.

KEEP YOUR RED CROSS AT HIS SIDE IN 1945!

Avon

COSMETICS • AT RADIO CITY, NEW YORK

ch 1945 Good Housekeeping   Copyright 1945, Avon Pro.

MARCH 1945
CMV $4.

Perfection
MOTHICIDE

Protect precious woolens and furs with Perfection Mothicide! Comes in the form of clean, white crystals. Destroys both moths and larvae more effectively than moth balls...offers a more pleasing odor which vanishes quickly when clothes are aired. A complete selection of Avon Perfection household and kitchen products plus fine quality Avon Cosmetics are available through the Avon Representative who brings them direct to your home. Welcome her when she calls. Enjoy this convenient shopping service.

Perfection
MOTHICIDE
An AVON Product

Guaranteed by Good Housekeeping

Radio City   New York

SEPTEMBER 1947
CMV $5

PERFECTION - ALL PRODUCTS

Grading condition is paramount. CMV can vary 60-90% on condition.

SILVER CREAM POLISH 1923
8 oz. metal can. OSP 30c. **CMV $40. mint.** 16 oz. can. OSP 54c. **CMV $45. mint. Add $5. MB.**

PERFECTION SILVER CREAM POLISH 1931-41
1/2 lb. brown, orange and white can. OSP 35c. **CMV $25. MB, $25. can only mint.**

PERFECTION SILVER CREAM POLISH 1941-52
Green, brown and white. 8 oz can. Sold 1941-43 then 1946-52. OSP 49c. **CMV $15 mint, $20. MB.**

SILVER CREAM POLISH 1943
Stick on white and green label over name of other products on can. Used during shortage of products during war. OSP 49c. **CMV $25. mint with label shown.**

SILVER PLATE POLISH 1906
4 oz. glass bottle with metal cap. OSP 25c. **CMV $100., $115. BO.**
CPC SILVER CREAM POLISH 1918
6 oz. jar, metal lid. OSP 30c. **CMV $85. mint.**

PERFECTION SPOTS OUT 1943-46
9 1/2 oz. glass jar, white metal lid. OSP 45c. **CMV $22., $25. MB.**
PERFECTION KWICK METAL POLISH 1943-46
11 oz. glass jar with white metal cap. OSP 39c. **CMV $40-$50 MB. Rare.**
PERFECTION SILVER CREAM POLISH 1943-46
10 1/2 glass jar with white metal lid. OSP 49c. **CMV $22., $25. MB.**

MOTHICIDE 1925
1 lb. metal can on right. Paper label around can is in English and French. OSP $1. **CMV $60. mint. CMV as shown with spots $20.** 1/2 lb. metal can on left, OSP 50c. **CMV $50. mint.**

MOTHICIDE 1925
1/2 lb. metal can with blue label. OSP 48c. **CMV $65. MB. $50. can mint only.**

PERFECTION MOTHICIDE 1931-41
1/2 lb. orange, brown and white can. OSP 50c. **CMV $25. MB, $20. can only mint.** Add $5. for CPC label.

MOTHICIDE 1923
1/2 lb. metal can 3 1/4" across. Paper label in English and French. OSP 48c. **CMV $40. mint.**

PERFECTION MOTHICIDE 1954-57
8 1/2 bronze metal can, green top, three different edges on lid. Sold 1954-57. **CMV $10.** Red metal can sold 1957 only. **CMV $12..** OSP each 55c. **Add $2 MB each.**

MOTHICIDE 1943-46
Glass jar with white lid, green and white label- Rare. OSP 55c. **CMV $30, $40 MB.** Green white and bronze label. **CMV $20., $30. MB.**

PERFECTION SPOTS OUT LIQUID 1929
(Left) 4 oz. bottle with CPC on black cork stopper and blue label. OSP 50c. **CMV $45. MB. $40. BO.**
PERFECTION LIQUID SPOTS OUT 1931-34
(Right) 4 oz. size. CPC on cork stopper. OSP 40c. **CMV $40. MB. $32.50. BO.**

LIQUID SPOTS OUT 1925-29
4 oz. clear glass bottle, black cork cap. blue label. OSP 40c. **CMV $50. MB, $45. BO mint.**

LIQUID SPOTS OUT 1934-41
4 oz. bottle. Orange, brown and white label. Black cap. OSP 40c. **CMV $30. MB - $25. BO.**

LIQUID SPOTS OUT 1946-58
4 oz. green smooth or threaded cap. 2 different labels. One box brown and one box bronze. OSP 50c. **CMV $20. MB., $15. BO.**

SPOTS OUT 1920
Metal can. OSP 33c. **CMV $70., can only mint $85. MB.**

SPOTS OUT 1923
8 oz metal can. OSP 33c. **CMV $40. mint.** 16 oz. can not shown, OSP 59c. **CMV $45. mint. Add $10 each MB.**

SPOTS OUT 1931-41
1/2 LB. ORANGE, BROWN AND WHITE CAN.
OSP 40C. **CMV $25. MB. $20.** can only
mint.

SHOE WHITE 1915
Box holds 5 oz. sack of Shoe White Powder.
OSP 25c. **CMV $90. MB.**

SHOE WHITE 1920
Green box holds 5 oz. sack of powder. OSP
25c. **CMV $90. MB.**

SPOTS OUT 1941-43
8 oz. green, brown and white can. Sold 1941-
43 then 1946-48. OSP 45c. **CMV $20., $25.
MB.**

**PERFECTION LIQUID SHOE WHITE 1931-
35**
(Right) Box holds 4 oz. bottle with cork
stopper. Brown, orange and white label. OSP
50c. **CMV $25., $30. MB.**
LIQUID SHOE WHITE 1928-30
(Left) 4 oz. glass bottle with cork stopper.
OSP 35c. **CMV $50. MB, $45. BO mint.**

**PERFECTION LIQUID SHOE WHITE 1935-
41**
Box holds 4 oz bottle with brown cap. Brown,
orange and white label. OSP 50c. **CMV
$25., $30. MB.**

LIQUID SHOE WHITE SAMPLE 1935-41
(Center) 1/2 oz. black cap. CPC on label.
CMV $40. Also with Avon Products label only
white cap. **CMV $25.**
LIQUID SHOE WHITE SAMPLE 1935-41
(Left) Same as above, different label. **CMV
$40.**
LIQUID SHOE WHITE SAMPLE 1941-57
(Right) 3/4 oz. white cap, green and brown
label. **CMV $35.**

Sample Courtesy Can

KWICK CLEANING POLISH SAMPLE 1922
Small sample can issued for one month on
introduction of this product. Rare. **CMV $75.**

**PERFECTION LIQUID SHOE WHITE 1941-
57**
4 oz. green smooth or threaded cap. Two
different labels. OSP 37c. **CMV $10. BO,
$12.50 MB.**

KWICK CLEANING POLISH 1922
8 oz. metal can, brown label. OSP 24c. **CMV
$70. MB. $55.** can only. Also came in 16 oz.
can. OSP 45c. **CMV $75. MB. $60.** can
only mint.

KWICK METAL POLISH 1925
1/2 lb. metal can with brown label. OSP 24c.
CMV $60., $45. only mint.

PERFECTION KWICK METAL POLISH 1931-41
1/2 lb. orange, brown and white can. OSP 35c. **CMV $35. MB. $30. can.**
KWICK METAL POLISH 1954-57
Green & brown 13 oz. can on right. Two different lids. OSP 55c. **CMV $30. mint.**

PERFECTION LAUNDRY CRYSTALS PERFUMED 1941-48
Green, brown and white can with green lid holds 13 crystals. Metal top and bottom and paper sides. Sold 1941-46. All metal sold 1946-48. OSP 29c. **CMV $20 each mint.**
PERFECTION LAUNDRY CRYSTALS PERFUMED 1943-46
All cardboard war time packaging. **CMV $30. mint.** Also came with white top and bottom. 4 different labels.

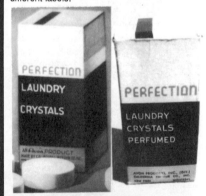

PERFECTION LAUNDRY CRYSTALS 1931-36
Brown, orange and white paper box. OSP 25c. **CMV $30. MB.**
LAUNDRY CRYSTALS PERFUMED 1934-36
(Right) Brown, white and orange box holds 13 white crystals. OSP 25c. **CMV $30. mint.**

LAUNDRY CRYSTALS PERFUMED 1938-41
Brown, orange and white paper sides, tin top and bottom. Top cut out to be used as bank. Held 13 crystals. Came with Avon and CPC labels. OSP 27c. **CMV $30. Avon label, $40. CPC label.**

POWDERED CLEANER 1928-31
12 oz. blue box. OSP 25c. **CMV $75. mint $90 MB.**

POWDERED CLEANER 1931-34
Red, white and blue. 16 oz. can. OSP 35c. **CMV $75. mint. $90. MB.**

PERFECTION PREPARED STARCH 1941-48
8 oz. brown, green and white can. Two different labels. Shiny top or painted top. OSP 39c. **CMV $20 mint. $25. MB.** 1943-46 had paper sides. **CMV $20 mint.**

PERFECTION POWDERED CLEANER 1934-41
16 oz. orange, brown and white can. Two different labels. Cardboard sides, metal bottom. OSP 35c. **CMV $25. MB. $20 can only mint.**

CARPET RENOVATOR 1906
Box holds 1 bar of soap. SSP 35c. **CMV $85. MB.**

FURNITURE POLISH 1912
8 oz. 1/2 pint bottle, cork stopper, clear glass. OSP 50c. **CMV $100., $125. BO.**

PERFECTION FURNITURE POLISH 1936-41
12 and 32 oz. brown, orange and white can.
Three different labels. OSP 75c. and $1.35.
**CMV $15., $20. MB. CMV 32 oz. size $20.,
$25. MB.**

FURNITURE POLISH 1915
(Left) 8 oz. clear glass bottle, cork stopper.
CMV $85. BO mint. $100. MB. Same label
is on rare amber bottle.
PERFECTION FURNITURE POLISH 1943-46
(Right) 12 oz. bottle, metal cap. Two different
labels. Green and white label, and white and
bronze. **CMV green and white add $5.** OSP
69c. **CMV $22., $25. MB.**

PERFECTION FURNITURE POLISH 1931-36
12 oz. brown, orange and white can. OSP
CMV $20., $25. MB.
FURNITURE POLISH 1944 Only
12 oz. bottle, black cap. OSP 79c. **CMV $40.
BO. $45. MB.**

FURNITURE POLISH 1916
12 oz metal can with green label. OSP 50c.
CMV $75. BO, $65 can only mint. Also
came in qt. size. OSP $1.20, 1/2 gal. size.
OSP $2.25, **CMV $75. mint.**
FURNITURE POLISH 1915
8 oz. amber glass, cork stopper. Very rare.
CMV $150. bottle only mint. $175. MB.

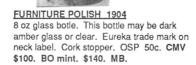

FURNITURE POLISH 1904
8 oz glass botle. This bottle may be dark
amber glass or clear. Eureka trade mark on
neck label. Cork stopper. OSP 50c. **CMV
$100. BO mint. $140. MB.**

CPC FURNITURE POLISH 1906
(Right Center) 8 oz. bottle with cork stopper.
Came as round or square bottle, same label.
OSP 50c. **CMV $100., $125. MB.**
FURNITURE POLISH 1912
(Left) 8 oz. bottle, cork stopper, label also read
for automobile bodies. OSP 50c. **CMV $125.
MB, $100. BO mint.**

FURNITURE POLISH 1925
12 oz. metal can with blue label on right. OSP
48c. Same as above only in 32 oz. on left,
blue metal can. OSP $1.20. Back side labels
in French on both cans. **CMV $70. can only
mint, $85. MB each.**

BAKING POWDER SAMPLE 1936-41
Orange, brown and white 1 oz can, 2 1/4" high.
Two different size samples. Rare. **CMV $40
each mint.**

PERFECTION MACHINE OIL 1941-48
3 oz. brown, green and white can. Sold 1941-
43 then 1946-48. OSP 29c. **CMV $15. MB.
$10. can only.**

255

POWDERED CLEANER 1943-46
16 oz. paper can, green, bronze and white. OSP 39c. **CMV $20. mint. $25. MB.**
POWDERED CLEANER 1941-43 then 1946-57
16 oz. paper sides with metal top and bottom. Green, bronze, and white. OSP 39c. **CMV $15., $20. MB** Five different labels & a Canada label.

PERFECTION AUTO POLISH 1933-36
1 pt. brown, orange and white can. Two different labels. OSP 75c. **CMV $50. MB. $40 can only. Rare.**

CARPET RENOVATOR SOAP 1915-20
Paper box with one bar carpet soap, 2 different boxes shown. First issued about 1893. OSP 35c. **CMV $90. each mint.**

AVON POWDERED CLEANER SAMPLE 1928-31
Small blue, orange and white paper box. 3 oz. size sample. CPC on label Rare. **CMV $100 mint.**

PERFECTION PREPARED STARCH 1931-41
6 oz. brown, orange and white can. Sold 1931-36. **CMV $25., $30. MB.** Same can in 8 oz. size sold 1936-41, two diffeent labels as shown. **CMV $20., $25. MB.**

FURNITURE POLISH 1941
All green, bronze and white metal can. 12 oz. can 1941-43 then 1946-48. OSP 69c. **CMV $12., $15. MB.** 16 oz can 1948-51. OSP 79c. **CMV $12.** 32 oz can 1941-43 OSP $1.29 **CMV $25.** Add $5 **MB.**

AUTO LUSTRE 1930-33
(Left) Blue 1 pt. can. OSP 75c. **CMV can only $75 mint. $85. MB.**
AUTO LUSTRE SAMPLE 1930-33
(Right) 1 oz. blue metal can. Rare. **CMV $90.**

OLIVE OIL 1895
8 oz. glass bottle with cork stopper. OSP 50c. **CMV $100 bottle only. $85. BO.** Also came in 1 pt., 1 qt., 1/2 gal, and 1 gal size. **CMV $125. rare.**
OLIVE OIL 1905
16 oz. bottle. OSP $1.25. **CMV $100. mint, rare.**

CPC EASYDAY OR SIMPLEX AUTOMATIC CLOTHES WASHER 1918
Made of pure zinc. Washer is 11" high and 9" in diameter. Has Easyday name on top and Pat. July 4, 1916. OSP $2. CMV $100.

CPC MARVEL ELECTRIC SILVER CLEANER 1918
Metal plate has Marvel name and Pat. Jan. 11, 1910. OSP 75c. CMV $50.

PERFECTION MACHINE OIL 1943-46
3 oz. smooth side glass, metal cap. OSP 29c. CMV $20. BO, $25. MB.

MACHINE OIL "RIBBED SIDE"
Short issue 3 oz. ribbed sided bottle, metal cap. OSP 29c. Came in two different boxes as shown. CMV $25. BO, $30. MB.

OLIVE OIL 1915
8 oz. glass bottle with cork stopper. OSP 50c. CMV $100. MB, $90. BO. Also came in 16 oz., 1 qt, 1/2 gal., 1 gal. size. CMV $100, $125 MB, rare.

BAKING POWDER 1915
16 oz. container. OSP 25c. CMV $80. MB, $65. container only mint.. Also came in 1 lb. and 5 lb. size. CMV $90 mint.

SUPREME HUILE D'OLIVE OIL 1923
Green & yellow can in 1 pt. size. OSP $1.35. CMV $75. MB, $60. can only mint. Also came in qt,. size can. OSP $2.50. CMV $85. MB, $70. can only mint.

PERFECTION MACHINE OIL 1931-41
3 oz. brown, orange and white can. Two different labels. OSP 26c. CMV $18 BO, $12.50 can only mint.

EXTRACT OF LEMON 1908
16 oz. glass stopper. OSP $3.25. CMV $150. BO mint. $175. MB.

PERFECTION OLIVE OIL 1931-41
1 pt. orange, brown and white can. Two different labels. OSP $1.35. CMV $40. MB, $35. can only.

FRUIT FLAVORING 1908
2 oz. embossed Fruit California Perfume Co. Flavors. Had paper label on reverse side. CMV $35. BO, $100. mint with paper label, $125. MB. Some came with reversed "A" in California. Add $5 for reversed "A".

BAKING POWDER 1943-46
16 oz. paper contianer used during the war. OSP 45c. CMV $40 mint.

VANILLA TONKA AND VANILLAN FLAVOR EXTRACT 1910
2 or 4 oz. glass bottle, cork stopper. Comes in 17 flavors. OSP 50c. & 90c. **CMV $100 mint. $125. MB.**

FLAVORING EXTRACTS 1908
Came in 1,2,4 and 8 oz. sizes with cork stoppers. Also came in 1 pt. and 1 qt. with glass stoppers. Flavors are almond, banana, celery, cinnamon, jamaica, ginger, lemon, maple, nutmeg, orange, onion, peppermint, pineapple, pistachio, rasberry, rose, strawberry, vanilla, tonka and vanillin, vanilla pure and wintergreen. The 2 oz. bottles are

embossed "California Perfume Co. Fruit Flavors" on back side, paper label on front. OSP 1 oz 25c. 2 oz. 45c. 4 oz. 90c. 8 oz. $1.75. 16 oz. $3.25. **CMV each $100 mint with label. CMV $125. embossed bottle with no label. $25. CMV 1 pt. and 1 qt size $125. BO, $150. MB with label and glass stopper.**

FLAVORING EXTRACT 1905-08
(Left) 8 oz and 16 oz. bottle, glass stopper. Came in all flavors listed under smaller bottles of 1893 Flavoring Extracts. OSP $1. **CMV $150. BO. $175. MB.**
FLAVORING EXTRACTS 1900-12
(Right) 2 oz. bottle shown is same as 4 oz. botle. Paper label. Came in almond, banana, blood orange, celery, cinnamon, cloves, lemon, nutmeg, onion, orange, peach, pear, peppermint, pineapple, pistachio, quince, jamaica ginger, rasberry rose, strawberry, vanilla and wintergreen. OSP 25c. and 45c. **CMV $100. MB, $85 BO mint.** Also came in 16 oz., 1 qt, 1/2 gal, and 1 gal. **CMV $125. BO, $150. MB.**

PERFECTION SAMPLES 1941
Sample size each. Perfection flavor sample came 20 in a box for 50c. Baking powder came in 16 for 50c. **CMV flavoring bottle. $20. each. Baking powder $45. each.**

BAKING POWDER 1906
1/2 and 1 lb can. OSP 25c. and 45c. **CMV $100. mint.**
BAKING POWDER 1906-15
5 lb container, paper label, metal can. OSP 25c. - 1 lb. **CMV $70. mint.** Pictured next to 1923-30 1 lb. can, for size comparison.

PERFECTION CAKE PAN
Tin pan marked "Perfection" We believe this was sold by Perfection Stove Co. and not by Perfection of Avon Products. If you have information on this please write to Bud Hastin.

PERFECTION MENDING CEMENT 1933-41
Brown, orange, and white tube. OSP 25c.
CMV $12. BO. Tube only **$10. mint.**
PERFECTION MENDING CEMENT 1941-48
White, green, and brown tube. OSP 29c.
CMV $12. BO. $10 tube only mint.

PERFECTION BAKING POWDER 1941-43-46-48
16 oz. red and white can, cardboard sides,
metal top or all metal can and top. OSP 45c.
CMV $20. mint, $25. MB. Also came 1946-
48 all metal can. Screw on lid. **CMV $50.
Rare**

KWICK METAL POLISH 1941-48
8 oz. green, brown and white can. Sold 1941-
43 then 1946-48. OSP 39c. **CMV $35., $45.
MB.**

PERFECTION BAKING POWDER 1923-30
(Left) 1 lb can. Also came in 1/2 lb. and 5 lb.
sizes. OSP 45c. **CMV $60. mint. $65. MB.**
PERFECTION BAKING POWDER 1931-41
(Right) 1 lb. orange, brown and white can.
OSP 45c. **CMV $25., $30. MB. Add $5 for
CPC label.**

EXTRACTS - FRUIT FLAVORING 1898
2 oz. clear glass. Fruit Flavors California
Perfume Co. embossed on backside.
Pineapple and wintergreen or rose. Cork
stopper. OSP 25c. **CMV $110. BO mint.,
$130. MB.**
ROOT BEER EXTRACT 1915
2 oz. cork stopper, clear glass. Very rare.
OSP 45c. **CMV $100. mint, $125. MB.**

PERFECTION MEASURING CUP 1940's
Metal cup
PERFECTION PIE PAN 1940's
9" pie pan with removable bottom. Center of
pan says" Trade Mark Perfection Patented".
We believe both items were sold by Perfection
Stove Co. and not by Perfection of Avon
Products. No value established

HARMLESS RED COLORING 1915
2 oz. clear glass, cork stopper. OSP 25c.
CMV $75. mint with label. $90. MB.
RASBERRY FLAVOR 1908
1 oz. size CPC New York Label. **CMV $50.**

SAVORY COLORING 1915
3 oz. clear glass bottle, cork stopper. 3 oz.
size is rare. OSP 25c. **CMV $80. with mint
label. $95. MB.**

FLAVORING EXTRACT 1934-41
8 oz. bottle plus cap. Came in vanilla, tonka,
lemon, almond, orange, peppermint,
wintergreen, pure vanilla, black walnut and
maple. OSP $1.45, **CMV $35. MB. $25.
BO.**

PERFECTION CAKE CHEST 1941-42

Brown and red designed cake chest has coloring set in can, 2 oz. bottles of lemon and almond extract, 2 oz. bottles of maple and black walnut flavoring, and 4 oz. bottle of vanilla. All bottles have red plastic caps. Can of baking powder, recipe book, cake chest is same as 1938 to 1941. Avon Perfection in bottom of cake pan. OSP $3.95. CMV set complete $110. MB. Chest only $35. mint.

PERFECTION CAKE CHEST 1938-41

Gold, red, brown, black cake chest. Contains can of baking powder, coloring set of 4 oz. vanilla extract. 2 oz each of lemon and almond extract, 2 oz each of black walnut and maple flavors. All have metal caps, recipe book. Avon Perfection in bottom of cake pan. OSP $3.50. CMV set complete $135. MB. chest only $35. mint.

FOOD FLAVORING SET 1914

Box holds 2 oz. bottle of vanilla tonka, a 2 oz bottle of lemon, and four 1 oz bottles of any other flavor. OSP $1., CMV $450. for set.

NO ALCOHOL FLAVORING SET 1920-21

Set came with five small tubes and one large tube. Choice of vanilla, lemon, pineapple, banana, maple, almond, orange, strawberry, jamaica, ginger, peppermint, nutmeg, wintergreen, cinnamon, rose, celery onion, pistachio, and rasberry. OSP $2. CMV $200. MB.

NO ALCOHOL FLAVOR IN TUBES 1921

Metal tubes came in small and large size, available in flavors as set. OSP small tube 30c., large tube 55c. CMV small tube $40. large tube $45.

PERFECTION CAKE CHEST 1933-38

Blue and gold cake pan 10 1/2" in diameter contains Perfection coloring set, metal caps. Can of Perfection baking powder. Bottles contain lemon, maple, black walnut, almond and vanilla flavoring and recipe book. Avon Perfection in bottom of cake pan. OSP $3.50. CMV set complete $135. chest only $50 mint. $70. MB.

FLAVORING EXTRACT SET 1920

Box holds two 2 oz. bottles and four 1 oz. bottles of any flavor desired. 1,2 and 4 oz. bottles shown. OSP $1.90. CMV $450. set mint in box.

NO ALCOHOL FLAVORS 1923

Lemon and vanilla only in small and large size tubes. OSP 24c. and 45c. CMV $40. MB. tube only $30 mint.

VEGETABLE COLORING 1908

2 oz. clear glass. Front white paper label. Embossed Fruit Flavors on back side. OSP 45c. CMV $100 mint, $125. MB.

SAVORY COLORING 1915

8 oz. clear glass. Cork stopper. Rare in 8 oz. size. CMV $125 mint - $150. MB.

IMITATION VANILLAN COUMARIN VANILLA AND TONKA FLAVOR 1939-41

4 oz. red cap. CMV $15. mint.

PERFECTION BLUE COLORING 1919
1 oz. size. Black & white label. Cork stopper.
New York-Montreal label. **CMV $75. mint.**
NUTMEG FLAVORING 1906
2 oz. cork stopper. Eureka Trade Mark label.
CMV $100. mint.
JAMAICA GINGER FLAVORING 1919
1 oz., cork stopper. **CMV $75. mint.**

**PERFECTION CONCENTRATED COLORING
1920-30**
(Right) 2 oz. No coloring listed on label. Cork
stopper. OSP 33c. **CMV $45. BO mint.
$55. MB.**
VEGTABLE COLOR SAMPLE 1900
(Left) Small clear glass vial with cork stopper.
CMV $50. mint.

SAVORY COLORING 1923-30
(Left) 2 and 3 oz. bottle with yellow labels and
brown letters, cork stoppers. Came in red,
yellow, blue, brown, and green. Also came
with brown label and yellow letters. OSP 33c.
and 59c. **CMV each with mint label $45.,
$55. MB.** 1/2 oz. bottle came in Coloring Set
only. **CMV same as above.**
PERFECTION SAVORY COLORING 1931-34
(Right) 4 oz. cork stopper. CPC label. OSP
35c. **CMV $35. MB. $30. BO.**

**CONCENTRATED FLAVORING EXTRACT
1923-30**
8 oz. size with handle. Same label as 1923-30
extracts. This bottle is very rare with handle.
Label in poor condition. **CMV $75. mint.**
**PERFECTION FLAVORING EXTRACT 1923-
30**
2 oz. clear glass bottle, cork stopper. Lemon,
orange, grape, cherry, rasberry, loganberry.
CMV $50., $60. MB.

**VANILLA TONKA & VANILLAN FLAVOR
SAMPLE 1910**
(Left) Small sample bottle, clear glass, cork
stopper. **CMV $100. mint. $125. MB.**
**"EXTRACT CONCENTRATED" VANILLA
EXTRACT 1906**
(Right) 2 and 4 oz. glass bottle with cork
stopper. OSP 50c. amd 90c. **CMV $100.,
$125. MB.**

PERFECTION EXTRACT 1934-41
Metal caps on 1/2 oz. 2, 4 and 8 oz. bottles.
Flavors are vanilla, tonka, lemon, almond,
orange, peppermint, wintergreen, pure vanilla,
black walnut, maple. OSP 2 oz. size 50c., 4
oz size 75c., and 8 oz. size OSP $1.45.
**CMV each 2 oz. and 4 oz. $12.50 each; 8
oz. size $20.; CMV each 1/2 oz. size $12.**

PERFECTION COLORING 1934-41
1/2 oz size in green, yellow, blue and brown.
Came in Coloring Set. **CMV $15 each.** 2 oz.
size in same colors plus red. OSP 25c. **CMV
$17.** 4 oz. size in savory coloring OSP 35c.
All have metal caps. **CMV $17. Add $3.
each MB.**

VANILLA TONKA VANILLAN SPECIAL ISSUE BOX 1937

Regular issue 2 oz. bottle in special issue box for 15c. with regular order. CMV $25. MB as shown.

SAVOURY COLORING 1941-48

4 oz. bottle with the word Savoury spelled different. Regular spelling is Savory. OSP 39c. CMV $15 BO. $17 MB.

PERFECTION IMITATION VANILLAN COUMARIN VANILLA AND TONKA SAMPLE 1939-41

1/4 oz. size bottle. Metal cap. CMV $25. mint.

VANILLA TONKA 1/4 OZ. SAMPLE 1934-39

(Right) 1/4 oz. size, 2 3/8" high, metal cap. On right shown next to 1/2 oz. size, on left that came in food flavor sets. CMV $25. 1/4 oz. size sample mint. CMV 1/2 oz. size $15. mint.

FOOD COLORING 1941-48

Red plastic caps. Savory coloring came in 4 oz. bottle. OSP 39c., red, yellow, blue, brown and green came in 2 oz. bottles. OSP 29c., all but red and savory coloring came in 1/2 oz bottles in coloring set. CMV $12. each size, $15. each MB.

PERFECTION FLAVORING EXTRACTS 1941-48

Vanilla and lemon came in 2 and 4 oz. sizes. 2 oz size only in maple, black walnut, orange, peppermint, almond, wintergreen. All have red plastic caps. OSP 49c., 2 oz., and 89c. 4 oz. CMV $9 each 1/2 oz. size came in Extract Set only. CMV $12., $15. MB.

HARMLESS COLORS SET 1915

Wood box with slide open lid, paper label on top. Holds eight 1/2 oz. bottles with cork stoppers. Paper labels on top of cork and front of bottles also. Came in chocolate, lemon, green, red, coffee, violet, lilac, and orange. OSP 50c. CMV $350. MB.

HARMLESS COLORING SET 1895-1920

Set of eight 1/2 oz. bottles with cork stoppers. Came in wood box. Lemon, chocolate, lilac, coffee, orange, red, violet and green. OSP 50c. CMV $400. set MB. or $45. each bottle.

FOOD FLAVORING DEMONSTRATOR SET 1909

Black leather covered wood case holds 24 1 oz. bottles of food flavoring. OSP toReps was $2., CMV mint with all labels $1800 complete.

HARMLESS COLORS SET 1920

Cardboard box holds eight 1/2 oz. bottles with cork stoppers. Red, chocolate, green, coffee, lemon, velvet, orange, lilac. OSP 50c. CMV $300. MB.

PERFECTION COLORING SET 1920-30
Bottles of green, yellow, blue and brown in 1/2 oz. size. Red in 2 oz. size. All have cork stoppers. Came with CPC Cook Booklet. OSP 74c. **CMV $250.**

PERFECTION COLORING SET 1941-48
Orange, brown and white can holds 2 oz. red coloring and 1/2 oz. each of yellow, brown, blue and green coloring, red plastic cap. OSP 98c. **CMV $65 MB.** Set came with Avon Recipe Booklet. Add $10. for Recipe Booklet. Can only $15. mint. This set also came in 1934-41 can. Only can is marked Avon and not CPC. Came with red caps and 1941-48 labels.. **CMV $70. MB.** Same set came 1942 only with matching caps to color content. Rare. **CMV $85. set MB.**

FLAVORING EXTRACT SET 1912
Black leather grain case with double handles and snaps. Holds 20 one ounce bottles of food flavor extract. Used by Reps. to show products. **CMV $1500. complete set mint.**

FRUIT FLAVORS BROCHURE 1923
Introducing new line of CPC Perfection fruit flavors. 1 page. **CMV $20.**

PERFECTION COLORING SET 1934-41
Orange, brown and white metal cans hold four 1/2 oz. bottles in blue, yellow, brown and green coloring and 2 oz. bottle of red. All have plain metal caps, or all color caps. Rare. Came with Perfection Cook Booklet OSP 85c. **CMV $75. MB. Can only $15. mint.**

HARMLESS COLORS SET 1910-15
Wood box, slide open lid, holds 8 1/2 oz. bottles with cork stoppers. Red, chocolate, green, coffee, lemon, velvet, orange, lilac. Labels on top of corks only. OSP 50c. **CMV $350. MB.**

CAKE CHEST PRODUCT BOX 1930's
CPC box with list of all contents that came in Perfection Cake Chest. **CMV $15 box only.**

PERFECTION FLAVORING EXTRACT SET 1930-34
In orange, brown and white can, has 2 oz. vanilla and 1.2 oz. each of almond, lemon, peppermint, and wintergreen extract. All have cork stoppers. OSP $1. **CMV $125. Can only $15. mint.**

FOOD FLAVORING DEMONSTRATOR SET 1900
Straw covered wood case holds 20 bottles of food flavoring extracts. **CMV complete set mint $1500.**

FOOD COLORING DIRECTIONS 1930's
Came in Perfection Food Coloring sets. CPC on back **CMV $15 mint.**

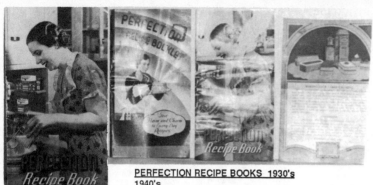

PERFECTION RECIPE BOOKS 1930's 1940's
Came in food coloring or flavoring sets. At lest four different booklets. CMV $15. each mint. 1920 far right CMV $25.

FACIAL SET 1936-37
Turquoise flip up box holds Ariel face powder, 2 oz. jar cleansing cream, tissue cream & 2 oz. bottle of astringent. All products are marked CPC. Also came with packet of tissues. OSP $1.60. CMV $50. MB.

PERFECTION FLAVORING SET 1941-48
Red, white and bronze can holds 2 oz. bottle of vanilla, 1/2 oz. bottle of maple, black walnut, almond and lemon. All have red plastic caps. OSP $1.15. CMV $60. complete set mint. Set came with Avon Recipe Booklet in can. Add $10 for Recipe Booklet. Can only $12 mint.

PERFECTION FLAVORING EXTRACT SET 1934-41
Orange, brown, and white metal can holds four 1/2 oz. bottles in wintergren, peppermint, almond and lemon, and a 2 oz. bottle of maple. All have metal caps. Came with Perfection Cook Booklet. CMV booklet only $12. OSP $1. CMV $75. MB can only $15. mint.

FACIAL SET 1911-48
Green box contains jar of cleansing cream, foundation cream, night cream with green lids. Skin freshener, 2 oz. green cap & box of face powder, blue and white feather design, 2 packs of Avon facial tissues. Jars had green or white metal lids. OSP $1.89. CMV $50. MB. Add $10 set for white lids.

AVON FACIAL SETS

WARNING!! Grading condition is paramount on sets. CMV can vary 50% to 90% on grade.

PERFECTION COLORING SET 1930-34
Brown and orange paper box. Red coloring in 2 oz. size brown, blue, yellow, green coloring in 1/2 oz. size. All have cork stoppers. OSP 85c. CMV $160. MB. Box only $20. mint.

FACIAL SET 1937-38
Green box contains choice of 2 oz. bottle of skin freshener or astringent, green caps, 2 oz. jar of cleansing cream, 1 oz. jar of tissue cream and Ariel of Vernafleur face powder. OSP $1.68. CMV $65. MB.

FACIAL SET 1933-36
Silver & blue box contains 2 oz. jar of cleansing cream & 1 oz. jar of tissue cream, 1 bottle of astringent, silver box of Ariel face powder, package of tissues. OSP $1.68. CMV $110. MB.

FACIAL SET 1938-40
Green box holds 4 oz. bottles of astringent & Lotus cream, jars of tissue cream & cleansing cream and box of face powder in Ariel or Cotillion. OSP $1.89. **CMV $65. MB.**

FACIAL SET FOR DRY SKIN 1949-54
Green box contains Fluffy cleansing cream, skin freshener, special dry skin cream & lipstick

SAME SET FOR OILY SKIN
Contained liquifying cleansing cream, astringent, night cream, & lipstick. OSP $3.39 each set. **CMV $50 MB each set.**

GOLD BOX SETS

GOLD BOX SET 1932
Metal gold with black strips. Can holds 3 1/2 oz. ribbed glass bottles of 391, Ariel and Vernafleur perfume. All have black octagonal caps. This is the same metal can as the 1925-30 manicure set. OSP $1.40. **CMV $140.**

GOLD BOX SET 1933-36
Gold box contained three 1/2 oz. bottles of Vernafleur, Ariel, 391, Bolero or Gardenia. Black caps. OSP $1.46. **CMV $125. MB.**

GOLD BOX SET 1937-38
Gold box holds three 1/8 oz. bottles of Cotillion, Narcissus, & Gardenia perfumes. OSP $1.25 **CMV $85. MB.**

GOLD BOX 1939-40
Gold open front box holds 3 bottles of perfume in Gardenia, Cotillion, Narcissus or Trailing Arbutus. White plastic caps on all. OSP $1.25 **CMV $90 MB.**

GOLD BOX SET 1947-48
Three 1/8 oz. perfume bottles, gold caps, pink labels. Ballad, Garden of Love, Cotillion. OSP $2.50 **CMV $85. MB.**

GOLD BOX SET 1949
Turquoise plastic bottom with gold insert, clear plastic lid contains three 1 dram bottles of Cotillion, Flowertime, & Golden Promise perfumes. All have gold caps and labels. OSP $2.25 **CMV $80. MB.**

GOLD BOX SET 1941-44
Pink & gold box contains 1/8 oz. perfumes in Gardenia, Cotillion & Trailing Arbutus. White caps, pink & gold box. OSP $1.35 **CMV $90. MB.**

GOLD BOX 1945-46
Pink & white box holds three 1/8 oz. bottles in Crimson Carnation, Gardenia & Cotillion perfume. OSP $1.50 **CMV $85. MB>**

GOLD BOX 1944
Ribbons & flower design box holds three 1/8 oz. perfumes in Trailing Arbutus, Cotillion, And Gardenia. OSP $1.50 **CMV $90. MB.**

MAKEUP ENSEMBLE SETS

MAKE-UP ENSEMBLE 1939-40
Box holds can of face powder in choice of Cotillion, Ariel or Vernafleur, and table rouge in green & gold boxes. Lipstick in green & gold. OSP $1.40. **CMV $40. MB.**

MAKE-UP ENSEMBLE 1945
Lipstick designed box holds feather design face powder, lipstick & rouge. Also came with metal bamboo lipstick. OSP $1.75 **CMV $37. MB.**

MAKE-UP ENSEMBLE 1947 Only
White, pink box with Eiffel Tower on box holds pink & blue feather design powder with bamboo lipstick & rouge. OSP $2.35 **CMV $45. MB.**

MAKE-UP ENSEMBLE 1948
Same except lipstick gold with swirl design around bottom. OSP $2.35 **CMV $45. MB.**

MAKE-UP ENSEMBLE 1943-44
Blue and pink box holds feathered box of face powder, rouge & plastic or cardboard lipstick. OSP $1.75 **CMV $40 MB.**

MAKE-UP ENSEMBLE 1946 Only
Pink & blue feather design box holds gold bamboo lipstick, rouge, & box of face powder. OSP $2.25 **CMV $45. MB.**

MAKE-UP ENSEMBLE 1949-51
Blue, pink and white box contains face powder, gold lipstick, & rouge. Eiffel Tower on box. OSP $2.35 **CMV $35. MB.**

MAKE-UP ENSEMBLE 1941-42
Box contains face powder, rouge in feather design, turqoise & gold lipstick. OSP $1.52 **CMV $40. MB.**

MAKE-UP ENSEMBLE 1952-53
Turquoise & gold box holds compact, lipstick & face powder or powder pak. OSP $2.75 **CMV $35. MB.**

MANICURE SETS

WARNING!! Grading condition is paramount on sets. CMV can vary 50% to 90% on grade.

MANICURE SET NO. 1 1930
Silver box holds 2 small bottles of nail polish remover. Black caps. Booklet "What Story Do Your Hands Tell?" came with set. OSP 52c. **CMV $65. MB.**

MANICURE SET NO. 1 1936-37
Green & white box has bottles of nail polish & polish remover with 2 rolls of cotton & booklet " What Story Do Your Hands Tell?" OSP 52c. **CMV $45. MB.**

MANICURE SET NO. 2 1931-36
Silver box holds 3 small ribbed glass bottles of polish remover, nail polish, cuticle softener. All have black caps. Two small silver cans of nail white & nail cream, 1 fingernail file & booklet "What Story Do Your Hands Tell?" OSP $1.67 **CMV $110. MB.** Same set also came with no stripe on box as shown & 2 different listings inside box as shown.

MANICURE SET NO.2 1938-39
Brown case holds orange stick, nail file, can of nail white, nail cream, bottles of cuticle softener, cream polish & polish remover. OSP $1.89 **CMV $60. MB>**

MANICURE SET NO. 2 1937
Turquoise & white lid, gold inside box holds cans of nail white & nail cream, bottles of nail polish remover, cuticle softener & nail polish, orange stick, nail file, 3 cotton rolls in glass tube & booklet "What Story Do Your Hands Tell?" OSP $1.67 **CMV $80. MB.**

MANICURE SET NO. 1 1938-49
Turquoise box holds 1/2 oz. nail polish and cream polish, 2 cotton rolls and booklet "What Story Do Your Hands Tell?" CPC on box, 2 different boxes. Some say Manicure Set No. 1 at top of box and some at bottom of box. Add $5 for CPC box. OSP 52c. **CMV $30. MB.**

TWOSOME SET 1938-49
Turquoise & white box holds 1/2 oz. of nail polish & 1/2 oz. of cuticle softener, 2 cotton rolls & booklet "What Story Do Your Hands Tell?" CPC on box in 1938-39. Add $5 for CPC box. OSP 52c. **CMV $30.**

NAIL POLISH THREESOME 1938-49
Turquoise & white box holds 1/2 oz. double coat, 1/2 oz. nail polish, 1/2 oz oily polish remover, 2 rolls cotton & booklet. OSP 85c. **CMV $42.50**

ROYAL WINDSOR SET 1941-44
Blue box holds choice 1/2 oz. nail polish base & 1/2 oz. cream polish or 1/2 oz. top coat. OSP 52c. **CMV $17. MB as shown**

MANICURE SET NO. 2 1940
Brown case holds fingernail file, orange stick, white Avon nail white pencil, 1/2 oz bottles of clear or cream nail polish, polish remover, cuticle softener & cuticle oil. Turquoise or black caps. OSP $2.25 **CMV $60. MB.**
MANICURE SET DELUXE 1941-43
Same set as above only name changed. OSP $2.25 **CMV $60 MB.**

THREESOME SET 1942-43
Pink & white box has 3 small bottles with turquoise caps of cream polish, nail polish base & oily polish remover. Comes with story booklet on hands. OSP 85c. **CMV $40 MB.**

DELUXE MANICURE SET 1950-51
Black & red box holds three 1/2 oz. bottles of nail polish, 1/2 oz. bottle of clear nail polish, 1/2 oz. bottle cuticle softener, 1 orange stick, 1 white nail white pencil & booklet. OSP $2.75 **CMV $25. MB.**

MANICURE SETS

MANICURE SET DELUXE 1944-49
Black & red bag holds 5 bottles of nail polish, top coat, nail polish base, cuticle softener, oily polish remover. All have black or turquoise caps. White nail white pencil, orange stick & 2 nail files. OSP $3. **CMV $45. MB.**

MANICURE SET DELUXE 1949
Same black & red bag only holds 4 bottles with turquoise caps in Cling Tite nail polish, nail polish remover & cuticle softener. OSP $2.50 **CMV $40 MB.**

NAIL POLISH TWOSOME 1945-50
Turquoise box holds 1/2 oz. bottles of cream polish & cuticle softener and small 30 page booklet. OSP 85c. **CMV $30. MB.**

AVON THREESOME SET 1948-49
Red, white & green tray with green box holds three 1/2 oz. bottles with white caps for oily polish remover, Cling Tite & nail polish. OSP $1.19 **CMV $30. MB.**

AVON THREESOME SET 1950-52
Red & white box holds 3 nail polish bottles with white caps. OSP $1.29 **CMV $30. MB.**

DELUXE MANICURE SET 1950-52
Black & red box holds bottles of cuticle softener, nail polish, oily polish remover & Cling Tite. OSP $2.50 **CMV $25. MB.**

MANICURE SET DELUXE 1953-54
Gray case holds 1/2 oz. bottles of cuticle softener, nail polish, double coat, 2 oz. oily polish remover, white caps on all. OSP $2.65. **CMV $25. MB.**

DELUXE MANICURE SET 1955
White plastic with gold dots, red lining holds oily nail polish remover, cuticle softener, Silvery Base, choice of nail enamel, all white caps & emery board. OSP $2.95 **CMV $25. MB.**

LITTLE FAVORITE SET 1955
Plastic turquoise case holds bottles of nail polish, oily polish remover & cuticle softener, all have white caps. OSP $1.50 **CMV $20. MB.**

POLKA DOT SET 1956-57
Red & white plastic case holds 1/2 oz. bottles of nail polish, top coat & 2 oz. oily polish remover. OSP $1.69 **CMV $20. MB.**

MANICURE SET DELUXE 1956-57
Pink plastic container holds 1/2 oz. bottles of polish remover, cuticle softener, silvery base, top coat & polish. All have white caps. OSP $3.25 **CMV $25. MB>**

COLOR CHANGE SET 1957
Pink, turquoise & gold design on white plastic case, holds 2 oz. bottle, white cap, oily polish remover & top coat & nail polish. OSP $1.95 **CMV $20. MB.**

COLOR BAR SET 1958
White plastic tray holds 4 bottles of nail polish or silvery base coat, top coat & cuticle softener. Mix or match. OSP $3. **CMV $15 complete - $20. MB**

MANICURE DELUXE SET 1959
Box holds cuticle softener, silvery coat, oily polish remover, top coat & cream polish. OSP $3.95 **CMV $25. MB.**

MANICURE PITITE SET 1960-61
Black vinyl case holds top coat, oily polish remover & cream or pearl nail polish, White caps. OSP $2.98 **CMV $15 MB.**

DELUXE MANICURE SET 1960-61
Black vinyl case holds silvery base, oily polish remover, cuticle softener, top coat & cream nail polish. All have white caps. OSP $4.98 **$20. MB.**

MANICURE KIT 1966
Gold & white plastic case holds 1 bottle of nail enamel, long last base coat, enamel set, cuticle remover cream, nail beauty, 10 nail enamel remover pads, emery board & orange stick. OSP $8.50 CMV $15 **complete set MB.**

MANICURE BEAUTI-KIT 1968-69
Black & white vinyl case holds 1/2 oz. bottles of nail enamels, 1 oz. plastic tube cuticle conditioner, 1 oz. plastic tube cuticle remover, 10 enamel remover pads, 1/2 oz. bottle of enamel set, long-last top coat, & emery boards. Red plastic tray. OSP $12. **CMV $8. MB.**

NAIL BUFFER SET 1974
Box holds .25 oz. tube of nail buffing cream & nail buffer. OSP $3. **CMV $1.50 MB.**

NAIL CARE KIT 1979-80
Blue plastic kit holds 5 bottles of nail care products & 3 emery boards & 1 cuticle stick. SSP $6.99 **CMV $5. complete.**

NAIL CARE KIT 1978-79
Same as above only beige color alligator grain case. **CMV $5. MB.**

PERFUME PAIR SETS

PERFUMED PAIR 1962
Box holds 2 1/4 oz. can of perfumed talc & perfumed soap in Somewhere, Topaze, Cotillion, Persian Wood, Here's My Heart, & to A Wild Rose. OSP $1.18 **CMV $15. MB.**

PERFEMUD PAIR 1964
Box holds perfumed talc & soap in Here's My Heart, Persian Wood, To A Wild Rose. OSP $1.18 Somewhere, Topaze, Cotillion. OSP $1.28 **CMV $14. MB.**

PERFUMED PAIR 1966
Brown, gold & white box holds 2 3/4 oz. perfumed talc & wrapped soap in Unforgettable, Rapture, Occur!, Cotillion, Somewhere, Topaze, Here's My Heart, To A Wild Rose & Wishing. OSP $1.39 **CMV $11. MB.**

PERFUMED PAIR 1967
Box contains perfumed talc and matching soap. Comes in Unforgettable, Here's My Heart, To A Wild Rose, Somewhere, Topaze, Cotillion, Rapture & Occur!. OSP $1.49 **CMV $10. MB.**

PERFUMED PAIR 1963
Gold & white with perfumed talc & bar of soap in To A Wild Rose, Here's My Heart, Persian Wood, Topaze, Somewhere, & Cotillion. OSP $1.18 **CMV $14 each set MB.**

PERFUMED PAIR 1968
Box holds 2 3/4 oz. can of talc and matching soap in Brocade, Regence, Unforgettable, Hawaiian White Ginger, Honeysuckle & To A Wild Rose. OSP $2. **CMV $8. MB.**

PERFUMED PAIR 1970
Each box contains perfumed talc & matching soap in Hawaiian White Ginger, Honeysuckle, Elusive, Blue Lotus, Bird of Paradise, & Charisma. OSP $2.25 **CMV $7. MB.**

PERFUMED PAIR 1969
Box holds perfumed talc & bar of soap in Charisma, Brocade, Blue Lotus, White Ginger, Honeysuckle, & To A Wild Rose. OSP $2. **CMV $8. MB.**

PERFUMED PAIR 1974-75
1.5 oz. perfumed talc & .5 oz. cologne. Choice of Roses Roses, Unforgettable, Cotillion, Sonnet or Moonwind. Came in 2 different boxes. OSP $3. **CMV $6. MB.**

PURSE SETS
WOMEN

EVENING CHARM SET 1949
Black purse holds gold compact, lipstick & 1 dram bottle in gold metal case with Golden Promise perfume. Also came with beige purse. OSP $10. **CMV $50. MB.**

EVENING CHARM SET 1952
Gold purse holds 1 dram perfume, lipstick & gold deluxe compact. OSP $10.95 **CMV $45. MB.**

LADY FAIR SET 1956
Gold box holds 1 dram prefume, gold lipstick & red leather billfold. OSP $5.95 **CMV $35. MB.**

EVENING CHARM SET 1953
Choice of black velvet bag or brocade bag. Came with 1 dram embossed top perfume, gold deluxe & gold jeweled lipstick. OSP $10.95 **CMV $35. MB.**

EVENING CHARM SET 1951
Brocade hand bag, or black satin bag with gold trim. Came with same contents as 1953 Evening Charm Set listed. OSP $10.95 **CMV purse only $6. complete set MB $30.**

EVENING CHARM PURSE 1953
Avon box holds black velvet purse. Avon on tag inside. **CMV $15 MB. purse only $6.**

EVENING CHARM SET 1954
Choice of black velvet or white brocade purse with 1 dram perfume, gold deluxe compact & jeweled lipstick. Both have zipper tops. OSP $12.50 **CMV $40. MB.**

DRESS UP SET 1955
Black & gold purse with gold satin lining holds 1 dram perfume, jeweled lipstick & deluxe gold compact. OSP $10.95 **CMV $40. MB.**

EVENING CHARM SET 1955
Gold brocade purse. Has Avon tag inside. Also came in matching black satin bag. Holds 2 dram embossed top perfume, gold deluxe compact, and gold jeweled lipstick. OSP $12.50 **CMV $40. MB.**

DRESS UP SET 1955-56
Black & gold reversible purse holds 1 dram perfume, gold compact & jeweled lipstick. OSP $10.95 **CMV $40. MB.**

AROUND TOWN SET 1956
Black leather bag holds gold lipstick, powder compact, 1 dram perfume & cologne stick. OSP $12.50 **CMV $35. MB.**

IN STYLE SET 1957
Black satin purse holds Persian Wood spray perfume, white compact, gold lipstick & black coin purse. OSP $12.95 **CMV $35. MB.**

MAKE-UP TUCK IN SET 1957
Black striped purse contains pink powder-pak, liquid rouge, & lipstick. OSP $3.50 **CMV $30. MB.**

PAK PURSE SET 1959
White leather purse holds lipstick, 1 dram perfume & compact. OSP $8.95 **CMV $20. MB.**

MODERN MOOD SET 1963
Gold & white or pink & gold purse holds deluxe compact & lipstick. On left: OSP $7. **CMV $17.50 MB.** Or pearl pink compact & floral fashion lipstick (on right). OSP $4.75 **CMV $20. MB.**

HIGH STYLE SET 1960
Blue satin lined bag holds gold deluxe compact & lipstick. OSP $5.95 **CMV $20 MB.**

ON THE AVENUE SET 1958
Black purse holds Top Style lipstick & Top Style compact with Here's My Heart or Persian Wood sparay perfume. OSP $12.95 **CMV $35. MB.**

GOING STEADY SET 1960
Gray bag holds white compact & lipstick. Purse does not say Avon on it. OSP **CMV $15. MB.**

MODERN MOOD SET 1961
Gold & white sequin bag holds deluxe lipstick & compact. OSP $6.50 **CMV $20. MB.**

DELUXE TWIN SET 1962
Blue clutch bag holds deluxe compact & lipstick. OSP $7.50 **CMV $20. MB.**

PURSE COMPANIONS SET 1964
Brocade beige purse with pockets to hold floral fashion lipstick & cameo compact. OSP $6.50 Same set in 1965 only with cameo lipstick. OSP $6.50 **CMV $20. each set MB.**

BEAUTY BOUND SET 1964
Black leather handbag deluxe compact & lipstick & choice of creme rollette. OSP $14.95. **CMV $30. MB.**
BEAUTY BOUND SET 1965
Same set as 1964 only with perfume rollete instead of creme rollette. OSP $14.95 **CMV $35. MB.**

EVENING LIGHTS PURSE SET 1965
White box with gold purse came with deluxe compact, lipstick, & perfume rollette. OSP $14.95 **CMV $20. MB.**

POLISHED GOLD EVENING BAG 1978-79
Gold plastic purse. Does not say Avon on it. Comes in white Avon box. SSP $6.50 **CMV $8. MB.**

MENS SETS OF 1930'S

WARNING!! Grading condition is paramonut on sets. CMV can vary 50% to 90% on grade.

HEADLINER FOR BOYS 1938-39
Maroon & gray striped box holds tubes of Hair Dress & Tooth Paste with Tooth Brush. OSP $1.10 **CMV $65 mint.**

MEN'S PACKAGES 1936-37
Maroon box holds can of Talc for Men, 4 oz. After Shave Lotion, turquioise can of Smokers Tooth Powder and tube of Shaving Cream. OSP $1.65 **CMV $100. MB.**

SMOKERS TRIO 1938-39
Green box holds 6 oz. Antiseptic, Tooth Brush and green can of Smokers Tooth Powder. OSP $1.39 **CMV $80. MB.**

ASSORTMENT NO. 7 FOR MEN 1931-34
Avon box holds can of Talc for Men, 4 oz. bottle of Bay Rum and tube of Bayberry Shaving Cream, 2 yellow Cannon wash cloths and 1 yellow Cannon towel. OSP $2. **CMV $110. set mint.**

ASSORTMENT FOR MEN 1931-36
Green box holds tube of Shaving Cream and green can Talc for Men with choice of 4 oz. Bay Rum or 2 oz. Lilac Vegetal. OSP $1.20 **CMV $110. MB.**

MENS TRAVEL KIT 1936-38
Leather case 7 1/4" x 6 1/2" x 2". Holds 4 oz. After Shave Lotion, Talc for Men, Shaving Cream and tube of Styptic. OSP $2.01 **CMV $90 mint.**

ASSORTMENT FOR MEN 1936-37
Wood grained paper box holds tube of Shaving Cream and can of Talc for Men with choice of 4 oz. Bay Rum or After Shave Lotion. OSP $1.15 **CMV $85. MB.**

ESQUIRE SET OR COUNTRY CLUB SET 1938-39
Same set as above and same price, only name changed. **CMV $85. each set.**

MEN'S TRAVEL KIT 1933-36
Black leather case 7 1/4" x 6 1/2" x 2". Holds green tube of Bayberry Shaving Cream, 4 oz. After Shave Lotion, Styptic Pencil and green can of Talc for Men. OSP $1.95 **CMV $110. mint.**

MEN'S TRAVEL KIT 1938-40
Brown leather zipper case holds maroon can of Talc for Men, tube of Shaving Cream, Styptic, and 4 oz. After Shave Lotion. OSP $2.16 **CMV $85. MB.**

VALET SET 1938-39
Speckled box holds 4 oz. After Shave, maroon can of Talc for Men, Smokers Tooth Powder & tube of Shaving Cream. OSP $1.65 **CMV $100. set mint.**

HAIR TREATMENT SET FOR MEN 1931-35
6 oz. Liquid Shampoo, 2 oz Pre-Shampoo, 6 oz. Hair Tonic, All have blue caps. Silver tube Hair Dress. White box. OSP $1.98 **CMV $135. MB.**

BRUSHLESS SHAVING SET 1937-39
Speckled box holds 4 oz. After Shave Lotion, maroon can of Talc for Men, and tube of Brushless Shaving Cream. OSP $1.10 **CMV $85.**

CHRISTMAS BOXES 1930
Special issue boxes came with seven different Avon sets at Christmas, 1931. **CMV $25. added to price of set for this box.**

MEN'S SHAVING SET 1934-35
Wood grained box holds 4 oz. After Shave Lotion, can of Talc for Men, Smokers Tooth Powder and tube of Bayberry Shaving Cream. OSP $1.65 CMV $175 set.

ASSORTMENT FOR MEN NO. 1 & NO. 2 1936
Avon box holds can of Talc for Men, tube of Bayberry Shaving Cream and choice of ribbed glass bottle after shave or Bay Rum. OSP $1. CMV $110. MB.

SHAVING CABINET 1930-34
White enamel cabinet with mirror on door. Cabinet is 8" high, 6 1/2" wide and 2 3/8" deep. Label on door reads "Gem Micromatic Shaving Cabinet, Avon Products" OSP $2.50 CMV $90 empty mint.

TRAVEL KIT FOR MEN 1938
Tan leather like case with zipper. Holds tube of Styptic Cream, 4 oz. after shave lotion, tube of shaving cream, can of Talc for Men. OSP $2.16. CMV $80. mint.

WOMEN'S SETS OF 1930'S

WARNING!! Grading condition is paramount on sets. CMV can vary 50% to 90% on grade.

BATH ENSEMBLE SET 1935
Box contains Jasmine Bath Salts, 2 bars Jasmine Bath Soap, Avon Dusting Powder in silver can and bottle of Trailing Arbutus Toilet Water. OSP $3.50 CMV $185. MB.

BATH ENSEMBLE SET 1936-39
Plaid box holds 9 oz. Jasmine Bath Salts, 2 oz. Trailing Arbutus Toilet Water, 2 bars of Jasmine Soap and can of Beauty Dust. OSP $3.50 CMV $160. MB.

CHRISTMAS SET NO. 49 1934
Red and green holly design box holds 2 white and green linen hand towels. 4 oz. bottle of Vanilla Tonka and Vanilla Extract in box with tube of Mending Cement in box. Rare set. Comes with outer sleeves with Set No. 49 on sleeve. OSP $1.29 CMV $115. MB with sleeve.

CHRISTMAS PERFUME SET 1933
Small blue box with winter snow scene holds 4 octagonal shaped perfumes with black caps. Came in choice perfumes. OSP 90c. CMV $225. Very Rare.

ASSORTMENT SET FOR WOMEN 1931-32
Contains 2 bars Verna Fleur Toilet soap, blue and silver can Avon Dusting Powder, bottle of Verna Fleur Bath Salts, 1 bath towel and 2 wash cloths. All in orange and blue box. $3.50 CMV $160. MB.

CHARMER SET 1938-41
Satin lined box contains lipstick, mascara and rouge. All green and gold. OSP $2.15 CMV $60. MB.

HAIR TREATMENT SET FOR WOMEN 1931-35
Contains Liquid Shampoo, Pre-Shampoo Oil, Wave Set, and Hair Tonic. All have blue plastic caps, blue and white box. OSP $2. **CMV $180. MB.**

WINGS TO BEAUTY SET 1938-40
Hinged lid box holds 4 oz. bottle of Lotus Cream and choice of Ariel or Cotillion Face Powder and choice of astringent or skin freshener. OSP $1.60 **CMV $75. MB.**

COLONIAL SET 1939
Blue and gold box holds 2 dram Gardenia Perfume and Face Powder in choice of Ariel or Cotillion. OSP $1.30 **CMV $75. MB.**

LYRIC SET 1937
White and gold box holds Trailing Arbutus Toilet Water, turquoise and white can, Daphne Talcum, turquoise and white can, turquoise cap, white jar, turquoise lid cold cream. OSP $1.65 **CMV $75. MB.**

HARMONY SET 1937
Blue and white box contains Lily of the Valley Toilet Water, gold cap and label. White milk glass jar with turquoise cap of Rose Cold Cream and turquoise and white tube Hand Cream. OSP $1.80 **CMV $75. MB.**

VANITY SET 1932-33
Gray velvet lined box contains blue and gold double Compact and Lipstick. OSP $2.50 **CMV $70. MB.**

VANITY BOOK SET 1931-32
Silver and blue box contains blue and silver Compact and Lipstick. OSP $1.82 **CMV $80. MB.** Also came in Christmas box. **CMV $90. MB.**

VANITY BOOK SET 1933
Silver and blue box contains blue and silver double Compact and Lipstick. OSP $1.75 **CMV $75. MB.**

MAYFAIR SET 1939
Blue lid box holds 2 dram glass stoppered bottle of Bolero Perfume box of Face Powder and turquoise double compact. OSP $3.57 **CMV $110. MB.**

VANITY BOOK SET 1936-37
Satin lined box holds green and gold Compact and Lipstick. OSP $2.27 **CMV $50. MB.**
SPORTS WISE SET 1938-40
Same set as 1936-37. Vanity Book only name changed. OSP $2.27 **CMV $50. MB.**

VANITY BOOK SET 1934-35
Blue and silver box holds blue and silver compact and lipstick. OSP $2.27 **CMV $70. MB.**

HANDKERCHIEF SET 1936 Only
Avon box holds 2 perfume bottles of Bolero and Ariel. OSP $1. **CMV $90. MB.**

PERFUME HANDKERCHIEF SET 1937-38
Two 1/8 oz. bottles of Gardenia and Cotillion Perfume on four colored handkerchiefs. OSP $1. CMV $70.

PERFUME HANDKERCHIEF SET 1933-36
Two small bottles of Ariel and 391 perfume or Bolero, with black caps, 4 handkerchiefs under green and red flower cutout. OSP $1. CMV $85. MB.

HANDKERCHIEF SET 1939 Only
Gardenia and Cotillion Perfumes with 4 handkerchiefs. OSP $1. CMV $75. MB.

FAIR LADY SET 1939-42
Green, yellow and white flowered box with gold base holds 4 perfumes in Narcissus, Gardenia, Cotillion, Trailing Arbutus, or Sweet Pes. Each came in different caps. OSP 94c. CMV $100. MB.

ATOMIZER SET NO. 6 1931-33
Blue and silver box contains red 1 oz. glass bottle with atomizer with Vernafleur perfume in 1 oz. bottle with cork stopper. Set comes in 2 different boxes. OSP $2.86 CMV $160. MB.

THREESOME SET 1934-35
Silver and blue box contains Compact Face Powder and 2 dram bottle Bolero Perfume. OSP $3.57 CMV $110. MB.

THREESOME SET 1936-37
Box has green and gold compact, box of face powder and glass stoppered 3 dram bottle of Bolero Perfume. OSP $3.57 CMV $115. MB.

POWDER COMPACT SET 1936-37
Box holds box of face powder and green and gold compact. OSP $2.50 CMV $50. MB.
ARISTOCRAT SET 1938
Same set as Powder Compact Set only name changed in 1938. OSP $2.50 CMV $50. MB.

BATH DUET 1937-39
Box holds turquoise and white can of Daphne Talc with choice of bath salts in Jasmine, Pine, Ariel, or Vernafleur. OSP $1. CMV $55. MB.

BEAUTY KIT FOR FINGERS 1938-39
Green box holds bar of Lemonal soap, turquoise tube of hand cream, bottle of polish remover and cream or nail polish. OSP $1.35 CMV $75. MB. Same set also came in gold design box as substitute.

SPECTATOR SET 1939
Turquoise and white box holds 2 dram bottle with gold cap ot Trailing Arbitus Perfume, lipstick and rouge compact. OSP $1.56. CMV $80. MB.

TRIO GIFT SET 1936
Box holds 2 oz. Trailing Arbutus toilet water with tulip label and gold ribbed cap. Silver can of Daphne Talcum and ribbed glass. Ariel powder sachet. OSP $1.29 CMV $110. MB.

TRIO SET 1934-35
Red and blue box contains Trailing Arbutus
Toilet Water, Daphne Talcum and Ariel Sachet.
OSP $1.60 **CMV $115. MB.**

GIFT SET "A" 1935
Satin lined box contains face powder in Ariel or
Vernafleur and 2 dram bottle of Gardenia
perfume with gold ribbed cap. OSP $1.30
CMV $85. MB.

GIFT SET "A" 1936-37
Box has box of face powder, 3 dram size of
Ariel, Vernafleur or Gardenia perfume with gold
caps. OSP $1.30 **CMV $75. MB.**

GIFT SET "B" 1936-37
Green and silver box holds green and gold
lipstick and rouge with 3 dram Trailing Arbutus
perfume with gold cap. OSP $1.56 **CMV
$90. MB.**

GIFT SET "B" 1935
Box contains blue and silver lipstick and rouge
compact and 2 dram bottle of Trailing Arbutus
perfume. OSP $1.56 **CMV $95. MB.**

GIFT SET "D" 1935
Blue and yellow box contains choice of Ariel or
Vernafleur face powder in silver and blue box
and 2 dram Ariel perfume with gold cap and
Ariel sachet with silver label. OSP $2.34
CMV $105. MB.

GIFT SET "D" 1936
Blue and yellow box contains Ariel or
Vernafleur face powder in green and gold and
2 dram Ariel perfume with gold cap and Ariel
powder sachet with black cap. OSP $2.34
CMV $90. MB.

GIFT SET "F" 1936-37
Box holds green and gold compact, lipstick and
box of face powder in Ariel or Vernafleur. OSP
$3.05 **CMV $60. MB.**
MASTERCRAFT SET 1938
Same set as Gift Set "F" only name changed in
1938. OSP $3.05 **CMV $60. MB.**

GIFT SET "F" 1935
Red and gold box contains blue compact, face
powder in Ariel or Vernafleur and lipstick. OSP
$2.80 **CMV $85. MB.**

GIFT SET "K" 1936-37
Blue and gold box has green and gold lipstick
and compact and 2 dram perfume with gold
cap. OSP $2.79 **CMV $90. MB.**
EMPRESS SET 1938
Same set as Gift Set "K" only name is
changed. **CMV $90. MB.**

GIFT SET NO. 19 1934
Red and green box contains Deluxe Hair
Brush, toothpaste, 1 bar of Savona soap, bottle
of antiseptic and tube of Dental Cream No. 2.
OSP $1.85. **CMV $110. MB.**

GIFT SET "K" 1935
Box contains blue compact, 2 dram perfume in
Gardenia and blue and silver lipstick. OSP
$2.54. **CMV $115. MB.**

GIFT SET "W" 1936-37
Satin lined box holds two ribbed bottles of nail polish and polish remover, green and gold lipstick and rouge. OSP $1.67. CMV $80. MB.

GIFT SET "W" 1935
Box contains nail polish, lipstick, rouge compact and polish remover. OSP $1.67 CMV $105. MB.

GIFT SET NO. 21 1936-37
Striped box holds turquoise and white box face powder, turquoise and white cake rouge, turquoise and gold lipstick. OSP $1.56. CMV $60. MB.

GIFT SET NO. 21 1933-35
Contains box of face powder and table rouge. Silver and blue. Blue lipstick in green, white and red box. OSP $1.56 CMV $65. MB.

GIFT SET NO. 24 1934
Holly decorated box contained box of face powder, rouge and jar of vanishing cream. OSP $1.56 CMV $85. MB.

GIFT SET NO. 36 1934
Red and green box contains bottle of Rosewater Glycerine, can of Daphne Talcum and Vernafleur Bath Salts. OSP $1.95 CMV $175. MB.

MEN'S SETS OF 1940'S

WARNING!! Grading condition is paramount on sets. CMV can vary 50% to 90% on grade. Refer to front of book for grading.

MODERN NIGHT 1946-49
Maroon and white box holds 2 oz. Deodorant for Men, can of Talc for Men and 4 oz. After Shaving Lotion. OSP $1.75. CMV $95. MB.

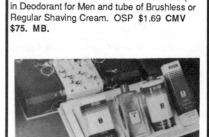

PLEASURE CAST SET 1948
Blue box holds 2 oz. bottles with maroon caps in Deodorant for Men and tube of Brushless or Regular Shaving Cream. OSP $1.69 CMV $75. MB.

VALET SET 1945-46
Maroon & ivory box holds 4 oz. After Shave Lotion, tube of Shaving Cream, Talc for Men and Smokers Tooth Powder. Both came in maroon paper containers with flat top lids and also pouring lids with caps. OSP $1.85. CMV $125. MB.

ARMY & NAVY KIT 1943-46
Blue and red box holds tube of Brushless Shaving Cream, maroon paper box of Elite Foot Powder and paper carton of Tooth Powder. OSP $1.46 CMV $100. MB.

ESQUIRE SET 1940-41
Maroon box holds 4 oz bottle of Bay Rum, tube of shaving cream, can of talc for men. OSP $1.15 CMV $90. MB.

ARMY & NAVY KIT 1941-42
Blue & red box with Eagle on lid, holds 4 oz. After Shave Lotion, maroon tube of Brushless Shaving Cream and maroon can of Elite Powder. Each in maroon & ivory boxes. OSP $1.35 **CMV $90 MB.**

TRAVELER KIT 1946-49
Maroon & white box holds 4 oz. After Shaving Lotion, maroon tubes of Smokers Tooth Paste and Shaving Cream. OSP $1.25 **CMV $75. MB.**

VALET SET 1943-45
Maroon & ivory box holds 4 oz. After Shave Lotion, 3 oz. tube in box of Shaving Cream, 2 5/8 oz. paper talc, 3.5 oz. paper side, tin flat top and bottom Smokers Tooth Powder. OSP $1.79 **CMV $115. MB.**

COUNTRY CLUB SET 1943-46
Maroon and white box holds 4 oz. After Shave Lotion, maroon flat top paper box of Talc for Men and tube Shaving Cream. OSP $1.15 **CMV $90. MB.**

VALET SET 1940-42
Maroon and white box holds 4 oz. After Shaving Lotion, maroon cans of Talc for Men, Smokers Tooth Powder and tube of Shaving Cream. OSP $1.69 **CMV $100. MB.**

VALET SET 1946-49
Maroon box holds maroon can of Smokers Tooth Powder, Talc for Men, 4 oz. After Shaving Lotion and tube of Shaving Cream. OSP $2. **CMV $90. MB.**

TRAVELER SET 1941-45
Maroon and ivory box holds 4 oz. After Shaving Lotion, maroon tubes of Smokers Tooth Paste and Shaving Cream. OSP $1. **CMV $75. MB.**

ARMY NAVY KIT 1943
Blue box with eagle holds turquoise can of Elite powder, 4 oz. of After Shave and maroon tube of Brushless Shaving Cream. OSP $1.35 **CMV $85. MB.**

MENS TRAVEL KIT 1946-49
Brown flip open leather case holds can of Talc for Men, 4 oz After Shaving Lotion, Styptic Cream and choice of tube of Shaving Cream or Brushless Shaving Cream. OSP $4.17 **CMV $85. MB.**

COUNTRY CLUB SET 1943-46
Maroon and white box holds 4 oz. After Shave Lotion, 2 5/8 oz. paper box of Talc for Men and 3 oz. tube of Shaving Cream. Talc came with flat paper top lid or cap lid as shown. OSP $1.15 **CMV $90. MB.**

COUNTRY CLUB SET 1940-42
Maroon and ivory box holds 4 oz. After Shaving Lotion, maroon can of Talc for Men and tube of Shaving Cream. OSP $1. **CMV $90. MB.**

COUNTRY CLUB SET 1946-49
Maroon and white box holds tube of Shaving
Cream, 4 oz. After Shaving Lotion and can of
Talc for Men. OSP $1.35 **CMV** $85. **MB.**

BRUSHLESS SHAVE SET 1946-49
Maroon and white box holds can of Talc for
Men, tube of Brushless Shaving Cream, and 4
oz. After Shaving Lotion. OSP $1.40 **CMV**
$85. **MB.**

COUNTRY CLUB SET 1939-41
Box holds 4 oz. bottle of After Shave, tube of
Shaving Cream, can of Talc for Men. OSP $1.
CMV $80. **MB.**

BRUSHLESS SHAVE SET 1940-42
Maroon and ivory box with man fishing,
maroon can of Talc for men and tube of
Brushless Shave Cream. OSP $1.10 **CMV**
$85. **MB.**

BRUSHLESS SHAVE SET 1943-46
Maroon and white box holds tube of Brushless
Shave Cream, 4 oz. After Shave Lotion and
maroon paper box of Talc for Men. OSP
$1.35. **CMV** $90. **MB.**

OLYMPIC SET 1940-46
Maroon and ivory box holds 6 oz. bottle of Hair
lotion, tube of Shaving Cream and 4 oz. After
Shave Lotion. OSP $1.29 **CMV** $95. **MB.**

COMODORE SET 1940-42
Maroon and ivory box holds 4 oz. After
Shaving Lotion, maroon can of Talc for Men
and 2 white handkerchiefs. OSP $1.35 **CMV**
$90. **MB.**

COMMODORE SET 1943-46
Maroon and white box holds 4 oz. After Shave
Lotion, 2 white handkerchiefs and maroon
paper box of Talc for Men. OSP $1.50 **CMV**
$90. **MB.**

OLYMPIC SET 1946-49
Maroon and white box holds tube of Shaving
Cream, 6 oz. bottle of Hair Lotion and 4 oz.
After Shaving Lotion. OSP $1.65. **CMV** $95.
MB.

WOMEN'S SETS OF 1940'S

**WARNING!! Grading condition is
paramount on sets. CMV can vary
50% to 90% on grade.**

BEAUTY BASKET SET 1947
Straw basket with pink ribbon holds two 6 oz.
bottles of Avon Cream Lotion and Rose
Gardenia Bath Oil. Both bottles are flat on the
back side and have pink caps. OSP $2. **CMV**
$55. basket mint with bottles, $75. **MB.**

LITTLE JEWELS SET 1944-45
Pink box holds 3 paper powder sachets in 1 1/4 oz. Cotillion, Attention, Garden of Love. OSP $3.25. **CMV $65. MB.**

RAINBOW WINGS SET 1943-44
Box holds 6 oz. bottles of Cream Lotion and Rose Geranium Bath Oil with pink caps. Both bottles are flat on one side. Butterflies on box. OSP $2. **CMV $65. MB.**

COLOR CLUSTER SET 1948
Red and gold box contains gold lipstick, gold rouge and 1/2 oz. nail polish with green cap. OSP $2. **CMV $45. MB.**

MINUET SET 1942
Box with music notes on lid, satin lined holds lipstick, powder compact, rouge, and face powder. All are blue and white feather design. OSP $2.95. **CMV $75. MB.**

RAINBOW WINGS SET 1945-46
Pink box holds two 6 oz. flat sided bottles of Cream Lotion and Rose Geranium Bath Oil. Pink net ribbon on top of box. OSP $2. **CMV $75. MB with net.**

MAYFAIR SET 1940
Blue box contains 1 dram perfume with gold cap. Green & gold compacts & box of face powder in Ariel or Cotillion. OSP $3.35. **CMV $75. MB.**

MINUET SET 1943-44
Pink and blue box with yellow satin lining holds blue plastic rouge compact, cardboard feather design lipstick, Cotillion perfume with gold cap and neck tag, and blue satin sachet pillowette. OSP $3.95. **CMV $110. MB.**

SPECTATOR SET 1940
Box contains green and gold rouge, 1 dram Garden of Love perfume, gold cap, green and gold lipstick. OSP $1.56. **CMV $65. MB.**

DOUBLE DARE SET 1946
Red and gold box holds bottle of Double Dare nail polish and gold Bamboo lipstick. OSP $1.25. **CMV $50. MB.**

LEADING LADY SET 1946 ONLY
Red, blue and gold box holds Bamboo lipstick and nail polish. OSP $1. **CMV $45. MB.**

COLOR CLUSTER SET 1946-47
Red and gold box holds gold Bamboo lipstick and rouge with 1/2 oz. nail polish with black cap. OSP $2.15. **CMV $50. MB.**

COLOR MAGIC THREE PIECE SET 1949-50
Multi-colored box holds gold lipstick, gold rouge and 1/2 oz. nail polish with green cap. OSP $2.19. **CMV $50. MB.**

BEAUTY MARK 1948
Red and gold box contains gold lipstick and 1/2 oz. nail polish with green cap. OSP $1.35. **CMV $40. MB.**

MILADY SET 1940-41
Satin lined box contains two small bottles of perfume in Gardenia, Cotillion, Apple Blossom or Ballad & white lace edged hanky. OSP $2.25. **CMV $85. MB.**

MR. & MRS. SET 1940-43
Blue & pink box contains smokers tooth-powder, after shaving lotion for men, Cotillion toilet water & Cotillion talcum for women. OSP $2.50. **CMV $140. MB.**

COLOR MAGIC TWO PIECE SET 1949-50
Multi-colored box contains gold lipstick and 1/2 oz. nail polish with green cap. OSP $1.35. **CMV $40. MB.**

COLONIAL DAYS SET 1943
6 oz. clear glass bottle, pink cap, cream lotion & cardboard body powder, shaker cap. OSP $1.60. **CMV $65. MB.**

BATH BOUQUET SET 1943-44
Blue box holds 6 oz. of Rose Geranium bath oil & Apple Blossom beauty dust. OSP $2.35. **CMV $75. MB.**

PEEK-A-BOO SET 1944 ONLY
Blue, white & pink box with yellow satin lining holds cardboard compact covered with pink satin & white net. Cake rouge in blue plastic compact & cardboard feather design lipstick. OSP $2.50. **CMV $60. MB.**

BATH DUET SET 1940-43
Blue, pink & white box box holds can of Daphne or Cotillion talc & choice of Jasmine, Pine, Ariel or Vernafleur bath salts. OSP $1. **CMV $60. MB.**

RECEPTION SET 1941-42
Satin lined box holds gold compact, blue box of face powder & 1/8 oz. perfume. OSP $2.75. **CMV $75. MB.**

COLONIAL SET 1940
Blue box holds 1 dram Garden of Love perfume, gold cap & label & box of face powder. OSP $1.25. **CMV $55. MB.**

COLONIAL SET 1940-41
Feather face powder & Garden of Love perfume in blue box. OSP $1.25. **CMV $60. MB.**

THAT'S FOR ME SET 1947-49
Multi-colored box contains choice of cream cake or cake makeup, gold lipstick & 1/2 oz. nail polish. OSP $2. **CMV $40. MB.**

ORCHID SET 1940
Red & white box, green & gold lipstick & rouge. Cream polish with green cap. OSP $1.50. **CMV $55.**

TANDEM SET 1941
(Left) Box holds gold bamboo compact & turquoise & gold lipstick. OSP $1.75. **CMV $50. MB.**
TANDEM SET 1942
(Right) Same set only with matching bamboo lipstick. **CMV $50. MB.**

ELYSIAN SET 1941-42
Satin lined box contains lipstick, rouge & 1 dram perfume with gold cap. OSP $1.75. **CMV $85. MB.**

FRAGRANT MIST 1950
Turquoise & gold box holds 2 oz. toilet water with green & gold atomizer in the choice of Flowertime, Cotillion, Lily of the Valley & Wishing. OSP $2.35. **CMV $50. MB.**

FAIR LADY SET 1945-47
Blue & white box holds 4 small bottles with colored caps of perfume in Cotillion, Lily of the Valley, Gardenia, Garden of Love, Trailing Arbutus & Sweet Pea. OSP $1.50. **CMV $75. MB.** Also came with all blue caps.

PEEK-A-BOO SET 1943
Pink & blue box with yellow satin lining holds blue & white feather design cardboard compact, cardboard lipstick & rouge. OSP $2.50. **CMV $65. MB.**

WINGS TO BEAUTY SET 1941
Red designed box contains choice of two 2 oz. skin conditioner, atringent, finishing lotion or Lotus cream, and box of face powder. OSP $1. **CMV $55. MB.**

PERFUMED DEODORANT SET 1947-54
Turquoise box holds two 2 oz. bottles of perfumed deodorant. OSP 98c. **CMV set $15. MB.**

FAIR LADY SET 1948--49
Pink & blue box contains four 1/8 oz. perfumes in Lily of the Valley, Garden of Love, Quaintance, Gardenia & Cotillion. All have blue caps. OSP $1.50. **CMV $85. MB.**

MERRIMENT SET 1940-42
Rouge, lipstick & eyebrow pencil. All green & gold. OSP $1.50. **CMV $45. MB.**

HANDKERCHIEF SET 1940-42
Box holds white, pink, blue & yellow handkerchiefs, 1/8 oz. Cotillion perfume with red cap. Gardenia perfume with blue cap. OSP $1. **CMV $60. MB.**

FRAGRANT MIST SET 1940-42
Blue & gold box holds 2 oz. toilet water with gold or plastic cap & label and spray atomizer. Came in Cotillion, Marionette, Sonnet, Jasmine or Apple Blossom. OSP $1.35. **CMV $50. MB.**

MEN'S SETS OF 1950s

WARNING!! Grading condition is paramount on sets. CMV can vary 50% to 90% on grade.

COMMODORE SET 1949-53
Stage coach on green flip open box holds 2 oz. cologne & 2 oz. deodorant for men & green tube of brushless or lather shaving cream. OSP $1.90. **CMV $55. MB.**

GROOMING GUARDS SET 1959
Black flip open box with red inner box holds can of After Shower Powder for Men, 2 oz. Spray Deodorant for Men in white plastic & tube of Attention Cream Hair Dress & choice of 4 oz. After Shower for Men or After Shaving Lotion. OSP $4.95. **CMV $60. MB.**

PARADE DRESS SET 1953-54
Red, white & blue soldier box holds 1 oz. bottle of liquid shampoo, 1 oz. cream or liquid hair lotion & 1 bar of Dr. Zabriskie's Soap. OSP $1.19. **CMV $75. MB.** Set also came with 2 shampoos & 1 hair lotion with no soap. **Same CMV.**

COAT OF ARMS SET 1958
Red, white, blue & gold box holds 6 oz. Kwick Foaming Shave Cream, 2 oz. Deodorant for Men & 2 oz. After Shave Lotion. OSP $1.98. **CMV $40. MB.**

CHANGING THE GUARD SET 1952
Red, white & blue guard house box holds 2 oz. hair guard with red cap. Came with outer box. OSP $1. **CMV $70. MV.**

GOOD MORNING SET 1955-56
Red box with geese holds choice of two 4 oz.
bottles of cream or liquid hair lotion. OSP
$1.18. **CMV $26. MB.**

ATTENTION SET 1957
Red & green box holds two 4 oz. bottles in
after shave lotion & choice of liquid or cream
hair lotion. OSP $1.49. **CMV $35. MB.**

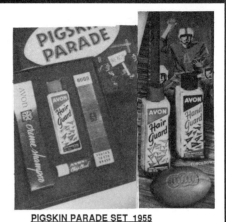

PIGSKIN PARADE SET 1955
(Left) Red & green box holds tube of creme
shampoo, youths toothbrush, chap check, 2
oz. bottle of hair guard & a plastic football.
OSP $1.95. **CMV $65. MB.**
TOUCHDOWN SET 1956-57
(Right) Green, red & gold box holds 2 oz.
bottles of hair guard with red cap, hand guard
with green cap & small football soap. OSP
$1.29. **CMV $65. MB.**

SPACE SHIP SET 1953
Blue box holds plastic spaceship with tubes of
chlorophyll toothpaste, creme shampoo &
toothbrush. OSP $2.10. **CMV $60. MB.**

HAIR TRAINER & COMB SET 1957
6 oz. bottle, white or blue cap, red & white
label. Came in box with comb. OSP 79c.
CMV $25. BO, $40. MB.

MAN'S WORLD SET 1957
Box has choice of 2 cream or liquid hair lotions
in 4 oz. size. OSP $1.49. **CMV $30. MB.**

SMOOTH SHAVING SET 1954
Green tubes with red caps has choice of
brushless or lather shaving cream. OSP 98c.
CMV $25. MB.

BEFORE & AFTER SET 1953-54
Silver, white & green box opens up to 4 oz.
cologne for men & choice of cream or liquid
hair lotion. OSP $1.69. **CMV $45. MB.**

PLEASURE SHAVE SET 1949-51
Green box holds green can of talc for men,
wood shaving bowl & 4 oz. after shave lotion
with silver label. OSP $2.35. **CMV $75. MB.**

BACKFIELD SET 1954
Red & green box holds 2 oz. bottle of hair guard with red cap, 2 oz. hand guard with green cap, tube of chap check & small brown football soap. OSP $1.95. **CMV $70. MB.**

DELUXE TRIO SET 1949-51
Stage coach on green flip open box with green & red inner box. Holds choice of 4 oz. cream or liquid hair lotion, 2 oz. deodorant for men & 2 oz. cologne for men. OSP $2. **CMV $60. MB.**

DELUXE TRIO SET 1952
Same as 1949 set only has green removable lid. OSP $2. **CMV $60. MB.**

KING PIN SET 1953
Red & green box holds two 4 oz. bottles of after shave lotion wrapped in green King Pin wrappings. OSP $1.18. **CMV $45. MB.**

PERSONAL NOTE SET 1954-56
Green & red box holds 4 oz. cologne & deodorant for men with green label & gold ball point pen. OSP $2.95. **CMV $60. MB.**

QUARTET SET 1953-54
Green & red box holds 2 tubes of shave cream brushless or lather, 2 oz. deodorant for men, green label & 4 oz. after shave lotion with silver label. OSP $2.20. **CMV $60. MB.**

HI PODNER SET 1950-51
White box holds 2 red leatherette cowboy cuffs with tubes of cream hair dress & ammoniated toothpaste or dental cream and toothbrush. OSP $2.39. **CMV $70. MB.** 1952 Hi Podner set is same except tube of cream hair dress was replaced with green tube of creme shampoo. **CMV $70. MB.**

PLEASURE SHAVE SET 1952-54
Green box with red & white barber pole holds 2 tubes of shaving cream in choice of brushless or lather. OSP 98c. **CMV $25. MB.**

OUT IN FRONT SET 1959
Box with soldier on horse holds 4 oz. cream or liquid hair lotion & 2 3/4 oz. spray deodorant for men in white plastic bottles. OSP $1.98. **CMV $30. MB.**

GOOD CHEER SET 1957
Man playing bass fiddle on green & red box. 2 oz. bottles of cologne, deodorant & after shave lotions. All have red caps. OSP $1.98. **CMV $45. MB.**

COUNTRY CLUB SET 1949-51
Green flip open box with red inner box, holds green can of talc for men, 4 oz. after shaving lotion & choice of lather or brushless shaving cream. OSP $1.85. **CMV $55. MB.**

COUNTRY CLUB SET 1952-53
Stage coach on green box lid with inner box in red. Holds green talc for men, 4 oz. after shave lotion & tube of brushless or lather shave cream. OSP $1.85. **CMV $55. MB.**

COUNTRY CLUB SET 1954-55
Red box holds green can of talc for men, 4 oz. after shaving lotion & tube of brushless or lather shaving cream. OSP $1.85. **CMV $60. MB.** 1956 Country Club Set came in green box with golf ball & red flag on lid & red lined box. Same contents as 1954 set. OSP $2.19. CMV $60. **MB.**

SPORT WISE SET 1954
Red, white & green box holds two 4 oz. bottles of after shave lotions. OSP $1.18. **CMV $30. MB.**

LAMPLIGHTER SET 1959-60
(Left) Lamp post on covered box. 2 oz. bottle of after shave lotion, 1 1/2 oz. white plastic bottle of spray deodorant for men & 2 oz. black plastic bottle of after shower for men. All have red caps. OSP $3. **CMV $45. MB.**

AVON GUARD SET 1958
(Right) Red & blue box holds 2 bottles of hair guard & hand guard with red caps, white Avon rocket soap sits on top of bottles. OSP $1.39. **CMV $65. MB.**

TOP OF THE MORNING SET 1956
Red, white, green & silver box holds can of Kwick Foaming shave cream & 2 oz. after shave lotion. OSP $1.59. **CMV $45. MB.**

ROUGN 'N' READY SET 1953
White, red & green box holds 4 oz. cream hair lotion, chap check & Dr. Zabriskie's soap. OSP $1.25. **CMV $47.50 MB.**

CAPTAIN OF THE GUARD SET 1959
White tube, red cap of cream hair dress and white plastic bottle, red cap of spray deodorant for men. OSP $1.98. **CMV $40.**

YOUNG MAN SET 1950
Red, white & green box holds tubes of cream hair dress & creme shampoo, comb & nail file in brown leather case. OSP $1.50. **CMV $60. MB.**

SAILING, SAILING SET 1957
4 oz. clear glass, red cap, silver label. Choice of any 2 bottles of after shaving lotion, electric pre-shave lotion or deodorant for men. OSP $2.07. **CMV $30. MB.**

HAPPY HOURS SET 1958
Coo-coo clock on black & brown box. 2 oz. cologne, deodorant & after shave lotion. All have red caps. OSP $1.98. **CMV $40. MB.**

REFRESHING HOURS SET 1957
Red & green hourglass box holds 4 oz. after shaving lotion & 4 oz. deodorant for men. OSP $1.69. **CMV $30. MB.**

MORE LOVE THAN MONEY SET 1956
Red, black & gold box holds 4 oz. cologne for men, 4 oz. after shave lotion & 2 oz. deodorant for men. Brown leather wallet with a new 1956 penny in it. OSP $5.95. **CMV $55. MB.**

PENNY ARCADE SET 1954-55
Red & white with center foil mirror, holds tubes of cream hair dress, creme shampoo & chlorophyll toothpaste, toothbrush & chap check. OSP $2.25. **CMV $70. MB.**

TRIUMPH SET 1959
Triumph box holds choice of 5 combinations of two 4 oz. after shave lotions or electric pre-shave lotion & after shave lotion or after shave lotion & after shower powder for men. OSP each set $1.78. **CMV each set $30. MB.** Electric pre-shave lotion & after shower for men in black glass, or after shower powder for men & after shower for men in black glass. OSP each set $2.14. **CMV $30. MB.**

SHAVE BOWL SET 1955-56
Bronzo box holds wood shave bowl & bronze 4 oz. deodorant for men. OSP $2.39. **CMV $55. MB.**

SEND OFF SET 1957
Red, white & black box holds two 4 oz. after shave lotions. OSP $1.49. **CMV $30. MB.**

TWO SUITER SET 1953-54
Two different olive tan box with airlines painted on sides. Holds choice of two 2 oz. deodorants for men or one 2 oz. deodorant and 4 oz. after shave or 2 oz. deodorant and 2 oz. cologne for men. Sold at Father's Day. OSP $1.26. **CMV $60. MB, light color box, $70. MB dark color box.**

FATHER'S SAIL DAY SPECIAL SET NO. 1
Box with sailboat holds two 4 oz. bottles of after shave with silver labels. Also came with choice of 4 oz. after shave and green can of talc for men or 4 oz. deodorant & 4 oz. shave lotion. OSP $1.39. **CMV $35. MB.**

PLEASURE CAST SET 1955
Green & white box holds two 4 oz. bottles of after shaving lotion. OSP $1.25. **CMV $30. MB.**

MODERN DECOY SET 1958
Blue & brown box with ducks on lid holds silver Paper Mate Capri pen, 4 oz. cream hair lotion & choice of 4 oz. after shave lotion, cologne, deodorant or electric pre-shave lotion. OSP $4.50. **CMV $40. MB.**

TRADING POST SET 1957
Red & brown box holds 2 oz. bottle of foamy bath & hair trainer. Both have red caps. OSP 98c. **CMV $40. MB.**

FLYING HIGH NO. 1 & NO. 2 SET 1955
Red & green box has 4 oz. after shave lotion & 4 oz. deodorant for men. No. 2 box has 4 oz. deodorant for men & green can talc for men. OSP $1.49. **CMV $35. each set MB.**

CAROLLERS SET 1959-60
Xmas box with red & gold base holds red & black stick deodorant for men & black and white can of after shower powder for men & choice of 4 oz. after shower for men in black glass of electric pre-shave lotion or after shave lotion. OSP $3.75. **CMV $55. MB.**

SPACE SCOUT SET 1955
Blue box holds wall charts of planets, toothbrush, white toothpaste, bottle of hair guard, tube of antiseptic cream & chap check. OSP $2.25. **CMV $60. MB.**

ROUND THE CORNER SET 1955
Red & white striped box holds 2 oz. deodorant for men & can of Kwick Foaming shave cream. OSP $1.59. **CMV $35. MB.**

STAGE COACH SET 1958
Yellow stage coach box holds 2 oz. bottles of hair trainer & foamy bath. Both have red caps. OSP 98c. **CMV $40. MB.**

SATURDAY NIGHT SET 1955
Plaid box holds 4 oz. deodorant for men, plaid bow tie & choice of 4 oz. cream or liquid hair lotion. OSP $2.69. **CMV $50. MB.**
VARSITY SET 1956
Same set as Saturday Night only name changed. OSP $2.19. **CMV $50. MB.**

MERRILY SET 1957
Red, white & green box holds can of Kwick Foaming shaving cream, 2 oz. deodorant for men & 2 oz. after shave lotion. OSP $1.98. **CMV $30. MB.**

MONEY ISN'T EVERYTHING SET 1957
Red box with money written all over lid, holds 4 oz. cologne for men, 4 oz. after shave lotion & 2 oz. deodorant for men, plus brown leather billfold. OSP $5.95. **CMV $60. MB.**

PLEASURE CAST NO. 2 SET 1954
(Left) Green & white box holds 4 oz. after shave lotion & green can of talc. OSP $1.25. **CMV $35. MB.**
PLEASURE CAST NO. 1 SET 1954
(Right) Red & white box holds 2 oz. deodorant for men & 4 oz. after shave lotion. OSP $1.25. **CMV $35. MB.**

BEFORE & AFTER SET 1956
Red & silver box holds 4 oz. electric pre-shave lotion & 4 oz. after shave lotion. OSP $1.59. **CMV $30. MB.**

BLACK SHEEP 1954-56
Red, white, green & black box holds black sheep soap with gold bell on neck & 4 oz. cologne for men & 4 oz. deodorant for men. OSP $2.50. **CMV $100. MB.**

U.S. MALE SET 1952-53
Green & white mailbox choice of two 4 oz. after shave lotions or 4 oz. after shave lotion & 2 oz. deodorant for men. OSP $1.22. **CMV $40. MB.**

HOLIDAY HOLLY SET 1957
Green & white box holds 4 oz. after shave lotion & green can of talc for men. OSP $1.39. **CMV $30. MB.**

NEW DAY SET 1957
Red top box holds 4 oz. electric pre-shave lotion & 4 oz. after shaving lotion. OSP $1.59. **CMV $30. MB.**

CLASSIC SET 1951
Green box holds 4 oz. cream hair lotion, tan bar of soap & 2 oz. deodorant. OSP $1.75 set. **CMV $65. MB.**

CLASSIC SET 1954
Red & white box with horse head on box holds green can of talc for men, 2 oz. deodorant green label, 4 oz. cologne, silver label, all have red caps. Rare. OSP $2.25. **CMV $80.**

AVON CLASSIC SET 1952-53
Silver & green box holds 2 oz. deodorant for men, green talc for men & 4 oz. cologne for men. OSP $2.25. **CMV $55. MB.**

CUFFLINKS SET 1957
Black velour covered box holds 2 gold cufflinks and 4 oz. cologne & deodorant for men. OSP $3.50. **CMV $55. MB.**

OVERNIGHTER SET 1956-57
Brown alligator type bag holds 2 oz. after shaving lotion & 2 oz. deodorant for men, & choice of 4 oz. cream or liquid hair lotion. OSP $2.75. **CMV $45. MB.**

VALET SET 1951
Green flip open box holds 2 oz. deodorant for men & tube of brushless or lather shaving cream & 4 oz. cream or liquid hair lotion. OSP $2. **CMV $50. MB.**

AVON SERVICE KIT 1953-54
Green & red box holds tan plastic apron with 4 oz. plastic bottle of after shaving lotion with red cap, tube of brushless shaving cream, chlorophyll toothpaste, Dr. Zabriskie's soap, comb & toothbrush. OSP $3.95. **CMV $55. MB.**

HAPPY HOURS SUBSTITUTE SET 1958
Outer sleeve marked Happy Hours Sub holds tan vinyl case with 2 oz. cologne, after shave lotion & deodorant. This is a rare set. Factory ran out of regular issue box & used overnighter case for short period. OSP $2. **CMV $45. set MB.** Must have outer sleeve.

VALET SET 1949-50
Green box with choice of green can talc for men or shaving soap & 4 oz. cologne for men. OSP $1.65. **CMV $50. MB.**

AVON SERICE KIT 1951-52
Red & green box holds canvas apron with 4 oz. plastic bottle of after shaving lotion with red cap, Dr. Zabriskie's soap, tube of brushless shaving cream, toothpaste, toothbrush & comb. OSP $3.90. **CMV $55. MB.**

OVERNIGHTER SET 1958
Tan case holds 2 oz. deodorant for men & 2 oz. after shaving lotion & choice of 4 oz. liquid or cream hair lotion. OSP $2.98. **CMV $35. MB.**

MAN'S SAMPLE CASE SET 1953
Very rare brown leather case has three partitions inside to hold a Gilette brass razor, 1/2 oz. green sample tube brushless shaving cream 3/4 oz. blue, white & green sample toothpaste tubes, 1 oz. bottle liquid shampoo, green label, 1 oz. bottle cream hair lotion, green label, 1/2 oz. bottle shaving lotion, green label, 1/2 oz. bottle deodorant for men, green label, 1/2 oz. bottle cologne for men, silver label. All bottles have red caps. **CMV $125. complete set mint.**

ON THE GO SET 1957
Brown leatherette bag holds green can of talc for men, 2 oz. deodorant for men, 4 oz. after shave lotion & can of shaving cream in choice of Kwick Foaming lather, brushless or electric pre-shave lotion. OSP $8.95. **CMV $50. MB.**

THE TRAVELER SET 1956
Brown leatherette bag holds choice of shaving cream in Kwick, lather or brushless, 4 oz. after shaving lotion, green can talc for men, 2 oz. deodorant for men & styptic cream. OSP $7.95. **CMV $50. MB.**

NEAT TRAVELER SET 1958
Tan soft leather case holds 2 oz. deodorant for men, 4 oz. after shaving lotion choice of Kwick Foaming, lather or brushless shaving cream or electric pre-shave lotion & choice of cream or liquid hair lotion. OSP $8.95. **CMv $45. MB.**

MEN'S TRAVELING KIT 1953-55
Choice of brown leatherette or plaid case. Holds 4 oz. after shave lotion, 2 oz. deodorant for men, styptic cream, green can of talc for men and tube of Lather Shaving Cream. OSP $7.50. **CMV $55. MB.**

DELUXE TRIO SET 1953-56
Tan leatherette bag holds 2 oz. cologne for men & 2 oz. deodorant for men & choice of 4 oz. cream or liquid hair lotion. Avon on bag. Fold open top, no zipper. OSP $2.25. **CMV $45.**

WOMEN'S SETS OF 1950s

WARNING!! Grading condition is paramount on sets. CMV can vary 50% to 90% on grade.

LADY BELLE SET 1954-55
White bell shaped box trimmed in blue & gold has two 1 dram perfumes. Ribbed glass with gold cap. Choice of Cotillion, To A Wild Rose, Golden Promise, Quaintance, Bright Night or Forever Spring. OSP $3. **CMV $60. MB.**

TOPS STYLE BEAUTY SET 1959
(Left) Red & white box holds lipstick & 1 dram perfume Top Style perfume. OSP $2.95. **CMV $25. MB.**
TWO LOVES SET 1956
(Right) Box holds 2 black lipsticks. OSP $1.40. **CMV $25. MB.**

CONCERTINA SET 1954
Two gold fashion lipsticks in red, white & green box. OSP $1.10. **CMV $35. MB.**

TWO LOVES SET 1955
Red, white, blue & gold Christmas tree ornament box holds 2 gold fashion lipsticks. OSP $1.10. **CMV $35. MB.**

AVONETTE SET 1950-51
Blue & white brocade bag holds 1 dram perfume & deluxe gold lipstick. OSP $2.65. **CMV $22. - $25. MB.**

2 LIPS SET 1959
Two white enamel lipsticks, white box with pink & gold design. OSP $1.69. **CMV $15. MB.**

TWO LOVES SET 1957
Red Christmas tree hang on box came with black fashion lipstick & liquid rouge. OSP $1.10. **CMV $35. MB.**

PRECIOUS PEAR SET 1953
Gold bell box holds 1 dram perfume in Golden Promise, Quaintance, Cotillion, To A Wild Rose & Forever Spring. OSP $2.75. **CMV $75. MB.**

JEWELED LIPSTICK 1955
(Left) Blue & gold box with gold lipstick with pearl & rhinestones on top. OSP $1.75. **CMV $20. MB.**

CHARMER SET 1955
(Right) White, gold & red brocade case holds jeweled lipstick & 1 dram perfume. OSP $3. **CMV $25. mint.**

FASHION FIRSTS SET 1958
White & gold box holds 2 light tan fashion lipsticks. OSP $1.69. **CMV $15. MB.**

FRAGRANCE RAINBOW SET 1954
Flowers on top of box. Choice of Cotillion, To A Wild Rose, Forever Spring, Quaintance. Cologne in 1/2 oz. bottles, white caps & painted labels. OSP $2.50. **CMV $70. MB.**

FRAGRANCE RAINBOW SET 1956
Box holds four 3 dram bottles with white painted caps. Came in To A Wild Rose, Nearness, Bright Night, Cotillion, Quaintance & Forever Spring. OSP $2.75. **CMV $75. MB.**

FRAGRANCE TIE INS SET 1953
White box with bows holds four 1/2 oz. bottles with white caps. Came in Cotillion, Forever Spring, Quaintance & To A Wild Rose cologne. OSP $2.50. **CMV $70. MB.**

SWEET AS HONEY SET 1951
Foam beehive holds four 5/8 dram bottles of perfume in Cotillion, Quaintance, Golden Promise, Luscious, Forever Spring & To A Wild Rose. All have different colored caps. OSP $2.50. **CMV MB $115. Beehive and bottles only $90. mint.**

AVON BLOSSOMS SET 1950
Four 1/8 oz. or 5/8 dram perfume bottles set in white foam with wire fence behind it. Flowers around bottles. Plastic cap. Quaintance, Cotillion, Luscious and Golden Promise. OSP $2. **CMV $85. set only, $100. MB.**

CREAM SACHET PETITES SET 1956
Gold box holds 4 plastic cream sachets in blue boxes. Came in Cotillion, Bright Night, Nearness and To A Wild Rose. OSP $3.25. **CMV $55. set, $10. each jar MB.**

CUPID'S BOW SET 1955
White and pink box holds four 1/2 oz. bottles of cologne with white caps. Bright Night, To A Wild Rose, Quaintance and Cotillion. OSP $2.50. **CMV $70. MB.**

AVONETTE SET 1953-54
Black case holds 1 dram perfume & gold deluxe lipstick. OSP $2.50. **CMV $22. - $25. MB.**

HOLIDAY FASHION SET 1953
White box holds 2 gold fashion lipsticks in green holly leaves. OSP $1.10. **CMV $25. MB.**

TIME FOR BEAUTY SET 1952
Blue, white & pink box with pink ribbon holds gold lipstick & nail polish. OSP $1.65. **CMV $30. MB.**

HOUSE OF CHARMS SET 1952-53
With windows open. You find four 1/8 oz. or 5/8 dram bottles or perfume: Lily of the Valley, Cotillion, Golden Promise or Quaintance. In pink box, all blue caps. OSP $1.95. **CMV $100. MB.**

HOUSE OF CHARMS PERFUMES
Shown only to identify size & labels, Left square bottle is 1954 set only. Center bottle has same label as short one on left issued in 1953-54. Right one issued 1952-53 sets only.

HOUSE OF CHARM SET 1954
Pink box holds four 5/8 dram bottles of perfume with turquoise caps or white caps. Choice of To A Wild Rose, Cotillion, Golden Promise or Quaintance. OSP $1.95. **CMV $110. MB.**

BEAUTY PAIR SET 1957
White, blue & yellow box with 2 black & pink fashion lipsticks. OSP $1.49. **CMV $30. MB.**

LITTLE LAMBS SET 1954-56
Box holds 2 lamb soaps and can of baby powder. Two different boxes. One has 2 lambs & the other has 2 lambs holding an umbrella. OSP $1.30. **CMV $80. each set MB.**

THAT'S FOR ME SET 1955-56
Pink box holds four 2 oz. bottles with pink caps of bath oil. Quaintance, To A Wild Rose, Cotillion & Pine. OSP $2.50. **CMV $85. MB.**

GEMS IN CRYSTAL SET 1957
1/2 oz. bottles of Nearness, Bright Night, Cotillion & To A Wild Rose. Pointed plastic caps. OSP $2.95. **CMV with flat top caps (left) $65., with pointed caps (right) $75. MB.**

OVER THE RAINBOW SET 1957
Blue box holds 4 cream sachet jars in Cotillion, To A Wild Rose, Bright Night and Nearness. Jars are white glass with green and yellow and have two pink lids. OSP $3.25. **CMV $50. set MB, $55. MB with outer box as shown, $8. each jar.**

WISHING COIN TRIO SET 1958
Blue and gold box. Holds choice of cream sachet, lotion sachet and 1/2 oz. cologne in To A Wild Rose, Cotillion, Nearness, Forever Spring, Bright Night, Elegante, Here's My Heart and Persian Wood fragrances. Blue caps on all three. OSP $2.50. **CMV $40. MB.**

SINGING BELLS SET 1956
White bell box holds 2 cans of talc in Cotillion or To A Wild Rose. OSP $1.10. **CMV $20. MB.**

JOLLY SURPRISE SET 1950
Pink, white and green Santa box holds 2 oz. cream lotion, nail polish and 1 dram perfume in ribbed glass. OSP $1.95. **CMV $55. MB.**

SILVER WINGS SET 1954
Box holds cream sachet and body powder in choice of To A Wild Rose, Quaintance, Golden Promise or Forever Spring. OSP $2.10. **CMV $40. each set MB.**

CHRISTMAS ANGELS SET 1953-55
Blue and white box holds gold lipstick and cream sachet in To A Wild Rose, Quaintance, Cotillion, Forever Spring and Golden Promise. To A Wild Rose pictured sold 1955 only and 1953-54 came with older 3 corner white jar with blue cap. Both are same CMV. OSP $2. **CMV $30.**

SHOWERS OF STARS SET 1955
Silver box with fluff on top holds cream sachet and body powder in choice of Golden Promise, Quaintance and Forever Spring. OSP $2.10. **CMV $40. MB.**

BATH DELIGHTS SET 1955
Box holds bottle of Avon Bubble Bath and shoice of body powder in Golden Promise, Quaintance or Forever Spring. OSP $2.10. **CMV $50. MB.**

SUNNY HOURS SET 1952-53
White umbrella holds 1 dram perfume and deluxe gold lipstick. OSP $2.50. **CMV MB $50. Umbrella and contents only $30.**

SPECIAL DATE SET 1955
Blue and white box holds gold lipstick, 2 different powder paks and 1/2 oz. Cotillion Toilet water. OSP $1.95. **CMV $40. MB.**

MODERN MOOD SET 1957
Pink and gold box holds 2 cans of talc in choice of Cotillion or To A Wild Rose. Same box in blue and gold holds 2 cans of talc in choice of Nearness or Forever Spring. OSP $1.29. **CMV $25. each set MB.**

TRI COLOR SET 1957
Blue and white box holds Nearness or choice of cream sachet, gold satin sheen lipstick and white leather purse trimmed in gold. OSP $7.75. **CMV $45. MB.**

CLASSIC STYLE SET 1958
Black and gold box holds Top Style lipstick and gold Top Style compact. OSP $5. **CMV $20. MB.**

AVON JEWELS SET 1957
Box contains liquid rouge, nail and longlife gold lipstick. OSP $2.50. **CMV $25. MB.**

LADY FAIR SET 1950-51
Red, white and silver box holds gold Deluxe Lipstick and bottle of nail polish. OSP $1.65. **CMV $30. MB.**

TOP STYLE SET 1955-56
Box holds gold lipstick, 1/2 oz. nail polish and liquid rouge. OSP $1.95. **CMV $25. MB.**

BEAUTY PAIR SET 1954
Red and gold box holds golds Deluxe Lipstick and nail polish. OSP $1.50. **CMV $25. MB.**

MAKEUP MATES SET 1958
Green box holds lipstick and face powder. OSP $1.98. **CMV $20. MB.**

TOUCH OF PARIS SET 1958
Box holds white lipstick and compact. OSP $2.10. **CMV $15. MB.**

GADABOUTS SET 1954-55
Gold and white box holds turquoise and white compact and gold lipstick. OSP $2.10. **CMV $20. MB.**

GADABOUTS SET 1952-53
Gold and white box holds compact and cologne stick. Both are turquoise in color. OSP $2.25. **CMV $25. MB.**

COLOR CORSAGE SET 1954-55
Turquoise box of face powder with gold lipstick on top. OSP $1.90. **CMV $25. MB.**

PEARL FAVORITES SET 1959
Blue, green and white box holds white compact and white enamel lipstick. OSP $2.19. **CMV $20. MB.**

BEAUTY BOUND SET 1955-56
Turquoise and white plastic compact, jeweled lipstick. Box pink and turquoise. OSP $2.75. **CMV $20. MB.**

ADORABLE SET 1950-51
White box holds blue satin with white lace pillow with powder pak and lipstick inside. OSP $2.95. **CMV $35. MB.**

ADORABLE SET 1950
Foam holder has powder pak and gold lipstick. Trimmed in blue feathers and pink ribbon and flowers. Came in green box. OSP $2. **CMV $35. mint as shown.**

FRAGRANCE MIST SET 1951-52
Turquoise box with pink and gold inside holds 2 oz. toilet water and 1 dram perfume in choice of Cotillion, Flowertime and Lily of the Valley. OSP $2.35. **CMV $50. MB.**

BEAUTIFUL JOURNEY SET 1957
Pink zippered bag holds 1 oz. bottles of Cotillion cologne, Deep Clean Cleansing Cream, Deodorant, Hand Lotion, Skin Freshener and 1/2 oz. jar of Rich Moisture Cream with peach colored cap. **$10. each bottle, $15. Cotillion cologne, $7. Rich Moisture Cream.** OSP $5.95. **CMV set $70. MB.**

HAND BEAUTY SET 1955
Pink box holds two 4 oz. bottles of hand lotion with turquoise caps. OSP $1.18. **CMV $20. MB.**

FOR YOUR LOVLINESS SET 1954-55
Green and silver box holds 3 1/2 oz. jar of Moisture Cream and choice of 4 oz. bottle of Hand Lotion or Skin Freshener. OSP $2.75. **CMV $20. MB.**

SPECIAL SET 1951
Blue and pink Christmas box holds 2 bottles of hand lotion. OSP $1. **CMV $30. MB.**

TWIN PAK SET 1952-53
Silver box holds 2 bottles of hand lotion. White caps, red ribbon on box. OSP $1.10. **CMV $30. MB.**

WOMEN'S SETS OF 1950s

SAFE JOURNEY SET 1958
Gold and white zippered travel kit holds 6 plastic containers of Perfumed Talc, Hand Lotion, Lotion Sachet, Cleansing Cream, Rich Moisture Cream and Deodorant. OSP $6.95. **CMV $35. mint.**

DRAMATIC MOMENTS SET 1958
Essence de Fleurs Cologne Mist and paper box of powder in blue box. Came in To A Wild Rose, Cotillion, Forever Spring. OSP $5. Nearness, Elegante and Bright Night. OSP $5.25. **CMV $40. MB.**

BEAUTIFUL YOU SET 1958
Pink and white box with ladies face holds 3 1/2 oz. Rich Moisture Cream, 2 oz. of Skin Freshener and Rich Moisture Suds or Deep Clean. OSP $3.50. **CMV $20. MB.**

HAND BEAUTY SET 1954
Red box holds two bottles of hand lotion. OSP $1.10. **CMV $20. MB.**

FOR YOUR BEAUTY SET 1956
Blue and gold box holds Cleansing Cream in plastic bottle, 2 oz. bottle of Skin Freshener and Rich Moisture Cream in jar. OSP $2.95. **CMV $20. MB.**

CLEAR-IT-SKIN CARE KIT 1959
White box holds shampoo and lotion in white plastic bottles and bar of Clear Skin soap. OSP $2.50. **CMV $20. MB.**

DOUBLY YOURS SET 1956
Blue and gold box holds two bottles of hand lotion. OSP $1.29. **CMV $20. MB.**

FOAM 'N' SPRAY SET 1955
Green box holds can of Avon Hair Spray and 6 oz. bottle of Cream Lotion Shampoo. OSP $2.19. **CMV $20. MB.**

BOUQUET OF FRESHNESS SET 1957
Pink and lavender box holds two 2 oz. bottles of Perfumed Deodorant. OSP $1.38. **CMV $15. MB.**

SHOWER OF FRESHNESS SET 1956
Turquoise and white box holds 2 bottles of Perfumed Deodorant. OSP $1.38. **CMV $15. MB.**

FASHION JEWELS SET 1954-55
Black velvet case holds 1 dram perfume, jeweled lipstick and gold compact. OSP $10.50. **CMV $40. MB.**

HIGH FASHION SET 1950-54
Black case with white satin lining holds 1 dram perfume, gold lipstick, gold compact and gold rouge compact. OSP $10. **CMV $45. MB.**

SPECIAL NAIL CARE SET 1955-57
Red and white box contained Silvery Base and Top Coat. OSP $1.10. **CMV $10. MB.**

HOME PERMANENT REFILL KIT 1951
Kit contains 4 oz. permanent wave lotion. **CMV $25.** Neutralizer, end tissues. OSP $1. **CMV $45. MB set.**

HAPPY TRAVELER SET 1955-56
Black bag with pink and blue stripes holds Cleansing Cream, Skin Freshener, Rich Moisture Cream, Hand Cream, Flowing Cream Deodorant, 1 empty plastic jar, packette of tissues. OSP $5.95. **CMV $35. MB.**

A THING OF BEAUTY SET 1957
White, pink and black box holds 6 oz. Avon Cleansing Cream, 2 oz. Skin Freshener and 3 1/2 oz. Rich Moisture Cream. OSP $3.50. **CMV $25. MB.**

HAPPY VACATION SET 1953
Plastic bag and tie string says Avon Happy Vacation. Bag holds Cotillion Talc, toothpaste, cream deodorant and tube of Ammoniated Toothpaste. OSP $1.39. **CMV $60. MB.**

HAPPY TRAVELER SET 1954
Black and white bag holds Perfumed Deodorant, Hand Cream, Rich Moisture Cream, Skin Freshener, Cleansing Cream and a plastic jar. OSP $5.95. **CMV $35. MB.**

CAMPING KIT 1954
Navy blue cotton twill draw string bag. Came with 2 oz. Sun Lotion, Chap Check, Antiseptic Cream and choice of either Creme Shampoo or Cream Hair Dress. OSP $1.95. **Value complete set $50. MB.**

HAPPY TRAVELER SET 1955
Black zipper bag with pink and blue stripes. Came with pack of Kleenex tissues, 2 turquoise and white plastic jars, tube of hand cream and cleansing cream and rare 2 oz. bottle of skin freshener with turquoise cap. OSP $5.95. **CMV $35. mint, $40. MB.**

HAPPY VACATION SPECIAL GIFT BAG SET 1951
Folder has plastic bag and Avon tie tag to hold cream deodorant, toothpaste, toothbrush and Cotillion Talcum, all boxed. **CMV $7. as pictured.**

MEN'S SETS OF 1960s

WARNING!! Grading condition is paramount on sets. CMV can vary 50% to 90% on grade.

CHRISTMAS CALL SET 1965
Red box holds two 4 oz. bottles of Original After Shave Lotion. Red caps. OSP $1.95. **CMV $20. MB.**

FRAGRANCE CHEST 1966-67
Brown chest type box holds four 1 oz. bottles with silver caps, of after shave lotion in Tribute, blue glass; Leather in amber glass; Spicy in clear glass; Island Lime in green glass. OSP $4. **CMV $40. MB. With outer sleeve $37. as pictured.**

MEN'S FRAGRANCE WARDROBE SET 1965
Red box holds three 2 oz. bottles of after shave lotion in choice of Set A: Leather, Blue Blazer, After Shower Cologne; Set B: Leather, Tribute, Spicy; Set C: "4-A", Tribute, Original; or Set D: Spicy, Bay Rum, Original. OSP $3.50 each set. **CMV $33. each set boxed with sleeve.**

ORIGINAL SET 1965
Horse box holds two 4 oz. bottles of Original after shave with red caps. OSP $1.96. **CMV $20. MB.**

MEN'S AFTER SHAVE CHOICE SET 1967-68
Black box holds 2 oz. after shave lotion in Wild Country with silver cap; Leather with gold cap; & Tribute with blue cap. Late issue set came with all silver or gold caps. OSP $5. **CMV $18. MB.**

AFTER SHAVE SELECTION SET 1966
Father's Day box holds three 2 oz. bottles in choice of Leather all purpose lotion for men, Blue Blazer, Island Lime, Tribute, after shave lotion Spicy, Bay Rum, Original & 4A after shave lotions. OSP $2.98. **CMV $33. boxed with outer sleeve.**

FIRST PRIZE SET 1960
Black, gold & red box holds three 2 oz. embossed Stage Coach bottles in choice of after shower for men, "Vigorate" after shaving lotion, cream hair lotion, deodorant for men, liquid hair lotion, electric pre-shave lotion, after shave for dry or sensitive skin. OSP $2.50. **CMV $55. set of 3 MB with outer sleeve.**

BUREAU ORGANIZER 1966-67
Wood grained plastic tray is 12 1/4" x 5 1/4". Came with 2 oz. bottles with black 4A embossed caps in Tribute after shave lotion, Blue Blazer after shave, Spicy after shave & Leather all purpose cologne. OSP $11.95. **CMV $50. MB, tray $15.**

GENTLEMAN'S COLLECTION SET 1968
Brown plastic box holds three 2 oz. bottles with gold, silver & bronze caps. Came in Leather, Windjammer & Wild Country cologne. OSP $8. **CMV $20. MB.**

FOX HUNT SET 1966
Fox hunt box holds two 4 oz. bottles with black caps in Leather all purpose cologne. OSP $4. **CMV $30. MB.**

AFTER SHAVE CADDY 1968
6 oz. rectangular bottle with silver cap & top fits in brown plastic box. Came in Leather & Island Lime after shave. OSP $7. **CMV $14. MB.**

GOLD MEDALLION GIFT SET 1961
Gold box holds three individual men's grooming products in 2 oz. glass or plastic bottles. Glass bottles are: Spicy after shave lotion, Vigorate after shaving lotion, after shaving lotion, after shower lotion, electric pre-shave lotion, liquid hair lotion & deodorant for men. Plastic bottles are: after shave for dry sensitive skin & cream hair lotion. Set of 3 bottles. OSP $2.50. **CMV $55. MB with outer sleeve.**

DELUXE SET FOR MEN 1962-63
Brown & gold box holds can of deluxe foam shave cream, deluxe after shave, after shower spray & deluxe stick deodorant normal. Box has outer sleeve. OSP $4.98. **CMV $45. MB.**

CHRISTMAS TRIO FOR MEN SET 1964
Winter scene box holds three 2 oz. red & white plastic bottles of any three of: Spicy after shave lotion, Original after shave lotion, "Vigorate" after shave lotion, after shower cologne, Spicy electric pre-shave lotion, liquid deodorant for men, liquid hair lotion, cream hair lotion or hair trainer. OSP $1.98. **CMV $15. MB.**

COLOGNE TRILOGY SET 1969-70
Brown & gold plastic box holds three 1 1/2 oz. bottles with gold caps & labels in Wild Country, Windjammer & Excalibur cologne. Box is 6" high. OSP $8. **CMV $18. MB.**

STRUCTURED FOR MEN SET 1969
Silver box holds black plastic stair step base with 3 oz. bottles of Glass, Wood & Steel cologne. OSP $8.50. **CMV $15. MB, bottles & base only $10.**

JOLLY HOLLY DAY SET 1963
Green & white box holds three 2 oz. white plastic bottles with red caps in choice of Vigorate, Spicy & Original after shave lotions, electric pre-shave lotion, liquid or cream hair lotion, hair trainer, after shower cologne for men, & liquid deodorant for men - gentle. OSP $1.98. **CMV $15. MB.**

KING FOR A DAY 1965
Box holds 3 white plastic bottles with red caps in choice of any 3 after shave lotion. Spicy, Original & Vigorate after shave, after shower cologne for men, cream or liquid hair lotion, liquid deodorant for men, electric pre-shave lotion. OSP $1.98. **CMV $15. MB.**

SMART MOVE SET 1967
Orange & black box holds three 2 oz. plastic bottles of after shave. Original or Spicy in red, Tribute or Spicy in black. White bottle came in both Original or Spicy. OSP $4. **CMV $20. MB.**

TAG-ALONGS SET 1967
Box holds 3 1/2 oz. red plastic bottle of after shave lotion Spicy & tan 3 oz. plastic bottle of Squeeze Spray deodorant. Both have black caps. OSP $2.50. **CMV $12. MB. Bottles only $3. each.**

THE TRAVELER SET 1969
Box holds 2 plastic bottles in Bravo or Spicy after shave & spray deodorant. OSP $2.50. **CMV $10. MB.**

OVERNIGHTER SET 1968
Black box holds 3 oz. white plastic bottle of Squeeze Spray deodorant & 3 1/2 oz. black plastic bottle of Spicy after shave lotion. OSP $2.50. **CMV $10. MB.**

FOR GENTLEMEN SET 1961
Black, gold & red box holds 4 oz. plastic cream hair lotion, roll-on deodorant for men, choice of Vigorate or after shower for men in 8 oz. embossed Stage Coach bottle and choice of 6 oz. Kwick foaming shave cream or 4 oz. electric pre-shave lotion. OSP $5.17. **CMV $62.50 each set MB, 2 different sets are shown.**

BOOTS & SADDLE SET 1968
Cowhide type box holds 3 oz. bottles of Leather after shave lotion with red cap & Wild Country after shave with black cap. OSP $3. **CMV $15. MB.**

MEN'S TRAVEL KIT 1963-64
Black leather bag holds can of after shave, after shower spray, Spicy, tube of cream hair dress, toothbrush, smokers toothpaste, spray deodorant for men & choice of foam shave cream, Spicy or electric pre-shave lotion. OSP $11.95. **CMV $32.50 MB.**

DASHING SLEIGHS SET 1960-61
Black, gold & red box holds 4 oz. plastic bottle of cream hair lotion, can of after shower powder for men, roll-on deodorant for men & choice of Vigorate or after shower for men in 8 oz. embossed stage coach bottle. OSP $5.17. **CMV $62.50 MB.**

TRAVEL DELUXE SET 1962
Tan plastic bag with front & top zipper. Holds only 2 items, after shave lotion & roll-on deodorant as pictured. Outer sleeve lists only 2 contents. OSP $6.95. **CMV $35. MB.**

UNDER THE MISTLETOE SET 1962-63
Green box holds 4 oz. electric pre-shave lotion Spicy & After Shave lotion Spicy. Red caps. OSP $1.78 **CMV $20. MB.**

TRAVEL DELUXE SET 1959-60
Brown leather case holds after shave lotion, choice of spray deodorant for men, 4 oz. hair lotion in cream or liquid or Attention & choice of shave cream in Kwick foaming, lather or brushless or electric pre-shave lotion. OSP $9,95 **CMV $35. MB.**

MEN'S TRAVEL KIT 1966
Brown travel bag holds smoker's toothpaste, clear hair dress, Spicy after shave lotion, Spicy talc for men, aerosol deodorant & choice of electric pre-shave lotion or foam shave cream in regular or mentholated. OSP $12.95 **CMV $30. MB.**

OVERNIGHTER SET 1960-62
Tan plastic travel case holds after shaving lotion, roll on deodorant for men & cream hair lotion, cream hair lotion or hair trainer. OSP $1.98 **CMV $25. MB.**

CHRISTMAS CLASSIC SET 1962-63
Blue box holds choice of two 4 oz. bottles of "Vigorate" after shave lotion, after shower cologne for men, original after shave lotion. OSP $1.79 **CMV $20. MB.**

HOLLY TIME SET 1962-63
Red white and green box holds choice of 2 plastic bottles in cream hair lotion or liquid hair lotion in glass bottle. OSP $1.78 **CMV $20. MB.**

SANTA'S TEAM SET 1964 Only
Blue box holds 4 oz. each of after shave lotion Spicy & liquid deodorant for men. OSP $1.59 **CMV $20. MB.**

GOOD CHEER SET 1962-63
Red & gold box holds Spicy talc for men & choice of Spicy or Original after shave lotion. OSP $1.78 **CMV $20. MB.**

HOLIDAY GREETINGS SET 1964
Gold box holds 4 oz. bottle of electric pre-shave lotion Spicy & after shave lotion Spicy. OSP $1.78 **CMV $20. MB.**

HOLLY STAR SET 1964
Red, white and green box holds 4 oz. each of after shave lotion, Spicy & 3 oz. talc for men, Spicy. OSP $1.59 **CMV $20. MB.**

CHRISTMAS DAY SET 1962-63
Partridge box holds 4 oz. liquid deodorant for men - gentle choice of Spicy or Original after shave lotion. OSP $1.78 **CMV $15. MB.**

CHRISTMAS MORNING SET 1964
Red & gold box holds two 4 oz. bottles of after shave lotion Spicy. OSP $1.78 **CMV $15. MB.**

WOMEN'S SETS OF 1960'S

WARNING!! Grading condition is paramount on sets. CMV can vary 50% to 90% on grade.

FRAGRANCE FLING TRIO 1968
1/2 oz. cologne gold cap. Set of three. Came in Occur!, Charisma, Brocade, Regence, Unforgettable, Rapture, Somewhere, Topaze, Cotillion, Here's My Heart, Wishing, To A Wild Rose, Persian Wood. OSP $4. **CMV $15. MB.**

FRAGRANCE GOLD SET 1964
Box holds 3 heart shaped 1/2 oz. colognes in Occur!, Somewhere, Wishing, Topaze, Cotillion, Here's My Heart, Persian Wood, To A Wild Rose. OSP $3.50 **CMV $20. MB.**

COLOGNE GEMS SET 1966-67
Gold & white box contains two 1 oz. Gem colognes, clear glass with plastic caps. Came in Unforgettable, Rapture, Occur!, Somewhere, Topaze, Cotillion, Here's My Heart, To A Wild Rose. OSP $3.50 **CMV $12. MB.**

FRAGRANCE ORNAMENTS SET 1965
Three bottles 5/8 dram perfume oil. Same as the Bullet bottle. White paper trimmed in gold. Gold & white box. Set A: Wishing, Somewhere, Occur!; Set B: Rapture, Topaze, To A Wild Rose; Set C: Unforgettable, Here's My Heart ,Cotillion. OSP $4.50 **CMV $35. MB.**

JEWEL COLLECTION SET 1964
(Left) With 6 gem shaped bottles of perfume oil & gold caps. Blue and gold box. Somewhere, Topaze, Cotillion, Persian Wood, Here's My Heart, To A Wild Rose. OSP $5.95 **CMV $35. MB.**

JEWEL COLLECTION- CANADASET 1964
(Right) Box is same as American set only center bottle hole is not punched out. Came in Somewhere, Topaze, Cotillion, Here's My Heart, To A Wild Rose in perfume oils, 5/8 dram each. Very rare set. OSP $6.95 **CMV $175. MB.**

FRAGRANCE FAVORITES SET 1965
Box holds 3 heart shaped 1/2 oz. colognes in Unforgettable, Rapture, Occur!, Cotillion, Somewhere, Topaze, Here's My Heart, Persian Wood, To A Wild Rose, Wishing. OSP $3.50 **CMV $20. MB.**

PERFUME OIL PETITES SET PIN CUSHION 1966
Gold box with red velvet pin cushion top & inner box holds three 5/8 dram heart shaped bottles with gold caps & labels. Came in choice of Wishing, Somewhere, Occur, Rapture, Topaze, To A Wild Rose, Here's My Heart, Unforgettable, Cotillion. OSP $4.50 **CMV $35. MB.**

RENAISSANCE TRIO 1966-67
Box holds 3 boxes with 1/2 oz. colognes in Unforgettable, Rapture, Occur!, Somewhere, Topaze, Cotillion, Here's My Heart, To A Wild Rose & Wishing. OSP $3.50 **CMV $20. MB.**

FRAGRANCE GOLD DUET 1965
Two heart shaped 1/2 oz. colognes in gold & white box. Came in Rapture, Occur!, Cotillion, Somewhere, Topaze, Here's My Heart, Persian Wood, To A Wild Rose, Wishing & Unforgettable. OSP $2.50 **CMV $20. MB.**

GIFT MAGIC SET 1960
Flat rocker bottles in same set that sold in 1967-68 with round cap rocker bottles. OSP $2.49 **CMV $20. MB.**

GOLDEN HEIRLOOM CHEST SET 1968
6" long gold metal, glass lid. Red velvet in bottom of chest. Avon on bottom. Came in perfume rollette in Brocade or Regence & deluxe refillable gold lipstick. Came in pink box. OSP $15 **CMV complete set in box $35. chest only $25.**

STAR ATTRACTIONS SET 1965
Box contains 1/2 oz. cologne & metal lipstick in Rapture, Occur!, Somewhere, Topaze, Cotillion, Here's My Heart, Persian Wood, To A Wild Rose, and Wishing. OSP $2.50 **CMV $20. MB.**

GOLDEN RINGS SET 1960
Red & gold box holds 2 pink & white lipsticks. OSP $1.79 **CMV $15. MB.**

GIFT MAGIC SET 1967-68
3 1/2 oz. clear glass rocker bottle with gold label & lid. Box red & purple with gold & white sleeve. Came in choice of Brocade, Regence, Unforgettable, Rapture, Occur!, Somewhere, Topaze, Cotillion, Here's My Heart, To A Wild Rose, Wishing, & Persian Wood. OSP $2.98 **CMV $15. MB.**

FRAGRANCE VANITY TRAY SET 1966
Three hearts on tray. 1/2 oz cologne. Heart shaped bottles on glass tray with Avon insignia on tray. OSP tray $1.25, **CMV $3. tray - MB. $4. colognes** OSP $3.75, **CMV $2. each- $4. MB. CMV set $20. MB.**

GOLDEN VANITY SET 1965-66
Gold metal stand with removable mirror in center. Came with perfume rollettte & gold refillable lipstick. OSP $10. **CMV complete set $30. MB. Stand with mirror only $15.**

VANITY SHOWCASE SET 1964-65
Silver & gold plastic holder. Avon on bottom. Came with 1 dram ribbed perfume & deluxe silver lipstick with 4A on top. OSP $5. **CMV complete set $20. in box-holder only $9.**

MANICURE TRAY SET 1967
Dark brown plastic tray with 4A design. Came with tubes Nail Beauty & Cuticle Remover, 1/2 oz. bottle of Double Coat & Nail Enamel with white caps & box of 10 enamel Remover Pads, 1 orange stick & emery board. OSP $5. **CMV complete set $16. MB. tray only $5. Also came in amber color tray. CMV $10 tray.**

MANICURE TRAY 1962-64
Clear plastic, Avon on bottom, 4A design. Came with 3 oz. bottle of Oily Polish Remover, 1/2 oz. bottle of Nail Polish & Base Coat or Double Coat & 2 tubes of Cuticle Remover & Nail Beauty. OSP $3.98 **CMV complete set $15. tray only $3.**

FRAGRANCE FORTUNE SET 1964
Matching boxes hold 2 oz. cologne & 1/2 oz. perfume oil in Somewhere, Here's My Heart, Cotillion, To A Wild Rose, Persian Wood & Topaze. OSP each $4.98 **CMV $30. MB.**

FRAGRANCE MAGIC SET 1962-63
Matching boxes holds cologne mist & beauty dust with claer plastic top. Came in To A Wild Rose, Persian Wood, Here's My Heart, Somewhere, Cotillion, & Topaze. OSP $6. **CMV $35. MB each.**

LADIES CHOICE SET 1960
Matching boxes hold 4 oz. cologne & beauty dust in Cotillion, Persian Wood, To A Wild Rose, Here's My Heart, OSP $5.45 **CMV $40. each set MB.**

MODERN SIMPLICITY SET 1960-61
Lavendar blue & white box contains soap, 4 oz. bath oil, 3 oz. beauty dust in choice of Cotillion, To A Wild Rose & Here's My Heart. OSP $3.98 **CMV $45. MB.**

FLOWER FANTASY SET 1965
Floral box holds cream sachet & Perfume rollette in Wild Rose, Wishing, Somewhere, Cotillion, Topaze, & Occurl. OSP $5. CMV **$15. each MB. $18. with carnival glass rollette.**

TWO LOVES SETS 1956-60
Matching boxes hold cologne mist & cream sachet in To A Wild Rose, Here's My Heart. **CMV $23.** 1959 only for Persian Wood **CMV $27.** Bright Night **CMV $30.** OSP $4.25.

VANITY TRAY SET 1968
Brown plastic tray. Came with brown plastic fashion lipstick shown on right & perfume rollette in choice of Unforgettable, Rapture, Occur!, Here's My Heart or To A Wild Rose. OSP $6. CMV complete set $11. MB. tray only $6. MB.

PERFUMED PILLOWETTES SET 1965
Box contains two sachet pillows & gold top powder sachet in Occur!, Somewhere, Cotillion, Topaze, Here's My Heart, To A Wild Rose, and Wishing. OSP $3. CMV $22. MB.

JUST TWO SET 1965
3 oz. each, Tribute after shave, black glass; clear Rapture cologne with gold tags. OSP $5.50 CMV $50 MB. bottles only with tags. $15. each.

TWO LOVES SET 1969
Red & gold box with red felt inside holds perfume rollette & cream sachet in Charisma, Brocade or Regence. OSP $6. CMV $12. Brocade is gray inside box.

SPLASH & SPRAY SET 1968
Purse size cologne spray & 2 1/2 oz. splash cologne botle with refill funnel. Both trimmed in gold. Gold box. Came in Brocade, & Regence, Unforgettable, Somewhere and Topaze. OSP $6.50 CMV $20. MB.

FLOWER FANTASIES SET 1963-64
Cream sachet & cream rollette in Here's My Heart, Persian Wood, To A Wild Rose, Cotillion, Somewhere, Topaze, Occur!. OSP $5. CMV $17. MB.

SCENTIMENTS SET 1969
Box holds 1/2 oz. clear glass with gold cap with cream sachet in Unforgettable, Rapture, Occur!, Somewhere, Topaze or Cotillion with 4A embossed soap. OSP $3.50 CMV $10 MB. Each fragrance came with different color soap.

MERRY FINGERTIPS SET 1967
Pink velvet box holds 2 bottles of nail polish. OSP $1.70 CMV $10 MB.

SCENTIMENTS SET 1968-69
Gold, white & silver box holds cream sachet & perfumed rollette in Brocade, Regence, Unforgettable, Rapture, Occur, Somewhere, Topaze, or Cotillion. OSP $4. CMV $12. MB.

1. Elusive

2. Bird of Paradise

3. Charisma

TWO LOVES SET 1970
Cream sachet & perfume rollette in Elusive in pink & gold box. Bird of Paradise in turquoise & gold box and Charisma in red & gold box with white , gold or red liner. OSP $6. each. CMV $12 each MB.

MERRY LIPTINTS SET 1967
Red flocked sleeve holds 2 white & gold Encore lipsticks with boxes to match sleeve but not flocked. OSP $1.99 CMV $9. MB.

TWO LOVES SET 1967
Gold & green box has cream sachet & perfume rollette in Unforgettable, Rapture, Occur!, Somewhere, To A Wild Rose, Topaze, Cotillion, Here's My Heart. OSP $5. **CMV $13. MB.**

FASHION TWINS SET 1965
Multi-colored box holds 2 Cameo lipsticks. OSP $1.95 **CMV $10. MB.**

CANDY CANE TWINS SET 1966
Candy cane box holds 2 cameo lipsticks. OSP $1.96 **CMV $20. MB.**

CLEVER MATCH SET 1962
Pink & red box holds black lipstick & nail polish with white cap. 1961 set same only has white plastic lipstick with pink flowered top. OSP $1.83 **CMV $10. MB.**

FASHION STAR SET 1963
Blue, pink and white box holds two Fashion lipsticks. OSP $1.69. **CMV $10. MB.**

COLOR TRICK SET 1962
Blue & gold foli box has 2 black Fashion lipstick tubes, gold bottom. OSP $1.96. **CMV $15. MB.**

GOLDEN ARCH SET 1964
Gold arch box holds 2 floral Fashion lipsticks. OSP $1.96. **CMV $17.50 MB.**

COLOR NOTE SET 1963
Gold & white box holds bottle of nail polish & pink Fashion lipstick. OSP $1.67. **CMV $10. MB.**

BEAUTY SCENTS SET 1963-64
Box holds 5 oz. perfumed skin softener & matching perfume creme rollette in Somewhere, Topaze, Cotillion, To A Wild Rose, Here's My Heart, & Persian Wood. OSP $5.25 **CMV $16. MB.** 1965 Beauty Scents issued same box but with perfume rollette and dropped Persian Wood and added Rapture and Occur! OSP $5.25. **CMV $15. each MB. $17 with carnival glass rollette**

TOUCH-UP TWINS SET 1963-64
Multi-colored box holds perfume cream rollette in Here's My Heart, Persian Wood, To A Wild Rose, Somewhere, Topaze, Cotillion, Occur! OSP $3.85 **CMV $17. MB.**

TOUCH-UP TWINS SET 1965
Angel box holds deluxe lipstick & perfume rollette in Here's My Heart, Wishing, To A Wild Rose, Somewhere, Topaze, Cotillion, Rapture, Occur! OSP $3.45. **CMV $10 Add $2 for carnival glass rollette.**

PAIR TREE SET 1964
Gold, white, & blue holds nail polish & floral lipstick. OSP $1.83 **CMV $15. MB.**

SLEIGH MATES SET 1966
Red and gold box holds Fashion Cameo lipstick & bottle of nail enamel. OSP $1.83 **CMV $20. MB.**

HAWAIIAN DELIGHTS SET 1962-63
Box holds 4 bottles of nail polish. White caps. OSP $2.98 **CMV $15. MB.**

BATH BOUQUET SET 1963
8 oz. plastic bottle of bath oil & soap in Royal Jasmine, Royal Pine, Rose Geranium. OSP $2.39 **CMV $10. MB.**

BATH BOUQUET SET 1965
Green box contains 1 1/2 oz. green cardboard talc, 2 oz. bath oil & 1/2 oz. cologne in Here's My Heart, To A Wild Rose, Wishing, Somewhere, Topaze, Cotillion, Rapture & Occur!. OSP $4. **CMV $35. MB.**

CLASSIC HARMONY SET 1960
Red, white & gold box holds Top Style lipstick compact & perfume. Came in choice of shades & fragrances. OSP $6.95 **CMV $25 each.**

COLOR GARDEN SET 1964
Red & white floral box holds 4 nail polish bottles with white caps. Came with pearl or cream polish only. OSP $2.76 **CMV $20. MB.**

BATH BOUQUET SET 1964
Pink & white plastic 6 oz. bottle of perfumed bath oil & perfumed soap in Topaze, Somewhere, To A Wild Rose, Persian Wood, Here's My Heart & Cotillion fragrances. OSP $2.89 **CMV $10. each MB.**

REFRESHING HOURS SET 1962-63
Red & white box holds 2 3/4 oz can of perfumed talc & 2 1/2 oz. bottle of cologne in Somewhere, Topaze, Cotillion, Here's My Heart, Persian Wood, & To A Wild Rose. OSP $2.50 **CMV $25. each set.**

WOMEN'S SETS OF 1960s

PARIS MOOD SET 1959-60
Gift set came with spray essence, beauty dust & cream sachet in Persian Wood, Here's My Heart, Cotillion, To A Wild Rose, Bright Night & Nearness fragrances. OSP $7.95. **CMV $47. MB.** See stockholders gifts for additional information.

FRAGRANCE DUETTE SET 1966
Blue and gold box holds 2 oz. splash on cologne & perfumed rollette in Occur!, Rapture & Unforgettable. OSP $5. **CMV $15. MB.**

BATH SPARKLERS SET 1965
Silver box holds 3 colored tubes of bubble bath powder in Lilac, Jasmine & Lily of the Valley. OSP $2.50. **CMV $25. MB.**

PARTY FUN SET 1960
Blue & gold box holds gold lipstick & 1 dram perfume in Topaze, Here's My Heart, Persian Wood, Cotillion, To A Wild Rose, Bright Night, Nearness. OSP $3.50. **CMV $20. MB.**

BEGUILING SET 1960
Multi-colored box holds spray essence & cream sachet in Bright Night, Nearness, To A Wild Rose, Cotillion. OSP $4.50. Here's My Heart & Persian Wood. OSP $5. **CMV $15. MB.**

FRAGRANCE GEMS SET 1962-63
Box holds creme sachet & cream lotion in Topaze, Cotillion, Somewhere, Persian Wood, Here's My Heart & To A Wild Rose. OSP $2.75. **CMV $12. MB.**

BATH CLASSIC SET 1962-63
1 1/2 oz. with gold design, gold cap in gold box with large red powder puff. Box has clear plastic top. Cologne came in Somewhere, Cotillion, Topaze, Here's My Heart, Persian Wood & To A Wild Rose. OSP $4.50. **CMV $35. MB.**

BATH BOUQUET SET 1963
Gift box holds 8 oz. plastic bottle of bath oil & soap in Lily of the Valley, Lilac. OSP $2.39. **CMV $10. each MB.**

FASHION TWIN SET 1962
Blue & white silk cosmetic case holds gold & black compact & lipstick. OSP $3.29. **CMV $15. MB.**

DECORATION GIFT SET 1964
Purple, gold & white box holds cream sachet & spray essence in Here's My Heart, Persian Wood, To A Wild Rose, Somewhere, Cotillion & Topaze. OSP $5.50. **CMV $15. MB.**

BATH BOUQUET SET 1962
White & gold box holds 6 oz. pink & white plastic bottle of bath oil & wrapped soap in Somewhere, Cotillion, Here's My Heart, Topaze, Persian Wood, Royal Jasmine, Rose Geranium, Royal Pine, Floral & To A Wild Rose. OSP $2.79. **CMV $12. MB.**

KEEPSAKES SET 1967-68
Gold, floral & white box holds 3 oz. cologne mist, perfume rollette in Occur!, Rapture & Unforgettable. OSP $8.50. **CMV $10. MB.**

MANICURE TRAY 1965-66
White plastic tray & tissue holder. Came with pink box of Kleenex Tissue with 4A design on box. 8 1/2 x 6 x 3 inches. OSP $5. **CMV tray only $5., MB $7. Avon Kleenex box mint $7. Complete set MB $15.**

FRAGRANCE CHIMES SET 1966
Red & gold box holds perfumed talc & cream sachet in Rapture, Occur!, Unforgettable, Somewhere, Topaze, Cotillion, Here's My Heart & To A Wild Rose & Wishing. OSP $2.89. **CMV $10. MB.**

FLORAL MEDLEY SET 1967
Floral box contains perfumed talc & cream sachet in Honeysuckle, Jasmine, Lily of the Valley, Lilac. OSP $2.89. **CMV $10. each set MB.**

FLORAL ENCHANTMENT SET 1963-64
Floral box holds cologne mist & cream sachet in Occur!, Persian Wood, Here's My Heart, To A Wild Rose, Topaze, Somewhere & Cotillion. Came with 2 different bottles. **CMV $15. MB.**

FLOWER BATH SET 1964
Talc & 2 bars of soap in choice of Lily of the Valley, Lilac, Jasmine & Rose Geranium. OSP $1.67. **CMV $10. MB.**

FLORAL TALC TRIO 1965
Floral box holds three 3 1/2 oz. talcs in Lily of the Valley, Lilac & Jasmine. OSP $2.65. **CMV $12.50 MB.**

MAKING EYES SET 1961-62
Blue & green box with checkerboard top holds Eye Shadow Stick, Curl 'N' Color & Eyebrow Pencil. Box came with outside sleeve. OSP $3.95. **CMV $15. MB.**

PRETTY NOTIONS SET 1965
Pink vinyl case contains pink compact & Cameo lipstick. OSP $4.50. **CMV $4 set only, $6. MB.**

FLUFF PUFF SET 1969
Cardboard talc, blue & gold design on white, puff white with marbleized handle, white knob with 4A. Came 3 different colors: Rapture, turquoise; Occurl, yellow; & Unforgettable, coral. OSP $4.99. **CMV $10. MB.**

DOUBLE PAK SET 1965
Box in green, pink & red foil design. Came with choice of 2 tubes of moisturized hand cream or Avon hand cream or silicone glove or bottle of hand lotion as shown. OSP $1.29. **CMV $10. MB.**

FLUFF PUFF SET 1967
Issued during bottle strike. Green box holds 2 boxes 3.5 oz. of powder. White plastic bottle, gold base & pink puff. Does not say Avon. Came in Unforgettable, To A Wild Rose, Cotillion, Regence. OSP $5.50. **CMV $18. MB.** Regence came in dark pink & light pink & green. Green is rare. **CMV green only $25. MB.**

ON THE WING SET 1959-60
Blue plastic bag holds choice of perfumed talc in Here's My Heart, Persian Wood, To A Wild Rose, Nearness, Cotillion & Floral. Skin freshener, deep clean & 2 oz. plastic bottle of choice of 1 1/2 oz. jar of Vita Moist or Rich Moisture cream. OSP $6.25. **CMV $30. MB.**

FLUFF PUFF SET 1967
Floral box contains one puff & beauty dust. White plastic. Comes in Unforgettable, To A Wild Rose, Cotillion & Regence. OSP $5.50. **CMV $12. MB.** Also came in white puff Regence. **CMV $20.**

FLUFF PUFFS SET 1968
3 1/2 oz. talc & matching puff comes in Somewhere with green puff, Honeysuckle with yellow puff, Here's My Heart with blue puff & To A Wild Rose with pink puff. OSP $6. **CMV $10. MB.**

TOTE ALONG SET 1962
Tapestry bag holds 4 oz. cologne & cream lotion, cream sachet, 3 cakes of wrapped soap in Somewhere, Topaze, Cotillion, Here's My Heart, Persian Wood & To A Wild Rose. OSP $12.95. **CMV $32. MB.**

ROLL-A-FLUFF SET 1967-70
Fluff holds 3 1/2 oz. beauty dust. Red puff is Charisma. Green puff is Regence. White puff is Brocade. Gold top & handle. OSP $13.50. **CMV $15. MB.**

WOMAN'S TRAVEL KIT 1963-64
White floral bag holds moisturized hand cream, perfumed talc, 4 oz. Skin-So-Soft, 2 oz. perfumed deodorant & choice of night cream. OSP $11.95. **CMV $25. MB.**

WOMEN'S TRAVEL KIT 1965-66
Yellow floral "hat box" contains cream deodorant, Skin-So-Soft, hand cream, white Velex Cleansing cream, Hormone cream, Rich Moisture, Vita Moisture & Cream Supreme. OSP $12.95. **CMV complete set $15. MB, hat box only $6.**

BATH LUXURY SET 1966-67
Box holds 4 oz. bottle of Skin-So-Soft & pink bath sponge. Came with 2 different sponges. Coarse as shown & fine grain. OSP $4.50. **CMV $11. MB.**

SKIN-SO-SOFT COMPLIMENTS SET 1967
Box holds 3 oz. box of Satin Talc & 2 bars of SSS soap. OSP $2.50. **CMV $9. MB.**

FRAGRANCE TRIO SET 1966
Box holds 3 bottles of Skin-So-Soft, 1 oz. each gold cap. In choice of Unforgettable, Rapture, Occur!, Somewhere, Topaze, Cotillion, Here's My Heart, To A Wild Rose & Wishing. OSP $4.50. **CMV $12. MB.**

SKIN-SO-SOFT SMOOTHIES SET 1968
Box holds 4 oz. bottle of Skin-So-Soft & 3 oz. Satin Talc. OSP $3.50. **CMV $8. MB.**

BATH MATES SET 1964-65
Box holds 4 oz. bottle Skin-So-Soft bath oil & cakes of soap. OSP $3.23. **CMV $11. MB.**

SHOWER MATES SET 1965
Green & white box holds 4 oz. can of after shower foam & 2 bars of SSS soap. OSP $3.20. **CMV $11. MB.**

MEN'S SETS OF 1970s

WARNING!! Grading condition is paramount on sets. CMV can vary 50% to 90% on grade.

FRAGRANCE GIFT SET FOR MEN 1979
Box holds choice of After Shave in plastic bottles in Cool Sage, Brisk Spice, or Light Musk or the same fragrance in cologne in glass bottles & matching talc. SSP $4. cologne set glass. **CMV $4. MB.** SSP $3. plastic. **CMV $3. MB.**

COLLECTORS ORGANIZER SET 1971 ONLY
Plastic brown duck holds two 3 oz. bottles of Cologne & After Shave. Tai Winds & Wild Country. Painted duck design on bottles & gold caps. 1 yellow bar of duck soap. OSP $25. **CMV $30. MB.**

WILD MALLARD SET 1978
Brown and green ceramic organizer and white Clint Soap On A Rope. Bottom says "Made in Brazil for Avon, May 1978". SSP $20. **CMV $16. - $20. MB.** Also came no date.

WHALE ORGANIZER SET 1973
Brown plastic whale holds 2-3 oz. ivory milk glass bottles and 5 oz. bar of soap. Came in Blend 7 or Deep Woods After Shave and Cologne. SSP $27. **CMV $30. MB.**

MASTER ORGANIZER SET 1970
Wood grained plastic flip open box, holds choice of 3 1/2 oz. Cologne or After Shave in Oland with tan bar of soap or Excalibur with blue bar of soap. OSP $25. **CMV $32.50 MB.**

AMERICAN EAGLE BUREAU ORGANIZER SET 1972
Plastic case, wood carved like finish. Case holds 2 clear glass bottles with embossed eagles & a 5 oz. bar of soap. The bottles hold 3 oz. One has cologne and one after shave. Came in Deep Woods or Tai Winds. SSP $20. **CMV $25. MB.**

WOMEN'S SETS OF 1970s

WARNING!! Grading condition is paramount on sets. CMV can vary 50% to 90% on grade.

TREASURE CHEST SET 1973
White plastic chest with deep purple velour inside & on top. Bottles are clear glass with white on front & gold rose & gold cap. One bottle holds 4 oz. Skin-So-Soft, other holds 4 oz. cologne in Moonwind or Sonnet. Soap 5 oz. in Moonwind (blue) or Sonnet (pink). SSP $20. **CMV $27.50 MB.**

ULTRA FLUFF SET 1970
Box holds 3 1/2 oz. beauty dust, 1/8 oz. perfume, Lamb's Wool Puff & white pedestal dish in Brocade, Charisma & Regence. OSP $10. **CMV $12. MB.**

PAST & PRESENT BRUSH & COMB SET 1972-73
Antique ivory colored, nylon bristled brush & comb. SSP $4. **CMV $6. MB.**

TRAVEL SET FOR MEN 1974-75
Brown box holds 3 oz. white plastic bottle with white cap. Choice of Deep Woods, Wild Country, Oland or Spicy After Shave and 1.5 oz. brown plastic bottle, white cap of Talc in choice of same fragrances. Short issue. OSP $4. **CMV $5. MB.**

LIGHTS & SHADOWS COLOGNE SET 1969-72
(Left) Lights is clear glass & gold cap. Shadows is smoked glass & cap. 2 oz. each. OSP $4. **CMV $6. MB.**

MINUETTE DUET SET 1973
5 oz. cologne in clear bottle with gold cap. 1.5 oz. talc in paper cylinder with Christmas scene. Came in set of Unforgettable, To A Wild Rose, Occur!, Somewhere, Topaze or Cotillion. SSP $3. **CMV $5. MB.**

FRAGRANCE NOTES SET 1977-78
Fragranced writing paper & sealing wax. Came with 18 notes scented with Earth Flowers fragrance, sealing wax stick, and goldtone seal. OSP $9. **CMV $7. MB.**

FRAGRANCE FANCY SET 1972-75
Pink, blue & white. Has .33 oz. rollette & 1.5 oz. perfumed talc. Choice of Unforgettable, Somewhere, Cotillion, Occur!, Topaze, Here's My Heart or Rapture. OSP $3. **CMV $4. MB.**

PRECIOUS PAIR SET 1971-73
Multi-colored box holds matching 1 1/2 oz. perfumed talc & 1/2 oz. cologne in Occur!, Rapture, Unforgettable, Somewhere, Topaze & Cotillion. OSP $4. **CMV $5. MB.**

FRAGRANCE TREASURES SET 1973-75
.66 oz. clear glass cream sachet with pink & gold lid. Pink & gold soap wrapper & box. Choice of Sonnet, Charisma or Moonwind. OSP $3. **CMV $4. MB.**

FRAGRANT NOTIONS SET 1978-79
Floral design box with gold & blue felt inner box holds .33 oz. bottle, gold cap & porcelain thimble with Avon stamped in bottom. Box came with outside sleeve. Choice of Ariane or Timeless cologne. SSP $6. **CMV $5. MB.**

FLUFF PUFF SET 1977-78
Perfumed talc dispenser. Pink plastic holder approx. 11 1/2" long. Came with 2 oz. cardboard talc in Roses Roses or Sonnet. SSP $5. **CMV $5. MB.**

SOPHISTICURL SET 1971
A salon permanent wave used only in Avon Beauty Salons. Box holds 4 oz. bottle of waving lotion and 3.75 oz. white tube of neutralizer. **CMV $10. set MB.**

HAIR PERFECT SET 1971-74
Blue & white box holds 2 oz. brown glass bottle of Color Perfect & 2 oz. white plastic bottle of cream developer. OSP $2.50. **CMV $4. MB.**

ORIGINAL BODY SALON PERMANENT WAVE SET 1971
Pink box holds 4 oz. bottle of neutralizer and waving lotion. Used only in Avon Beauty Salons. Not sold. **CMV $12. MB.**

HAIR COLOR SET 1969
2 oz. brown glass bottle of hair color & 2 oz. white plastic bottle of cream developer in blue box. Short issue. OSP $2.50. **CMV $16. MB.**

BUILT-IN BODY SALON PERMANENT WAVE SET 1971
White box holds 4 oz. bottle of waving lotion & 4 oz. bottle of neutralizer. Used only in Avon Beauty Salons and not sold. **CMV $12. MB.**

EMPRISE PERFUME 1977-80
Box holds 1/4 oz. bottle with glass stopper with plastic base seal. OSP $15. **CMV $10. BO, $14. MB.**

EMPRISE ULTRA GIFT SET 1977-78
Box came with 1.8 oz. Ultra cologne spray and .33 oz. Ultra purse concentre. OSP $11.50. **CMV $11.50 MB.**

MEN'S SETS OF 1980s

CURL SUPREME SALON PERMANENT WAVE SET 1971
Purple box holds 3.75 oz. white tube of neutralizer & 4 oz. bottle of waving lotion. Used only in Avon Beauty Salons. Not sold. **CMV $12. MB.**

SWEET HONESTY GIFT SET 1977-78
Came with 2 oz. cologne and 2 perfumed soaps. OSP $9. **CMV $7. MB.**

TIMELESS GIFT SET 1976
Amber bottles with gold caps. Box yellow & gold. Contains Ultra cream sachet & cologne mist. OSP $10. **CMV $10. MB.**

TIMELESS ULTRA GIFT SET 1977-78
Box came with 1.8 oz. Ultra cologne spray and .33 oz. Ultra perfume rolette. OSP $10. **CMV $10. MB.**

COUNTRY CHRISTMAS COLLECTION FOR HIM SET 1982
Green plastic box with green outer sleeve, holds matching bar of soap, talc 1.5 oz. & 2 oz. ribbed clear glass bottle, green cap cologne in choice of Clint, Weekend, Black Suede or Wild Country. SSP $9. **CMV $9. with sleeve.**

TRAVELER GIFT SET 1981
Green and red box with deer, holds 1.5 oz. deer decor Talc and 2 oz. plastic After Shave in own box, in choice of Weekend, Wild Country, Black Suede. SSP $5. **CMV $5. MB set.**

UNSPOKEN ULTRA GIFT SET 1976-77
Box came with 1.8 oz. Ultra cologne spray and .33 oz. Ultra perfume rollette. OSP $10. **CMV $10. MB.**

BUCKAROO GIFT SET FOR BOYS 1981
Brown leather look box holds 2 oz. Buckaroo Talc and matching tan 2 oz. plastic bottle of Buckaroo Cologne for Boys. SSP $5. **CMV $5. MB set.**

NATURALS AFTER SHAVE & SOAP SET 1981
Wood look box holds 3 oz. plastic bottle and bar of soap to match box. Choice of Crisp Lime, Brisk Spice, Light Musk. SSP $4. MB. **CMV $4. MB.**

HOWDY PARDNERS SET 1982-83
Box holds 2 oz. Talc & 2 oz. plastic bottle of Buckaroo Cologne with 2 piece blue cowboy hat cap. SSP $5. **CMV $5. MB.**

GIFT COLLECTION FOR MEN SET 1984
Triangle box holds 1 oz. talc, deodorant & after shave conditioner. Choice of Wild Country, Cordovan, Musk for Men or Black Suede. OSP $2. **CMV $2. MB.**

MEN'S TRAVELER GIFT SET 1985
Box holds 2 oz. after shave, deodorant & small bar soap. Choice of Black Suede, Wild Country, Cordovan, Musk for Men. OSP $4. **CMV $4. MB.**

FERAUD POUR HOMME GIFT SET 1985
(Top) Box holds cologne, soap & talc. OSP $10. **CMV $10. MB.**
GENTLEMEN'S GIFT SET 1985
(Bottom) Box holds 3 oz. cologne in flannel pouch & can of talc. Choice of Cordovan, Black Suede, Musk for Men or Wild Country. SSP $6. **CMV $6. set MB.**

GENTLEMEN'S GIFT COLLECTION 1986
Box holds 3.5 oz. Talc & 3 oz. cologne in choice of Wild Country "shown", Musk for Men or Black Suede. DP $6. **CMV $6. MB.**

AURES GIFT SET 1986
Box holds 4 oz. Aures after shave & soap on a rope. DP $7.25. **CMV $7.25 MB.**
AMERICAN CLASSIC GIFT SET
Box holds 4 oz. American Classic after shave & soap on a rope. DP $7.25. **CMV $7.25 MB.**

FERAUD POUR HOMME GIFT SET 1986
Black box holds 2.5 oz. after shave & razor with clear black plastic handle. DP $13.50. **CMV $13.50 MB.**

MEN'S FRAGRANCE DUO SET 1980
Brown box holds choice of 5 oz. After Shave and 1 1/2 oz. Talc in Wild Country, Trazarra, Weekend or Clint. SSP $6. **CMV $4. MB each set.**
NATURALS AFTER SHAVE SAMPLER SET 1980-81
Box holds 3 plastic bottles of Brisk Spice, Crisp Lime and Light Musk After Shave. SSP $9. **CMV $2. MB.**

FLORAL ACCENT GIFT SET 1982
Box holds 1 oz. cologne & matching trim handkerchief. Choice of Wild Jasmine & Honeysuckle in yellow trim; Hawaiian White Ginger or Field Flowers in green trim; Roses Roses or Sweet Honesty in pink trim. SSP $6. **CMV $6. MB each set.**
ENVIRA SKIN CARE KIT 1982
Handle carton holds .5 oz. tube of conditioning cleansing cream, .5 oz. plastic bottles of clarifying toner & protective moisturizing lotion. Short issue. SSP $2. **CMV $2. mint set.**

HOLIDAY GIFT SET ULTRA 1981
Red & green carry box holds gold 1.5 oz. talc & 1 oz. Ultra cologne spray in gold box. Choice of Timeless, Candid, Ariane, Tempo or Tasha. SSP $8. **CMV $8. MB.**

HOLIDAY TAPESTRY GIFT SET 1981
Red & green handle carry box holds green & red tapestry design 1.5 oz. talc & 1.8 oz. cologne spray in choice of Occur!, Topaze, Moonwind, Charisma, Sweet Honesty or Zany. Colognes come in own box. SSP $8. **CMV $8. MB set.**

HOLIDAY GIFT SOAP SET 1981
Red & green handle box holds 3 bars soap in gold wrappers. Choice of mix & match in Tasha, Foxfire, Odyssey, Candid, Timeless, Unspoken, Ariane or Emprise. SSP $5. set. **CMV $5. MB set.**

NUTURA GET ACQUAINTED PACK SET 1982
Carry carton holds tube of 2.5 oz. Replenishing body cream, .25 oz. eye cream & 1 oz. jar of Replenishing cream. Short issue. SSP $4. **CMV $4. mint set.**

APPLE BLOSSOM TIME SET 1983
Fancy box from early Avon days holds .5 oz. bottle of Apple Blossom cologne. Box has outer sleeve. SSP $7. **CMV $7. MB.**

COLORCREME & ULTRA WEAR GIFT SET 1980
Blue & red box holds blue & silver Colorcreme moisture lipstick & Ultra Wear nail enamel. Each item in own box inside set box. SSP $4. **CMV $4. MB.**

TOCCARA DELUXE GIFT SET 1982
Blue box holds white bar of soap & jar of renewable creme cologne. Short issue. SSP $9. **CMV $9. MB.**

GAY NINETIES SET 1983
Fancy box from early Avon days holds .5 oz. of White Lilac cologne. Box has outer sleeve. SSP $7. **CMV $7. MB.**

FANTASQUE GIFT COLLECTION SET 1983
Black box, gray plastic liner holds Eau de Cologne Flacon spray, 5 oz. Perfumed Body Veil & .5 oz. Perfumed Bath Essence. SSP $6.50. **CMV $6.50 MB.**

COUNTRY CHRISTMAS COLLECTION FOR HER SET 1982
Red & tan plastic box & outer sleeve holds matching soap, talc & .33 oz. cologne. Choice of Odyssey, Timeless, Tasha, Foxfire, Ariane or Candid. SSP $9. **CMV $9. MB.**

GOLD STAMPS SET 1982
Blue & gold box sleeve holds small bottle of golden fixative & small container of Beauty Dust & plastic stamps. SSP $6. **CMV $6. MB.**

HALLOWEEN MAKE A FACE KIT 1982
Carton box holds jar of Make a Face Base, blue lid, 3 pomettes of face color, orange, black & blue. SSP $6. **CMV $6. MB.**

COORDINATES SET 1982
White & red box holds small red checked bag marked Avon. Comes with choice of 2 of 4 different coordinates make up products, lipstick & nail enamel shown. Each boxed separately. SSP $4.50 set. **CMV $4.50 set MB.**

NAIL ACCENTS SET 1982
Yellow container box holds .5 oz. top shield & packet of 3 sheets of decals. SSP $3. **CMV $3. MB.**

GIFT COLLECTION FOR WOMEN 1984
Triangle box holds 1 oz. bath foam, Talc & 1 oz. cologne. Choice of Pavi Elle, Odyssey or Soft Musk. DP $2. **CMV $2. MB.**

GILDED PERFUME SET 1985
Gold & black box holds .33 oz. cologne & .6 oz. perfume in Pavi Elle, Soft Musk or Odyssey. DP $6.00. **CMV $6. MB.**

FANTASQUE ELEGANT EVENING SET 1985
Black box holds .33 oz. cologne & black earrings. DP $10. **CMV $10. MB.**

PEARLS & LACE CLASSIC COLLECTION SET 1985
Pink box holds 1.5 oz. cologne spray & pair of pearlized earrings. DP $8.75. **CMV $8.75 MB.**

VIVAGE RADIANCE GIFT SET 1985
Box holds blue earrings & .33 oz. cologne. DP $9. **CMV $9. MB.**

SOFT MUSK GILDED PERFUME SET 1985
Box holds .06 oz. perfume & .33 oz. cologne. DP $7. **CMV $7. MB.**

CELEBRATION OF BEAUTY SET 1985
Black plastic box holds makeup. DP $6. **CMV $6. MB.**

IMARI GIFT SET 1986
Maroon box holds .33 oz. cologne purse spray & pair of red & gold enamel like earrings. DP $11. **CMV $11. MB.**

ROARING TWENTIES SET 1983
.5 oz. bottle of Trailing Arbutus cologne. Fancy blue & gold box. SSP $7. **CMV $7. MB with outer sleeve.**

CELEBRATION SAMPLER SET 1983
Trial size products given to customers 1 campaign only for $7.50 purchase. Box holds trial size tubes of Care Deeply Hand Cream, Aqua Clean Shower Gel, Nutura Creamy Wash Off Cleanser & small bottle of Naturally Gentle Shampoo. **CMV $5. set MB.**

GOING TO GRANDMA'S HOUSE SET 1982
Carton box holds 1.25. oz. white plastic bottles with turquoise caps of bubble bath for children & Little Blossom Whisper Soft Cologne, 1 small green childs toothbrush. SSP $5. **CMV $5.**

PEARLS & LACE FRAGRANT TREASURE GIFT SET 1986
Pink box holds 8 bath pearls & .33 oz. cologne. DP $5. **CMV $5. MB.**

FRAGRANCE DUET COLLECTION SET 1986
Box holds .33 oz. cologne spray & 1.5 oz. Perfumed Talc in choice of Soft Musk "shown", Pavi Elle, Odyssey & Pearls & Lace. DP $4.25. **CMV $4.25 MB.**

SOMERSAULTS PASTEL TALC & PUFF SETS 1986
2 oz. talc with Tallulah in pink, Zippy in yellow, and Miss Pear in green puff. DP $3. **CMV $3. MB.**

LAVENDER FLORAL GIFT SET 1987
Box holds 4 oz. Lavender Floral toilet water & bar of soap. DP $5.50. **CMV $5.50 MB.**

FANTASQUE GIFT SET 1986
Black box holds 1 oz. cologne spray & 2 bars of soap. DP $12. **CMV $12.**

SILK TAFFETA GIFT SET 1986
Box holds 2 square goldtone earrings & .33 oz. cologne spray in choice of Soft Musk, Pavi Elle, Odyssey or Pearls & Lace. DP $7. **CMV $7. MB.**

SWITCH GIFT SET 1982
Blue sleeve over red box. Holds 7 oz. New Vitality Shampoo, 10 oz. Care Deeply lotion, Lots O' Lash, Ultra Wear Eye Shadow & 3 oz. Beauty Fluid. This set was given to first people around U.S. to call in on radio advertisement to switch to Avon Products. Rare. **CMV $30. MB.**

SOAPS CPC

All Soaps Must Be Mint For CMV.

JAPAN TOILET SOAP 1905
Box of 3 cakes. OSP 25c. **CMV $110. MB.**

ALMOND BOUQUET TOILET SOAP 1925
Yellow, green & pink wrapping around 3 bars of soap. Soap is embossed. OSP 30c. **CMV $90. MB.**

ALMOND MEAL TOILET SOAP 1905
Box of 3 cakes. OSP 25c. **CMV $110. MB.**

PEROXIDE TOILET SOAP 1915
Box of 3 cakes. OSP 50c. **CMV $95. MB.**

SAVONA BOUQUET SOAP 1896
Maroon colored box & wrapping. Two bars.
OSP 50c. **CMV $110. MB.**

SAVONA BOUQUET SOAP SAMPLES 1936
(Left) **CMV $15. each.**
SAVONA BOUQUET TOILET SOAP SAMPLES 1929
(Right) **CMV $15. each.**

SAVONA BOUQUET TOILET SOAP 1932-36
Box of 6 bars. OSP 50c. **CMV $70. MB.**

ALMOND, BUTTERMILK & CUCUMBER SOAP 1906
Yellow, pink & green box & wrapping holds 3 bars soap. OSP 40c. **CMV $100. MB.**

CASTILE IMPORTED SOAP 1923-25
Box holds 2 silver wrapped bars. OSP 60c.
CMV $45. MB. Same box also came with 1 large bar. OSP 33c. **CMV $60. MB.**

VEGETABLE OIL SOAP 1936-38
Three light orange colored bars wrapped in turquoise & white paper & box. OSP 46c.
CMV $45. MB.

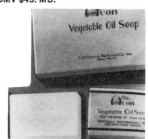

VEGETABLE OIL SOAP 1931-36
Box of 3 bars. OSP 45c. **CMV $50. MB.**

CPC IMPORTED CASTILE SOAP 1908
5 oz. cake. First came out about 1893. OSP 25c. **CMV $60. MB.**

CASTILE IMPORTED SOAP 1931-36
Box holds 2 silver wrapped bars. OSP 60c.
CMV $45. MB.

CASTILE SOAP 1925
One bar of soap. OSP 33c. **CMV $50. MB.**

A.B.C. SOAP 1915
Six bars in yellow box with pink flowers on box.
OSP 40c. **CMV $110. MB.**

CASTILE SOAP 1936-43
Two white bars wrapped in silver paper & turquoise box. OSP 62c. **CMV $45. MB.**

STARCH DRESSING SAMPLE 1911
1" size box holds 3 samples. **CMV $60. MB.**

SAVONA BOUQUET TOILET SOAP 1936-43
Turquoise & white box holds 6 square bars. OSP 72c. 1936-39 has cpc label on soap & box. **CMV $75. MB.** 1940-43 Avon label only on soap and box. **CMV $65. MB.**

EASY CLEANER 1925
Box of two 1/2 lb. cakes. OSP 33c. **CMV $75. MB.**

NAPTHA LAUNDRY CRYSTALS 1925
Two different box labels. One box has blue letters & 1 box has green letters. Thirteen white crystals in box, with instruction sheet. OSP 33c. **CMV $45. MB.**

STARCH DRESSING 1925
25 tablets in box. Each tablet is marked CPC & has instruction sheet in box. OSP 33c. **CMV $45. MB.**

DR. ZABRISKIE'S SOAP

DR. ZABRISKIE'S CUTANEOUS SOAP 1936-56
Green bar in turquoise box. OSP 33c. **CMV $25. MB.** Add $5. for CPC label on box.

DR. ZABRISKIE'S CUTANEOUS SOAP 1940-47
3 oz. green bar and box with Ichthynat. OSP 33c. **CMV $25. MB.**

STARCH DRESSING DIRECTIONS SHEET 1911
Came in box of Starch Dressing. Printed on both sides. **CMV $5. mint.**

CPC STARCH DRESSING 1911
(Right) Paper box holds 25 blue tablets. OSP 25c. **CMV $50. MB.**

CPC NAPTHA LAUNDRY CRYSTALS 1915
(Left) White tablets, paper box. OSP 25c. **CMV $50. MB.**

DR. ZABRISKIE'S CUTANEOUS SOAP 1895
One bar in box. OSP 25c. **CMV $70. MB.**

DR. ZABRISKIE'S SOAP 1915
Brown or green bar embossed, came in blue box. OSP 25c. **CMV $60. MB.**

DR. ZABRISKIE'S CUTANEOUS SOAP 1920
Green cake & box. OSP 24c. **CMV $50. MB.**

CHILDREN'S SOAPS

DR. ZABRISKIE'S CUTANEOUS SOAP 1931-33
(Right) Gray box holds 1 bar. OSP 31c. **CMV $30. MB.**

DR. ZABRISKIE'S SOAP 1933-36
Gray box holds 1 bar. CPC & Avon on box & soap. Two different labels on boxes. OSP 33c. CMV $30. MB.

DR. ZABRISKIE'S CUTANEOUS SOAP 1956-62
Turquoise box holds 1 green bar. OSP 43c. **CMV $20. MB.**

CIRCUS SOAP SET 1939-41
5 ring circus on box holds 5 figural soaps. This set is Avon's first figurals. Soaps are clown, elephant, monkey, seal & horse. OSP $1.19. **CMV $300. MB.** Very rare.

FORWARD PASS 1958
7 1/2 oz. brown football soap on a white rope on side of soap. OSP $1. **CMV $45. MB.**

"OLD 99" SOAP 1958
Yellow train engine soap. OSP 69c. **CMV $60. MB.**

POOL PADDLERS SOAP 1959
Pond display box holds green frog, yellow fish & blue turtle soap. OSP $1.39. **CMV $40. MB.**

FIRE ENGINE SOAP 1957
Red box contains red fire truck soap. OSP 59c. **CMV $60. MB.**

CIRCUS WAGON SOAP SET 1957-58
Pink, yellow, black & white circus wagon box contains 1 blue elephant, 1 pink monkey, 1 yellow lion soaps. OSP $1.25. **CMV $65. MB.**

BO PEEP SOAP 1953-54
Blue & green box holds 3 white sheep soaps. OSP $1. **CMV $65. MB.**

BEST FRIEND SOAP 1956
Blue & white box holds blue dog soap. OSP 59c. **CMV $55. MB.**

KIDDIE KENNEL SOAP 1955
Blue & yellow box holds blue, yellow & pink dog soaps. OSP $1.49. **CMV $150. MB.**

CASEY JONES JR. 1956-57
Red, white & blue box holds red engine soap, yellow passenger car & red carboose. OSP $1.19. **CMV $55. MB.**

LI'L FOLKS TIME SOAP ON A ROPE 1961-62
Red box holds yellow clock soap on a rope. OSP $1.19. **CMV $30. MB.**

AWAY IN THE MANGER SOAP SET 1955
Box holds 4 bars of pink, blue, white & yellow soap. 2 different scenes as shown. Remove panel on bottom picture to show inner panel as shown on top picture. OSP $1.49. **CMV $75. each set, MB.**

THREE LITTLE BEARS SOAP SET 1954
3 brown bear soaps. OSP $1.19. **CMV $80. MB.**

SANTA'S HELPER SOAP 1956
(Left) Box holds 3 green, yellow & red Santa & 2 helpers soaps. OSP $1.19. **CMV $115. MB.**
SANTA'S HELPER SOAP 1955
(Right) Box holds green, red & yellow soap. Red Santa soap much larger than 1956 set. OP $1.49. **CMV $105. MB.**

FRILLY DUCK SOAP 1960
Box contains yellow & blue soap 5 3/4 oz. OSP 89c. **CMV $25. MB.**

A HIT! SOAP ON A ROPE 1961-62
Box holds white baseball soap on a rope. OSP $1.19. **CMV $30. MB.**

HIGH SCORE 1959
Green net box holds brown basketball soap on a rope. OSP $1.19. **CMV $15. soap only mint, $30. MB.**

AVONLITE SOAP ON A ROPE 1960-61
Green bowling ball shaped soap in green box. Brochure says "Bowl 'em Over", soap says "Avon Lite". OSP $1.19. **CMV $35. MB, soap only $20. mint.**

SHERIFF'S BADGE SOAP 1962-63
Box holds yellow soap on a rope with embossed sheriff's badge. OSP $1.19. **CMV $35. MB.**

HANSEL & GRETAL SOAP 1965
Blue & pink soap in a box. OSP $1.35. **CMV $30. MB.**

"WATCH THE BIRDIE" SOAP 1962-64
White molded camera soap on a rope. OSP $1.19. **CMV $35. MB.**

LIFE PRESERVER SOAP 1963-64
White life preserver soap on a rope. OSP $1.19. **CMV $30. MB.**

LIL TOM TURTLE SOAP 1962-63
Box holds green turtle soap with white hat. OSP 98c. **CMV $30. MB.**

LITTLE SHAVER SOAP 1966-67
(Left) Yellow shaver soap on a rope. OSP $1.35. **CMV $25. MB.**
TEXAS SHERIFF SOAP 1958
(Right) Box holds 2 blue pistol soaps & silver sheriff's badge. Box comes with band around outside of box as shown at top. OSP $1.19. **CMV $60. MB.**

PACKY THE ELEPHANT SOAP 1964-65
Green box holds pink elephant with white hat. OSP 98c. **CMV $30. MB.**

GINGERBREAD SOAP TWINS 1965
Pink, white & brown box holds 2 blue plastic gingerbread cookie cutters with 2 yellow bars of gingerbread soap. OSP $1.50. **CMV $25.**

SPEEDY THE SNAIL 1966
Green snail soap on a rope. OSP $1.35. **CMV $25.**

GOLDILOCKS SOAP 1966-67
5 oz. yellow soap. OSP $1. **CMV $15. MB.**

MR. MONKEY SOAP ON A ROPE 1965
(Left) Brown monkey soap. OSP $1.35. **CMV $20. MB.**
LIGHT BULB SOAP ON A ROPE 1967
(Right) Yellow soap on black, orange & yellow rope. OSP $1.50. **CMV $18. MB.**

SUNNY THE SUNFISH SOAP 1966
Yellow fish soap on a rope. OSP $1.19. **CMV $20. MB.**

YO YO SOAP SET 1966-67
Pink & red wood Yo Yo & pink soap. OSP $1.50. **CMV $20. MB, Yo Yo only $6.**

TUB RACERS SOAP 1969
Green box holds red, yellow & green racer soap. OSP $1.75. **CMV $10. MB.**

BUNNY'S DREAM SOAP ON A ROPE 1967
Box holds orange carrot soap on a green rope. OSP $1.25. **CMV $17. MB.**

MIGHTY MITT SOAP ON A ROPE 1969-72
Brown soap. OSP $2. **CMV $10. MB.**

SEA BISCUIT - THE SEA HORSE SOAP ON A ROPE 1964-66
Box holds green soap on a rope. Sea Horse. OSP $1.25. **CMV $20. MB.**

EASTER QUACKER SOAP ON A ROPE 1968
Yellow soap. OSP $1.35. **CMV $12. MB.**

YANKEE DOODLE SHOWER SOAP 1969-70
White drum shaped soap on a rope. OSP $2. **CMV $10. MB.**

CHICK-A-DEE SOAP 1966-67
Yellow soap on a rope. OSP $1.35. **CMV $15. MB.**

RUFF, TUFF & MUFF SOAP SET 1968-69
Blue, pink & yellow dog soaps. OSP $1.25. **CMV $9. MB.**

MODELING SOAP 1969-70
Pink 6 oz. soap in blue & pink box. OSP $2. **CMV $7. MB.**

MIITTENS KITTENS SOAP 1969-70
Pink, green & yellow soap. Blue box. OSP $2.
CMV $10. MB.

M.C.P. SOAP 1977-79
Tan color Male Chauvinist Pig soap. Came in
Deep Woods scent. OSP $5. **CMV $6. MB.**
BUTTON BUTTON GUEST SOAPS 1977-79
Cardboard spool container holds 5 blue button
shaped soaps. OSP $6. **CMV $6. MB.**

FIRST DOWN SOAP 1970-71
Box holds brown 5 oz. football soap on a rope.
This soap is different from older one. Rope is
on end of football. OSP $1.50. **CMV $10. MB.**

TWEETSTERS SOAPS 1971
Yellow box holds 3 pink bird soaps. OSP $2.
CMV $9. MB.

TUBBY TIGERS SOAP SET 1974-75
3 orange soaps in orange & green box. OSP
$2. **CMV $4. MB.**

FOOTBALL HELMET SOAP ON A ROPE
1974-75
(Left) Yellow soap, white cord. OSP $2. **CMV
$6. MB.**
WILBUR THE WHALE SOAP ON A ROPE,
1974-75
(Right) 5 oz. blue soap with white rope. SSP
$2. **CMV $6. MB.**

PERCY PELICAN SOAP ON A ROPE 1972-
73
5 oz. yellow soap on white rope. SSP $1.50.
CMV $7. MB.
PETUNIA PIGLET SOAP ON A ROPE 1973-
74
5 oz. pink soap on white rope. SSP $2. **CMV
$6. MB.**

SCRUB TUG SOAP 1971
4" long plastic boat scrub brush holds 2 oz.
yellow boat soap. OSP $2.50. **CMV brush &
soap $6. MB, brush only $1.**
PIG IN A TUB SOAP 1973-75
3" long yellow scrub brush holds 2 oz. pink pig
soap. SSP $2.20. **CMV $4. MB.** Reissued
1979.

SNOOPY'S PAL SOAP DISH & SOAPS
1973-74
4 1/2" diameter red plastic dish says "Snoopy"
on front with yellow bird. Comes with two 2 oz.
white bone shaped soaps. SSP $3. **CMV $7.
MB.**

HOOTY & TOOTY TUGBOAT SOAPS 1973-
75
2 oz. yellow & orange tugboat shaped soaps.
SSP $2. **CMV $6. MB.**

PEEP A BOO SOAP ON A ROPE 1970
Yellow chick soap on pink or white rope. OSP
$1.35. **CMV $10. MB.**
EASTER BONNET SOAP ON A ROPE 1970
Yellow soap. OSP $1.35. **CMV $10. MB.**

SURE WINNER SOAPS 1973-75
(Left) 3 snowmobile soaps in blue, red & yellow. SSP $2. CMV $5. MB.
SURE WINNER SHOWER SOAP 1972-73
White with blue cord. SSP $2. CMV $7. MB.

FURRY, PURRY & SCURRY SOAPS 1978-79
Red box with white dots holds 3 kitten shaped soaps in yellow, blue & green. SSP $3. CMV $4. MB.

TREE TOTS SOAP 1970-72
Red & green box holds 3 squirrel soaps. OSP $1.75. CMV $7. MB.

BLUE MOO SOAP ON A ROPE 1972
(Left) 5 oz. blue cow soap on a rope. OSP $1.75. CMV $7. MB.
HONEY LAMB SOAP ON A ROPE 1971-72
(Center) 5" high yellow soap on blue rope. OSP $1.19. CMV $7. MB.
AL E. GATOR SOAP ON A ROPE 1971-72
5" high green soap on white rope. OSP $2. CMV $7. MB.

TUBBO THE HIPPO SOAP DISH & SOAP 1978-80
(Left) Blue box holds light green plastic hippo soap dish & 3 oz. pink embossed wrapped bar of hippo soap. SSP $5. CMV $5. MB, soap dish only $1, soap only wrapped $1.50.
ALKA SELTZER SOAPS 1978-79
Blue, white & red box holds 2 white embossed bars. SSP $4. CMV $5. MB.

ARISTOCAT KITTENS SOAP 1971
Box holds white, brown & blue kitten soaps. OSP $2. CMV $7. MB.

HOOPER THE HOUND SOAP HOLDER & SOAP 1974
White & black plastic head with pink, green & yellow hoops. Has yellow soap. SSP $4. CMV $7. MB.

SAFE COMBINATION BANK SOAPS 1978-79
Black & gold tin bank comes with 2 yellow bars of soap embossed "Avon, 99.9 mint". Bottom of bank says "Made in England, exclusively for Avon". SSP $8. CMV $8. MB.

TUB RACERS 1970-72
Three speed boat soaps in red, blue & yellow. OSP $2. CMV $7. MB.

HYDROJET SCRUB BRUSH & SOAP 1972-73
Red plastic jet with yellow soap. SSP $2. CMV $6. MB.

HAPPY HIPPOS NAIL BRUSH & SOAP 1973-74
3" Long pink nail brush with yellow soap. SSp $2. CMV $6. MB.

PEANUTS GANG SOAP 1970-72
Red Lucy, yellow Charlie, white Snoopy soaps. OSP $2. CMV $10. MB.

THREE MICE SOAPS 1971-72
Box holds green, white & pink mice soaps.
OSP $2. **CMV $7. MB.**

ALL STAR BASE BALL MITT & SOAP 1987
7" orange sponge mitt & white baseball soap.
No box. DP $3.25 **CMV $3.25 MB.**
SEA SUB & CREW SOAPS 1987
Orange plastic boat holds 2 small sea creature
soaps. D P $4. **CMV $4. MB.**

SCRIBBLE DEE DOO PENCIL SOAPS 1980-81
(Top) 3 pencil shaped yellow soaps. SSP
$4.50 **CMV $5. MB.**
ORCHARD FRESH GUEST SOAPS 1980-81
(Bottom) Choice of orange, lemon or peach
shaped soaps. 6 bars in each box. SSP $5.
CMV $5. each kind.

DARLING DUCKLINGS SOAP 1983
Box holds 3 yellow duck soaps. SSP $4.
CMV $4. MB.

EGGOSAURS SOAPS 1986
Yellow & blue shells hold soaps. Comes with
20 pg. mini book. DP $3. **CMV $3. MB.**

GOOD HABIT RABBIT SCRUB BRUSH & SOAP 1975
(Left) Pink plastic with white bristles. OSP
$2.50 **CMV $5. MB.**
GAYLORD GATOR SCRUB BRUSH & SOAP 1974-75
(Right) Green plastic with white bristles. OSP
$2.50 **CMV $5. MB.**

BUBBLE BLAZER SOAP 1982-83
(Left) Box holds 4 oz. yellow space gun bar.
SSP $3. **CMV $3. MB.**
PARTY LINE SOAP ON A ROPE 1982-83
(Right) Box holds 5 oz. yellow telephone bar
on white rope. SSP $4. **CMV $4. MB.**
TRAIN SOAP 1982-83
(Bottom) 5 3/4" long blue train soap breaks
into 3 cars. Must be all together or of no value.
SSP $3.50 **CMV $3.50 MB.**

STORY BOOK SOAPS 1984
Book shaped soaps. Pinnochio, Hansel &
Gretel or Cinderella. DP $1. **CMV $1. MB.**

GRIDIRON SCRUB BRUSH & SOAP 1976-77
Brown plastic with yellow soap. OSP $4.
CMV $5. MB.

BATH TUB BUGGIES SOAP SET 1986
Box holds blue, red or yellow truck soaps.
OSP $2.50 **CMV $2.50 MB.**

SWEET PEA SOAPS 1986
(Top) different soaps, 2 oz. each. Mud puppy, Goldie Purrsha, Sea Star, and Starfish. DP $1. **CMV $1 MB.**

DUCKS ON PARADE 1987
Box holds 3 small yellow duck soaps. DP $1.50 **CMV $1.50 MB.**

SOUNDS OF CHRISTMAS SOAPS 1986
3 different small bars. Drum, Horn or Harp soap. DP .75c **CMV .75c. MB.**

ANIMAL SOAPS 1985
Choice of Elephant, Hippo or Lion. DP $1. **CMV $1 MB.**

EASTER FUN BATH CUBES 1985
Box holds 6 Easter cubes. SSP $2.50 **CMV $2.50 MB.**

SOMERSAULTS SOAP & MINI BOOKS 1985
Each box has different colored soaps. DP $2. **CMV $2. MB.**

SOAPS WITH SPONGES

BATH FLOWERS SOAP & SPONGE 1965-66
Pink and white floral box contains 1 bar To A Wild Rose soap pink, green and white sponge. OSP $2.50 **CMV $12. MB.**

CHARLIE BROWN BATH MITT & SOAP 1969-71
Red and white sponge with white bar of Snoopy embossed soap. OSP $3. **CMV $8. MB.**

SPONGAROO SOAP & SPONGE 1966-67
Brown kangaroo sponge is 15" x 5 3/4". White kangaroo soap. OSP $2.25. **CMV $14., soap only $7. mint.**

MINNIE THE MOO SOAP & SPONGE 1965-66
White foam cow with yellow ears and black eyes. Soap is in green wrapper. OSP $1.75 **CMV $6 soap and sponge only mint. $12. MB.**

POLLY PARROT PUPPET SPONGE & SOAP 1969-70
Green and orange sponge with bar of soap. OSP $3. **CMV $10 MB. Soap and sponge only $4.**

CLARENCE THE SEA SERPENT 1968-69
Orange and yellow sponge with bar of serpent soap in blue and yellow wrapper. OSP $2.25 **CMV $9. MB.**

MISTERJAW BATH MITT & SOAP 1978
Blue sponge mitt 9" long with fish design bar of soap. SSP $5. **CMV $5. MB.**

YAKETY YAK TAXI SOAP AND SPONGE 1978-79
Box holds yellow taxi and bar of wrapped Sweet Pickles soap. SSP $4. **CMV $5 MB.**

BABY KERMIT & MISS PIGGY SPONGE & SOAP 1986
3 1/2" high sponge with soap inside, doubles in side when wet. Kermit in green & Piggy in red. DP $2. **CMV $2. MB.**

LITTLE PRO SOAP 1966
White baseball soap and brown sponge. OSP $2.25 **CMV $14. MB. $8 soap and sponge only.**

NEST EGG SOAP & SPONGE 1967-68
Box holds yellow nest sponge and pink soap. OSP $2.25 **CMV $12. MB.**

BATH BLOSSOMS 1969
Pink and yellow sponge with pink soap. OSP $3.50 **CMV $10 MB. $4. soap and sponge only.**

GOOD HABIT RABBIT BATH MITT & SOAP 1974
White and pink foam mitt with yellow carrot soap. SSP $2.50 **CMV $7 MB.**

MONKEY SHINES 1969
Brown and pink sponge and bar of soap. OSP $3. **CMV $9 MB. Soap and sponge only $5.**

BATH BLOSSOM SPONGE AND SOAP 1979-80
(Left) Box holds yellow, green and blue sponge and yellow soap. SSP $6. **CMV $6 MB.**

SWEET PICKLES WORRIED WALRUS SOAP AND SPONGE 1979-80
(Center) Purple, green and brown sponge. Comes with wrapped bar of Sweet Pickles childrens bath soap. SSP $5. **CMV $5. MB.**

FEARLESS FISH SPONGE AND SOAP 1979-809
(Right) Green fish sponge and Sweet Pickles wrapped soap with fish on a scooter. SSP $4. **CMV $4 MB.**

PINK PANTHER SPONGE MITT AND SOAP 1977-80
Pink mitt, yellow eyes. Blue, green and pink wrapped soap. OSP $6. **CMV $6. MB.**

LITTLE LEAGUER SOAP AND SPONGE 1972
Tan sponge mitt and white baseball soap. Sponge is different from Little Pro soap and sponge in 1966. **CMV $10 MB. $6 soap and sponge only mint.**

HUBIE THE HIPPO SOAP & SPONGE 1970-71
Turquoise and red sponge with Hippo wrapped soap. OSP $4. **CMV $10 MB.**

SOAPY THE WHALE BATH MITT AND SOAP 1973-74
8 1/2" long blue and red sponge mitt with blue soap. SSP $3. **CMV $7 MB.**

CEDRIC SEA SERPENT SPONGE AND SOAP 1973
(Left) 9 1/2" long, green and pink sponge, white soap. OSP $2.50 **CMV $7 MB.**
CEDRIC SEA SERPENT SPONGE AND SOAP 1974-75
(Right) 9 1/2" long, purple and pink sponge. OSP $3. **CMV $6. MB.**

SPIDERMAN SPONGE & SOAP 1980
Blue and red sponge. Red wrapped soap. SSP $4. **CMV $5 MB.**

OSCAR OCTUPUS & SOAP 1980-81
Yellow and orange with blue and green trim sponge. Green, red and purple rings, 1 bar of Oscar Octupus soap. SSP $6. **CMV $6. MB.**

MEN'S SOAPS

MOST VALUABLE SOAP SET 1963-64
Yellow box holds 3 yellow bars. OSP $1.35 **CMV $25. MB.**

CPC SHAVING SOAP 1908
White bar embossed. Came in yellow box. OSP 20c. **CMV $60 MB.**

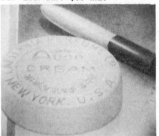

SHAVING SOAP 1930-36
White bar. OSP 25c. **CMV $30. MB.**
STYPTIC PENCIL 1930
OSP 10c. **CMV $10. MB.**

SHAVING SOAP 1936-49
Two bars in maroon box, white soap. OSP 31c. **CMV $42.50 MB.**

SHAVING SOAP 1949-57
Two bars in green & red box. OSP 59c. **CMV $32.50 MB.**

CARRIAGE SHOWER SOAP 1960-62
Red, white and black box contains 6 oz. cake embossed Stage Coach soap on red or white rope. OSP $1.35 **CMV $30.**

OATMEAL SOAP 1961-63
Two brown bars, 2 different boxes. "A spicy fragrance." OSP $1.35 **CMV $25. MB, deluxe box $30. MB.**

OATMEAL SOAP FOR MEN SPICY 1963-64
Embossed stage coach on brown bar of soap. OSP 39c. **CMV $10 in wrapping.**

LONESOME PINE SOAP 1966-67
Green & gold box holds woodgrained soap cut in half. OSP $2. **CMV $20. MB.**

BATH SOAP FOR MEN 1966-67
Two white soaps with red buttons, silver & white box. OSP $2.50 **CMV $22.50 MB.**

SHAMPOO SHOWER SOAP FOR MEN 1972-73
5 oz. bar on red & black rope. Also came with white rope. Red & black box. OSP $2.50 **CMV $7. MB.**

MODEL 'A' 1928 SOAP SET 1975
Two 3 oz. white bars of soap with dark & light blue wrapper & box. OSP $3. **CMV $5. MB.**

GOLF BALL SOAPS 1975
Three white soaps in yellow & green box. Spicy scented OSP $2. **CMV $5 MB.**

ON DUTY 24 SOAP 1977-84
Deodorant soap. OSP 3 for $1. **CMV 50c. each. 3 different labels.**
MUSK FOR MEN 1983-84
Shower soap on rope. SSP $3. **CMV $3. MB.**

ROYAL HEARTS SOAP 1978-79
(Left) King & Queen box holds 2 white bars with king & queen of hearts soaps. SSP $5. **CMV $5 MB.**
SUITABLY GIFTED SOAP 1978-79
(Right) Blue box holds blue bar that is shaped like a shirt and tie. SSP $5. **CMV $5. MB.**

BUFFALO NICKEL 1913 SOAP DISH & SOAP 1978-79
5" nickel plated Buffalo Nickel metal soap dish & light gray or off white color soap. SSP $8. **CMV $8 MB.**

BARBER SHOP DUET MUSTACHE COMB & SOAP SET 1978-79
Box holds white bar man's face soap & small brown plastic mustache comb. SSP $4. **CMV $4. MB. set.**

FARMERS ALMANAC THERMOMETER & SOAPS 1979-80
Box holds tin top with plastic bottom with 2 bars of Farmers Almanac soap. Comes with copy of Avon 1980 Farmers Almanac. SSP $9. **CMV $9 MB complete. CMV Farmers Almanac only $1.**

LUCKY SHOEHORSE SOAP DISH & SOAP 1979-80
(Left) Brown box holds amber glass horseshoe soapdish & soap. SSP $8. **CMV $8 MB.**
PERPETUAL CALENDAR CONTAINER & SOAP 1979-80
(Right) Yellow box holds Avon tin can calendar & white bar of soap. Bottom of can says Made in England for Avon. SSP $8. **CMV $8. MB.**

WEEKEND SOAP ON A ROPE 1979-80
Tan soap on green rope. **CMV $3.**

ANCIENT MARINER BOX & SOAP 1982-83
Tin box with bar compass design soap. SSP $6. **CMV $6. MB.**

THATS MY DAD DECAL SOAPS 1983
(Left) Choice of 3 different decal soaps. "We love you dad" or "You taught me all the important things Dad" or "You're always there when I need you Dad" SSP $2. **CMV $2 each bar MB.**

GRANDFATHERS & GRANDMOTHERS ARE SPECIAL SOAPS 1983
(Right) Metal can holds choice of black or white grandfather or black or white grandmother. SSP $6. **CMV $4 MB.**

HUDDLES SOAP ON A ROPE & CARDS 1984
Box holds brown football marked Huddles & deck of NFL football team playing cards. DP $4. **CMV $4. MB.**

DAD SOAP ON A ROPE 1985
Yellow bar. DP $3. **CMV $3. MB.**

AURES SOAP ON A ROPE 1986 AMERICAN CLASSIC SOAP ON A ROPE 1987
Both boxed single bar on rope. DP $2.75 **CMV $2.75 MB.**

MEN'S SOAPS 1984
Cool soap, Cordovan, Wild Country, Musk for Men. **CMV $1. Each.**

DADS LUCKY DEAL DECAL SOAP & CARDS 1984
Bar of dog soap & deck of cards. DP $4. **CMV $4. MB.**

WOMEN'S SOAPS

LEMONOL TOILET SOAP 1931-36
Yellow soap wrapped in blue and silver paper. Came in box of 3. OSP 50c. **CMV $45. MB. Box of 12 bars $1.75 CMV $65. MB.**

LEMONOL SOAP 1921-33
Box of 12 cakes. OSP $1.50 **CMV $100 MB.**

LEMONOL TOILET SOAP 1923-31
Box of 3 bars. OSP 45c. **CMV $80 MB.**

LEMONOL SOAP 1941-58
Yellow and green lemon box holds 3 flat bars with round edges and flat on bottom. OSP $1. **CMV $30 MB.**

LEMONOL TOILET SOAP 1936-41
Three yellow bars in turquoise and white box and wrapping. OSP 51c. **CMV $40. MB.** Box of 12 bars OSP $1.79 **CMV $60 MB. Add $3 per bar for CPC label mint.**

LEMONOL SOAP 1958-66
Yellow and green box holds 3 yellow bars with flat edges. Box comes lift off, (older) and flip up as shown. OSP $1.19 **CMV $22.50 MB.**

LEMONOL SOAP 1966-67
Blue and yellow box holds six 2 1/2" yellow bars. OSP $2.25 **CMV $22.50 MB.**

HOSTESS BOUQUET SOAP 1959-61
Pink and yellow box holds bars OSP $1.39 **CMV $25. MB.**

GIFT BOWS SOAP 1962-64
Box holds 6 bow tie soaps. OSP $2.25. **CMV $25. MB.**

FACIAL SOAP 1945-55
Box holds 2 bars. OSP 89c. **CMV $25. MB.**

FACIAL SOAP 1955-61
Turquoise box holds 2 bars. OSP 89c. **CMV $20. MB.**

HOSTESS SOAP SAMPLER 1964-65
Floral box holds 12 cakes of soap. OSP $2.50 **CMV $25. MB.**

WHIPPED CREAM SOAP 1968
Green, blue, pink and yellow soap. OSP $3. **CMV $10. MB.**

SOAP TREASURE 1963
Gold and white box holds 5 bars of perfumed soap in choice of Lilac, Lily of the Valley, Floral, Lemonol, Cotillion, Here's My Heart, Rose Geranium, To A Wild Rose, Royal Jasmine, Persian Wood, Somewhere, Royal Pine, and Topaze Set. Came with 2 different kinds of soap as shown. OSP $1.95. **CMV $25. MB each set.**

LADY SLIPPERS SOAP 1965-66
4 shoe soaps in box. OSP $2.25 **CMV $25. MB.**

BAY BERRY SOAP 1967
Blue and gold box holds 3 wrapped bars in plastic holder. OSP $3. **CMV $25. Soap only $5. each.**

DECORATOR SOAPS 1969
Pink box holds 3 egg shaped soaps in green, pink and blue. OSP $3. **CMV $10. MB.**

BUTTERFLY SOAP 1966-67
4 bars in box. OSP $2. **CMV $25. MB.**

CHERUB SOAP SET 1966-67
Blue box holds 2 pink angel soaps. $2. **CMV $25. MB.**

PARTRIDGE & PEAR SOAPS 1968-70
Two green pears and white partridge. OSP $3. **CMV $10 MB.**

FRUIT BOUQUET SOAP 1969
Orange, lavender, and green soap. OSP $3. **CMV $10. MB.**

PINE CONE GIFT SOAPS 1970-73
Box contains blue, yellow and green pine scented soaps. OSP $3. **CMV $10. MB.**

SLIPPER SOAP & PERFUME 1970-71
1/8 oz. bow tie perfume sits in light pink slipper soap in Cotillion, and dark pink soap in Charisma. OSP $5. **CMV $10. MB. soap and perfume only mint.**

SPRING TULIPS SOAP 1970-73
Blue and pink box holds 6 green white and pink soaps. OSP $3.50 **CMV $12. MB.**

CUP CAKE SOAP 1972-73
Green, pink and orange soap. 2 oz. each. SP $2.50 **CMV $8. MB.**

GRADE AVON HOSTESS SOAPS 1971-72
Plastic carton holds 2 blue and 2 pink egg shaped soaps. OSP $4.50 **CMV $8. MB.**

HIDDEN TREASURE SOAP 1972-75
Two 3 oz. turquoise soaps with pearl colored and shaped 1/8 oz. bottle of perfume. Came in Bird of Paradise only. SSP $5. **CMV $8. MB.**

LACERY HOSTESS BATH SOAP 1972-73
Cream colored with foil center design. Box gold and pink. SSP $3. **CMV $6. MB.**

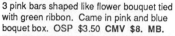

HOSTESS BOUQUET GUEST SOAP 1972-73
3 pink bars shaped like flower bouquet tied with green ribbon. Came in pink and blue boquet box. OSP $3.50 **CMV $8. MB.**

FRAGRANCE & FRILLS SOAP 1972-75
4 lavendar soaps in lavender plastic box. In center a 1/8 oz. bottle of Dazzling perfume in Field Flowers or Bird of Paradise. SSP $6. **CMV $10. MB.**

MELON BALL GUEST SOAP 1973
1 oz. honey dew and cantaloupe colored balls inside cantaloupe shaped plastic container. SSP $4. **CMV $8 MB.**

SOAP SAVERS 1973
9 oz. total of green soaps in spearmint fragrance. SSP $3. **CMV $10. MB.**

SOAP FOR ALL SEASONS 1973
1.5 oz. each, 4 soaps, yellow, green, blue and orange. SSP $3. **CMV $8 MB.**

RECIPE TREASURES 1974-75
5 orange scented soaps in yellow and orange decorative metal file box. OSP $5. **CMV $8. MB.**

COUNTRY KITCHEN SOAPDISH AND SOAP 1974-75
Red plastic scooped dish contains 5 green apple fragranced soaps. OSP $6. **CMV $8. MB.**

1876 WINTERSCAPES HOSTESS SOAPS 1976
Two Currier and Ives scenes soaps. Came in Special Occasion fragrance. OSP $5.50 **CMV $7. MB.**

PETIT FOURS GUEST SOAPS 1975-76
Eight 1 oz. soaps, 3 pink hearts, 2 yellow squares. 3 rounds. OSP $4. **CMV $8. MB.**

BAYBERRY WREATHS GIFT 1975
3 Bayberry scented in Christmas box. OSP $3. **CMV $6. MB.**

ANGEL LACE SOAPS 1975-76
3 blue soaps in blue and white box. OSP $3. **CMV $7 MB.**

TOUCH OF LOVE SOAPS 1975
3 white soaps in lavender box. Spring lavender frgrance. OSP $4. **CMV $6. MB.**

PICK A BERRY STRAWBERRY SOAPS & CONTAINER 1975-76
4 1/2" high red plastic with 6 strawberry scented soaps. OSP $6. **CMV $8. MB.**

LITTLE CHOIR BOYS HOSTESS SOAPS 1976
Box holds 3 pink soaps. Came in light or dark pink. SSP $2.88 **CMV $6 MB.**

TAPESTRY HOSTESS SOAPS 1981
Box holds 2 decorator bars. SSP $4. **CMV $4. MB.**

TIDINGS OF LOVE SOAPS 1976
3 pink soaps in pink and white box. OSP $3. **CMV $6. MB.**

PARTRIDGE 'N PEAR HOSTESS SOAP 1974-75
3 yellow soaps in festive Christmas box. OSP $3. **CMV $7. MB.**

GOLDEN BEAUTIES HOSTESS SOAP 1974-76
2 oz. each, 3 cakes yellow soap. SSP $2. **CMV $7. MB.**

MERRY ELFKINS GUEST SOAPS 1977
Box holds 3 green soaps. OSP $5.50 **CMV $7. MB.**

BLUE TRANQUILITY REFRESHING SOAP 1978-80
5 oz. blue embossed bar on white rope. Blue box. SSP $3. **CMV $3. MB.**

BOUQUET OF PANSIES SOAP 1976-77
Blue box holds 2 flower decorated special occasion white soaps. OSP $5.50 CMV $7. MB.

ANGEL FISH HOSTESS SOAPS 1978
Box holds 3 blue fish soaps. SSP $3.66 CMV $5. MB.

BALLET PICTURE SOAPS 1978-80
White plastic box and lid holds 2 blue picture decal bars of soap. SSP $6. CMV $6. MB.

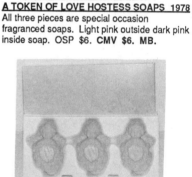

TENDER BLOSSOMS GUEST TOWELS & SOAPS 1977-78
Came with 12 paper hand towels and 3 special occasion fragranced soaps. OSP $6.50. CMV $7. MB.

TREASURE BASKET GUEST SOAPS 1978-79
Silver basket holds 2 yellow and 2 pink tulip soaps. SSP $9. CMV $9. MB.

A TOKEN OF LOVE HOSTESS SOAPS 1978
All three pieces are special occasion fragranced soaps. Light pink outside dark pink inside soap. OSP $6. CMV $6. MB.

WINTER FROLICS HOSTESS SOAPS 1977-78
Came with 2 Festive Fragrance scented soaps with long lasting decals. 3 oz. each. OSP $5.50 CMV $7. MB.

COUNTRY GARDEN SOAPS 1978-80
Box holds 2 Avon bar flower soaps with 2 different flower decals. SSP $4. CMV $5. MB.

CHRISTMAS CAROLLERS SOAPS 1978-79
Box holds 2 turquoise color carollers. SSP $3. CMV $5. MB.

LITTLE ANGELS HOSTESS SOAPS 1980-81
Blue box holds 3 blue angel soaps. SSP $4. CMV $5. MB.

SUMMER BUTTERFLIES HOSTESS SOAPS 1977-78
Two scented soaps with long lasting decals. 3 oz. each. OSP $5.50 CMV $7. MB.

PERFUMED SOAP CHRISTMAS WRAP 1979-80
Single fragrance bar in red. Tempo or Ariane, bronze Candid, Blue Emprise or Unspoken. SSP $1. CMV $1.50 MB.

COMPLEXION BAR 1966-70
4 oz. bar. OSP $1.25 CMV $4. MB.

BUBBLY BEAR SOAP-IN-SOAP 1980-81
Blue box holds small ribbon box of blue soap with small white bear soap inside. SSP $6.
CMV $6. MB.
CALIFORNIA PERFUME CO. 1980 ANNIVERSARY SOAPS 1980-81
1980 CPC box holds two Violet bars. SSP $4.
CMV $5. MB.

PERFUMED DEODORANT SOAP 1963-67
OSP 39c. **CMV $4. mint.**

PERFUMED SOAP HOLIDAY WRAPPING 1977
Came in Charisma and Touch of Roses in red poinsettia wrap. Sonnet and Field Flowers in green and Moonwind and Bird of Paradise in blue. SSP $1.25. **CMV $2. each.**

CLEAR SKIN SOAP 1960-63
Brown bar in gray and white box. OSP 49c.
CMV $4.
CLEAR SKIN SOAP 1964-69
Brown bar in gray and white wrapper. OSP 59c. **CMV $3.**

FRESH AS NATURE SOAP 1982-83
3 different bars in Aloe Vera, Wheat Germ and Glycerine, Witch Hazel and Lyme. SSP $2.
CMV $1.50 each MB.

PERFUMED SOAPS & PERFUMED DEODORANT SOAPS 1961-64
1 bar of each in Lemonol, Persian Wood, Somewhere, Facial, Floral, Royal Pink, Royal Jasmine, Here's My Heart, Cotillion, To A Wild Rose, Topaze and Rose Geranium. OSP 39c.
CMV $4. each mint.

SCENTED SOAPS 1971-73
3 oz. bars in matching soap and wrapping. Mint, Pine Tar, Almond, Camomile, Papaya, Avacado. OSP 75c. **CMV $4. MB.**

CANDID PERFUMED SOAPS 1977-78
Open end box, 3 cakes each. 3 oz. white bars. OSP $7. **CMV $5. MB.**

FEELIN' FRESH SOAP 1978-83
Regular issue bar on left. **CMV 50c.**
Introductory trial size bar on right., short issue.
CMV $2.

CREAM SOAPS 1981-83
1 pink, yellow or blue wrapped bar. SSP 50c.
CMV 50c.
HEARTS & LACE SPECIAL OCCASION SOAP 1981
Pink flower wrapped bar. SSP 75c. **CMV 75c mint.**

EMPRISE PERFUMED SOAPS 1977-78
Open end box holds 3 beige color bars. OSP $7. **CMV $5. MB.**

ARIANE PERFUMED SOAPS 1978
Red box holds 3 white soaps. SSP $5. CMV
$5. MB.

**CHRISTMAS WISHES DECAL SOAPS
1983**
3 different boxed bars. Choice of Happiness in
pink, Togetherness in green & Sharing in tan
color soap. SSP $1.50. each. CMV $1.50.
each MB.

TIMELESS SOAP 1975-78
3 cakes amber soap in amber, gold & yellow
box. OSP $4. CMV $4.
TIMELESS PERFUMED SOAP 1976-78
3 oz. bar. OSP $1.25. CMV $1.

SOFT MUSK SOAP 1982-84
Single 3 oz. bar. SSP $1.50. CMV $1. mint.

A MOTHER'S JOY SOAP SET 1983
Blue box holds 2 white mother & child soaps.
SSP $4. CMV $4. MB.

**SWEET HONESTY PERFUMED SOAPS
1978**
Boxed 3 cakes, 3 oz. each. OSP $6.50. CMV
$5.50 MB.
SWEET HONESTY SOAP 1982-83
Single bar. CMV 75c.
**SEA GARDEN PERFUMED BATH SOAP
1970-73**
6 oz. blue bar with blue box. OSP $2. CMV
$4. MB.

FIVE GUEST SOAPS 1983
Flower design box holds 5 small bars in
Timeless, Candid, Ariane, Tasha, Foxfire,
Odyssey or Soft Musk. SSP $4. CMV $4. MB.

**COUNTRY CHRISTMAS DECAL SOAPS
1982**
Box holds 2 bars. SSP $4. CMV $4. MB.

TIS THE SEASON SOAPS 1985
Small bars of Mistletoe, Poinsettia or Holly.
DP $1. CMV $1. each MB.
**SPRING GARDEN GLYCERINE SOAPS
1985**
White, pink or yellow bars. CMV $1. each MB.
FIVE GUEST SOAPS 1984
Flowered box has 5 small bars in choice of 7
fragrances. DP $3. CMV $3. MB.

FLORAL BOXED SOAPS 1983
(Left) Box has different flower design for each
fragrance. 4 flowered bars. Choice of Wild
Jasmine "gold", Hawaiian White Ginger
"white", Honeysuckle "yellow" or Roses Roses
"pink". SSP $4. CMV $4. MB.
FLORAL GUEST SOAP 1983
(Right) Single 1 oz. bar in box. Different color
soap for each fragrance. Choice of Roses
Roses, Wild Jasmine, Hawaiian White Ginger.
SSP 75c. CMV 75c MB.

**RICH MOISTURE BATH BAR SOAP 1972-
82**
Single 5 oz. bar, turquoise & white wrapper.
SSP $1. CMV $1. mint.

GARDEN FRESH SOAPS 1985
Box holds 3 peach shaped soaps or box of 6 strawberry soaps. DP $3. each. **CMV $3. each MB.**

ENCHANTED LAND SOAP SET 1984
(Right) Box holds 2 white bars with fairy decals. DP $2.50. **CMV $2.50 MB.**
CALIFORNIA PERFUME CO. SOAP 1984
(Left) Small bars, choice of Violet, Apple Blossom or Lilac. DP $1. **CMV $1. each MB.**

FLORAL BATH CUBES 1984
Box of 6 wrapped cubes. DP $2. **CMV $2. MB.**
LIGHT ACCENT SOAP 1984
Single bar, choice of Tea Garden, Willow, Amber Mist. **CMV 50c each.**
VALENTINE SOAP SET 1986
Pink box holds 3 pink heart soaps. DP $3. **CMV $3. MB.**

IMARI LUXURY PERFUMED SOAPS 1986
Maroon & gold box holds 2 bars. DP $4.50. **CMV $4.50 MB.**
FIFTH AVENUE SCULPTURED SOAPS 1986
Black, white & purple box holds 2 lavender bars. DP $4.50. **CMV $4.50 MB.**

TRANQUIL MOMENTS SOAP 1986
SILK TAFFETA SOAP 19866
Single bars each. DP $1.25. **CMV $1.25 each.**

LETTER PERFECT GUEST SOAP 1984
Single bar with choice of pesonal letter on soap. DP $1. **CMV $1. MB.**
ULTRA GUEST SOAPS 1984
Silver box holds choice of 5 small bars in 7 fragrances. DP $3. **CMV $3. MB.**
WATER LILY BATH CUBES 1985
Blue box holds 6 soap cubes. DP $3. **CMV $3. MB.**

PEACEFUL TIDINGS SOAP & BATH CUBE SET 1985
Blue box has soap bar & 2 bath cubes. DP $3. **CMV $3. MB.**
COLONIAL ACCENT SOAP & SACHET 1985
Box holds decorator bar soap & 3 packets of sachet. DP $4. **CMV $4. MB.**

SOAP DISHES & SOAP

Soaps must be mint for CMV.

SKIN-SO-SOFT SOAP 1965-74
3 oz. bar. OSP 49c. **CMV $1. mint.**
WINTER GLOW SOAP 1981
Green & white. **CMV $1.**
SOFT MUSK SOAP 1983-84
Single bar. **CMV $1.**
5 GUEST SOAPS
CMV $4. MB.

FERAUD SOAP 1985-87
5 oz. bar. Silver, black wrapper. **CMV $1.**
SOFT MUSK SOAP 1982-85
TOCCARA SOAP 1981-85
CLEAR SKIN SOAP 1984-86
PEARLS & LACE SOAP 1984-87
All single bars. **CMV 50c each.**

COLLECTORS:

All Containers are Priced Empty

BO means . . . . Bottle only (empty)
CMV means . . Current Market Value (mint)
SSP means . . . . Special Selling Price
OSP means . . . . Original Selling Price
MB means . . . . Mint and Boxed
DP means . . . . Avon Rep Cost
(This is used on all new products 1984 or newer.)

ULTRA CRYSTAL SOAP DISH & SOAP 1981-82
5" long clear glass soap dish and bar of cream color soap. SSP $10. CMV $10. MB.

FLOWER FROST SHERBERT GLASS AND SOAPS 1979-80
Frosted glass holds 6 yellow Avon balls of soap. SSP $10. CMV $9. MB.

BIRD IN HAND SOAP DISH AND SOAPS 1978-80
5 1/2" long white glass hand soap dish with 3 small blue bird soaps. SSP $6. CMV $5. MB.

MOUNT VERNON PLATE & SOAPS 1979-80
9" long blue glass plate. Has Mount Vernon, George and Martha Washington on front. Came with 2 white George and Martha bars of soap. SSP $11. CMV $11. MB.

AVON SOAP JAR 1965-66
Pink ribbon on clear glass jar and lid. Came with 12 cakes of soap. OSP $4.50. CMV $20. MB, jar only with ribbon and no soap $6. Jar and soap with ribbons mint $16.

HOSTESS FANCY SOAP DISH & SOAP 1975-76
8" wide clear glass with 5 pink soaps. OSP $6. CMV $7. MB.

BUTTERFLY FANTASY DISHES & SOAPS 1979-80
Two 4" porcelain with butterfly design. 1 pink butterfly soap. SSP $10. CMV $10. MB.

SITTIN' KITTENS SOAP DISH AND SOAPS 1973-75
White milk glass dish with 3 kitten soaps in gold colored, yellow and orange. SSP $4. CMV $7.50 MB.

BICENTENNIAL PLATE & SOAP 1975-76
Clear glass plate with blue soaps embossed with the face of George & Martha Washington on each. Some have Avon on bottom and some don't. OSP $7. CMV $8. MB.

FLOWER FROST COLLECTION CRESCENT PLATE & GUEST SOAPS 1979-80
Frosted glass soap dish holds 3 yellow flower soap bars. SSP $13. CMV $12. MB.

DOLPHIN SOAP DISH AND HOSTESS SOAPS 1970-71
Silver and aqua plastic soap dish holds 4 blue soaps. OSP $8. CMV $11. MB.

WINGS OF BEAUTY SOAP DISH & SOAP 1975-76
White milk glass dish with 2 pink soaps. OSP $5. CMV $7. MB.

NUTTY SOAP DISH & SOAPS 1974-76
Plastic dish with 2 peanut scented soaps. OSP $4. CMV $6. MB.

BIRDS OF FLIGHT CERAMIC BOX & SOAP 1980-81
Embossed ducks on lid and sides. Bar of duck soap inside. Made in Brazil. SSP $23. **CMV $15. MB.**

COUNTRY PEACHES SOAP JAR & SOAPS 1977-79
Replica of a 19th century mason jar. Holds 6 yellow peach seed soaps. Blue glass jar with wire bail. Avon on bottom. OSP $8.50. **CMV $8. MB. Jar only $3.**

SKIN-SO-SOFT DISH & SOAP 1965
Blue & white plastic soap dish with white bar of SSS soap. OSP $1.50. **CMV $10. MB, soap & dish $8., dish only $3.**

GIFTS OF THE SEA SOAPS & BASKET 1987
6 1/2" wide wicker basket holds 4 pink sea shell soaps. DP $4.25. **CMV $4.25 MB.**
SEA TREASURE SOAPS 1986
Black & gold trim tin box holds 4 pink sea shell soaps. DP $4. **CMV $4. MB.**

FOSTORIA EGG SOAP DISH & SOAP 1977
Blue soap came in Spring Lilacs fragrance. Egg dish about 4 1/2" long clear glass. Avon on bottom. OSP $15. **CMV $10. MB. Egg dish only $5.** 1st issue had "Mother's Day 1977" on bottom. **CMV $12. MB.**

FOSTORIA HEART VASE & SOAPS 1985
(Right) 5" high heart shape vase with 5 pink heart soaps. DP $6. **CMV $6. MB.**
CITRUS FRESH SOAPS 1984
(Left) Glass jar holds 5 lemon soaps. DP $7. **CMV $7. MB.**

NESTING HEN SOAP DISH & SOAP 1973
White milk glass hen with beige painted nest. Holds 4 yellow egg soap, 2 oz. each. SSP $7. **CMV $10. MB.**

LOVE NEST SOAPS 1978
Light green glass holds 3 yellow bird soaps in Special Occasion fragrance. SSP $5. **CMV $5. MB.**

HOLIDAY CACHEPOT SOAPS 1985
(Right) Metal can holds 5 red apple soaps. DP $5. **CMV $5. MB.**
WATER LILY SOAP DISH & SOAPS 1985
(Left) Blue glass dish. 3 white flower soaps. DP $6. **CMV $6. MB.**

TOUCH OF BEAUTY 1969-70
White milk glass hand holds 4 small bars of pink soap. OSP $5. **CMV $10. MB.**

"HEART AND DIAMOND" SOAP DISH & SOAP 1977
Fostoria clear glass soap dish. Came with red heart shaped Special Occasion fragranced soap. Avon on dish. OSP $9. **CMV $8. MB.**

BUTTER DISH & HOSTESS SOAPS 1973-74
Clear glass with 2 yellow 3 oz. butter pats. SSP $7. **CMV $12. MB.**

NATURE BOUNTIFUL CERAMIC PLATE & SOAPS 1976-78
Wedgewood ceramic plate made in England, edged in 22K gold. Two soaps decorated with pears decals. Avon stamped on plate. OSP $25. **CMV $16. MB. Plate only $7.**

CRYSTALUCENT COVERED BUTTER DISH & SOAP 1975-76
7" long clear glass with 2 yellow soaps. OSP $10. **CMV $12. MB.**
SUNNY LEMON SOAP DISH & SOAP 1975-76
8 1/2" long clear glass with 3 lemon scented yellow soaps. OSP $4. **CMV $7. MB.**

LOVEBIRDS SOAP DISH & SOAPS 1974
White milk glass dish with two 4 oz. pink soaps. SSP $6. **CMV $8. MB.**

OWL SOAP DISH 1971-73
5 1/2" long white glass soap dish with 2 owl eyes in bottom of dish. Holds 2 yellow bars of owl soap. OSP $4.50. **CMV $8. MB.**

DECORATOR SOAP DISH & SOAPS 1971-73
7" long frosted glass dish on gold stand. Came with 2 pink soaps. OSP $7. **CMV $8. MB.**

GIFT OF THE SEA SOAP DISH & SOAPS 1972-73
Iridescent white glass dish looks like a shell. 6 cakes, 1 oz. each, pink soap. 2 each of 3 different shells. SSP $5. **CMV $8. MB.**
LOVE NEST SOAP DISH & SOAPS 1973-75
White dish with green plastic lining, holds 2 aqua and 1 blue bird soap. OSP $4. **CMV $6. MB.**

BEAUTY BUDS SOAP DISH & SOAP 1974-76
6" long white milk glass with 4 yellow soaps. OSP $5. **CMV $6. MB.**
HOSTESS BLOSSOMS FLOWER ARRANGER SOAP DISH & SOAP 1975-76
4 1/2" high white milk glass, plastic top and light green soap. OSP $6. **CMV $6. MB.**

HEAVENLY SOAP SET 1970
White glass dish and 2 pink soaps. OSP $5. **CMV $10. MB.**

FLOWER BASKET SOAP DISH & SOAP 1972-74
Clear glass dish with gold handle. Came with 5 cakes of soap (2 yellow, 3 pink) 1 oz. each. Hostess Fragrance. SSP $5. **CMV $8. MB.** Also came with double stamp on bottom, add $4.

PERFUME GLACE

PERFUME JEWEL GLACE 1965-66
Gold & white box contains gold locket. Came as pin or on a chain with solid perfume in Unforgettable, Rapture, Occur!, Somewhere, Topaze, Cotillion, Here's My Heart, To A Wild Rose and Wishing. OSP $5.50. **CMV $17. each MB, $12. locket only.**

MEMORY BOOK PERFUME GLACE 1971-75
1 1/2" long gold book. Choice of Moonwind, Elusive, Brocade, Regence or Bird of Paradise perfume glace. OSP $7. **CMV $9. MB, $6. no box.**
BABY GRAND PIANO PERFUME GLACE 1971-72
2" wide gold piano. Came in same fragrances as Memory Book. OSP $10. **CMV $14. MB, $10. piano only.**

RING OF PEARLS GLACE 1969-70
Perfume glace ring is gold with white pearls.
Comes in Charisma, Regence & Bracade.
OSP $7.50 **CMV $10. MB $7. ring only.**

OWL PIN PERFUME GLACE 1968-69
(Left) Gold metal pin with green eyes. Green &
gold box. Came in Unforgettable, Brocade,
Regence, Rapture, Occur!, Cotillion, Here's My
Heart, To A Wild Rose. OSP $6. **CMV Owl
only $9. $12 MB.**

FLOWER BASKET PERFUME GLACE 1970-71
(Right) 1 1/2" x 1 1/4" gold tone. Choice of
Bird of Paradise, Elusive, Charisma, Brocade,
or Regence. OSP $7. **CMV $10. MB. $6
pin only.**

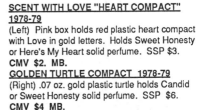

**SCENT WITH LOVE "HEART COMPACT"
1978-79**
(Left) Pink box holds red plastic heart compact
with Love in gold letters. Holds Sweet Honesty
or Here's My Heart solid perfume. SSP $3.
CMV $2. MB.

GOLDEN TURTLE COMPACT 1978-79
(Right) .07 oz. gold plastic turtle holds Candid
or Sweet Honesty solid perfume. SSP $6.
CMV $4 MB.

MANDOLIN PERFUME GLACE 1971-72
2 1/2" long gold mandolin Choice of Moonwind,
Elusive, Charisma, Brocade, Regence, or Bird
of Paradise perfume glace. OSP $9. **CMV
$14. MB $8 no box.**

TORTOISE PERFUME GLACE 1971-75
2 1/2" long gold turtle with turquoise back.
Came in same fragrances as Mandolin. OSP
$9. **CMV $10 MB. $7. turtle only.**

GOLDEN CHARMER LOCKET 1968-70
(Left) Gold locket holds perfume glace in
Somewhere, Topaze, Cotillion, Here's My
Heart, To A Wild Rose, Unforgettable, Rapture,
Occur!, Brocade, & Regence. OSP $9.50
CMV $14. MB $9 locket only.

PILLBOX PERFUME GLACE 1967
(Top Right) Black & gold with red rose on top.
Came in Occur!, Rapture, Unforgettable,
Somewhere, Topaze, Cotillion,Here's My
Heart, To A Wild Rose. OSP $4.50 **CMV
$15. MB. pill box only $10 mint.**

DAISY PIN PERFUME GLACE 1969
(Bottom Right) White & gold pin Charisma,
Brocade, Regence, Rapture, Occur!,
Unforgettable,Somewhere, Topaze, Cotillion.
OSP $6. **CMV $7. $10. MB.**

GOLDEN LEAF PIN 1969-70
Blue box contains gold leaf pin with pearl at
stem. Perfume glace comes in Elusive,
Charisma, Brocade, Unforgettable,
Rapture, Occur!, Topaze, Somewhere, &
Cotillion. Same pin also issued with out glace.
OSP $6.50 **CMV $11 MB. $7. Pin only.**

PERFUME GLACE NECKLACE 1966-67
Silver with black stone & gold with brown
stone. Came in Unforgettable, Rapture,
Somewhere, Cotillion, Topaze, To A Wild
Rose, Here's My Heart, Wishing. OSP $8.
CMV $17. each MB. $12 locket only.

PERFUME GLACE NECKLACE 1966-67
Special issue gold round box. Came with
either silver with black stone or gold necklace
with brown stone. **CMV $20. as shown.**

**DELICATE HEART PERFUME COMPACT
1982**
Pink plastic heart holds solid perfume. Red &
white heart decor box. SSP $4. **CMV $2.
MB.**

CAMEO RING & PIN 1970
Both are perfume glace. Comes in Elusive,
Charisma, Brocade, Regence, & Bird of
Paradise. OSP $10. each. **CMV $9. each
$15 each MB.**

PLATES

FREEDOM PLATE 1974-77
9" ceramic plate, blue trim with gold edge.
Blue printing on back. Made by Wedgewood,
England for Avon. SSP $13. **CMV $15 MB.**

**STRAWBERRY PORCELAIN PLATE &
GUEST SOAPS 1978-79**
7 1/2" plate made in Brazil for Avon. Comes
with 6 red strawberry soaps SSP $13 **CMV
$13 MB. $8 plate only.**

TENDERNESS PLATE 1974-75
9 1/4" Ironstone plate. Blue & white with gold
edge. Made in Spain for Avon by Pontesa.
The plate sold to public with word "Pontesa" on
the back side in blue letters. This was also
awarded to Avon Reps. Plate was also sold
with no inscription on back. No. 1 (Regular
issue)-all blue lettering on back of plate, No. 2
(Reps Award)- all blue lettering including
Pontesa logo. No. 3 (Reps Award)- all blue
lettering on back of plate except the Pontesa
logo which is red. **CMV $20 MB. regular
issue- $25 Rep plate MB.**

GENTLE MOMENTS PLATE 1975-77
8 3/4 ceramic plate. Green letters on back.
Made by Wedgewood, England. SSP $15
CMV $15 MB.

MOTHER'S DAY PLATE 1982
5" size plate. Little Things Mean A Lot
inscribed on face. Comes in yellow box &
plastic plate stand. SSP $10 CMV $8 MB.
**Same plate given to presidents Club Reps.
Label on back reads "January 1982
Presidents Club Luncheon". CMV $15 MB.**

BETSY ROSS PLATE 1973-77
White with colored scene, gold trim and
lettering. 9" plate. SSP $13. **CMV $15 MB.**

CHRISTMAS PLATE - 15 YEAR 1978
Same plate as 15 year anniversary plate
inscribed on back. We have no info on this or
where it came from. Write Bud Hastin if you
know what this plate is for. **CMV $50.**

**CHILDRENS PERSONAL TOUCH PLATE
1982-83**
7 5/8 ceramic plate. SSP $12 **CMV $12 MB.**

**CARDINAL NORTH AMERICAN SONG
BIRD PLATE 1974-76**
10" ceramic plate. Gold & green letters on
back. SSP $13. **CMV $15 MB.**

**MOTHERS DAY PLATE "CHERISHED
MOMENTS" 1981**
5" porcelain plate dated 1981, with stand. SSP
$10 **CMV $10 MB.**

**CHRISTMAS ON THE FARM 1973
CHRISTMAS PLATE 1973-75**
White with colored scene, turquoise border,
gold edge and lettering. 9" plate SSP $13
CMV $55 MB.

PINK ROSES CUP & SAUCER 1974-76
(Left) White china with pink flowers & green leaves with gold trim. Made by Stoke-on Trent, England. OSP $10 **CMV $12 MB.** Also came with double printed letters on bottom. **CMV $20 MB.**

BLUE BLOSSOMS CUP & SAUCER 1974-75
(Right) White china with blue & pink flowers and 22K gold rim. Made in England. OSP $10 **CMV $12. MB.**

CHRISTMAS "BETSY ROSS" PLATE 1973
Factory mistake 1973 Christmas plate has inscription on back for Betsy Ross plate. Very Rare. **CMV $100.**

COUNTRY CHURCH 1974 CHRISTMAS PLATE
9" ceramic plate. Second in a series of Christmas plates by Avon. Made by Wedgewood, England. Blue writing on back. Blue & white front, gold edge. SSP $13. **CMV $35 MB.** Rare issue came without Christmas 1974 on front of plate. **CMV $75 MB.**

SKATERS ON THE POND 1975 CHRIST-MAS PLATE 1976-80
8 3/4 ceramic green & white plate. Green letters on the back. Made by Wedgewood, England for Avon. This plate was not sold till 1976 Christmas selling season. SSP $17. **CMV $15. MB. Some have 1976 on back Add $10.**

BRINGING HOME THE TREE 1976 CHRISTMAS PLATE 1976-80
9" blue ceremic plate, gold edge. Blue printing on back. Made by Wedgewood, England for Avon. SSP $16. **CMV $15. MB. Some have 1975 on back Add $10.**

CHRISTMAS PLATE TEST 1976
8 3/4 test plate. Does not say Avon. Christmas 1976 on front 6 times in gold. Was never sold by Avon. Came from factory. Has blue border. **CMV $75.**

COUNTRY CHRISTMAS PLATE 1980-82
9" ceramic 1980 Christmas plate. SSP $22. **CMV $15. MB.**

"CAROLLERS IN THE SNOW" 1977 CHRISTMAS PLATE 1977-80
8 3/4 ceramic blue & white plate, gold edge. Blue letters on back. Made by Wedgewood, England for Avon. SSP $17. **CMV $15. MB.**

"TRIMMING THE TREE" 1978 CHRIST-MAS PLATE 1978-79
(6th edition) 8 5/8 ceramic plate. Turquoise rim with gold edge trim. Made for Avon by Enoch Wedgewood in England. SSP $20. **CMV $15. MB.**

DASHING THROUGH THE SNOW 1979 CHRISTMAS PLATE 1979-80
8 3/4 blue and white ceramic plate with gold trim. Christmas 1979 on front. Back of plate says Made for Avon Products by Enoch Wedgewood in England. SSP. $20. **CMV $15 MB.**

SHARING THE CHRISTMAS SPIRIT 1981 CHRISTMAS PLATE 1981
9" porcelain plate has 2 lids carrying Christmas tree, Christmas 1981 on front. SSP $21.50 **CMV $15 MB.** Rare issue came with no Christmas 1981 on front. **CMV $75.**

CHRISTMAS PLATE 1983-85
"Enjoying the night before Christmas". 9" porcelain plate. SSP $23.50 CMV $20 MB.

BAKED WITH LOVE PLATE 1982-83
9" porcelain plate dated 1982 SSP $18 CMV $18 MB.

SWEET DREAMS KEEPSAKE PLATE 1983
7 5/8" porcelain plate. SSP $15 CMV $15 MB.

CUPIDS MESSAGE PORCELAIN DISH 1984
White heart shaped dish with Angel Love in red letters. red box. SSP $10 CMV $10 MB.

CHRISTMAS PLATE "KEEPING THE CHRISTMAS TRADITION" 1982-84
9" ceramic plate, back says Christmas Memories, 1982. Comes in green & gold box. SSP $23.50 CMV $23.50 MB.

HOSPITALITY SWEETS RECIPE PLATE 1982-83
3 different 7" metal plates, made to hang on wall, choice of Plum Pudding, Buche de Noel or Blue Berry Orange Nut Bread. Comes with Avon recipe on box. SSP $6. CMV $4 each MB.

SINGIN IN THE RAIN PLATE 1986
8" porcelain plate. Both came with or without wood base music box. DP $12. CMV $12 MB. Add $5 for music box base.
EASTER PARADE PLATE 1986
8" porcelain plate came with wood base music stand, plays Easter Parade. DP $12. CMV $12. MB. Add $5. for music box base.

BOUQUET OF LOVE PLATE 1987
7" white porcelain Bisque plate. DP $8.25 CMV $8.25 MB.
CHRISTMAS PLATE 1986
8" white bisque porcelain. "A Childs Christmas" DP $12. CMV $12 MB.

CHRISTMAS PLATE 1985
"A Childs Christmas" 7 3/4 white bisque porcelain. DP $8. CMV $8. MB.
CHRISTMAS PLATE 1984
9" porcelain decal plate. Last in this series. DP $15. CMV $15. MB.

ABIGAIL ADAMS PLATE 1985
9" porcelain plate. Wood stand. DP $15. CMV $15. MB.
CHORUS LINE PLATE 1986
8" porcelain plate. Wood music box stand. DP $12. CMV $12. MB.

CLASSIC WEDDING PLATE 1986
9" bisque porcelain plate with 2 boxes on face. Gold trim. DP $12 CMV $12 MB.
FOUR SEASONS CALENDAR PLATE 1987
9" porcelain plate. DP $11 CMV $11 MB.

MOMENTS OF VICTORY SPORTS PLATES 1985
Set of 4 different 7" porcelain plates Football, Basketball, Hockey, or Baseball. SSP $8. **CMV $8. each MB.**

AMERICAN PORTRAITS PLATE COLLECTIONS 1985
Set of six 4 1/2" porcelain plates. Choice of The East, The West, The Rockies, The Southwest, The Midwest, The South. DP $6. **CMV $6. each MB.**

MOTHER'S DAY SPECIAL MEMORIES PLATES 1985
5" porcelain plate, choice of white or black body and child. DP $7. **CMV $7. each MB.**

MOTHER'S DAY PLATES 1983-84
5" ceramic plates. Both dated on back. DP $7. **CMV $7. each MB.**

MOTHER'S DAY PLATE 1986
5" porcelain plate called "A New Tooth" Comes in White or Black body & child. DP $6. **CMV $6. MB.**

MOTHER'S DAY PLATE 1987
"A Mother In Love" 5" porcelain plate. DP $5.25 **CMV $5.25 MB.**

SCHOOL IS A NEW BEGINNING PLATE 1986
5" porcelain plate. DP $6. **CMV $6. MB.**

12 DAYS OF CHRISTMAS COLLECTIONS 1985
All white porcelain.

CANDLE HOLDERS
DP $9. Pair. **CMV $9 Pair.**

DESSERT PLATES
Set of 4 DP $16 **CMV $16 Set.**

MUGS
Set of 4 DP $13 **CMV $13 Set.**

BABY KEEPSAKE SPOON & BOWL SET 1984
6 1/4 porcelain bowl & 5" spoon. DP $12 **CMV $12 MB.**

CHRISTMAS LIGHTS DESSERT PLATE 1985
7" white ceramic plate with X-mas light design. DP $4. **CMV $4. MB.**

CANDLES

Whats hot & whats not? Candles are very popular in Avon Collecting. Most popular are all glass figurine type candles. They are selling faster & at better prices then the non figurine type glass candles. All wax Figurine candles are popular but are hard to keep clean & in mint condition. Tin containers with candles are popular but not as much as glass figurines candles. The Tall or short wax taper type candles are hard to display & will not be as popular as the figurine candles. Keep these thoughts in mind when buying & collecting candles. Candle refills & wax chips are no longer considered collectable. There is no resale interest to most collectors in these items.

COLLECTORS
All containers are priced empty.

CO means............. Container Only
BO means............. Bottle Only (empty)
CMV means........... Current Market Value
SSP means............. Special Selling Price
OSP means............ Original Selling Price
MB means............... Mint and Boxed
DP means................ Avon Rep Cost
This is used on all new products 1984 & newer.

DANISH MODERN CANDLE 1970
(Left) Stainless steel candleholder with red candle. OSP $8. **CMV $8 with candle. MB.**

FLAMING TULIP FRAGRANCE CANDLE 1973
(Right) Red candle in Floral Medley fragrance. Gold holder. OSP $7. **CMV $7 CO. $9. MB.**

JOYOUS MESSAGE CANDLES 1985
3 elf candles 1 1/2 high. DP $2. **CMV $2 MB.**

FLORAL FRAGRANCE CANDLE 1971-75
(Left) Metal gold leaf stand & pink or yellow flower candle. OSP $8.50 **CMV $7 - $9 MB.**
WATER LILY FRAGRANCE CANDLE 1972-73
(Right) Green lily pad base with white plastic petals with yellow center candle. OSP $5. **CMV $4 CO, $6 MB.**

REVOLUTIONARY SOLDIER SMOKERS CANDLE 1979-80
Clear, or dark amber glass, clear harder to find, 2 different. Red & gold box. SSP $4. **CMV $4 MB.**
FOSTORIA CRYSTAL POOL FLOATING CANDLE 1979-80
6" clear crystal dish, green & white flower candle. SSP $12 **CMV $8.**

OVALIQUE PERFUME CANDLEHOLDER 1974-75
(Left) 4" high, clear gloss, choice of Sonnet, Moonwind, Patchwork, Roses Roses, Charisma, Bird of Paradise, Bayberry, Frankincense & Myrrh or Wassail. OSP $8. **CMV $6 MB.**
FACETS OF LIGHT FRAGRANCE CANDLETTE 1975-76
(Center) 4" high, clear glass. Came with Bayberry candle but any refill candlette will fit. OSP $5. **CMV $5. MB.**
GOLDEN PINE CONE FRAGRANCE CANDLETTE 1974-75
(Right) Gold toned glass. Choice of Bayberry only. OSP $5. **CMV $5 MB.**

CRYSTALLITE COLOGNE CANDLE 1970-71
(Left) Clear glass bottle with gold cap holds 4 oz. cologne in Unforgettable, Rapture, Occur!, Somewhere, Topaze, & Cotillion. OSP $5.50 **CMV $6. MB. $5. BO.**
CANDLESTICK COLOGNE 1972-75
(Right) 5 oz. silver painted over clear glass with silver cap. Came in Moonwind, Field Flowers, Bird of Paradise, Roses Roses. SSP $6. **CMV $4 MB. $3. BO. 1975 came only in Imperial Garden, Moonwind, or Sonnett CMV $6. MB. $5 BO.**

WASHINGTON GOBLET FOSTORIA CANDLEHOLDER 1975-77
Blue glass by Fostoria. Came with Frankincense & Myrrh or Floral Medley candle. OSP $10 **CMV $10 CO $12 MB.**
MARTHA WASHINGTON GOBLET 1976-77
Blue glass Fostoria candleholder. OSP $12.50 **CMV $10 CO. $12. MB.**

TURTLE CANDLE 1972
(Left) White glass turtle candle with green glass shell top. OSP $5. **CMV $7-$9 MB.**
MUSHROOM CANDLE 1972
(Right) White glass candle with pink glass mushroom top. OSP $5. **CMV $7-$9 MB.**

COLOGNE & CANDLELIGHT 1975-76
(Left) 2 oz. clear glass with gold cap and clear plastic collar. Hold Imperial Gardens, Roses Roses, or Charisma. OSP $3. **CMV $4. BO. $3. MB.**
CANDLESTICK COLOGNE 1970-71
(Right) 4 oz. red glass bottle, gold cap. Holds Elusive, Charisma, Brocade, Regence, Bird of Paradise. OSP $6. **CMV $6 MB. $5. BO.** Also came in smoked red glass. Appears much darker than red glass issue. It looks smokey red. **CMV $12 MB.**

CANDLESTICK COLOGNE 1966
3 oz. silver coated over clear glass. Silver cap. Came in Occur!, Rapture, Unforgettable. OSP $3.75 **CMV $12. mint. $16 MB.**

FLORAL MEDLEY PERFUMED CANDLES 1971-72
Box holds yellow & purple frosted glass candleholders. OSP $5.50 **CMV $8 MB.**

REGENCY CANDLESTICK COLOGNE 1973-74
(Left) 4 oz. clear glass. Came in Bird of Paradise, Charisma, Elusive, or Roses Roses. SSP $7. **CMV $5. MB. $4 BO.**

OPALIQUE CANDLESTICK COLOGNE 1976-77
(Right) 5 oz. swirl glass & cap. Came in Charisma or Sweet Honesty. SSP $8. **CMV $6. MB. $5. BO.**

CRYSTAL GLOW PERFUMED CANDLE-HOLDER 1972-73
(Left) Clear glass. Came in Moonwind, Bird of Paradise, Elusive, Charisma, Brocade, Regence, Wassail, Bayberry, Frankincense, Myrrh, Roses Roses. SSP $8. **CMV $8-$10 MB.**

FOSTORIA PERFUMED CANDLEHOLDER 1973
(Right) Clear glass. Came with Patchwork, Sonnet, Moonwind, Roses Roses, Charisma, Bird of Paradise, Bayberry, Wassail, Frankincense, & Myrrh candles. SSP $6. **CMV $6-$8 MB.**

CHESAPEAKE COLLECTION JIGGER CANDLE 1981
Amber glass dog head candle, candle in bottom. SSP $10 **CMV $7 MB.**

FOSTORIA CANDLELIGHT BASKET CANDLEHOLDER 1975
(Left) Clear glass, gold handle. Choice of Sonnet, Moonwind, Patchwork, Charisma, Roses Roses, Bird of Paradise, Wassail, Frankincense, & Myrrh or Bayberry candle refill. OSP $9 **CMV $9 MB. $7 CO.**

FOSTORIA SALT CELLAR CANDLE 1969-70 & 1981
(Right) Clear glass with small silver spoon. OSP $6 **CMV $10 MB. $7 candle only.** Reissued in 1981 with "R" on bottom of foot for reissue. SSP $10 **CMV $6 MB.**

TULIP CLEARFIRE TRANSPARENT CANDLE 1980-82
(Left) Clear glass. 4" high. SSP $6 **CMV $5. MB.**

SPARKLING SWIRL CLEARFIRE CANDLE 1980-82
(Center) Clear glass 5 1/8" high. SSP $11 **CMV $8. MB.**

SHERBERT DESSERT CANDLE 1980-82
(Right) 5" high clear glass. Comes with red, yellow or pink candle. SSP $8 **CMV $5 MB.**

HEARTS & FLOWERS FRAGRANCE CANDLE 1973-74
(Left) White milk glass with red green & pink design. Came in Floral Medley fragrance. SSP $4 **CMV $5 MB. $4 CO.**

POTPOURRI FRAGRANCE CANDLE 1972-73
(Right) White milk glass, came with Potpourri candle. SSP $4 **CMV $4 CO. $5. MB.**

HEART & DIAMOND FOSTORIA LOVING CUP PERFUMED CANDLEHOLDER 1978
(Left) Approx. 7" high claer Fostoria glass. Came with floral Medley perfumed candle. Embossed with "Avon 1978" on it's base. Refillable. OSP $15 **CMV $12. MB. glass only $7.**

MOUNT VERNON SAUCE PITCHER 1977-79
(Right) Approx. 5 1/2" high. Blue Fostoria glass. Came with Floral Medley perfumed candle. Refillable. Avon on bottom. OSP $15.50 **CMV $10 MB. pitcher only $6.**

WHITE MILK GLASS CANDLE 1964-66
(Left) OSP $3.50 **CMV $9-$13 MB.**

AMBER GLASS CANDLE 1965-66
(Center) Amber Paint over clear glass. OSP $4 **CMV $17 MB. $12 candle only.**

RED GLASS CANDLE 1965-66
(Right) Red paint over clear glass OSP $4 **CMV $11-$16 MB.** Dark red 1968 glass candle, not painted. **CMV $50.**

CANDLE PERFUMED REFILLS 1970'S
Candle refills for the many candle holders. Avon has made over the years Comes in many fragrances. SSP $2.50 **CMV $2.50 MB.**

SUNNY BUNNY CERAMIC CANDLE-HOLDER 1981-82

5 1/2" high ceramic candleholder Dated 1981. $15 **CMV $10 MB.**

HEART & DIAMOND CANDLESTICK 1978-79

7" high heart embossed Fostoria clear glass candle. Avon 1979 on bottom. COmes with long red candle for one end or turn it over and insert the small glass candleholder on other end. Comes in red box. SSP $13. **CMV $10 MB.**

KITCHEN CROCK FRAGRANCE CANDLETTE 1974-75

(Left) Yellow crock with red, yellow & blue flowers with cork cap. Came in Meadow Morn fragrance. SSP $4 **CV $5 CO. $6 MB.**

WASSAIL BOWL CANDLE 1969-70

(Right) Silver paint over red glass with silver spoon. OSP $8. **CMV $9 CO. $11 MB.**

FROSTED GLASS CANDLE 1967

(Left) Gold band around edge. lid makes stand for base. OSP $5 **CMV $12 MB. $9 CO.**

WHITE & GOLD CANDLE 1966-67

(Right) White glass top & bottom with gold band. Top makes stand for base. OSP $5. **CMV $9-$12 MB.**

CHINA TEA POT CANDLE 1972-73

White china with blue flower design or without decal. Thousands came from factory, not sold by Avon, with or without decals, some decals were on front, some on back. The factory rejects **CMV $9 each.** Came from Avon with Roses Roses, Moonwind, Bird of Paradise, Elusive, Charisma, Brocade, Regence, Wassail, Bayberry, Frankincense & Myrrh candles. SSP $10 **CMV $10 MB. $6 CO.**

REGENCE CANDLE 1967

(Left) Gold paint over clear glass with green paper band. Lid makes base for bottom. OSP $6. **CMV $20. MB. $15 CO.**

REGENCE CANDLE 1968-69

(Right) Green glass candleholder with gold handle & base. OSP $10 **CMV $13. candle only $18 MB.**

CRYSTAL CANDLEIER 1969-70

(Left) 7" high, clear glass with blue crystals inside, gold handle on glass lid. OSP $7. **CMV $10 MB. $8 CO.**

GOLD & WHITE CANDLE 1969-70

(Right) Painted gold & white over clear glass, lid makes stand for base. OSP $8 **CMV $9-$11 MB.**

FIRST CHRISTMAS CANDLE 1967

All gold, red inside 1967 had label on bottom and no Avon. OSP $5. **CMV $9 CO. $12 MB.** 1972 Reissued-Avon on Bottom, no label. **CMV $9 MB. $7 CO.**

FIRST CHRISTMAS CANDLE FOREIGN

(Right) All silver with red inside. **CMV $20.**

NESTING DOVE CANDLE 1970

White base glass & lid with dove on top. OSP $7.50 **CMV $7 - $9 MB.**

HOBNAIL PATIO CANDLE 1973

(Right) White milk base clear glass top. Came with Sonnet, Moonwind, Roses Roses, Bird of Paradise, Charisma, Wassail, Bayberry, and Frankincense & Myrrh candles. SSP $8. **CMV $10 MB. $8 CO.**

GOLDEN APPLE CANDLE 1968-69

Shiny gold over clear glass. OSP $6. **CMV $14 mint. $18 MB.**

SILVER APPLE CANDLE 1968

Factory test sample same as gold apple only in shiny silver over clear glass. Was not filled. **CMV $90 on silver top & bottom. Silver bottom with gold top CMV $55 mint.**

SCENTIMENTS CANDLES 1982-83
2" high metal can candles, 2 different designs. Lid says "May Love Always Fill Your Heart" or "The Beauty of Friendship is Everlasting." SSP $7. each. **CMV $4. MB each.**

ULTRA CRYSTAL CANDLE 1981-82
(Left) 2 1/2" high clear glass. Gray box. SSP $10. **CMV $5. MB.**
ULTRA SHIMMER CANDLE 1981-82
(Right) 2 1/2" high clear glass octagonal shaped. Gold box. SSP $9. **CMV $5. MB.**

FLORAL LIGHT CANDLE REFILL 1980-81
(Left) Comes in lavender, green or yellow. Flower shaped. SSP $4. **CMV $2. MB.**
FLORAL LIGHT FRAGRANCE CANDLE 1980-81
(Right) Clear glass flower shaped base holds flower shaped refill candle. SSP $7. **CMV $5. MB.**

GAMESMAN CANDLE GIFT SET 1981-82
Green & red box holds small metal green can with candle & set of green playing cards with deer in 2 corners. Made by Arco Playing Card Co., Chicago. Cards do not say Avon. SSP $10. **CMV $8. MB complete set.**

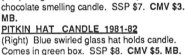

HOT CHOCO-LITE CANDLE 1981-82
(Left) Beige or white color wax cup with brown chocolate smelling candle. SSP $7. **CMV $3. MB.**
PITKIN HAT CANDLE 1981-82
(Right) Blue swirled glass hat holds candle. Comes in green box. SSP $8. **CMV $5. MB.**

SHIMMERING PEACOCK CANDLE 1979-80
(Left) Box holds clear glass peacock. SSP $10. **CMV $8. MB.**

PERSONALLY YOURS FRAGRANCE CANDLE 1980-82
(Left) Clear glass with refillable candle. Comes with sheet of stick on gold letters. SSP $12. **CMV $8. MB.**
STAR BRIGHT FRAGRANCE CANDLE 1980-81
(Right) Icy clear glass holds refillable candle. SSP $7. **CMV $5. MB.**

BRIGHT CHIPMUNK CANDLETTE 1978-79
Clear glass candleholder. Refillable. SSP $6. **CMV $6. MB.**
FRESH AROMA SMOKERS CANDLE 1978-79
Non refillable brown wax like pipe with black plastic and chrome top. Bottom cardboard label. SSP $7. **CMV $5. MB.**

FLOWER FANCY CANDLES 1982
(Left) Same box as Easter Surprise set below only different name. Two 10" green candles with flowers. SSP $8. **CMV $5. MB.**
EASTER SURPRISE CANDLES 1982
(Right) Green flower box holds two 10" yellow candles with white rabbits. SSP $8. **CMV $5. set MB.**

SNUG 'N COZY "CAT" FRAGRANCE CANDLE 1980-82
Clear glass cat candleholder. SSP $10. **CMV $7. MB.**

CHRISTMAS CHIMES CANDLES 1981
(Left) Red 10" candles with gold bells in red box.
HOLIDAY HOSTESS CANDLES 1981
(Center) Green & white holly box holds 2 white 10" candles with green & red holly.
MR. & MRS. CHRISTMAS CANDLES 1981
(Right) Red box holds two 10" green candles with Mr. & Mrs. Santa Clause. SSP $7. each. **CMV $5. MB each set.**

GEM GLOW CANDLE 1981-82
(Left) Clear glass multi-faceted. Comes with green, amber or red filled candle. SSP $10. **CMV $7. MB.**
CAPE COD CREAMER CANDLE 1981-83
(Right) 4" high ruby red glass. Holds candle. See Cape Cod in Women's Decanters for other Cape Cod candles. SSP $9. **CMV $6.**

GLISTENING TREE CLEARFIRE CANDLE 1981-82
4 1/2" high clear ribbed glass tree shaped candle. SSP $10. **CMV $7. MB.**
LOVE LIGHT CLEARFIRE CANDLE 1982
Clear ribbed glass heart shape candle. SSP $10. **CMV $7. MB.**

CATNIP FRAGRANCE CANDLE 1975-76
4" high yellow plastic. Floral Medley fragrance. OSP $3. **CMV $4. MB.**
DYNAMITE FRAGRANCE CANDLETTE 1975-76
Red & white. OSP $4. **CMV $5. MB.**

HOLIDAY CANDLE DISH & WREATH 1980
Clear glass candleholder, red candle and holly wreath. SSP $9. **CMV $7. MB.**

DAPPER SNOWMAN CANDLES 1980
(Pictured) 10" high red candles with snowman on base. Set of 2.
WINTER ROSE CANDLES 1980
(Left in book picture) 10" white candles with roses at base. Set of 2.
CANDY CANE & HOLLY CANDLES 1980
(Center in book picture) 10" high green candles with candy cane at base. Set of 2. SSP $6. each set. **CMV $6. MB each set.**

PLUM PUDDING CANDLE 1978-79
(Left) 4" high brown, green & white candle. Bottom label. SSP $6. **CMV $6. MB.**
WINTER LIGHTS CANDLETTE 1978-79
(Right) Clear glass square candleholder. Holds glass candlette. Avon on bottom of both. SSP $8. **CMV $8. MB.**

CAROLLING TRIO CANDLES 1981-82
Comes in separate boxes. Melodic Mouse candle, Howling Hound candle, Crooning Cat candle. SSP $5. each. **CMV $3. each MB.**
HARVEST TIME FRAGRANCE CANDLE 1980-81
Tan wax candle, 6" high. SSP $10. **CMV $6. MB.**

MRS. SNOWLIGHT CANDLE 1979-81
(Left) White, red & green wax candle. SSP $7. **CMV $5. MB.**
WINTER WONDERLAND CENTERPIECE CANDLE 1979-80
(Right) White wax base, green wax trees, red & white wax house. Center holds glass candlette. SSP $15. **CMV $12. MB.**

ENCHANTED MUSHROOM FRAGRANCE CANDLE 1975
(Left) White wax shell / yellow cover. Meadow Morn fragrance. OSP $4. **CMV $5. MB, $4. CO.**
SLEIGH LIGHT FRAGRANCE CANDLE 1975-76
(Right) 4" high, red & green. Bayberry scented. OSP $5. **CMV $5. MB, $4. CO.**

MR. SNOWLIGHT CANDLE 1981
5 1/2" high white wax, green trim. SSP $7. **CMV $5.**

BLACK-EYED SUSAN FRAGRANCE CANDLE 1975-76
Yellow with brown center. Wild Flowers fragrance. OSP $5. **CMV $6. MB, $5. CO.**
GRAPEFRUIT FRAGRANCE CANDLE 1974-76
Yellow with red center. Has grapefruit fragrance. OSP $3. **CMV $5. MB, $4. CO.**

CRYSTALGLOW CLEARFIRE CANDLE 1980
(Left) Clear glass. Avon on bottom under candle. SSP $10. **CMV $8. MB.**
BUNNY BRIGHT CERAMIC CANDLE 1980
(Right) White ceramic with pink & green trim. "1980 Avon" on bottom. SSP $12. **CMV $8. MB.**

TERRA COTTA BIRD CANDLETTE 1976-77
Reddish brown clay bird candleholder. Avon on bottom. OSP $8. **CMV $6. MB, $3. bird only.**

GINGERBREAD HOUSE FRAGRANCE CANDLE 1977-79
Brown & white candle. Came in Frankincense & Myrrh fragrance. OSP $8.50. **CMV $7. MB, $5. no box.**

GLOW OF CHRISTMAS CANDLE 1980
White wax with red center refillable candle. SSP $10. **CMV $7. MB.**

DOVE IN FLIGHT CANDLETTE 1977-78
Clear glass dove candleholder. Came in Meadow Morn fragrance candlette. Refillable. SSP $6. **CMV $6. MB.**
BUNNY CERAMIC PLANTER CANDLE-HOLDER 1977-79
3 different rabbits. One made in Brazil and recesses on bottom; one flat bottom made in U.S. and lighter in weight; 1978 issue same flat bottom only different type letters on bottom. Came with Floral Medley or Roses Roses perfumed candle. SSP $11. **CMV $10. MB each, rabbit only $6. each.**

LOTUS BLOSSOM PERFUMED CANDLE-HOLDER 1974-75
(Left) Black glass with green & white design. Available with candle fragrance: Bayberry, Frankincense & Myrrh, Wassail, Sonnet, Moonwind, Roses Roses, Bird of Paradise or Charisma. OSP $8. CMV $10. - $12. MB.

DYNASTY PERFUMED CANDLE 1971-72
(Right) 6" high, white glass jar & lid. OSP $7.50. CMV $9. - $11. MB.

AMERICAN HEIRLOOM CANDLESTICK & CANDLE 1982-84
Pewter metal candlestick & 6" red candle. SSP $11. CMV $7. MB.

CORAL GLOW CANDLE 1983-84
Clear glass Conch shell design candle. SSP $12. CMV $8. MB.

GARDEN BOUNTY CANDLE 1979-80
(Left) Beige & pink cart, red candle. SSP $8. CMV $6. MB.

COUNTRY SPICE CANDLE 1979-80
(Center) Light blue green glass jar & lid. Wire bale. Comes with candle inside. SSP $8. CMV $6. MB.

FLOWER FROST COLLECTION WATER GOBLET CANDLETTE 1979-80
(Right) Frosted glass goblet holds glass candle insert. SSP $10. CMV $8. MB.

TOCCARA SPECIAL EDITION CANDLE 1982-83
(Left) Clear cut glass Fostoria candle. Blue box. SSP $13. CMV $7. MB.

HARVEST GLOW CANDLE 1982-83
(Right) Clear glass pumpkin shaped candle and lid. SSP $13. CMV $8. MB.

NATURE'S FRESH PETITE CANDLES 1983-84
3 miniature candles on connecting wick, choice of strawberry, pine cone or mushroom. SSP $6. set of 3. CMV $4. each set MB.

BUNNY CERAMIC PLANTER CANDLE 1979-80
Made of ceramic in Brazil for Avon. Green, pink & yellow flowers. Brown eyes, pink inner ears. Comes with Floral Medley or Spiced Garden candle. SSP $15. CMV $10. MB.

TENDER BLOSSOM CANDLE 1977-80
Light pink wax base with dark pink inner candle. SSP $7. CMV $5. MB.

SNUGGLY MOUSE CANDLEHOLDER 1983
Ceramic mouse holder base 4 1/4" wide. Comes with 6" red candle. SSP $13. CMV $8. MB.

SPICE CUPBOARD CANDLE 1982
(Left) 1 1/2" high clear glass refillable candle. SSP $5. CMV $3. MB.

RAIN OR SHINE GREETING CANDLE 1983
(Right) 2" high candle with mouse decal on side. SSP $5. CMV $3. MB.

HOLIDAY FLOATING CANDLES 1983
Box of 2 candles in choice of Red Poinsettia flowers or green & red wreath, 2 1/2" wide. SSP $5. each set. **CMV $4. set MB.**

LITTLE DRUMMERS CANDLES 1982
Box holds two 10" red candles with boy & girl drummers. SSP $9. **CMV $5. MB.**

SPARKLING TURTLE CANDLETTE 1978-79
4 1/2" long clear glass turtle. SSP $7. **CMV $7. MB, $6. CO.**

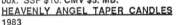

LOVE BIRDS TAPER CANDLES 1983-84
(Left) 2 white 10" candles, has 2 ceramic love bird rings. Box has blue birds & felt lined inner box. SSP $10. **CMV $5. MB.**
HEAVENLY ANGEL TAPER CANDLES 1983
(Right) 10" white candles with 2 ceramic angels rings. Angels on box. SSP $10. **CMV $5. MB.**

YEAR TO YEAR BIRTHDAY CANDLE 1983-84
4 1/2" ceramic clown candle holder with yellow candle, 1-2-3-4 on sides. SSP $10. **CMV $7. MB.**

AUTUMN HARVEST CANDLES 1983-84
Box of 2 - 10" brown & beige candles with corn decoration. SSP $9. **CMV $5. MB.**

SHADES OF AUTUMN CANDLES 1982
2 - 10" white candles in Christmas box. SSP $9. **CMV $5. MB.**

HO HO GLOW "SANTA" CANDLE 1982-83
5" ceramic red, white & black Santa candle. SSP $16. **CMV $10. MB.**

SUMMER LIGHTS INDOOR-OUTDOOR CANDLE 1984
(Left) 2 1/4" high green glass. DP $4. **CMV $4. MB.**
CLEARFIRE TULIP CUP CANDLE 1986
(Right) Clear glass. 4" high. DP $6. **CMV $6. MB.**

CANDLES

CHRISTMAS FUN CANDLE GIFT SET 1985
Green horse, white doll, red soldier candles. DP $3. **CMV $3. set MB.**

GLISTENING GLOW CANDLE 1986
Clear glass candle. DP $6. **CMV $6. MB.**

GINGERBREAD HOUSE CANDLE 1986
Ceramic house holds glass cup candle. DP. $13.50. **CMV $13.50.**

NATURAL HOME FRAGRANCE CANDLE HOLDER 1986
(Left) 3 3/4" high ceramic top & bottom dish. Bot marked Avon. Currier & Ives Scene. Comes with small candle. DP $9. **CMV $9. MB.**

SPRING HOSTESS CANDLE HOLDERS 1987
(Right) 2 white ceramic candle holders 2 3/4" high. Not marked Avon. DP $6.75. **CMV $6.75 MB.**

SHIMMERING GLASS CONVERTIBLE CANDLEHOLDER 1985
2 3/4" high clear glass. Holds big candle on 1 side, flip it over to holds taper candle. DP $5. **CMV $5. MB.**

PERSONAL CREATION CANDLE 1985
GLISTENING CREATING CANDLE 1985
(Right & Center) Both glass candles the same. Different boxes & candle mix. DP $4. **CMV $4. each MB.**

AUTUMN IMPRESSIONS CANDLE 1984
(Left) 2 1/4" high clear glass. DP $3. **CMV $3. MB.**

ANNIVERSARY TAPER CANDLE HOLDER 1985
Small porcelain doves & flowers. DP $9. **CMV $9. MB.**

PORCELAIN ANGELS CANDLE HOLDER 1985
5" high white porcelain. Empty DP $11. **CMV $11. MB.**

SPARKLING JEWEL STACKABLE CANDLES 1984
Green or blue glass. DP $5. **CMV $5. MB each.**

MOTHERS DAY CANDLE 1986
4" high wax candle. Decal on front says "A Mother's Gift is Love 1986". DP $2. **CMV $2. MB.**

TRINKET BOX "SEA SHELL" CANDLE 1987
Small ceramic 3 1/2" pearlized sea shell. DP $4.75. **CMV $4.75. MB.**

DOVE CANDLE HOLDERS 1986
2 white bisque porcelain candle holders. DP $7.25. **CMV $7.25 MB.**

BUNNY TAPER CANDLE HOLDERS 1987
2 small ceramic rabbit candle holders. DP $8.25. **CMV $8.25 MB.**

SOFT MUSK CANDLE 1985
Small tin can candle, lid. DP. $4. **CMV $4. MB.**

FRAGRANCE CANDLE 1985
Tin can. DP $4. **CMV $4. MB.**

STRIPED TAPER CANDLES 1985
Candy cane design 10" candles. 2 in a box.
Green or red. DP $4. **CMV $4. MB.**

STAR COLOR CANDLES 1985
Short & tall yellow, green & blue wax candles.
DP $2. each. **CMV $2. each.**
COUNTRY JAM CANDLES 1985
2" high clear glass. Cloth covers over lid.
Comes in Mint, Black Raspberry, Strawberry
and Orange. DP $4. **CMV $4. each MB.**

HURRICANE LAMP CANDLE 1986
8" high glass dome sits on wood base. Does
not come with candle. Is not marked Avon.
DP $11. **CMV $11. MB.**

COLOR GLOW CANDLES 1985
Red, white or green in 1 1/2" high , 10" tapers
or 6" high columns. DP $2. **CMV $2. each
box.**

EGG CANDLES MARBELIZED 1987
2 1/4" high wax egg candles in Blue, Pink or
Green. DP $2.25. **CMV $2.25. MB.**
JACK 0-LANTERN TRIO CANDLES
1 1/4" high orange candles. Box of 3. DP
$2.50. **CMV $2.50 MB.**

JOLLY SANTA CANDLE 1986
5 1/2" high Santa candle. DP $3. **CMV $3.
MB.**
FESTIVE HOLIDAY CANDLES 1986
Box of 2 white or 2 red candles. DP $3. **CMV
$3. MB.**

FESTIVE GLITTER CANDLES 1985
Gold, green or red in 10" taper or 4" column
candles. DP. $3. **CMV $3. MB.**

AVON COUNTRY FRESH CANDLE 1985
Chicken egg candle with blue or red base. DP
$2. **CMV $3. MB.**

FESTIVAL OF COLORS CANDLES 1985
(Right) 2" high tin cans in Green Apple-stripes,
Raspberry-polka dots, or Lemon-confetti. DP
$4. each. **CMV $4. MB each.**
SOFT ROSE FLOATING CANDLES 1985
(Left) Box holds white, pink & red flower
candle. DP $4. **CMV $4. MB.**

GLOWING MESSAGE CANDLE 1984
1" high each. Flower - Star - Apple. DP $2.50.
CMV $2.50 MB each.

PEARLS & LACE CANDLE 1987
1 1/2" high candle in pink lace design, tin can &
white lid. DP $3.50. **CMV $3.50.**
SUPERSTAR FOOTBALL CANDLE 1986
3" wide green tin can holds candle. DP $3.
CMV $3. MB.

**PAMPERED PIGLET CERAMIC POMANDER
1978-79**
Avon's 1st ceramic pomander is made in
Brazil. White with pink and green flowers.
Came in Meadow Morn wax chip refill. Pink
box. SSP $8. **CMV $6. MB.**

**PORCELAIN UNICORN POMANDER 1981-
82**
5" long white porcelain. Comes with Garlandia
wax chips. SSP $16. **CMV $10. MB.**
**BASKETS OF VIOLETS POMANDER 1981-
82**
White glass basket with fabric flowers. Comes
with Violet fragrance wax chips. SSP $10.
CMV $6. MB.

POMANDERS

POMANDERS MUST BE IN THE BOX TO BE MINT.

FLORENTINE LADY POMANDER 1977-78
Pink wax, approx. 9 1/2" high. Came in
Fragrant Seasons scent. OSP $8. **CMV $5.
MB.**
ORIENTAL FIGURINE POMANDER 1972
10" high. Scented pink wax figurine. OSP $6.
CMV $8. MB.
ORIENTAL FIGURINE POMANDER 1973
Same as above except green. SSP $6. **CMV
$8. MB.**

TWO TURTLEDOVES POMANDER 1979-80
Blue box holds white wax doves. SSP $9.
CMV $9. MB.
**UNDER THE MISTLETOE POMANDER
1979-80**
Light blue wax with wire hanging mistletoe.
SSP $8. **CMV $8. MB.**

HONEY BEARS POMANDER 1979-80
Light yellow wax figure. SSP $6. **CMV $6.
MB.**
FRILLY BOOT POMANDER 1978-79
Pink plastic boot came with wax chip refill.
SSP $2.89. **CMV $2.50 MB.**

THE NESTLINGS 1978-79
Yellow wax bird Pomander. 6 1/2" high. SSP
$6. **CMV $6. MB.**

**WOODLAND CHARMERS MINI POMAN-
DERS 1982-83**
Wax figures in Racoons, Skunk, Rabbit or
Turtle.. SSP $6. each. **CMV $4. each MB.**

**SNEAKIN' 'ROUND SHOE POMANDER
1981-82**
White plastic tennis shoe with white cord and
blue stick on decals. Comes with Country
Morning wax chips. SSP $6. **CMV $3. MB.**
CHICK POMANDER 1981
White egg shaped wax pomander. 3" high.
SSP $5. **CMV $2. MB.**

BOUNTIFUL HARVEST POMANDER 1978-79
Red spiced apple with tan wax basket. SSP $8. **CMV $8. MB.**
VIENNESE WALTZ POMANDER 1978-79
6 1/2" high blue wax figurine, bottom label. SSP $7. **CMV $7. MB.**

PARISIAN MODE POMANDER 1976-77
Pink wax. OSP $7.50. **CMV $6. MB.**
ROYAL PEKINGESE POMANDER 1977-79
White wax. OSP $7.50. **CMV $6. to MB.**

DUCK DECOY DECORATIVE POMANDER 1974-75
Wax statuette (not a bottle) scented with Deep Woods or Wild Country. OSP $6. **CMV $7. MB.**

FLORENTINE CHERUB POMANDER 1975-76
7 1/2" high sculptured wax figurine. OSP $6. **CMV $6. MB.**
DELICATE DOVE POMANDER 1974-76
4" high light green or olive wax pomander scent Summer Breeze or Sun Forest. OSP $5. **CMV $5. MB.**

SIGN OF SPRING POMANDER 1974
6" high yellow fern scented wax. OSP $4. **CMV $5. MB.**
MEADOW BIRD POMANDER 1975-76
6" high white and blue wax pomander, Fernerie scented. OSP $6. **CMV $6. MB.**

CORAL EMPRESS POMANDER 1975
6 1/2" high coral colored wax figurine. Fragrant Seasons scent. OSP $5. **CMV $7. MB.**
CHRISTMAS CAROLLERS POMANDER 1974-75
7" high red wax pomander. Bayberry scented. OSP $6. **CMV $7. MB.**

MODEL T CAR FRESHENER 1979
3" high light yellow wax pomander comes in green and yellow box with green hang up rope. SSP $1.99. **CMV $1.99 MB.**

PAMPERED PERSIANS DECANTER POMANDER 1974-76
Wax sculptured cats with Floral Medley fragrance. SSP $5. **CMV $5. MB. Yellow cat $7. MB.**
'LIL CUPID MINI POMANDER 1982
2 1/4" high wax angel with red heart. Short issue. SSP $3. **CMV $3. MB.**

COCKATOO POMANDER 1972-73
8 1/2" tall blue scented wax pomander. Came in Floral Medley fragrance. SSP $5. **CMV $7. MB.**

FRAGRANT TREE TRIMMING POMANDERS 1980
Set of 3 double sided ornaments 4" high each. Cloth covered, gold hanging cords. SSP $8. set. **CMV $5. MB.**

SWAN TENDER LOVE POMANDER 1980-82
6" long white wax. SSP $10 CMV $6 MB.
LION PEACEFUL PARTNERS POMANDER 1980-82
6 1/2" long wax lion and sheep. SSP $11 CMV $7 MB.

HERALDS OF SPRING MINI POMANDERS 1981
Choice of Owl (yellow), Chipmunk (pink), Mouse (blue), chick (white), 3" high each. SSP $5 CMV $3 each. MB.

AUTUMN HARVEST POMANDER 1979-80
10" long, yellow and green wax. Hangs on wall. SSP $8 CMV $6. MB.

CALICO GARDEN FABRIC POMANDER 1983
Choice of corn (yellow & green), carrot (orange & green), pepper (green), tomato (red & green. SSP$7. CMV $2 each MB.

GRADUATE POMANDER 1982
Small blue "82" plastic pomander on white cord in yellow box. SSP $4 CMV $2 MB.

KEEP ON TRUCKIN TRUCK POMANDER 1981
Small blue truck wax on red cord. SSP $3.50 CMV $2 MB.
GO FOR IT POMANDERS 1981-82
Box of 2 hanging pomanders. Basket Ball & Football scenes. Red cords. SSP $6 CMV $2 MB.

AMERICAN TRADITION POMANDER 1982
5 x 7 plastic wood look frame with green fabric pomander. Does not say Avon. Must be in Avon box. SSP $10 CMV $5 MB.

CUCKOO CLOCK WALL POMANDER 1981-82
Light brown wax with blue bird. SSP $9 CMV $5 MB.
GINGER BREAD JOYS POMANDER 1981-82
Pink and brown wax with gold hanging cords. Set of 2 SSP $6. CMV $4 set MB.

SURE START CAR KEY POMANDER 1981-82
Tan wax key. 3" long. SSP $4 CMV $2 MB.
PARASOL CLOSET POMANDER 1976-77
Lavender with cord & tassel. Came with Potpourri Fragrance wax chips. OSP $3. CMV $2. MB.

VINTAGE MOTOR CAR POMANDER 1981-82
Green box holds 6" wide antique car hanging pomander. SSP $10 CMV $3 MB.
TROPICAL SPLENDOR WINDOW POMANDER 1981-82
Parrot box holds parrot hanging pomander. Cord not included. SSP $10 CMV $3 MB.

FRAGRANT FLIGHT POMANDER 1980
Metal frame around soft plastic. Stain glass look. SSP $10 CMV $5 MB.
WILD GAME POMANDER 1980-81
3" long blue plastic, green cord. SSP $4 CMV $1 MB.

SANTA'S HELPERS POMANDER 1982-83
Wax elves, choice of girl in red and boy in green. SSP $7 CMV $4 each MB.

LACY GLOVES CLOSET POMANDER 1979-80
Lavender box holds Lavender plastic glove. It does not say Avon on it. Comes with packet of Garlandia wax chips. SSP $3 **CMV $2 MB.**

FLIRTATION FROG CERAMIC POMANDER 1980-82
3" high white ceramic frog, yellow and green trim. Made in Brazil. Comes with Fernerie wax chip refill. SSP $10 **CMV $6 MB.**

TRAFFIC STOPPER CAR POMANDER 1980-82
Small soft green plastic, yellow cord. SSP $3 **CMV $2 MB.**

PINE CONE CLUSTER POMANDER 1980-82
Small light brown wax with red satin ribbon. SSP $4 **CMV $2 MB.**

LAVENDER POMANDER 1967-69
Gold tassel on white, pink & gold plastic container. 4" high. Filled with lavender Fragrance tablet. OSP $5 **CMV $3 MB.**

POTPOURRI POMANDER 1970
Holder is yellow plastic & 4" high in shape & design as Lavender Pomander. OSP $5 **CMV $3 MB.**

SWEET CHERUBS CLOSET POMANDER 1977-78
Blue & white plastic with blue tassel. Came in Potpourri fragrance wax chips. OSP $5 **CMV $2 MB.**

WOODLAND CHARMERS MINI POMANDERS 1982-83
Small wax figurines. Came in Raccoons, Turtle & Rabbit, Skunk in Flower basket. SSP $7 each **CMV $4 each MB.**

FRESH FLIGHT CLOSET POMANDER 1979-80
Blue plastic bird holds Potpourri wax chips. Came in colorful box. SSP $4 **CMV $2 MB.**

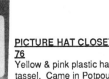

PICTURE HAT CLOSET POMANDER 1975-76
Yellow & pink plastic hat with yellow cord & tassel. Came in Potpourri fragrance. OSP $4 **CMV $2 MB.**

MERRY MESSENGER POMETTE 1984
Choice of three different small pomettes.
HAPPY BIRTHDAY MOUSE THANK YOU RABBIT KOALA BEAR
Each 1 1/2" to 2" high in display boxes. SSP $4 **CMV $2 each MB.**

CAT NAPPER CERAMIC POMANDER 1983-84
4" long ceramic cat in basket pomander. Comes with pack of Meadow Morn wax chips. SSP $13 **CMV $7 MB.**

NATURAL BLEND POTPOURRI 1983-84
Pink paper box holds dried flowers. SSP $10 **CMV $2 MB.**

LITTLEST BOO POMETTS 1983
1 3/4" high orange and white pumpkin and ghost pomander. SSP $3 **CMV $1 MB.**

PUPPY LUV POMETTE 1983
2 1/4" high wax dog with red heart. SSP $3 **CMV $1 MB.**

HEARTSCENT CLOSET POMANDER 1973-74
Wedgewood blue and white plastic heart with white tassel holds Potpourri scented chips. SSP $3. **CMV $3 MB.**

CAMEO CLOSET POMANDER 1980-82
4 1/2" long yellow plastic with white cord. Comes with wax chip Potpourri refill. Comes with wax chip Potpourri refill. SSP $5 CMV $3 MB.

MOON ROCK A BYE BABY POMANDER 1980-82
5" long yellow wax with blue hanging cord. SSP $7 CMV $3 MB.

CHRISTMAS SURPRISE FRAGRANCE ORNAMENT 1981
(Left) 3 x 3 inch tree ornament. Teddy Bear on one side & bells on box on the other side. SSP $3 CMV $2 MB.

HIDDEN SCENTS SACHET NUGGETS 1981
(Right) Box holds 3 small tulip shaped see thru fragranced flowers. SSP $5 CMV $2 MB.

WHISPER OF FLOWERS CLOSET POMANDER 1980
Small hat box type with green hanging cord & package of Garlandia Fragrance wax chips. SSP $4 CMV $2 MB.

WHISPER OF FLOWERS SACHET PILLOWS 1980
Flowered box holds 5 silk like sachet pillows. SSP $8 CMV $2 MB.

WISE EYES CLOSET POMANDER 1974-75
Brown plastic with yellow cord & tassel. Came with Fernerie fragranced wax chips. OSP $4 CMV $3 MB.

GIFT OF THE SEA POMANDER 1987
Pearl glazed porcelain sea shell. 5 1/4" long. DP $5.25 CMV $3 MB.

COUNTRY EGG BASKET POMANDER 1986
4 x 5 wicker basket has 3 fabric scented eggs. DP $5.50 CMV $3. MB.

MEN'S DECANTERS CERAMICS & FIGURINES

COLLECTORS:
All Containers are
Priced Empty

BO means.......... Bottle Only (empty)
CMV means........ Current Market Value (mint)
SSP means..........Special Selling Price
OSP means......... Original Selling Price
MB means.......... Mint and Boxed
DP means.......... Avon Rep Cost
This is used on all new products 1984 or newer.

BIG MACK 1973-75
6 oz. green glass with beige bed. Holds Oland or Windjammer After Shave. SSP $5 CMV $7 MB. $5 BO.

WINNEBAGO MOTOR HOME 1978-79
(Top) 5 oz. white painted over clear glass. Stick on trim decals. Holds Wild Country or Deep Woods After Shave. SSP $7 CMV $9.

STANLEY STEAMER 1978
(Bottom) Silver, 5 oz. silver paint over clear glass. Came in Tai Winds or Deep Woods After Shave. SSP $9 CMV $10 MB.

RED SENTINAL "FIRE TRUCK" 1978-79
4 piece decanter. Engine is 3 1/2 oz. clear glass painted red. Holds Wild Country or Deep Woods After Shave. Plastic hook and ladder center section and 6 oz. rear red plastic section holds talc. Comes with stick on decals. SSP $12 CMV $13 MB.

GREYHOUND BUS '31 1976-77
5 oz. blue painted over clear glass. Blue plastic front cap. White plastic roof will pop off. Came in Avon Spicy or Everest. SSP $6 CMV $6 BO. $8 MB.

EXTRA SPECIAL MALE 1977-79
(Left) 3 oz. blue glass, dark blue cap and white plastic roof. Separate American eagle and red striped stick on decals. Came in Deep Woods or Everest After Shave. SSP $4.44 **CMV $3.50 BO $5. MB.**

MUSTANG '64 1976-78
(Right) 2 oz. size blue glass and blue tail cap. Came in Spicy or Tai Winds. SSP $3. **CMV $3 . BO $5. MB.**

THE CAMPER 1972-74
5 oz. green glass truck with After Shave. 4 oz. Talc in beige plastic camper. Came in Deep Woods or Oland. SSP $8. **CMV $10. MB. $8. MB.**

1973 FORD RANGER PICK-UP 1978-79
5 oz. blue paint over clear glass, blue plastic bed cap. Stick on decals. Came in Wild Country or Deep woods. SSP $6 **CMV $6. BO. $8. MB.**

FERRARI '53' 1974-75
(Left) 2 oz. dark amber glass with plastic closure. Came in Wild Country After Shave or Avon Protein Hair Lotion for Men. OSP $3 **CMV $4. BO $5 MB.**

THUNDERBIRD '55 1974-75
(Right) 2 oz. blue glass with blue plastic closure. Came in Wild Country or Deep Woods After Shave. OSP $3 **CMV $5. BO $6 MB.**

TRIUMPH TR-3 '56 1975-76
(Left) 2 oz. blue-green glass with plastic cap. Came with Spicy or Wild Country After Shave. OSP $4 **CMV $4. BO. $6. MB.**

PORSCHE DECANTER '68 1976
(Right) 2 oz. amber glass with amber plastic cap. Holds Wild Country or Spicy After Shave. OSP $3 **CMV $5. BO $7 MB.**

GOLD CADILLAC 1969-73
(Left) 6 oz. gold paint over clear glass. Came in Oland & wild Country After Shave. OSP $6. **CMV $8. BO. mint, $10. MB.**

SILVER DUESENBERG 1970-72
(Right) 6 oz. silver paint over clear glass. Came in Oland & Wild Country After Shave. OSP $6. **CMV $8 BO. mint, $10 MB.**

SURE WINNER RACING CAR 1972-75
(Left) 5.5 oz. blue glass with blue cap. Came in Sure Winner Bracing Lotion and Wild Country. OSP $5 **CMV $5. MB. $3. BO.**

JAGUAR CAR DECANTER 1973-76
5 oz. jade green glass with green plastic trunk over cap. Holds Deep Woods or Wild Country After Shave. SSP $5 **CMV $6. MB. $5. BO.**

PIERCE ARROW '33 1975-77
(Left) 5 oz. dark blue sprayed glass with beige plastic cap. Came in Wild Country or Deep Woods After Shave. OSP $6 **CMV $6. BO $7 MB.**

STOCK CAR RACER 1974-75
(Right) 5 oz. blue glass with blue plastic cap. Holds Wild Country After Shave or Electric Pre-Shave Lotion. OSP $6 **CMV $6. BO $7. MB.**

STUDEBAKER '51 1975-76
(Left) 2 oz. blue glass with blue plastic parts. Holds Avon Spicy or Wild Country. OSP $2.50 **CMV $4. BO. $5 MB.**

CORVETTE STINGRAY '65 1975
(Right) 2 oz. green glass with green plastic cap. Holds Wild Country, Deep Woods or Avon Spicy After Shave. OSP $3 **CMV $5. BO. $7 MB.**

'36 FORD 1976-77
5 oz. orange paint over clear glass. Plastic stick on hub caps and grill. Came in Tai Winds or Oland. SSP $5. **CMV $6. BO. $7. MB.**

CHRYSLER TOWN & COUNTRY '48 1976
4.25 oz. off red painted over clear glass. Beige plastic top. Came in Everest or Wild COuntry. SSP $5 **CMV $7. BO. $8. MB.**

ROLLS ROYCE 1972-75
6 oz. beige painted over glass with dark brown and silver plastic parts. Came in Deep Woods or Tai Winds After Shave. SSP $7. CMV $8. BO. $9. MB.

BUGATTI '27 1974-75
6.5 oz. black glass with chrome colored plastic trim. Came in Wild Country or Deep Woods Cologne or After Shave. OSP $6. CMV $10. - $12. MB.

'37 CORD 1974-76
7 oz. yellow painted with yellow plastic cap and black plastic top. Came in Tai Winds or Wild Country After Shave. SSP $7. CMV $8. MB. $6. BO.

JEEP RENEGADE 1981-82
3 oz. black glass, stick on decals. Tan plastic top. Black cap. Sure Winner Bracing Lotion or Trazerra Cologne. SSP $9. CMV $9. MB. $7. BO.

VOLKSWAGON RABBIT 1980-82
3 oz. blue glass and blue plastic cap. Comes with silver stick on windows and hub caps. Choice of Light Musk Cologne or Sure Winner Bracing Lotion. SSP $8. CMV $6. MB. $5. BO.

BUICK SKYLARK '53 1979-80
(Left) 4 oz. emerald green glass and cap. Stick on decals. Came in Clint or Everest After Shave. SSP $9. CMV $8. MB. $7. BO.
VANTASTIC 1979-80
(Right) 5 oz. burgandy color galss. Stick on decals. Comes in Wild Country or Everest After Shave. SSP $6. CMV $6. MB. $5. BO.

BLUE VOLKSWAGON 1973-74
(left) 4 oz. light blue painted with plastic cap. Holds Oland or Windjammer After Shave. SSP $3. CMV $5. BO. $7. MB.
BLACK VOLKSWAGON 1970-72
(Right) 4 oz. black glass with black plastic cap. Holds Wild Country, Spicy or Electric Pre-Shave Lotion. SSP $2. CMV $7. MB. $5. BO.
RED VOLKSWAGON 1972
(Center) 4 oz. painted red with red cap. Came in Oland or Wild Country After Shave or Sports Rally Bracing Lotion. SSP $3. CMV $5. BO. $7. MB.

MINI-BIKE 1972-73
(Left) 4 oz. light amber glass coated over clear glass with light amber plastic wheel and silver handlebars with yellow grips. Came in Wild Country After Shave, Sure Winner Bracing Lotion, or Protein Hair Lotion for Men. SSP $5. CMV $6. MB. $4. BO.
ROAD RUNNER DECANTER 1973-74
(Right) 5.5 oz. blue glass with blue plastic front wheel, silver handle bars with black grips. Holds Sure Winner Bracing Lotion or Wild Country After Shave. SSP. $6. CMV $6. MB. $4. BO.

SUPER CYCLE 1971-72
(Left) 4 oz. gray glass. Came in Wild Country, Island Lime or Sports Rally Bracing Lotion. SSP $5. CMV $7. MB. $5. BO.
SUPER CYCLE II 1974-75
(Right) Issued in blue glass. Came in Wild Country and Spicy After Shave. SSP $5. CMV $5. BO. $7. MB.

AVON OPEN GOLF CART 1972-75
(Left) 5 1/2" long, green glass bottle with green plastic front end, red plastic golf bags. Holds 5 oz. Wild Country or Windjammer After Shave. Came in light or darker green glass. OSP $6. CMV $7. MB. $6. BO.
SNOWMOBILE 1974-75
(Right) 4 oz. blue glass with yellow plastic front and back runners. Came in Oland or Windjammer After Shave. SSP $6. CMV $6. BO. $7. MB.

HARVESTER TRACTOR 1973-75
5.5 oz. amber glass with amber plastic front. Holds Wild Country After Shave or Protein Hair Lotion for men. OSP $5. **CMV $10. BO.** $14. **MB.**

'55 CHEVY 1975-76
5 oz. sprayed green glass with white plastic parts. Holds Wild Country or Electric Pre-Shave Lotion. SSP $5. **CMV $7. BO. $8. MB.**

TOURING T SILVER 1978
6 oz. silver plated over clear glass. May, 1978 on bottom. Came in Deep Woods or Everest. SSP $8. **CMV $7. BO. $8. MB.**

STERLING SIX SILVER 1978
7 oz. plated over clear glass. Came in Tai Winds or Deep Woods After Shave. May 1978 on Bottom. SSP $8. **CMV $7. BO. $8. MB.**

1914 STUTZ BEARCAT 1974-77
(Left) 6 oz. red painted with black plastic seats and cap. Came in Oland or Blend 7 After Shave. SSP $6. **CMV $6. MB. $5. BO.**

1936 MG DECANTER 1974-75
(Right) 5 oz. red painted with red plastic cap and white plastic top. Came in Avon Blend 7, Tai Winds or Wild Country After Shave. SSP $4. **CMV $4. BO. $5. MB.**

COVERED WAGON 1970-71
6 oz.. 4 1/2" long. Dark amber glass bottom, white painted top and gold cap. Came in Spicy and Wild Country After Shave. OSP $5. **CMV $5. MB. $7.**

SIDE WHEELER 1971-72
5 oz. dark amber glass, black plastic stacks, silver cap, brown label. Came in Wild Country and Spicy After Shave. OSP $6. **CMV $3. BO. $5. MB.** Reissued 1976 in Tai Winds gold cap, white label, same CMV.

ARMY JEEP 1974-75
4 oz. olive drab green with plastic closure. Came with Wild Country or Avon Spicy After Shave. OSP $5. **CMV $5. BO. $7. MB.**

GOLDEN ROCKET 0-2-2 1974-76
(Right) 6 oz. smokey gold over clear glass with gold plastic cap. Came in Tai Winds or Wild Country After Shave. OSP $7. **CMV $7. MB. $6. BO.** Factory reject from factory is indented sides and gold coated. **CMV $20.**

FIRST VOLUNTEER 1971-72
6 oz. gold coated over clear glass. Oland or Tai Winds Cologne. OSP $8.50. **CMV $9. BO. $11. MB.**

MAXWELL '23 DECANTER 1972-74
6 oz. green glass with beige plastic top and trunk over cap. Came in Deep Woods or Tribute Cologne or After Shave. SSP $5. **CMV $6. $8. MB.**

1910 FIRE FIGHTER 1975
6 oz. painted over glass with red plastic back. Came in Wild Country or Tai Winds After Shave. OSP $6. **CMV $7. MB. $5. BO.**

COUNTRY VENDOR 1973
5 oz. brown glass with brown plastic top, has picture of fruits and vegetables on side. Holds Wild Country or Avon Spicy After Shave. SSP $7. **CMV $8. MB. $7. BO.**

1926 CHECKER CAB 1977-78
5 oz. yellow painted over clear glass. Black plastic trunk cap and top. Stick on decal hub caps, bumper and checker design. Came in Everest or Wild Country. SSP $6. **CMV $7. BO. $7. MB.**

STERLING SIX 1968-70
7 oz. came in 4 different shades of amber glass, black tire cap, rough top roof. Came in Spicy, Tribute, Leather After Shave. OSP $4. **CMV $6. BO. $8. MB.** Smooth top in very light amber glass. **CMV $45.**

STERLING SIX II 1973-74
7 oz. green glass with white tire cap. Came in Wild Country or Tai Winds After Shave. SSP. $4. **CMV $5. BO. $7. MB.**

STRAIGHT 8 1969-71
(Left) 5 oz. dark green glass with black trunk cap. No. 8 on hoood. Came in Wild Country, Windjammer, and Island Lime After Shave. Label says "Avon for Men" OSP $3.50. **CMV $7 MB. $5 BO.**

STRAIGHT 8 1973-75
(Left) 5 oz. green glass. Came in Wild Country and Island Lime After Shave. Label says Avon-Keep out of reach of children. OSP $3.50 **CMV $4. BO. $5. BO.**

DUNE BUGGY 1971-73
(Right) 5 oz. blue glass, silver motor cap. Came in Spicy After Shave, Liquid Hair Lotion and Sports Rally Bracing Lotion. OSP $5. **CMV $5. MB. $6.**

TOURING T 1969-70
(Left) 6 1/2" long, 6 oz. black glass with black plastic top and tire cap. Came in Excalibur or Tribute After Shave. OSP $6. **CMV $6. BO. $7. MB.**

MODEL A 1972-74
(Right) 4 oz. yellow painted over clear glass, yellow cap. Holds Wild Country or Leather After Shave. SSP $4. **CMV $5. BO. $6. MB.**

ELECTRIC CHARGER 1970-72
(Left) 5 oz. black glass with red cap and red side decals. Came in Spicy, Leather or Wild Country After Shave. OSP $4. **CMV $5. BO. $7. MB.**

STAGE COACH 1970-77
(Right) 5 oz. dark amber glass with gold cap. Came in Wild Country, Tai Winds or Oland After Shave. 1977 issue has "R" on bottom for reissue, hard to find silver cap. **CMV $7 for reissue.** OSP $5. **CMV $5. BO. $7. MB.**

VOLKSWAGON BUS 1975-76
(Left) 5 oz. red painted glass with silver gray motorcycle plastic closure. Set of 4 "decorate-it-yourself" labels come with each decanter. Came with Tai Winds After Shave or Sure Winner Bracing Lotion. OSP $5. **CMV $6. BO, $8. MB.**

THE THOMAS FLYER 1908 1974-75
(Right) 6 oz. white painted glass with red and blue plastic parts with white tire cap on back. Came in Wild Country or Oland After Shave. OSP $6. **CMV $6. BO, $7. MB.**

STATION WAGON 1971-73
6 oz. green glass car with tan plastic top. Came in Wild Country or Tai Winds After Shave. OSP $6. **CMV $7. BO, $9. MB.**

STANLEY STEAMER 1971-72
5 oz. blue glass bottle with black plastic seats and tire cap. Came in Wild Country or Windjammer After Shave. OSP $5. **CMV $6. BO, $8. MB.**

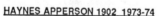

HAYNES APPERSON 1902 1973-74
4.5 oz. green glass with green plastic front over cap. Has silver tiller steering rod. Holds Avon Blend 7 or Tai Winds After Shave. SSP $5. **CMV $7. MB, $5. BO.**

REO DEPOT WAGON 1972-73
5" long, 5 oz. amber glass with black plastic top and cap. Holds Tai Winds and Oland After Shave Lotion. OSP $6. **CMV $6. MB, $8.**

PACKARD ROADSTER 1970-72
6 oz. light amber glass and matching plastic rumble seat cap. Came in Oland and Leather Cologne. 6 1/2" long. OSP $6. **CMV $6. MB, $8.**

HIGHWAY KING 1977-79
4 oz. green glass bottle with white plastic center connection piece and rear section is 6.5 oz. white plastic talc bottle. Came in Wild Country or Everest. OSP $12.50. **CMV $8. BO, $9. MB.**

CEMENT MIXER 1979-80
3 piece bottle. Front section is dark amber glass. Comes in Wild Country or Everest After Shave. Center plastic section connects to 6 oz. pale yellow plastic rear section bottle. Holds talc. Has stick on decals. SSP $12. **CMV $11. BO., $13. MB.**

BIG RIG 1975-76
3.5 oz. blue glass cab with 6 oz. white & blue plastic trailer. Cab holds After Shave, trailer holds Talc in Wild Country or Deep Woods. OSP $10. **CMV $9. BO, $10. MB.**

RAINBOW TROUT 1973-74
(Left) Plastic head over cap. Holds Deep Woods or Tai Winds. SSP $5. **CMV $6. MB, $5. BO.**
SEA TROPHY 1972
(Right) 5.5 oz. lt. blue with plastic blue head over cap. Came in Wild Country or Windjammer After Shave. SSP $5. **CMV $7. BO, $9. MB.**

TRAIN 1876 CENTENNIAL EXPRESS DECANTER 1978-86
5.5 oz. dark green glass with stick on trim decals. Holds Wild Country or Everest After Shave. SSP $6. **CMV $4. BO, $6. MB.** Reissues 1986.

CANNONBALL EXPRESS 4-6-0 1976-77
3.25 oz. black glass, black cap. Came in Deep Woods or Wild Country or After Shave. SSP $6. CMV $5. BO, $6. MB.

AMERICAN SCHOONER 1972-73
4.5 oz. blue glass with blue plastic end over cap. Some are blue painted over clear glass. Came in Oland or Spicy After Shave. SSP $5. **CMV $6. MB, $5. BO.**

CABLE CAR DECANTER 1974-75
4 oz. green painted over clear glass has plastic green and white top. Came in Wild Country or Avon Leather. SSP $7. **CMV $6. BO, $8. MB.**

GENERAL 4-4-0 1971-72
5 1/2 oz. dark blue glass and cap. Came in Tai Winds or Wild Country After Shave. OSP $7.50. **CMV $7. MB, $9.**

BLOOD HOUND PIPE 1976
5 oz. lt. tan paint over clear glass, brown & silver cap. Came in Wild Country or Deep Woods After Shave. OSP $7. **CMV $7. MB, $6. BO.**
CHIEF PONTIAC CAR ORNAMENT CLASSIC 1976
4 oz. black ribbed glass with silver Indian. Came in Tai Winds or Deep Woods After Shave. OSP $8. **CMV $6. BO, $7. MB.**

ATLANTIC 4-4-2 DECANTER 1973-75
5 oz. silver over clear glass with silver plastic parts. Holds Deep Woods or Leather After Shave or Cologne. SSP $8. **CMV $8. MB, $6. BO.**

GONE FISHING DECANTER 1973-74
5 oz. lt. blue boat with white plastic man, yellow fishing rod. Came in Tai Winds or Spicy. SSP $6. **CMV $7. MB, $6. BO.**

CAPTAINS PRIDE 1970
6 oz. bottle with ship decal, tan cap & blue neck label. Sits on black plastic stand. Came in Oland & Windjammer After Shave. OSP $5. **CMV $5. BO, $7. MB.**

AMERICAN EAGLE PIPE 1974-75
5 oz. dark amber glass with gold plastic top & black handle. Holds Wild Country or Tai Winds Cologne. OSP $5. **CMV $6. MB, $5. BO.**

CALABASH PIPE 1974-75
3 oz. yellow gold sprayed glass with yellow gold plastic cap & black plastic stand. Holds Wild Country or Deep Woods After Shave. OSP $5. **CMV $6. MB, $5. BO.**

BULL DOG PIPE 1972-73
6 oz. cream colored milk glass with black stem. Came in Wild Country or Oland After Shave or Cologne. SSP $4. **CMV $6. BO, $7. MB.**

DUTCH PIPE 1973-74
2 oz. white milk glass, blue design, silver handle & cap. Came in Tribute or Tai Winds Cologne. SSP $7. **CMV $7. BO, $9. MB.**

VIKING DISCOVERER 1977-79
4 oz. blue-green glass & matching plastic cap. Red & white metal sail. Black plastic sail post. Came in Wild Country or Everest. SSP $9. **CMV $7. BO, $8. MB.**

UNCLE SAM PIPE 1975-76
3 oz. white opal glass with blue band & blue plastic stem. Holds Wild Country or Deep Woods After Shave. OSP $5. **CMV $6. MB, $5. BO.**

PONY EXPRESS RIDER PIPE 1975-76
3 oz. white milk glass with black plastic stem. Holds Wild Country or Tai Winds Cologne. OSP $5. **CMV $6. MB, $5. BO.**

CORNCOB PIPE 1974-75
3 oz. amber glass with black plastic stem. Holds Wild Country or Avon Spicy. OSP $3. **CMV $4. BO, $5. MB.**

PIPE FULL DECANTER 1971-72
2 oz. brown glass with black stem. Holds Spicy, Oland, Tai Winds or Excalibur After Shave. SSP $2. **CMV $5. MB, $4. BO.**

PIPE FULL DECANTER 1972-74
2 oz. lt. green glass with brown plastic stem. Holds Tai Winds or Spicy After Shave. SSP $2. **CMV $4. BO, $5. MB.**

PIPE DREAM 1967
6 oz. dark amber glass, black cap, tan plastic base. Came in Spicy, Tribute & Leather After Shave. OSP $5. **CMV $15. BO, $20. MB.**

PIPE DREAM CLEAR TEST 1967
6 oz. clear glass factory test bottle. Very rare. **CMV $250.**

WILD MUSTANG PIPE 1976-77
3 oz. white paint over clear glass. Holds Wild Country or Deep Woods cologne. SSP $5. **CMV $6. MB, $5. BO.**

PHILADELPHIA DERRINGER 1980-82
2 oz. dark amber glass with gray stick on parts & gold trim. Came in Light Musk or Brisk Spice After Shave. SSP $10. **CMV $10. MB, $9. BO.**

COLLECTOR'S PIPE 1973-74
3 oz. brown glass with black stem. Holds Deep Woods or Windjammer After Shave or Cologne. SSP $3. **CMV $5. MB, $4. BO.**

SHORT PONY DECANTER 1968-69
(Right) 4 oz. green glass, gold cap. Came in Wild Country, Windjammer, Spicy, Leather or Electric Pre-Shave. OSP $3.50. **CMV $4. BO, $5. MB.**
SHORT PONY, FOREIGN, DECANTER 1968-69
Gold cap, greenish amber color. $7. Bright green from Germany. **CMV $15. MB.**

BLUNDERBUSS PISTOL 1780 1976
(Top) 12 1/2" long, 5.5 oz. dark amber glass, gold cap & plastic trigger. Came in Everest & Wild Country. OSP $12. **CMV $10. MB, $9. BO.**
THOMAS JEFFERSON HAND GUN 1978-79
(Bottom) 10" long, 2.5 oz. dark amber glass with gold & silver plastic cap. Holds Deep Woods or Everest cologne. SSP $9. **CMV $9. MB, $8. BO.**

PONY POST MINIATURE 1973-74
1.5 oz. clear glass with gold cap & ring. Holds Oland or Spicy After Shave. OSP $3. **CMV $3. BO, $4. MB.**
PONY POST 1972-73
5 oz. bronze paint over clear glass with bronze cap & nose ring. Holds Tai Winds or Leather After Shave. OSP $5. **CMV $6. BO, $7. MB.**
PONY POST "TALL" 1966-67
8 oz. green glass with gold cap & nose ring. Holds Island Lime, Tribute or Leather After Shave. OSP $4. **CMV $13. MB, $7. BO.**

TWENTY PACES 1967-69
3 oz. each, 10" long. Gold paint over clear glass, gold cap. Red paper labels on end of barrel. Came in All Purpose Cologne, Wild Country & Leather After Shave. OSP $11.95. **CMV brown box lined with red $40, black lined box $120, blue lined box $160. Very rare gun with raised sight did not break off in glass mold. CMV $100. Raised sight gun only. Regular issue guns $10. each mint.**

LONGHORN STEER 1975-76
5 oz. dark amber glass with amber plastic head, ivory colored horns. Holds Wild Country or Tai Winds After Shave. OSP $6. **CMV $6. BO, $7. MB.**

PEPPERBOX PISTOL 1850
(Top) 3 oz. silver plated over clear glass barrel bottle with gold and brown plastic handle cap. Came in Everest or Tai Winds. SSP $7. **CMV $8. MB, $6. BO.**
PEPPERBOX PISTOL 1982-83
Reissued in gold tone instead of silver came in Clint and Wild Country. SSP $11. **CMV $8. MB.**
DERRINGER 1977
(Bottom) 2 oz. gold plated over amber glass. Came in Deep Woods or Wild Country. SSP $6. **CMV $6. BO, $7. MB.**

GAS PUMP - REMEMBER WHEN DE-CANTER 1979-80
4 oz. clear glass painted yellow, white top, yellow cap. Came in Light Musk or Cool Sage. SSP $6. **CMV $6. MB, $5. BO.**
VOLCANIC REPEATING PISTOL DE-CANTER 1979-80
2 oz. silver coated over clear glass. Silver & pearl plastic handle. Holds Wild Country or Brisk Spice Cologne. SSP $10. **CMV $9. BO, $10. MB.**

DUELING PISTOL 1760 1973-74
(Top) 4 oz. brown glass with silver clamp on parts, silver cap. Holds Deep Woods or Tai Winds After Shave. SSP $8. CMV $8. MB, $7. BO.

DUELING PISTOL II 1975
Same as above but black glass & gold plastic parts. Came in Wild Country or Tai Winds. SSP $8. CMV $8. BO, $9. MB.

COLT REVOLVER 1851 1975-76
(Bottom) 3 oz. amber glass with silver plastic barrel. Holds Wild Country or Deep Woods After Shave. OSP $9. CMV $9. MB, $8. BO.

AT POINT DECANTER 1973-74
5 oz. reddish brown glass with reddish brown plastic head. Came in Deep Woods or Tribute. SSP $4. CMV $5. MB, $4. BO.

SNOOPY SURPRISE 1969-71
5 oz., 5 1/2" high. White glass with blue or yellow hat & black ears. Came in Wild Country, Excalibur After Shave & Sports Rally Bracing Lotion. OSP $4. CMV $5., $6. MB.

PHEASANT 1972-74
5 oz. brown glass with green plastic head. Holds Oland or Leather After Shave. OSP $6. CMV $8. MB, $7. BO.

CANADA GOOSE 1973-74
5 oz. brown glass with black plastic head. Holds Deep Woods, Wild Country or Everest After Shave or Cologne. OSP $6. CMV $6. BO, $8. MB. Reissued in 1976 in smaller box in After Shave only. Same CMV.

OLD FAITHFUL 1972-73
5 oz. brown glass with brown plastic head & gold keg. Holds Wild Country or Spicy After Shave. SSP $5. CMV $6. BO, $8. MB. Small German St. Bernard on right (silver barrel). CMV $12.

FAITHFUL LADDIE 1977-79
4 oz. light amber glass & amber head cap. Came in Wild Country or Deep Woods. SSP $4.99. CMV $5. MB, $4. BO.

KODIAK BEAR 1977
6 oz. dark amber glass & head. Came in Wild Country or Deep Woods. SSP $5. CMV $4. BO, $5. MB.

PONY EXPRESS 1971-72
5 oz. brown glass with copper colored man on cap. Came in Avon Leather or Wild Country After Shave. SSP $4. CMV $7. MB, $6. BO.

BUCKING BRONCO 1971-72
6 oz. dark amber glass horse with bronze plastic cowboy cap. Came in Oland or Excalibur. OSP $6. CMV $8. MB, $7. BO.

MAJESTIC ELEPHANT 1977
5.5 oz. gray painted over clear glass. Gray head cap. Came in Wild Country or Deep Woods. SSP $9. CMV $7. BO, $9. MB.

PHEASANT DECANTER 1977
Same bottle as 1972-74 issue only came in Deep Woods or Wild Country and box is smaller than early issue. SSP $6. CMV $8. MB, $7. BO.

WILDERNESS CLASSIC 1976-77
6 oz. silver plated over clear glass. Silver plastic head. Came in Sweet Honesty or Deep Woods. SSP $9. CMV $11. MB, $10. BO.

NOBLE PRINCE 1975-77
4 oz. brown glass with plastic head. Holds Wild Country After Shave or Electric Pre-Shave Lotion. OSP $3.25 CMV $5 MB. $4 BO.

CLASSIC LION 1973-75
8 oz. green glass with green plastic head. Holds Wild Country, Tribute After Shave or Deep Woods Emollient After Shave. OSP $6 CMV $7 MB. $6 BO.

ALASKAN MOOSE 1974-75
8 oz. amber glass with cream colored plastic antlers. Holds Deep Woods or Wild COuntry After Shave. OSP $7. CMV $7. BO. $9. MB.

TEN-POINT DUCK 1973-74
6 oz. reddish brown glass with reddish brown plastic head & gold antlers. Holds Wild Country or Leather After Shave. OSP $7. CMV $8. MB. $7. BO.

DUCK AFTER SHAVE 1971
3 oz. glass bottles with gold caps & ducks painted on sides. Came in Collector's Organizer Set only in Tai Winds & Wild Country After Shave. CMV $4. each.

AMERICAN EAGLE 1971-72
6" high, dark amber glass with silver eagle head. Holds 5 oz. Oland or Windjammer After Shave. OSP $5. CMV $6. MB. $5. BO.
1973-75
Eagle is black glass with dark gold ead. CMV $6. BO. $7. MB.

CAPTAIN'S CHOICE 1964-65
(Right) 8 oz. green glass with green paper label, gold cap. Came in Spicy & Original After Shave Lotion, Electric Pre-Shave Lotion, Spicy After Shower Cologne for Men & Vigorate After Shave Lotion. OSP $2.50 CMV $8. $11. MB.

SPORT OF KINGS DECANTER 1975
5 oz. amber glass with plastic head. Holds Wild Country, Avon Spicy or Avon Leather After Shave. OSP $5 CMV $6. MB. $5. BO.

AMERICAN BUFFALO 1975-76
5 oz. amber glass with amber plastic head & ivory colored horns. Holds Wild Country or Deep Woods After Shave. OSP $6. CMV $6. BO. $7. MB.

MALLARD DUCK 1967-68
6 oz. green glass, silver head. Came in Spicy, Tribute, Blue Blazer, Windjammer After Shave. OSP $5. CMV $7. BO. $11. MB.

MALLARD-IN-FLIGHT 1974-76
5 oz. amber glass with green plastic head. Holds Wild Country or Tai Winds Cologne or After Shave. OSP $6. CMV $7. MB. $6. BO.

WESTERN BOOT 1973-75
5 oz. dark amber glass bottle, silver cap & clamp on spurs. Came in Wild Country or Leather. SSP $4. CMV $5. MB. $4. BO.

WILD TURKEY 1974-76
6 oz. amber glass with silver & red plastic head. Holds Wild Country or Deep Woods After Shave. OSP $5. CMV $6. BO. $7. MB.

QUAIL DECANTER 1973-75
5.5 oz. brown glass, gold cap. Came in Avon Blend 7, Deep Woods or Wild Country After Shave. OSP $6. CMV $7. MB. $6. BO.

REVOLUTIONARY CANNON 1975-76
2 oz. bronze spray over glass with plastic cap. Holds Avon Spicy or Avon Blend 7 After Shave. OSP $4. CMV $5. MB. $4. BO.

HOMESTEAD DECANTER 1973-74
4 oz. brown glass with gray plastic chimney over cap. Holds Wild Country After Shave or Electric Pre-Shave. OSP $3. CMV $5. MB. $4. BO.

BIG GAME RHINO 1972-73
4 oz. green glass with green plastic head over cap. Came in Spicy or Tai Winds After Shave. SSP $4. **CMV $5. BO. $6. MB.**
BLACKSMITH'S ANVIL 1972-73
4 oz. black glass with silver cap. Came in Deep Woods or Avon Leather After Shave. SSP $4. **CMV $5. MB. $4. BO.**

CAPITOL DECANTER 1976-77
4.5 oz. white milk glass with white cap & gold tip. Came in Spicy or Wild Country After Shave. OSP $4. **CMV $5. MB. $4. BO.**
CAPITOL DECANTER 1970-72
5 oz. amber glass or clear glass coated amber, gold cap. Came in Leather & Tribute After Shave. OSP $5. **CMV $8. MB. $6. BO.**

WISE CHOICE OWL 1969-70
4 oz. silver top, light amber bottom. Came in Excalibur or Leather After Shave. OSP $4. **CMV $5. MB. $7.**
RADIO 1972-73
5" high dark amber glass with gold cap & paper dial on front. Holds 5 oz. liquid Hair Lotion, Wild Country or Spicy After Shave. OSP $4. **CMV $5. MB. $6.**

KING PIN 1969-70
(Left) 4 oz. 6 1/2" high. White glass & cap, red label. Came in Wild Country & Bravo After Shave. OSP $3. **CMV $5. MB. $4. BO.**
STRIKE DECANTER 1978-79
(Right) 4 oz. white milk glass, white cap. Red painted on AMF designs. Came in Sweet Honesty of Wild Country. SSP $3. **CMV $4. MB. $3. BO.**

RAM'S HEAD 1975-76
5 oz. white opal glass on brown plastic base. Holds Wild Country or Avon Blend 7 After Shave. OSP $5. **CMV $5 MB. $4 BO.**
MINUTEMAN 1975-76
4 oz. white opal glass with plastic top. Holds Wild Country or Tai Winds After Shave. OSP $7. **CMV $7. BO. $8. MB.**

LONG DRIVE 1973-75
4 oz. brown glass with black cap. Holds Deep Woods After Shave or Electric Pre-Shave Lotion. SSP $3. **CMV $4 MB. $3. BO.**
TEE-OFF DECANTER 1973-75
3 oz. white golf ball on a plastic yellow tee & fits into a green plastic green. Holds Protein Hair Lotion for Men. SSP $3. **CMV $4. MB. $3. BO.**

BOOT "SILVER TOP" 1965-66
8 oz. amber glass, silver cap with hook on cap. Came in Leather All Purpose Lotion for Men. OSP $5. **CMV $5. $7. MB.**
BOOT "GOLD TOP" 1966-71
8 oz. amber glass with hook on cap. Came in Leather All purpose Cologne for Men. OSP $5. **CMV $3. MB. $4.** Gold top boot with no hook on cap is 1971-72 with Leather Cologne. OSP $5. **CMV $3. BO. $4. MB.**
BOOT SPRAY COLOGNE 1967-70
3 oz. tan plastic coated with black cap. Came in Leather All Purpose Cologne in early issues. **CMV $6. MB. & Leather Cologne Spray in later issues. OSP $4. CMV $4 MB. $5.**

OPENING PLAY 1968-69
6 oz. each, 4" high. Gold caps, white plastic face guards. Came in Sports Rally Bracing Lotion, Spicy & Wild Country After Shave. OSP each $4. Shiny gold over blue glass was issued one campaign only, on last campaign Open Play was sold. **CMV Shiny gold $25. BO $30. Dull gold over blue glass with blue stripe CMV $10, $12 MB. Dull gold over blue glass, no stripe, CMV $14 BO. $16. MB.**

MARINE BINOCULARS 1973-74
Black over clear glass with gold caps. One side holds 4 oz. Tai Winds or Tribute Cologne, other side holds 4 oz. Tai Winds or Tribute After Shave. SSP $8. **CMV $9. MB. $8.**

SURE WINNER BASEBALL 1973-74
White ball with dark blue lettering, blue blue base contains Liquid Hair Trainer. SSP $2. **CMV $3.50 MB. $2. BO.**

FIRST DOWN 1970
5 oz. brown glass, white plastic base. Came in Wild Country or Sports Rally Bracing Lotion. OSP $4. **CMV $6. MB. $5. BO.**

FIRST DOWN 1973-74
5 oz. brown glass, white base. Came in Deep Woods & Sure Winner Bracing Lotion. SSP $3. **CMV $5. MB. $4. BO.**

THEODORE ROOSEVELT 1975-76
(Left) 6 oz. white paint over clear glass. Came in Wild Country or Tai Winds After Shave. OSP $9. **CMV $7. BO. $9. MB.**

THOMAS JEFFERSON 1977-78
(Right) 5 oz. white paint over clear glass. White head cap. Came in Wild Country or Everest After Shave. SSP $8. **CMV $6. BO. $8. MB.**

PASS PLAY 1973-75
5 oz. blue glass with white soft plastic top over cap. Came in Sure Winner Bracing Lotion or Wild Country After shave. OSP $5. **CMV $7. BO. $8. MB.**

PERFECT DRIVE 1975-76
4 oz. green glass with white plastic top over cap. Holds Avon Spicy After Shave or Avon Protein Hair/Scalp Conditioner. OSP $6. **CMV $7. BO. $8. MB.**

PRESIDENT WASHINGTON 1974-76
6 oz. white spray over clear glass, white plastic head. Holds Wild Country or Tai Winds After Shave. 1976 came in Deep Woods or Tai Winds After Shave. OSP $6. **CMV $6. BO. $7. MB.**

PRESIDENT LINCOLN 1973
6 oz. white spray over clear glass, white plastic head. Holds Wild Country or Tai Winds After Shave. OSP $5. **CMV $9. BO. $12. MB.**

BENJAMIN FRANKLIN 1974-76
6 oz. white spray over clear glass, white plastic head. Holds Wild Country or Tai Winds After Shave. OSP $6. **CMV $6. BO. $7. MB.**

PRESIDENT LINCOLN BRONZE 1979
6 oz. bronze tone over clear glass. Dated 1979 on bottom. Holds Deep Woods or Everest After Shave. SSP $11 **CMV $8 MB.**

PRESIDENT WASHINGTON BRONZE 1979
6 oz. bronze tone over clear glass. Dated 1979 on bottom. Holds Wild Country or Tai Winds After Shave. SSP $11 **CMV $8 MB.**

WASHINGTON BOTTLE 1970-72
5 1/2" high, 4 oz. bottle with gold eagle cap. Holds Spicy or Tribute After Shave. OSP $3.50 **CMV $4. MB. $3. BO.**

LINCOLN BOTTLE 1971-72
5 1/2" high, 4 oz. bottle with gold eagle cap. Holds Wild Country or Leather After Shave. OSP $3.50 **CMV $4. MB. $3. BO.**

CHESS PIECE "BROWN" (THE ORIGINAL SET)
3 oz. dark amber glass with silver toned tops. OSP $4. each.

SMART MOVE 1971-72
1973-78 Tribune & Oland Cologne. **CMV $8.** Smart move came in Wild Country After Shave or Protein Hair/Scalp Conditioner. **CMV $4. MB.**

THE KING 1972-73
Came in Tai Winds or Oland After Shave. **CMV $8. MB.**

1973-78
The King came in Wild Country or Oland. **CMV $4 MB.**

THE QUEEN 1973-74
Came in Tai Winds or Oland After Shave. **CMV $7. MB.**

1974-78
The Queen came in Wild Country or Deep Woods After Shave. **CMV $4 MB.**

THE ROOK 1973-74
Came in Oland & Spicy After Shave. **CMV $7. MB.**

1974-78
The rook came in Wild Country, Avon Blend 7 or Avon Protein Hair Lotion for Men. **CMV $4. MB.**

THE BISHOP 1974-78
Came in Wild Country, Avon Blend 7 or Avon Protein Hair Lotion for Men. **CMV $4 MB.**

THE PAWN 1974-78
Came in Wild Country, Oland or Electric Pre-Shave Lotion. **CMV $6. BO. $8. MB. (Pieces needed for one side are 2 Smart Moves, 1 King, 1 Queen, 2 Rooks, 2 Bishops, 8 Pawns.) Early issues Chess Pieces do not have to have name on label.**

COLLECTOR'S STEIN 1976-79
Hand made ceramic blue stein. Made in Brazil and numbered on botom. Came with 8 oz. plastic bottle of Everest or Wild Country. SSP $25. **CMV $35. MB. $30 BO. stein only.**

CHESS PIECE DECANTER (THE OPPOS-ING SET)
3 oz. silver over clear or amber glass with amber plastic tips. OSP $3. CMV $3. BO. $4. MB. Pawns CMV $6. BO. $8. MB. Silver over clear are hard to find.
SMART MOVE II 1975-78
Came in Wild Country After Shave, Avon Protein Hair Lotion or Avon Protein Hair/Scalp Conditioner for Men.
THE KING II 1975-78
Came in Avon Spicy After Shave or Avon Protein Hair Lotion.
THE QUEEN II 1975-78
Came in Avon Spicy After Shave or Avon Protein Hair/Scalp Conditioner.
THE ROOK II 1975-78
Came in Wild Country After Shave or Protein Hair Lotion for Men.
THE BISHOP II 1975-78
Came in Avon Spicy After Shave or Avon Protein Hair Lotion for Men. CMV $5. MB $4. BO.
THE PAWN II 1975-78
Came in Avon Spicy After Shave or Avon Protein Hair/Scalp Conditioner for Men.
(Pieces needed for one side are 2 Smart Moves, 1 King, 1 Queen, 2 Rooks, 2 Bishops, 8 Pawns.)

AVON CALLING '1905 DECANTER 1973
7 oz. brown glass with brown plastic top, has gold bell & black plastic receiver. Holds 7 oz. After Shave and .75 oz. Talc. Came in Wild Country or Avon Spicy. SSP $9. CMV $8. BO. $10. MB.
AVON CALLING FOR MEN 1969-70
8 1/2" high, 6 oz. gold paint over clear glass, gold cap, black mouth piece, black plastic ear piece. Holds 1 1/4 oz. Talc. Came in Wild Country and Leather Cologne. OSP $8. CMV $10. MB. $12.

WESTERN SADDLE 1971-72
5 oz. brown glass with brown cap, sets on beige fence. Came in Wild Country or Avon Leather After Shave. SSP $6. CMV $5. BO. and fence $7. MB.

MIXED DOUBLES TENNIS BALL 1977-78
(Left) 3 oz. light green flock over clear glass. Green cap base. Came in Sweet Honesty Body Splash or Avon Spicy. SSP $3. CMV $3. BO. $4. MB.
SURE CATCH 1977
(Right) 1 oz. white milk glass, with red cap, yellow tassel, black eyes. Came in Spicy or Wild Country. SSP $4. CMV $3. BO. $4. MB.

WHALE ORGANIZER BOTTLES 1973
3 oz. ivory milk glass with dark blue design. Holds After Shave & Cologne in Deep Woods or Avon Blend7. Sold only in Whale Organizer. CMV $5. each.

GOOD SHOT 1976-80
(Left) 2 oz. plastic bottle, gold cap. Red bottle in Wild Country or Brisk Spice After Shave and yellow bottle in Deep Woods or Cool Sage After Shave. SSP $2. CMV $2. BO. $3. MB. Add $5. for cap on wrong end.
WILD WEST" BULLET" 1977-78
(Right) 1.5 oz. bronze plated over clear glass. Silver top. Wild Country or Everest. SSP $2.50 CMV $2. BO. $3. MB.

FIRM GRIP 1977-78
(Left) 1.5 oz. silver plated clear glass. Came in Wild Country or Everest. SSP $3. CMV $3. BO. $4. MB.
WEATHER VANE 1977-78
(Right) 4 oz. red painted over clear glass. Silver top with black horse weather vane. Came in Wild Country or Deep Woods. SSP $4. CMV $4. MB.

EAGLE - PRIDE OF AMERICA 1982-83
7 3/4" high porcelain eagle figurine. SSP $29.50 CMV $25. MB.

GET THE MESSAGE DECANTER 1978-79
(Left) 3 oz. black glass with silver & black plastic top. Came in Clint or Sweet Honesty. SSP $5. **CMV $4. MB. $3. BO.**

NO CAUSE FOR ALARM DECANTER 1979-80
(Right) 4 oz. silver plated over clear glass. Silver plastic top. Came in Deep Woods, or Tai Winds. SSP $7. **CMV $6.50 MB. $5.50. BO.**

ARCTIC KING 1976-79
(Left) 5 oz. blue glass bottle, silver bear cap. Came in Everest only. SSP $5. **CMV $5. MB. $4. BO.**

BOLD EAGLE 1976-78
(Right) 3 oz. gold plated over clear glass, gold top. Came in Tai Winds or Wild Country. SSP $7. **CMV $6. MB. $5. BO.**

NBA DECANTER 1977-80
(Left) Came with your choice of individual NBA team labels. Came in Wild Country or Sure Winner Bracing Lotion. 6 oz. dark amber glass. Silver top. SSP $6. **CMV $6. MB. $5. BO.**

NFL DECANTER 1976-77
(Right) Came with your choice of NFL team emblem out of 28 member clubs of the National Football League. Came in Wild Country or Sure Winner Bracing Lotion. 6 oz. black glass with silver top. SSP $5. **CMV $6. MB. $5. BO.**

INDIAN CHIEFTAIN 1972-75
(Left) 4 oz. brown glass with gold cap. Came in Avon Spicy After Shave or Avon Protein Hair Lotion for Men. OSP $2.50 **CMV $3. MB.**

INDIAN TEPEE DECANTER 1974-75
(Right) 4 oz. amber glass with brown plastic cap. Holds Wild Country or Avon Spicy. OSP $3. **CMV $3. MB. $2. BO.**

MOTOCROSS HELMET 1976-78
6 oz. white plastic botle with stick on decals, blue plastic face guard cap. Came in Wild Country or Avon Protein Hair Lotion for Men. SSP $3. **CMV $4. MB. $3. BO.**

BIG BOLT 1976-77
(Left) 2 oz. silver plated over clear glass. Silver cap. Came in Dep Woods or Wild Country. SSP $2. **CMV $3. MB.**

DURACELL SUPER CHARGE 1976-78
(Center) 1 1/2 oz. black glass with bronze & silver cap. Came in Spicy or Everest. SSP $2. **CMV $2. MB.**

RIGHT CONNECTION "FUSE" 1977
(Right) 1.5 oz. clear glass, with gold & brown cap. Came in Oland or Wild Country. SSP $2. **CMV $3. MB.**

REMEMBER WHEN GAS PUMP 1976-77
(Left) 4 oz. red painted over clear glass. Red & white plastic cap. Came in Deep Woods or Wild Country. SSP $5. **CMV $5. BO. $6. MB.**

ONE GOOD TURN "SCREWDRIVER" 1976
(Right) 4 oz. clear glass, silver cap. Came in Tai Winds or Avon Spicy. SSP $3. **CMV $4. MB. $3. BO.**

CHESAPEAKE COLLECTION TRAY 1981-82
12" green metal tray. Back says "Mallards in Flight" Avon. SSP $7. **CMV $4. MB.**

CHESAPEAKE COLLECTION COASTERS 1981-82
Set of 4 metal duck coasters with green felt backs. Does not say Avon. SSP $8. **CMV $3. MB.**

CAR CLASSIC STEIN 1979-80
9" high ceramic stein made in Brazil & numbered on the bottom. Comes with 8 oz plastic of Trazarra Cologne. SSP $33. **CMV $35. MB. $30 stein only.**

CHESAPEAKE COLLECTION GLASSES 1981-82
(Left) Glass with after shave. 8 oz. drinking glass with 3 ducks on side. Glass does not say Avon. Comes with 7 oz. plastic bottle, green cap. Duck scene on side. Choice of Wild Country & Weekend After Shave. SSP $9. **CMV $5 MB.** (Right) Drinking Glasses. Green & brown box holds 2-8oz. drinking glasses with 3 ducks on side. Glasses do not say Avon. SSP $8. set. **CMV $6. MB.**

DAD'S PRIDE & JOY PICTURE FRAME 1982-83
6 1/2" long clear glass. Holds pictures. SSP $8. **CMV $5. MB.**

PERFECT COMBO MUG & POPCORN 1982
Box holds 12. oz. clear glass mug with geese on side & 10 oz. gold foil wrapped can of popcorn. SSP $10. **CMV $10. MB. set, mug only. $5.**

ROOKIE COLOGNE FOR BOYS 1980-81
2.5 oz. clear glass. Red cap & label. SSP $2.80 **CMV $1. MB.**

AVON'S FINEST DECANTER 1980-81
2 oz. dark amber glass. Gold tone cap. Comes in Clint or Trazarra cologne. SSP. $5. **CMV $2. MB.**

BOOTS 'N SADDLE DECANTER 1980-81
7 1/2" high, 7 oz. dark amber glass. Silver label, brown leather look wrap around label. Choice of Wild Country or Weekend After Shave. SP $10. **CMV $2. MB.**

SPIRIT OF ST. LOUIS 1970-72
6 oz. silver paint over clear glass. Came in Windjammer & Excalibur After Shave. 7 1/2" long. OSP $8.50 **CMV $6. MB. $8.50.**

VIKING HORN 1966
7 oz. dark amber glass with gold cap & decoration. Came in Spicy, Blue Blazer & Original After Shave. OSP $5. **CMV $10. BO. $15 . MB.**

IRON HORSE SHAVING MUG 1974-76
White milk glass mug holds 7 oz. plastic bottle with gold cap. Came in Avon Blend, Deep Woods or Avon Leather After Shave. SSP $6. **CMV $6. MB. $2. BO. mug only.**

DESK CADDY 1977-80
Brown cork holder, silver top made in Spain. Holds 4 oz. clear glass bottle of Clint cologne, red letters, silver cap or Wild Country. **CMV $5. MB.**

DEFENDER CANNON 1966
6 oz. 9 1/2" long, amber glass, brown plastic stand, gold cap, & gold center band, small paper label. Came in Leather, Island Lime & Tribute After Shave. OSP $5. **CMV $10 bottle & stand mint. $15 MB.**

SCIMITAR 1968-69
10'long, 6 oz. gold paint with red windows over clear glass, gold cap. Came in Tribune & Windjammer After Shave Lotion. OSP $6. **CMV $15. mint. $18 MB.**

TRIBUTE SILVER WARRIOR 1967
6" high, 6 oz. silver & blue paint over clear glass, silver cap. Came in Tribute After Shave. OSP $4.50 **CMV $12.50 BO. mint $18. MB. All blue glass $30 mint.**

TRIBUTE RIBBED WARRIOR 1971-73
6" high, 6 oz. clear ribbed glass, silver cap. Came in Tribute Cologne. OSP $4. **CMV $6. MB. $7.**

TRIBUTE RIBBED WARRIOR 1968-71
6" high, 6 oz. frosted glass, silver cap. Came in Tribute Cologne. OSP $4. **CMV $3. BO> $5. MB.**

WEATHER-OR-NOT 1969-71
5 oz. dark amber glass, regular issue on left, gold cap. Came in Leather & Oland, Tribute, Wild Country & Spicy After Shave. OSP $5. **There are 5 different Thermometers starting with 20 below, 10 below, 0, 10 above, & 20 above. All same price. CMV $6. BO. $8. MB.**

SUPER SHIFT 1978
4 oz. black glass bottle with silver & black shifter cap. Came in Sure Winner Bracing Lotion or Everest Cologne. 7" high. SSP $5. **CMV $5. MB. $4. BO.**

GAVEL 1967-68
5 oz. dark amber glass with brown plastic handle. 8" long. Came in Island Lime, Original, & Spicy. OSP $4. **CMV $10. BO. $14. MB.**

GOODYEAR BLIMP 1978
2 oz. silver gray paint over clear glass, blue letters. Came in Everest or Wild Country After Shave. SSP $5. **CMV $2. BO. $3. MB.**

WESTERN CHOICE (STEER HORNS) 1967
Brown plastic base with red center, Holds 2-3 bottles with silver caps. Came in Wild Country & Leather After Shave. OSP $6. **CMV $15. BO. $20. MB.**

PAID STAMP 1970-71
5" high, dark amber glass with black cap & red rubber paid stamp on bottom. Holds 4 oz. of Spicy or Windjammer After Shave. OSP $4. **CMV $5. BO. $7. MB.**

SWINGER GOLF BAG 1969-71
5 oz. black glass, red & silver clubs. Came in Wild Country & Bravo After Shave. OSP $5. **CMV $6. BO. $8. MB.**

INKWELL 1969-70
(Right) 6 oz. amber with purple tint, black cap with gold or silver pen. Came in Windjammer & Spicy After Shave. OSP $6. **CMV $7. BO. $9. MB.** (Left) Factory test. No value established

POT BELLY STOVE 1970-71
5" high, 5 oz. black glass bottle with black cap. Came in Bravo or Excalibur After shave. OSP $4. **CMV $5. BO. $6. MB.**

BAY RUM KEG 1965-67
(Right) 6 oz. brown & silver paint over clear glass bottle. OSP $2.50 **CMV $15. BO. $20. MB.**

DECISIONS 1965
8 oz. red painted labels, black caps with red centers that say Panic Buttons. Came in Spicy After shave Lotion. OSP $2.50 **CMV $20. MB. $15. BO.**

TOWN PUMP 1968-69
8" high black glass bottle with gold cap & plastic shoe horn. Holds 6 oz. of Leather, Windjammer, Wild Country. OSP $5. **CMV $6. BO. $8. MB.**

FIRST CLASS MALE 1970-71
(Left) 4 1/2" high, 4 oz. blue glass with red cap. Came in Bravo or Wild Country after Shave or Liquid Hair Lotion. OSP $3. **CMV $6. MB. $5. BO.**

DAYLIGHT SHAVING TIME 1968-70
6 oz. gold paint over clear glass. Came in Spicy, Wild Country, Windjammer, Bravo & Leather After Shave. OSP $5. **CMV $6. BO. $8. MB.**

CASSEY'S LANTERN 1966-67
10 oz. gold paint on clear glass bottle gold caps. Came in Leather After Shave in red window & Island Lime in green window. OSP each. $6. **CMV amber & green $55. MB. Red $45 MB. BO $5 less each mint.**

CLOSE HARMONY (BARBER BOTTLE) 1963
8 oz. white glass bottle, gold painted letter & neck band. White cap with tip. Came in Spicy & Original After Shave. OSP $2.25 Vigorate & After Shower Cologne. OSP $2.50 **CMV without tip. $7.50 with tip. $15 BO. $25 MB.**

DOLLARS 'N SCENTS 1966-67
8 oz. white glass bottle with green dollar painted on silver cap. Came in Spicy After Shave. Red rubber band around bottle. OSP $2.50 **CMV $15. MB. $10. BO.**

TOP DOLLAR SOAP ON A ROPE 1966-67
White 1886 dollar soap. OSP $1.75 **CMV $30 MB. $20 soap only mint.**

AVON CLASSICS 1969
6 oz. each OSP $3.50 Leather in clear & dark amber glass. Wild Country in light & dark amber glass & clear glass. Tribute After Shave in clear glass, light & dark amber glass. All bottle caps & labels must match color, gold or silver. **CMV $6. BO. $8. MB.**

FIRST EDITION 1967-68
6 oz. gold cap. Came in Bay Rum, **CMV $9 BO. $12. MB.** Wild Country & Leather After Shave. OSP $3.50 **CMV $7. BO. $9. MB.**

ROYAL ORB 1965-66
8 oz. round bottle, gold cap, red felt around neck. Came in Spicy & Original After Shave. Red letters painted on bottle common issue. OSP $3.50 **CMV $15. MB. $20 White letter Orb. $75.**

ALPINE FLASK 1966-67
8 oz. 8 3/4" high, brown glass, gold cap & neck chain. Came in Spicy, Original, Blue Blazer & Leather After Shave. OSP $4. **CMV $30. MB. $25. BO.**

GENTLEMAN'S REGIMENT COLLECTION 1982-83
Talc in beige tin can, SSP $5. No box,- **CMV $1.**

SHAVING MUG AND SOAP
Beige in color glass mug and matching bar of soap. SSP $15. **CMV $8. MB.**

SHAVING BRUSH
Beige plastic brush. SSP $9. **CMV $3. MB.**

AFTER SHAVE DECANTER
4.5 oz. clear glass painted beige. Gold cap. SSP $10. **CMV $4. MB.** Fragrance choice was Wild Country or Black Suede.

DAD'S BREW CRACKERS 1983
7" high paper sides can holds Dad's Crackers. SSP $7. **CMV $3 mint.**

JUST A TWIST 1977-78
2 oz. silver plated over clear glass. Came in Sweet Honesty or Deep Woods. SSP $3. CMV $3 BO. $4. MB.

HARD HAT 1977-78
4 oz. yellow paint over clear glass. Yellow plastic base. Came with seven decals. Came in Everest or Deep Woods. SSP $4. CMV $4 BO. $5. MB.

NO PARKING FIRE PLUG 1975-76
(Left) 6 oz. red painted glass with red cap. Came in Wild Country After Shave or Electric Pre-Shave. OSP $4. CMV $4 BO. $5. MB.

FIRE ALARM BOX 1975-76
(Right) 4 oz. red painted glass with black cap. Came in Avon Spicy After Shave, Avon Protein Hair Lotion or Electric Pre-Shave. OSP $3. CMV $4. BO. $5. MB.

ANGLER 1970
5 oz., 4 1/2" high blue glass with silver reel cap & trim. Came in WIndjammer & Wild Country After Shave. OSP $5. CMV $6. BO. $7. MB.

EIGHT BALL DECANTER 1973
3 oz. black glass with black cap & white 8. Came in Spicy After Shave, Avon Protein Lotion for Men, or Electric Pre-Shave Lotion. SSP $2. CMV $5. MB. $4. BO.

BARBER POLE 1974-75
3 oz. white milk glass with red & blue paper striped label & white plastic cap. Holds Avon Protein Hair/Scalp Conditioner or Wild Country After shave. OSP $3. CMV $4. BO. $5. MB.

BARBER SHOP BRUSH 1976
1.5 oz. brown glass with black & white plastic brush cap. Came in Tai Winds or Wild Country Cologne. CMV $4. BO. $5. MB.

ELECTRIC GUITAR DECANTER 1974-75
6 oz. brown glass with silver plastic handle. Came in Avon Sure Winner Bracing Lotion or Wild Country After Shave. SSP $4. CMV $5. BO. $6. MB.

TOTEM POLE DECANTER 1975
6 oz. dark amber glass with plastic cap. Holds Wild Country, Deep Woods or Avon Spicy After Shave. OSP $5. CMV $5. BO. $6. MB.

SMOOTH GOING OIL CAN 1978
1.5 silver plated over clear glass. Came in Deep Woods or Everest After Shave. SSP $3. CMV $4. MB. $3. BO.

BUFFALO NICKEL 1971-72
5 oz. plated over clear glass with matching cap. Came in Spicy, Wild Country After Shave or Liquid Hair Lotion. SSP $4. CMV $6. MB. $5. BO.

INDIAN HEAD PENNY 1970-72
4 oz. 4" high. Bronze paint & cap over clear glass. Came in Bravo, Tribute, Excalibur After shave. OSP $4. CMV $6. MB. $5. BO.

LIBERTY DOLLAR 1970-72
(Left) 6 oz. silver paint over clear glass, silver cap with eagle. 6" high. Came in Oland, and Tribute After Shave. OSP $5. CMV $7. MB. $6. BO. Same bottle only gold, rare, $40. MB.

TWENTY DOLLAR GOLD PIECE 1971-72
(Right) 6 oz. gold paint over clear glass. Gold cap. Came in Windjammer After Shave & Electric Pre-Shave Lotion. OSP $5. CMV $6. BO. $7. MB.

LIBERTY BELL 1971-72
(Left) 5 oz. light amber glass coated over clear glass, brown cap. Came in Tribute or Oland After Shave or Cologne. OSP $5. CMV $7. MB. $5. BO.

LIBERTY BELL 1976
(Right) 5 oz. sprayed bronze with bronze cap. Came in Oland or Deep Woods After Shave. OSP $5. CMV $6. MB. $5. BO.

AFTER SHAVE ON TAP 1974-75
(Left) 5 oz. dark amber glass with gold plastic spigot cap. Holds Wild Country or Oland After Shave. OSP $3. **CMV $5. MB. $4. BO.**
AFTER SHAVE ON TAP 1976
5 oz. amber glass, red spigot cap. Holds Spicy or Wild Country. OSP $4. **CMV $5. MB. $4. BO.**
TRIPLE CROWN 1974-76
(Right) 4 oz. brown glass with red plastic cap. Holds Spicy After Shave or Avon Protein Hair/Scalp Conditioner. OSP $3. **CMV $4. MB. $3. BO.**

IT'S A BLAST 1970-71
(Left) 5 oz. 8 1/2" high, gold paint over clear glass, black rubber horn on cap. Came in Oland or Windjammer After Shave. OSP $7. **CMV $7. BO. $9. MB.**
MAN'S WORLD 1969-70
(Right) Brown plastic stand holds 6 oz. globe. Gold paint over clear glass, gold cap. Came in Bravo, Windjammer & Tribute After Shave. 4" high. OSP $5. **CMV $7. BO. $8. MB.**

BREAKER 19 1977-79
(Left) 2 oz. black glass with black & silver plastic cap. Wild Country or Sweet Honesty. SSP $3. **CMV $3. BO. $4. MB.**
COLEMAN LANTERN 1977-79
(Right) 5 oz. green painted over clear glass. Green cap, silver bail handle. Came in Wild Country or Deep Woods. SSP $5. **CMV $5. BO. $6. MB.**

CAPTAINS LANTERN 1864 1976-77
(Left) 7 oz. black glass with black plastic cap & gold ring. Came in Wild Country or Oland After Shave. OSP $5. **CMV $5. MB. $4. BO.**
WHALE OIL LANTERN 1974-75
(Right) 5 oz. green glass with silver toned plastic top & base. Holds Wild Country, Oland or Tai Winds. OSP $4. **CMV $5. MB. $4. BO.**

JUKE BOX 1977-78
4.5 oz. amber glass, silver top. Came in Sweet Honesty or Wild Country. Came with decals. SSP $4. **CMV $5. MB. $4. BO.**
AVON ON THE AIR 1975-76
3 oz. black glass with silver plastic stand. Holds Wild Country, Deep Woods or Spicy After Shave. OSP $4. **CMV $5. MB. $4. BO.**

PIANO 1972
(Left) 4" high, 4 oz. dark amber glass piano with white music stack cap. Holds Tai Winds or Tribute After Shave Lotion. OSP $4. **CMV $5. BO. $6. MB.**
FIELDER'S CHOICE 1971-72
(Right) 5 oz. dark amber glass, black cap. Came in Sports Rally Bracing Lotion, Liquid Hair Trainer, or Wild Country After Shave. OSP $4. **CMV $5. BO. $6. MB.**

HISTORIC FLIGHT "1903 FLYER" 1986
3/3/4" high pewter plane. Wood base. DP $21. **CMV $21. MB.**
SPIRIT OF ST. LOIUS 1986
4 1/2" wide pewter plane with wood base. DP $21. **CMV $21. MB.**
PEWTER CAR COLLECTION 1984
Wood base with '63 Corvette, '63 Riviera, '55 Thunderbird, '57 Chrysler 300, and '64 Mustang. DP $15. **CMV $15. each MB.**

BENJAMIN J BEARINGTON FIGURINES 1983-84
2" high pewter "First Day Back", "Hard At Work", "Report Card Day", "Schools Out". 4 in a series. DP $8 each. **CMV $8. each MB.**
"FATHER'S ARMS" FIGURINE 1984
Wood base. Pewter figurine. DP. $10. **CMV $10. MB.**

CORD CAR '1937' 1984
9" long car, yellow. DP $18. **CMV $18. MB.**

"ON THE ROAD AGAIN" PRODUCTS 1982 Only
Each green and white with license plates design. Choice of Talc, lather shave cream or Anti-Perspirant Deodorant in Wild Country fragrance. No boxes. SSP $1. each **CMV $1. each.**

DUCK SERIES 1983-84
6 different hand painted metal ducks. 4" long, 2" high. SSP $13. each. **CMV $8. each MB.**

DUCK DISPLAY RACK 1983-84
12 1/2 " long two tier wood rack to display all six duck figurines. SSP $15. **CMV $10. MB.**

ALL AMERICAN SPORTS FAN MUG & POPCORN 1983
5 1/2" high clear glass mug with red white and blue design. Comes with red white and blue cannister of popcorn. SSP $8. **CMV $5. set MB., or $3 mug only.**

AUBURN BOATTAIL SPEEDSTER 1983-84
1st in series. Black & red ceramic car figurine. 8 1/2" long. Dated 1983. SSP $29.50 **CMV $15. MB.**

SPORTING MINIATURE STEIN 1983-84
5" tall ceramic stein. Hunting scene on side. SSP $13. **CMV $8. MB.**

AGE OF THE IRON HORSE STEIN 1982-84
8 1/2" ceramic stein made in Brazil. Numbered and dated. Metal top. Has train design on side. Sold Empty. SSP $40. **CMV $25. MB.**

MINIATURE STEINS 1982-83
4 1/2" to 5 1/2" high ceramic steins. Choice of Tall Ships, Vintage Cars or Flying Classics. Each numbered and dated 1982. SSP $13. **CMV $8. each MB.**

GREAT AMERICAN FOOTBALL STEIN 1982-83
9" high ceramic stein made in Brazil. Metal flip top. SSP $40. **CMV $25. MB.**

WESTERN ROUND UP MINI STEIN 1983-84
5" mini ceramic tan & white stein, made in Brazil and numbered on bottom. Cowboys on side. SSP $13. **CMV $8. MB.**

ENDANGERED SPECIES MINI STEIN 1983-84
Blue and white 5" mini stein, moose and goat on side. SSP. $13. **CMV $8. MB.**

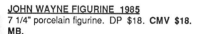

JOHN WAYNE FIGURINE 1985
7 1/4" porcelain figurine. DP $18. **CMV $18. MB.**

BLACKSMITH STEIN 1985
Ceramic stein, pewter top, Made in Brazil & numbered. DP $22. **CMV $22. MB.**

SHIP BUILDER STEIN 1986
Both ceramic steins 8 1/2" high, numbered on bottom. Pewter lids. DP. $24.CMV $24. **each MB.**

BIG SHOT MUG - TEST AREA 1983
Chrome plated brass jigger about 2 1/2" inches high. Comes with or without stick on initials. Sold only in Test area in Mid-West. OSP $13. **CMV $40. in white test box.**

WRIGHT BROTHERS MUG 1985
3" high. Hand painted porcelain mug. DP $12. **CMV $12. MB.**

LEWIS & CLARK MUG 1985
Hand painted porcelain mug. 3" high. DP. $12. **CMV $12. MB.**

IRON HORSE MINI STEIN 1985
5 1/4" high ceramic stein. DP $6. **CMv $6. MB.**

GREAT AMERICAN BASEBALL STEIN 1984
Ceramic stein 8 3/4" high , Metal top, Made in Brazil. SSP $22. **CMV $22. MB.**

WOMEN'S DECANTERS, CERAMICS & FIGURINES

COLLECTORS:
All containers are Priced Empty

BO means . . . . Bottle only (empty)
CMV means . . . . Current Market Value
SSP means . . . . Special Selling Price
OSP means . . . . Original Selling Price
MB means . . . . Mint and Boxed
DP means Demo Price . . . . .Avon Rep Cost
DP is used on all new products 1984 or newer.

PRECIOUS TURTLE 1975-76
.66 oz. gold jar with plastic lid. Came in Patchwork, or Roses Roses Cream Sachet. OSP $4. **CMV $5. MB, $4. BO.**

TREASURE TURTLE 1971-73
1 oz. brown glass turtle with gold head. Holds Field Flowers, Hana Gasa, Bird of Paradise, Elusive, Charisma, Brocade, Unforgettable, Rapture, Occur!, Somewhere, Topaze, Cotillion, Here's My Heart and Persian Wood. OSP $3.50. **CMV $6. MB, $4. BO.**

TRESAURE TURTLE 1977
1 oz. clear glass turtle with gold cap. Came in Sweet Honesty or Charisma cologne. Avon on bottom & 'R' for reissue on tail. OSP $4.50. **CMV $4. MB, $3. BO.**

EMERALD PRINCE FROG 1977-79
1 oz. green frosted paint over clear glass. Came in Sweet Honesty or Moonwind cologne. OSP $5. **CMV $4. MB, $3. BO.**

WHAT'S HOT AND WHAT'S NOT IN WOMEN'S FIGURINES

What's hot is any decanter or figurine that's made of glass or ceramic. It has to look like something. This is what collectors are after today. What's not hot is plain looking bottles of no particular shape. Almost all plastic bottles, wall tiles & wall decorations, plain tin can items, jars, fabric items such as sachet pillows etc., ceramic items not marked Avon on bottom & kitchen items that have no shape that would appeal to most collectors.

Avon collecting is 20 years old as we know it and the Avon product line has expanded well beyond most people's ability to collect everything in their product line. There are thousands of products to collect. Choose the one's that appeal to most collectors & you should have a market when you decide to sell your collection in years to come.

This book has been researched to include all products that are hot with most collectors. Some new products not shown in this book fall in the catagory of new collectable. We also are pricing all new products at the "DP" Demo Price. This is the cost the Avon Representative pays for a product. Because there are over 400,000 Avon Reps, we feel there are more than ample supplies to collectors. It will take several years for almost any new products to become scarce & start to rise in value due to supply & demand. Keep this in mind in buying new collectables. Only the older products are true collectables. This is why the CPC items, the first Avon products, are so scarce & have risen so high in price. We hope you find this information helpful in guiding your collecting.

Candy products from Avon are not in this book unless they come in a figurine type container. Boxes & cans of candy will not be considered collectable as it easily melts & is dangerous when it gets old & could cause harm to children. We suggest you buy this type of product to use & dispose of the box it came in.

COLOGNE ROYAL 1972-74
1 oz. clear glass, gold cap. Came in Field Flowers, Roses Roses, Bird of Paradise, Sonnet, Charisma, Unforgettable, Somewhere. SSP $1.75. **CMV $4. MB, $3. BO.**
COURTING CARRIAGE 1973-74
1 oz. clear glass, gold cap. Came in Moonwind, Sonnet, Field Flowers or Flower Talk. SSP $2. **CMV $5. MB, $4. BO.**
PINEAPPLE PETITE 1972-74
1 oz. clear glass, gold cap. Came in Roses Roses, Charisma, Elusive, Brocade or Regence. SSP $2. **CMV $4. MB, $3. BO.** Reissued in 1977 in Field Flowers & Unforgettable.

KEY NOTE PERFUME 1967
1/4 oz. glass key with gold plastic cap. 4A design on cap. Came in Here's My Heart, To A Wild Rose. OSP $5. Somewhere, Topaze, Cotillion. OSP $5.50. Unforgettable, Rapture, Occur!. OSP $6.50. **CMV $20. MB, $12. key only.**
LADY BUG PERFUME 1975-76
1/8 oz. frosted glass, gold cap. Came in Sonnet, Moonwind or Patchwork. OSP $4. **CMV $4. BO, $5. MB.**
SCENT WITH LOVE 1971-72
1/4 oz. frosted glass with gold pen cap, white and gold label around bottle. Came in Field Flowers, Moonwind, Bird of paradise, Charisma, Elusive, Moonwind. OSP $6. **CMV $12. MB, $8. BO.**

AUTUMN ASTER DECANTER 1978-80
(Left) .75 oz. clear glass, gold cap. Holds Topaze or Sun Blossoms cologne. SSP $2. **CMV $2. MB.**
DOGWOOD DEMI DECANTER 1978-80
(Right) .75 oz. flower shaped bottle, gold flower lid. Came in Apple Blossom, Moonwind or Topaze cologne. SSP $3. **CMV $2. MB.**

BOW TIE PERFUME 1970
1/8 oz. clear glass. Shape of bow with gold cap. Came in Pink Slipper Soap in Charisma & Cotillion. **CMV $4. mint.**

ICICLE PERFUME 1967-68
1 dram, gold cap. Came in Here's My Heart, To A Wild Rose, Somewhere, Topaz, Cotillion, Unforgettable, Rapture, Occur!, Regence. OSP $3. with gold neck label. **CMV $6. MB, $5. BO.**

ONE DRAM PERFUME 1974-76
Clear glass with gold cap. Came in Bird of Paradise, Charisma or Field Flowers. OSP $3.75. Sonnet, Moonwind or Imperial Garden. OSP $4.25. **CMV $3. MB, $2. BO.**

STRAWBERRY FAIR PERFUME 1974-75
1/8 oz. red glass, silver cap. Came in Moonwind, Charisma or Sonnet. OSP $4. **CMV $5. MB, $4. BO.**

SEWING NOTIONS 1975
1 oz. pink and white glass with silver cap. Holds Sweet Honesty, To A Wild Rose or Cotillion. OSP $3. **CMV $4. MB, $3. BO.**

CRYSTALIER COLOGNE 1975
2 oz. clear glass. Filled with Field Flowers, Bird of Paradise or Roses Roses Cologne. OSP $4. **CMV $4. MB, $3. BO.**

BABY OWL 1975-77
1 oz. clear glass, goldc ap. Holds Sweet Honesty or Occur! Cologne. OSP $2. **CMV $2. BO, $3. MB.**

PERT PENGUIN 1975-76
1 oz. clear glass, gold cap. Holds Field Flowers or Cotillion Cologne. OSP $2. **CMV $2. BO, $3. MB.**

PRECIOUS SLIPPER 1973-74
.25 oz. frosted glass bottle with gold cap. Came in Sonnet or Moonwind. OSP $4. **CMV $7. MB, $5. BO.**

LOVE BIRD PERFUME 1969-70
1/4 oz. frosted bird with silver cap. 2 1/2" long. Came in Charisma, Elusive, Brocade, Regence, Unforgettable, Rapture, Occur!. OSP $6.25. **CMV $9. MB, $5. BO.**

SMALL WONDER PERFUME 1972-73
1/8 oz. frosted glass with gold cap. Holds Field Flowers, Bird of Paradise, Charisma. OSP $2.50. **CMV $7. MB, $5. BO.**

NEW Frisky Friends Cologne Decanter

FRISKY FRIENDS 1981
3 different frosted 1 oz. glass cats. With blue cap, Honeysuckle, yellow cap has Roses Roses & pink cap has Hawaiian White Ginger. SSP $5. **CMV $5. MB each.**

CHRISTMAS CHARMER CANDLESTICK 1981
Small white, red & green girl, plastic candle holder. Remove top sleeve to fit small bottle of cologne with red cap. Choice of Zany or Charisma. .33 oz. cologne, red box. SSP $6. **CMV $4. set MB.**

DREAM GARDEN 1972-73
1/2 oz. pink frosted glass with gold cap. Came in Moonwind, Bird of Paradise, Charisma, Elusive or Unforgettable perfume oil. OSP $5. **CMV $15. MB, $8. BO.**

SNOW MAN PETITE PERFUME 1973
.25 oz. textured glass with pink eyes, mouth & scarf. Gold cap. Came in Cotillion, Bird of Paradise, Field Flowers. OSP $4. **CMV $6. BO, $8. MB.**

PRECIOUS SWAN PERFUME 1974-76
1/8 oz. frosted glass with gold cap. Came in Field Flowers, Bird of Paradise or Charisma. OSP $4. **CMV $5. BO, $6. MB.**

HEAVENLY ANGEL 1981
(Left) .5 oz. blue glass angel, silver cap. Choice of Ariane, Candid, Timeless. Red box dated 1981. SSP $2. **CMV $2. MB.**

WINGED PRINCESS 1981
(Center) .5 oz. swan shaped iridescent glass, gold cap. Choice of Occur!, Charisma, Sweet Honesty. Box dated 1981. SSP $2.25. **CMV $2.25. MB.**

LOVE CHIMES 1981-82
(Right) .5 oz. clear glass bell shape, gold cap. Choice of Roses Roses, Charisma, Moonwind, Sweet Honesty. SSP $1.75. **CMV $1.75. MB.**

ROLLIN GREAT ROLLER SKATE 1980-81
2 oz. glass red top. Choice of Zany Cologne or Lover Boy Cologne. SSP $4. **CMV $3. MB.**

PETITE PIGLET 1972
2" long embossed clear glass with gold cap. Holds 1/4 oz. perfume in Field Flowers, Bird of Paradise, Elusive & Charisma. OSP $5. **CMV $7. BO, $8. MB.**

SNAIL PERFUME 1968-69
1/4 oz. gold cap, clear glass. Came in Charisma, Brocade, Regence, Unforgettable, Rapture & Occur!. OSP $6.25. **CMV $13.50 MB, $7. BO.**

PERFUME PETITE MOUSE 1970
Frosted glass with gold head and tail, holds 1/4 oz. perfume in Elusive, Charisma, Brocade, Regence. OSP $7.50. Unforgettable, Rapture & Occur!. OSP $6.25. **CMV $17.50 MB, $12. BO.**

COLOGNE GO ROUND 1980
.5 oz. clear glass, gold cap. Choice of Roses Roses, Honeysuckle, Hawaiian White Ginger, Field Flowers. SSP $1.75. **CMV $1. MB.**

SEAHORSE MINIATURE 1980-81
.5 oz. clear glass, gold cap. Choice of Sweet Honesty, Charisma, Occur! or Moonwind. SSP $3. **CMV $2. MB.**

COLOGNE RONDELLE 1980
5 oz. clear glass, gold cap. Choice of Moonwind, Charisma, Topaze, Occur!, Sweet Honesty, Zany Sportif or Country Breeze. In special Christmas box. SSP $1.40. **CMV $1. MB.**

WEDDING FLOWER MAIDEN 1979-80
(Left) 1.75 oz. white painted over clear glass. Holds Unforgettable or Sweet Honesty cologne. SSP $6. **CMV $5. BO, $6. MB.**

GARDEN GIRL 1978-79
4 oz. pink painted over clear glass. Holds Charisma or Sweet Honesty cologne. SSP $5. **CMV $4. BO, $5. MB.**

ANGEL SONG DECANTER 1978-79
1 oz. frosted glass base with off white plastic top. Holds Here's My Heart or Charisma cologne. SSP $3. **CMV $2. BO, $3. MB.**

HUGGABLE HOP-A-LONG 1982
1 oz. green glass frog. Plastic hat. Comes with 20 stick on decals. Choice of Sweet Honesty for girls or Light Musk for guys. SSP $5. **CMV $3. MB.**

SCENTIMENTAL DOLL ADORABLE ABIGAIL 1979-80
4.5 oz. clear glass painted beige. Beige plastic top. Comes in Regence or Sweet Honesty cologne. SSP $10. **CMV $6. BO, $7. MB.**

MRS. QUACKLESS 1979-80
2 oz. clear glass painted off white. Off white plastic top with white lace and green bonnet. Comes in Delicate Daisies Cologne. SSP $6. **CMV $3. BO, $4. MB.**

SWEET TOOTH TERRIER 1979-80
1 oz. white glass and white plastic top. Comes in Topaze or Cotillion Cologne. SSP $4. **CMV $3. BO, $4. MB.**

FASHION FIGURINE 1971-72
(Left) 4 oz. white plastic top & white painted bottom, over clear glass. 6" high. Came in Field Flowers, Elusive, Bird of Paradise, Brocade. SSP $4. **CMV $9. BO, $12. MB.**

VICTORIAN FASHION FIGURINE 1973-74
(Center) 4 oz. light green (some call it blue or aqua) painted over clear glass base with green plastic top. Came in Charisma, Field Flowers, Bird of Paradise Cologne. SSP $4. **CMV $30. BO, $33. MB.**

ELIZABETHAN FASHION FIGURINE 1972
(Right) 4 oz. pink painted glass bottom over clear glass with pink plastic top. 6" high. Came in Moonwind, Charisma, Field Flowers & Bird of Paradise Cologne. SSP $5. **CMV $16. BO, $20. MB.** Also came pink painted over white milk glass. Remove cap to see difference. **CMV $15.**

SONG OF CHRISTMAS 1980
.75 oz. frosted glass. Red cap. Choice of Moonwind, Sweet Honesty or Bird of Paradise. SSP $2.22. **CMV $2. MB.**

CHRISTMAS SOLDIER 1980
.75 oz. clear glass, gold cap. Choice of Sportif, Sweet Honesty, Charisma or Moonwind. SSP $2. **CMV $2. MB.**

OWL MINIATURE 1980-81
.6 oz. clear glass, gold owl cap. Choice of Tasha, Ariane, Candid or Timeless. SSP $1.95. **CMV $1. MB.**

ON THE AVENUE 1978-79
2 oz. blue painted over clear glass. Pink plastic top with lavender hat. White detachable umbrella. Holds Topaze or Unforgettable cologne. SSP $8. **CMV $7. BO, $8. MB.**

PROUD GROOM 1978-80
2 oz. white painted over clear glass. Holds Sweet Honesty or Unforgettable Cologne. SSP $7. **CMV $6. BO, $7. MB.**

TUG-A-BRELLA 1979-80
2.5 oz. clear glass painted yellow, yellow plastic top. Black plastic umbrella on wire. Holds Moonwind or Cotillion Cologne. SSP $10. CMV $9. BO, $10. MB.

GOOD FAIRY 1978-80
3 oz. clear glass painted blue. Blue plastic top. Plastic wand. Blue and pink fabric purse and wings. Holds Delicate Daisies cologne. SSP $6. CMV $5. BO, $6. MB.

ANGEL SONG WITH MANDOLIN 1979-80
(Left) 1 oz. frosted over clear glass. White plastic top. Holds Moonwind or Unforgettable cologne. SSP $3. CMV $3. MB.

SKATER'S WALTZ 1979-80
(Center) 4 oz. blue flock base over clear glass. Light blue plastic top. Holds Charisma or Cotillion cologne. SSP $8. CMV $8. MB.

LITTLE JACK HORNER 1979-80
(Right) 1.5 oz. white glass painted white frosted. Came in Topaze or Roses Roses cologne. SSP $6. CMV $6. MB.

BETSY ROSS 1976
4 oz. white painted over clear glass. Came in Sonnet or Topaze Cologne. Sold 2 campaigns only. SSP $7. CMV $6. MB, $5. BO. Also came white painted over white milk glass. Remove cap to see color of bottle. CMV $20. MB. The regular issue Betsy Ross bottle was one of the all time biggest sellers in Avon history.

MAGIC PUMPKIN COACH 1976-77
1 oz. clear glass, gold cap. Comes in Bird of Paradise or Occur! Cologne. OSP $5. CMV $4. BO, $5. MB.

GARDEN GIRL 1975
4 oz. sprayed frosted glass with yellow plastic top. Holds Sweet Honesty, Somewhere, Cotillion ot To A Wild Rose. OSP $3.50. CMV $9. BO, $11. MB.

FLOWER MAIDEN 1973-74
4 oz. yellow skirt painted over clear glass with white plastic top. Came in Unforgettable, Somewhere, Topaze, Cotillion. SSP $5. CMV $7. MB, $5. BO.

DEAR FRIENDS 1974
4 oz. pink painted with light pink plastic top. Came in Field Flowers, Bird of Paradise or Roses Roses Cologne. SSP $4. CMV $10. BO, $13. MB.

FLY-A-BALLOON 1975-77
3 oz. glass sprayed blue with light blue top & red plastic balloon. Holds Moonwind or Bird of Paradise cologne. OSP $7. CMV $7. BO, $8. MB.

SKIP-A-ROPE 1977-77
4 oz. yellow sprayed glass with yellow plastic top and white plastic rope. Holds Sweet Honesty, Bird of Paradise or Roses Roses cologne. OSP $7. CMV $7. BO, $8. MB.

PRETTY GIRL PINK 1974-75
(Left) 6 oz. glass sprayed pink base with light pink top. Holds Unforgettable, Topaze, Occur! or Somewhere cologne. OSP $4. CMV $7. BO, $9. MB.

LITTLE GIRL BLUE 1972-73
(Center) 3 oz. blue painted glass with blue plastic cap. Came in Brocade, Unforgettable, Somewhere or Cotillion. SSP $4. CMV $7. BO, $9. MB.

LITTLE KATE 1973-74
(Right) 3 oz. pastel orange painted glass with orange plastic hat over cap. Came in Bird of Paradise, Charisma, Unforgettable. SSP $4. CMV $8. BO, $10. MB.

SONG OF SPRING 1977
(Left) 1 oz. frosted glass with frosted plastic bird bath top. Blue plastic bird attachment. Came in Sweet Honesty or Topaze. OSP $6. CMV $4. MB.

FELINA FLUFFLES 1977-78
(Right) 2 oz. blue paint over clear glass, white plastic top, blue ribbon on head. Pink cheeks. Came in Pink & Pretty Cologne. OSP $6. CMV $4. BO, $5. MB.

MY PET FIGURINE 1973
(Left) Green & brown, white kitten, ceramic figurine. 1973 embossed in ceramic & printed on box. OSP $10. **CMV $35.**

JENNIFER FIGURINE 1973
(Right) Pastel turquoise dress & hat figurine. 1973 embossed in ceramic & printed on box. Some came with flowers in center of hat & some with flowers on the right side of hat. OSP $10. **CMV $45.** Both issued from Springdale, Ohio branch only.

AMERICAN BELLE 1976-78
(Left) 4 oz. yellow dull paint over clear glass, yellow cap. Came in Cotillion or Sonnet cologne. SSP $5. **CMV $6. MB, $5. BO.**

LITTLE BO PEEP DECANTER 1976-78
(Right) 2 oz. white dull paint over white milk glass base, white plastic top & can. Came in Sweet Honesty or Unforgettable cologne. SSP $5. **CMV $6. MB, $5. BO.**

VICTORIAN LADY 1972-73
5 oz. white milk glass, white plastic cap. Came in Bird of Paradise, Unforgettable, Occur!, Charisma Foaming Bath Oil. SSP $4. **CMV $6. BO, $7. MB.**

18th CENTURY CLASSIC FIGURINE YOUNG BOY 1974-75
(Left) 4 oz. white sprayed glass with white plastic head. Choice of Sonnet or Moonwind cologne or foaming bath oil. OSP $5. **CMV $7. BO., $9. MB.**

18th CENTURY CLASSIC FIGURINE YOUNG GIRL 1974-75
(Right) 4 oz. white sprayed glass with white plastic head. Choice of Sonnet or Moonwind cologne or foaming bath oil. OSP $5. **CMV $5. BO, $7. MB.**

CATCH-A-FISH 1976-78
3 oz. dark tan, painted over clear glass, light tan plastic top, yellow hat & brown plastic removable pole. Came in Field Flowers or Sonnet cologne. OSP $9.50. **CMV $8. BO, $9. MB.**

ROLL-A-HOOP 1977-78
3.75 oz. dull pink painted over clear glass base. Light pink plastic top, white plastic hoop. Came in Field Flowers or Cotillion cologne. OSP $10. **CMV $8. BO, $9. MB.**

WISHFUL THOUGHTS 1982-83
5 1/2" high porcelain figurine. Blue & white. SSP $15. **CMV $10. MB.**

LITTLE MISS MUFFET 1978-80
(Left) 2 oz. white painted over milk glass. Came in Sweet Honesty or Topaze. OSP $7. **CMV $5. MB, $4. BO.**

CHURCH MOUSE BRIDE 1978-79
Plastic top with separate white veil. Came in Delicate Daisies cologne. Base is white dull paint over milk glass. OSP $6. **CMV $5. BO, $6. MB.**

LIBRARY LAMP 1976--77
(Left) 4 oz. gold plated base over clear glass, gold cap. Came in Topaze & Charisma cologne. OSP $9. **CMV $5. BO, $6. MB.**

BRIDAL MOMENTS 1976-79
(Right) 5 oz. white paint over clear glass. White plastic top. Came in Sweet Honesty or Unforgettable cologne. OSP $9. **CMV $7. MB, $6. BO.**

SCOTTISH LASS 1975
(Left) 4 oz. blue with red, green & blue plaid skirt, blue plastic top. Holds Sweet Honesty, Bird of Paradise, Roses Roses or Cotillion cologne. OSP $5. **CMV $6. BO, $8. MB.**

SPANISH SENORITA 1975-76
(Center) 4 oz. red base with white designs and pink plastic top. Holds Moonwind, To A Wild Rose or Topaze cologne. OSP $5. **CMV $10. BO, $12. MB.**

ROARING TWENTIES FASHION FIGURINE 1972-74
(Right) 3 oz. purple painted over clear glass with plastic purple top. Came in Unforgettable, Topaze, Somewhere, Cotillion. SSP $4. **CMV $8. BO, $10. MB.**

DUTCH MAID 1977-79
(Left) 4 oz. blue painted base over clear glass, flower design & blue plastic top. Came in Sonnet or Moonwind cologne. OSP $7. **CMV $7. MB, $6. BO.**

MARY MARY 1977-79
(Center) 2 oz. frosted white over milk glass & white plastic top. Came in Sweet Honesty or Topaze. OSP $7. **CMV $6. MB, $5. BO.**

SKATERS WALTZ - RED 1977-78
(Right) 4 oz. red flock on clear glass & pink plastic tip. Came in Moonwind or Charisma cologne. OSP $8.50. **CMV $8. BO, $9. MB.**

PIERROT COLOGNE 1982-83
(Left) 1.75 oz. bottle. Black & white. Choice of Charisma or Occur! SSP $10. **CMV $6. MB.**

PIERRETTE COLOGNE 1982-83
(Right) Same as Pierrot. SSP $10. **CMV $6. MB.**

DUTCH GIRL FIGURINE 1973-74
(Left) 3 oz. blue painted with light blue plastic top. Came in Unforgettable, Topaze or Somewhere. SSP $5. **CMV $8. BO, $11. MB.**

GAY NINETIES 1974
(Center) 3 oz. orange sprayed bottle with white top and orange hat. Holds Unforgettable, Topaze or Somewhere. OSP $4. **CMV $10. BO, $13. MB.**

SWEET DREAMS 1974
(Right) 3 oz. sprayed white bottom with blue top. Holds Pink & Pretty or Sweet Honesty cologne. OSP $4. **CMV $13. BO, $15. MB.**

FIRST PRAYER 1981-82
(Left) 1.5 oz. light bisque yellow painted bottom over clear glass. Light yellow top. Choice of Charisma, Occur!, Topaze cologne. 4" high. SSP $7. **CMV $5. MB.**

PRIMA BALLERINA 1981
(Center) Pink frosted glass over clear glass, 1 oz. Choice of Zany or Sweet Honesty. Bottle & box label dated 1981. SSP $7. **CMV $4. MB.**

NOSTALGIC GLOW 1981-82
(Right) 1 oz. clear glass lamp bottom, blue plastic shade top. Choice of Moonwind, Wild Jasmine or Topaze. SSP $6. **CMV $4. MB.**

CLASSIC DECANTER 1969-70
(Left) 8 oz. white glass bottle with gold cap. 11" high, filled with Skin-So-Soft bath oil. SSP $5. **CMV $8. MB, $6. BO.**

SEA MAIDEN SKIN-SO-SOFT 1971-72
(Right) 6 oz. gold cap, clear glass, 10" high. SSP $5. **CMV $7. MB, $5. BO.**

PRECIOUS PRISCILLA 1982-83
(Left) 3 oz. pale pink paint over clear glass. Plastic head top. Holds Sweet Honesty or Moonwind. SSP $10. **CMV $6. MB.**

AMERICAN HEIRLOOM PORCELAIN HEAD DOLL 1981
(Right) 11" high fabric doll with porcelain head. Blue ribbon around waist. SSP $16.50. **CMV $10. MB.**

BEST FRIENDS PORCELAIN FIGURINE 1981
(Left) 6" high boy figurine. Dated 1981. SSP $19.50. **CMV $12. MB.** 1 made in Taiwan and 1 in Japan.

MOTHER'S LOVE PORCELAIN FIGURINE 1981
(Center) 5 1/2" high girl figurine holding a baby. Bottom tan painted label is dated 1981. Made in Taiwan sticker is tan color. SSP $19.50. **CMV $12. MB.**

MOTHER'S LOVE FIGURINE ADVANCED 1981
(Right) Factory sample. About 75 were given by Avon Products Inc. to Avon collectors at the 10th Annual National Association of Avon Collectors Convention in Long Beach, California. These factory samples do not have Avon label on bottom & is 1/4" higher. Made in Taiwan label is green. Rare. Came in plain box. **CMV $100. mint.**

MOTHER'S LOVE PORCELAIN FIGURINE TEST PRODUCTS 1981
24 were given to Avon collectors at the 10th Annual National Association of Avon Collectors Convention on the Queen Mary Ship June 1981. It is not in the regular issue box & figurine is not marked on bottom. Came with letter from Avon as very rare. **CMV $150 with letter & plain box.**

LOVING TREATS BUTTERMINTS 1982
Flowered tin box filled with buttermint candy. Tin dated 1982. Comes in lavendar box. SSP $10 **CMV $2. MB. empty.**

HOLIDAY TREATS CAN 1981
(Left) Green metal can made in England for Avon Christmas 1981. Full of Candy. SSP $9. **CMV $2. MB.** Empty.

SWEET SCENTIMENTS VALENTINE CANDY 1981
(Right) Metal pink & tan can full of candy. Bottom stamped "Avon Valentine's Day 1981" SSP $8. **CMV $2. MB empty.**

SPRING DYNASTY VASE 1982-83
7" high glass vase with fragranced outer coating in blue, pink or green. SSP $11 **CMV $6. MB each color.**

FOSTORIA CRYSTAL BUD VASE 1980
(Left) 6" high clear glass. Dated 1980 on bottom. Comes with white scented carnation. SSP $13. **CMV $8. MB.**

CRYSTAL SNOWFLAKE CHRISTMAS BELL 1980
(Center) 3.75 oz. clear glass. Bottom label dated 1980. Choice of Charisma, Topaze, Occur! or Cotillion cologne. SSP $8. **CMV $5. MB.**

MARCHING PROUD 1980-81
(Right) 8 1/2" high, 2 oz. blue base paint over clear glass. White top, red hat, cloth flag. Choice of Sweet Honesty or Topaze cologne. SSP $12. **CMV $7. MB.**

LITTLE DREAM GIRL 1980-81
(Left) 1.25 oz. aqua paint over clear glass. Cream color top. Choice of Sweet Honesty or Occur! cologne. SSP $5. **CMV $3. MB.**

BUNDLE OF LOVE 1980-81
(Center) .75 oz. light blue paint over clear glass. Sits on red plastic sled. Choice of Hello Sunshine cologne or Sure Winner Bracing Lotion. SSP $5. **CMV $3. MB.**

FLOWER MOUSE 1980-81
(Right) .75 oz. dull red paint over clear glass and white & yellow mouse cap. Choice of Cotillion or Zany cologne. SSP $4. **CMV $2. MB.**

LIP POP COLA'S 1973-74
.13 o. plastic tube with plastic top. Came in Cherry (light red case), Cola (brown case), Strawberry (pink case) lip pomade. Strawberry & Cherry also came solid red plastic **(rare CMV $7.)** others OSP $1.50. **CMV $2. BO, $3. MB.**

NATIVITY HOLY FAMILY FIGURINE SET 1981
Box holds 3 piece white porcelain bisque nativity scene. Each dated 1981. SSP $38.50 **CMV $25. set MB.**

DAPPER SNOWMAN 1978-79
(Left) 1 oz. white milk glass with black painted spots and black hat cap. Holds Moonwind or Sweet Honesty cologne. Brown, blue and red neck scarf. SSP $3. **CMV $3. MB.**

JOLLY SANTA 1978-79
(Right) 1 oz. clear glass, white painted beard. Red cap. Came in Here's My Heart or Topaze cologne. SSP $1.50 **CMV $1.50**

SHARING THE CHRISTMAS SPIRIT FIGURINE 1981
First in a series of Christmas figurines from Avon. Dated 1981. 6" high. SSP $45. **CMV $45. MB.**

CUPID'S MESSAGE SACHET PILLOW & STICKPIN 1979-80
Red & white box holds 4" red satin heart with white lace trim. Avon on back side of arrow stickpin. Pilow has Timeless Fragrance. SSP $8. **CMV $3. MB.**

BEARING GIFTS LIP BALM 1981-82
Small fuzzy bear, head turns, holds red & green lip balm in red box. SSP $5. **CMV $3. MB.**

SPRING BOQUET VASE 1981
6" glass vase with special plastic coated scented outside. Comes in red, green or amber. SSP $9. each **CMV $6. each MB.**

HOLIDAY PLATTER 1981
11" clear glass, holly & berry decal. Plate does not say Avon. SSP $15 **CMV $10 MB.**

HOLIDAY COMPOTE 1981
4" high clear glass, holly decoration. Avon on bottom. SSP $12. **CMV $7. MB.**

HOLIDAY CANDLESTICKS 1981
3" high clear glass, holly decoration. Avon on bottom. SSP $10 set. **CMV $7. MB.**

CHRISTMAS TREE HOSTESS SET 1979
9" high ceramic green tree. Comes with Mountain Pine fragrance wax chips and rag Doll & Teddy Bear ceramic salt & pepper shakers. This was a very short issue at X-mas. 1979. SSP $25. **CMV $18. MB.**

HEARTHSIDE 1976-77
(Left) .6 oz. bronze plated over clear glass. Came in Sweet Honesty or Occur!. SSP $3.50 **CMV $4. MB. $3. BO.**

GOLDEN ANGEL 1976-77
(Right) 1 oz. gold plated over clear glass. White angel head cap. Came in Sweet Honesty or Occur!. SSP $3. **CMV $3. BO. $4. MB**

CHRISTMAS TREES 1968-70
4 oz. bubble bath. Came in red, green gold silver painted over clear glass. OSP $2.50 **CMV $9. MB. $7. BO mint.**

HEAVENLY ANGEL 1974-75
(Left) 2 oz. clear glass with white top. Holds Occur!, Unforgettable, Somewhere, Here's My Heart, or Sweet Honesty cologne. OSP $4. **CMV $6. MB. $5. BO.**

GOLDEN ANGEL BATH OIL 1968-69
(Right) 4 oz. gold bottle, gold paper wings. Gold & white cap. OSP $3.50 **CMV $7. MB. $6. BO mint.**

CHRISTMAS ORNAMENT 1970-71
5 oz. Christmas ornament with bubble bath in red, orange or green plastic bottles with silver caps. OSP $2.50 **CMV $3. MB. $2. BO.**

CHRISTMAS SPARKLERS 1968-69
4 oz. bubble bath. Came in gold, green, blue and red with gold caps. 2 sides of bottle are indented. OSP $2.50 **CMV $9. MB. $7. BO. Mint.**

CHRISTMAS SPARKLER PURPLE 1968
4 oz. painted over clear glass, gold cap. OSP $2.50 **CMV $22.50 Mint. Sold only in West Coast Area.**

FESTIVE FACETS DECANTER 1979-80
1 oz. with gold caps. Comes in Charisma "red glass", Sweet Honesty "green glass", and Here's My Heart in "blue glass". SSP $1.50 each. **CMV $2. BO, $3. MB.**

GOLDEN NOTES (CANARY) 1979-80
1.75 oz. clear glass coated light yellow, Yellow head. Came in Charisma or Woonwind cologne. SSP $3. **CMV $3. MB.**

CHURCH MOUSE GROOM 1979-80
.75 oz. white glass, white plastic top. Holds Delicate Daisies cologne. SSP $6. **CMV $6. MB.**

FUZZY BUNNY 1979-80
1 oz. clear glass coated with white flock. Pink ears, orange carrot. Holds Sweet Honesty or Honeysuckle cologne. SSP $6. **CMV $6. MB.**

YULE TREE 1974-79
(Left) 3 oz. green with plastic with green plastic top and gold star. Came in Sonnet, Moonwind or Field Flowers cologne. OSP $4. **CMV $3. BO. $4. MB.**

TOUCH OF CHRISTMAS 1975
(Center) 1 oz. green glass with red cap. Holds Unforgettable or Imperial Garden. OSP $2.50 **CMV $3. MB. $2. BO. Reissued 1979 in Zany & Here's My Heart. Same CMV.**

CRYSTAL TREE COLOGNE 1975
(Right) 3 oz. clear glass with gold plastic star cap. Holds Moonwind or Sonnet. OSP $6. **CMV $5. BO. $6. MB.**

HEAVENLY MUSIC 1978-80
(Left) 1 oz. clear glass, gold cap. Holds Charisma or Topaze cologne. SSP $3. **CMV $3. MB.**

LITTLE BURRO 1978-79
(Center) 1 oz. light gray glass. Straw hat with red flower. Holds Sweet Honesty or Charisma cologne. SSP $3. **CMV $3. BO, $4. MB.**

HONEY BEE 1978-80
(Right) 1.25 oz. amber coated over clear glass. Gold bee on lid. Holds Honeysuckle or Moonwind cologne. SSP $4. **CMV $4. MB.**

SNIFFY "SKUNK" 1978-80
1.25 oz. black glass, white trim. Holds Sweet Honesty or Topaze cologne. SSP $5. **CMV $5. MB.**

"CALCULATOR" IT ALL ADDS UP 1979-80
4 oz. black glass. Holds Deep Woods After Shave or Sweet Honesty Body Splash. SSP $6. **CMV $6. MB.**

CHRISTMAS COLOGNE 1969-70
3 oz. each. Unforgettable is silver & pink, Occur! is gold & blue, Somewhere is silver & green, Topaze is bronze and yellow. OSP $3.50 **CMV $8. BO. $10. MB.**

KANGAROO TWO 1978-79
8" red calico stuffed Kangaroo with Avon tag. Green neck ribbon. Came with .75 oz. frosted glass kangaroo bottle with gold head. Holds Topaze or Sweet Honesty cologne. SSP $10. **CMV $10. both MB, BO $4., Stuffed toy $5.**

FAIRYTALE FROG 1976
1 oz. clear glass with gold frog cap. Choice of Sweet Honesty or Sonnet Cologne. OSP $3. **CMV $3. MB, $2. BO.**

LUCKY PENNY LIP GLOSS 1976-80
2" diameter copper colored. Contains 2 colors lip gloss. OSP $3. **CMV $2. MB, $1. no box.** Reissued in 1980 with R on bottom.

CHRISTMAS ORNAMENTS 1967
Round 4 oz. bubble bath. Came in gold, silver, red, green. Silver caps. OSP $1.75. **CMV $10. MB, $8. BO mint.**

ROCKING HORSE TREE ORNAMENT 1979-80
.75 oz. clear glass rocker shapes bottle with gold plastic rocking horse top. Bottom of horse says 1979. Holds Sweet Honesty or Moonwind cologne. SSP $5. **CMV $4. MB.**

BABY HIPPO 1977-80
1 oz. frosted glass with silver head. Came in Sweet Honesty or Topaze cologne. OSP $5. **CMV $4. MB, $3. BO.**
LITTLE LAMB 1977-78
.75 oz. white milk glass, white head. Came in Sweet Honesty or Topaze cologne. OSP $5. **CMV $4. BO, $5. MB.**

PRETTY PIGLET 1979-80
(Left) .75 oz. clear glass. Holds Roses Roses, pink cap; Honeysuckle, yellow cap; Hawaiian White Ginger, blue-green cap. Fabric flower around neck. SSP $3. **CMV $3. MB.**
MONKEY SHINES 1979-80
(Inside Left) 1 oz. clear glass painted light gray, brown eyes and ears. Red cap and neck strap. Holds Sonnet or Moonwind cologne. SSP $6. **CMV $5. BO, $6. MB.**
BON BON 1979-80
(Inside Right) .75 oz. dark amber glass. Pink and green top came with Sweet Honesty cologne or Cotillion with yellow and green top. SSP $4. **CMV $4. MB.**
GENTLE FOAL 1979-80
(Right) 1.5 oz. dark amber glass and plastic head. Comes in Charisma or Sun Blossoms cologne. SSP $5. **CMV $5. MB.**

LOVE SONG 1973-75
6 oz. frosted glass with gold cap. Holds Skin-So-Soft bath oil. OSP $6. **CMV $5. MB, $3. BO.**
BATH TREASURE SNAIL 1973-76
6 oz. clear glass with gold head. Holds Skin-So-Soft. OSP $6. **CMV $6. MB, $5. BO.**

ENCHANTED FROG CREAM SACHET 1973-76
(Left) 1.25 oz. cream colored milk glass with cream colored plastic lid. Came in Sonnet, Moonwind or Occur!. OSP $3. **CMV $4. MB, $3. BO.**
HANDY FROG 1975-76
(Right) 8 oz. white milk glass with red cap. OSP $6. **CMV $5. MB, $4. BO.**

MERRY MOUSE 1979-80
(Left) .75 oz. white milk glass bottle & head. Stick on holly leaf. Choice of Zany or Cotillion cologne. SSP $5. **CMV $4. MB.**
PRECIOUS CHICKADEE 1979-80
(Center) 1 oz. white glass. Red & white cap. Came in Here's My Heart or Sun Blossoms cologne. SSP $4. **CMV $3. MB.**
SNUG CUB 1979-80
(Right) 1 oz. milk glass. Green cap. Pink & green paint. Comes in Occur! or Sweet Honesty cologne. SSP $3. **CMV $2. MB.**

PERFUME CONCENTRE 1974-76
1 oz. clear glass with gold cap. Came in Imperial Garden, Moonwind, Sonnet, Charisma or Bird of Paradise. SSP $4. **CMV $3. MB, $2. BO.**
UNICORN 1974-75
2 oz. clear glass with gold cap. Came in Field Flowers, Charisma, Bired of Paradise or Brocade. SSP $4. **CMV $4. MB, $3. BO.**

SNOW BUNNY 1975-76
3 oz. clear glass with gold cap. Holds Moonwind, Charisma, Bird of Paradise or Sweet Honesty cologne. OSP $4. **CMV $5. MB, $4. BO.**
LA BELLE TELEPHONE 1974-76
1 oz. clear glass with gold top. Holds Moonwind, Sonnet or Charisma perfume concentre. OSP $7. **CMV $8. MB, $7. BO.**

TEDDY BEAR 1976-78
.75 oz. frosted glass, gold cap. Came in Sweet Honesty or Topaze. SSP $3. **CMV $2.50 MB, $2. BO.**

PRECIOUS DOE 1976-78
1/2 oz. frosted glass bottle. Came in Field Flowers or Sweet Honesty. SSP $3. **CMV $2.50 MB, $2. BO.**

HUGGABLE HIPPO 1980
1.75 oz. white glass. Red hat. Holds Zany cologne or Light Musk After Shave. Comes with card of stick on decals. SSP $4. **CMV $3. MB.**

GREEN-BLUE-BROWN EYED SUSAN COMPACT 1980
3 different color centers with yellow flower rim. SSP $5. **CMV $2. each MB.**

COUNTRY KITCHEN 1973-75
6 oz. white milk glass with red plastic head. Holds moisturized hand lotion. SSP $5. **CMV $6. MB, $5. BO.**

HIGH-BUTTONED SHOE 1975-76
2 oz. clear glass with gold cap. holds Occur! or Unforgettable cologne. OSP $3. **CMV $3. MB, $2. BO.**

GRACEFUL GIRAFFE 1976
1.5 oz. clear glass with plastic top. Holds Topaze or To A Wild Rose cologne. OSP $4. **CMV $5. MB, $4. BO.**

FLOWER FAIR SSS 1975-76
(Left) 5 oz. marbleized glass jar with plastic cap. Holds Skin-So-Soft Skin Softener. SSP $4. **CMV $2. MB, $1. BO.**

FLOWER FAIR COLOGNE 1975-76
(Right) 3 oz. marbleized glass with plastic top. Holds Roses Roses, Moonwind or Sonnet. SSP $4. **CMV $1. BO, $2. MB.**

ROYAL COACH 1972-73
5 oz. white milk glass, gold cap. Holds Moonwind, Bird of Paradise, Charisma or Field Flowers foaming bath oil. OSP $5. **CMV $6. MB, $5. BO.**

SITTING PRETTY 1971-73
4 oz. white milk glass with gold cat cap. Came in Topaze, Rapture, Cotillion, Somewhere or persian Wood. OSP $5. **CMV $8. MB, $6. BO.**

GOOD LUCK ELEPHANT 1975-76
1.5 oz. frosted glass, gold cap. holds Sonnet, Imperial Garden or Patchwork cologne. OSP $3. **CMV $4. MB, $3. BO.**

SWISS MOUSE 1974-75
3 oz. frosted glass, gold cap. Holds Roses Roses, Field Flowers or Bird of Paradise cologne. OSP $4. **CMV $5. MB, $4. BO.**

VENETIAN PITCHER COLOGNE MIST 1973-75
3 oz. blue plastic coated bottle with silver plastic top. Came in Imperial Garden, Patchwork, Sonnet or Moonwind. SSP $6. **CMV $5. MB, $3. BO.**

COMPOTE DECANTER 1972-75
5 oz. white milk glass bottle, gold cap. Came in Moonwind, Field Flowers, Elusive or Brocade. SSP $5. **CMV $5. MB, $4. BO.**

BATH URN 1971-73
5 oz. white glass & cap with gold top plate. Foaming bath oil in Elusive & Charisma or bath foam in Lemon Velvet & Silk & Honey. 6" high. SSP $4. **CMV $5. MB, $4. BO.**

KOFFEE KLATCH 1971-74
5 oz. yellow paint over clear glass pot with gold top. Foaming Bath Oil in Field Flowers, Honeysuckle or Lilac. Also Lemon Velvet Bath Foam. SSP $5. **CMV $6. MB, $5. BO.**

VICTORIAN MANOR 1972-73
(Left) 5 oz. white painted over clear glass with pink plastic roof. Holds Roses Roses, Bird of Paradise, Unforgettable, Cotillion. SSP $5. **CMV $9. MB, $8. BO.**

HOBNAIL DECANTER 1972-74
(Center) 5 oz. white opal glass. Came in Moonwind, Elusive, Roses Roses Bath Foam, Lemon Velvet Bath Foam. SSP $6. **CMV $6. MB, $4. BO.**

HOBNAIL BUD VASE 1973-74
(Right) 4 oz. white milk glass with red & yellow roses. Holds Charisma, Topaze, Roses Roses cologne. SSP $6. **CMV $5. MB, $4. BO.** Also came 4.75 oz. size.

FRAGRANCE HOURS 1971-73
6 oz. ivory glass grandfathers clock, gold cap. Bird of Paradise, Field Flowers, Charisma or Elusive. SSP $5. **CMV $7. MB, $6. BO.**

EIFFEL TOWER 1970
3 oz., 9" high clear glass with gold cap. Came in Occur!, Rapture, Somewhere, Topaze, Cotillion or Unforgettable. SSP $4. **CMV $8. MB, $6. BO.**

SWEET SHOPPE PIN CUSHION 1972-74
(Left) 1 oz. white milk glass bottom with white plastic back with hot pink pin cushion seat. Came in Sonnet, Moonwind, Field Flowers, Roses Roses, Bird of Paradise or Charisma. SSP $4. **CMV $7. MB, $5. BO.**

FRAGRANCE TOUCH 1969-70
(Right) 3 oz. white milk glass. Cologne came in Elusive, Charisma, Brocade or Regence. OSP $5. **CMV $5. MB, $4. BO.**

BATH SEASONS 1967
3 oz. foaming oil. Each is white glass & top with orange design in Honeysuckle, green in Lily of the Valley. **CMV $7. BO, $9. MB each.** Lavender in Lilac, yellow in Jasmine. Matching ribbons on each. OSP $2.50 each. **CMV $7. BO each, $9. MB.**

BUTTERCUP CANDLESTICK 1974
(Left) 6 oz. white milk glass, yellow & white flowers. Holds Moonwind, Sonnet or Imperial Garden cologne. OSP $7. First issue has yellow band around neck. **CMV $9. MB.** Later issue was plain with no band on neck and yellow or brown decals. **CMV $7. MB, $2. less no box.**

BUTTERCUP FLOWER HOLDER 1974
(Center) 5 oz. milk glass with plastic white top. Holds Moonwind, Imperial Garden or Sonnet. OSP $5. **CMV $5. MB, $3. BO.**

BUTTERCUP SALT SHAKER 1974
(Right) 1.5 oz. white milk glass with yellow & white flowers, yellow plastic cap. Came in Moonwind, Sonnet or Imperial Garden. OSP $2.50. **CMV $3. MB, $2. BO.**

DUTCH TREAT DEMI-CUPS 1971
3 oz. white glass filled with Cream Lotion in Honeysuckle, yellow cap; Blue lotus, blue cap; Hawaiian White Ginger, pink cap. OSP $3.50. **CMV $7. MB, $5. BO.** Also each came with white caps.

SALT SHAKERS 1968-70
3 oz. pink ribbon, pink flowers. Yellow ribbon & flowers in Hawaiian Ginger White, Honeysuckle & Lilac bath oil. OSP $2.50. **CMV $8. MB each, $6. BO.**

ORIENTAL EGG - CHINESE PHEASANT 1975
Upside down label mistake made at factory. Upside down bottle only. **CMV $18.**

BLUE DEMI-CUP 1968-70
(Left) 3 oz. white glass, blue cap & design, some came with gold top with blue lid. Came in Brocade, Topaze or Unforgettable. OSP $3.50. **CMV $8. MB, $6. BO.**

DEMI-CUP 1969-70
(Center Two) 3 oz. white milk glass. Charisma has red cap and design. Regence has green cap and design. OSP $3.50. **CMV $8. MB, $6. BO.**

TO A WILD ROSE DEMI-CUP 1969
(Right) 3 oz. white glass, red rose, pink cap. 6 1/2" high. Contains Foaming Bath Oil. OSP $3.50. **CMV $9. MB, $7. BO.**

ENCHANTED HOURS 1972-73
(Left) 5 oz. blue glass bottle with gold cap. Came in Roses Roses, Charisma, Unforgettable or Somewhere cologne. SSP $5. **CMV $7. MB, $6. BO.**

BEAUTIFUL AWAKENING 1973-74
(Right) 3 oz. gold painted over clear glass front paper clock face, gold cap. Came in Elusive, Roses Roses or Topaze. SSP $5. **CMV $5. BO, $6. MB.**

LEISURE HOURS 1970-72
5 oz. white milk glass bottle contains foaming bath oil in 6 fragrances. Gold cap. OSP $4. **CMV $6., $8. MB.**

LEISURE HOURS MINIATURE 1974
1.5 oz. white milk glass bottle, gold cap. Holds Field Flowers, Bird of Paradise or Charisma cologne. OSP $3. **CMV $5., $6. MB.**

ORIENTAL EGG CHINESE PHEASANT 1975
(Left) 1 oz. white opal glass, black plastic base. Came in Imperial Garden, Charisma and Bird of Paradise cologne. OSP $6.50. **CMV $10. MB, $8. BO.**

ORIENTAL EGG PEACH ORCHARD 1974-75
(Right) 1 oz. white opal glass with green marbleized plastic base. Came in Imperial Garden, Sonnet or Moonwind or Patchwork perfume concentre. SSP $5. **CMV $8. MB, $7. BO.**

ORIENTAL EGG DELICATE BLOSSOMS 1975-76
(Center) 1 oz. light blue opal glass with blue-green plastic base. Came in Patchwork, Sonnet & Charisma cologne. OSP $7.50. **CMV $8. MB, $7. BO.**

HEARTSCENT CREAM SACHET 1976-77
.66 oz. white glass bottom with white plastic top. Gold dove design. Came in Charisma, Occurl or Roses Roses. OSP $3. **CMV $4. MB, $3. BO.**

FOSTORIA COMPOTE 1975-76
12 Skin-So-Soft capsules. Clear glass with glass top. OSP $8. **CMV $6. MB, $5. BO.**

VICTORIANA SOAP DISH 1978
Blue marbleized glass - white soap. May 1978 on bottom. SSP $5. **CMV $6., $4. no box, $2. dish only.**

VICTORIANA PITCHER & BOWL 1978
Blue marbleized glass bowl and 6 oz. pitcher. Holds bubble bath. May 1978 on bottom. SSP $9. **CMV $8. MB, $6. no box.**

BUTTERFLY FANTASY PORCELAIN TREASURE EGG 1974-80
5 1/2" long white porcelain multi-colored butterfly decals. Sold empty. 1974 stamped on bottom. Sold 1974-75 then reissued 1978. The 1978 issue was a 1974 "R" for reissue on bottom and the big butterfly on top is much lighter than the 1974 issue. OSP $12. **CMV $25. MB for 1974 issue. CMV $15, MB for 1974 "R" issue.** 1979-80 issue has "R" 1979 on bottom. **CMV $15. MB.** Also came with bottom label upside down or backwards. **Add $6. CMV.**

FRENCH TELEPHONE 1971
6 oz. white milk glass base with gold cap & trim. Holds Foaming Bath Oil. Center of receiver holds 1/4 oz. of perfume in frosted glass. Came in Moonwind. OSP $22. Bird of Paradise, Elusive or Charisma. OSP $20. **CMV $27.50 MB, $22. BO.**

GRECIAN PITCHER 1972-76
6 1/2" high, 5 oz. white glass bottle & white stopper holds Skin-So-Soft. SSP $5. **CMV $6. MB, $5. BO.**

CORNUCOPIA 1971-76
6 oz. white glass, gold cap. 5 1/2" high. SSP $5. **CMV $6. MB, $5. BO.**

VICTORIANA PITCHER & BOWL 1971-72
6 oz. turquoise glass pitcher with Skin-So-Soft bath oil & turquoise glass bowl with Avon bottom. Some bowls have double Avon stamp on bottom. OSP $7.50. **CMV $11. MB, $9. no box, $12. with double stamp on bottom.**

VICTORIANA PITCHER & BOWL 1972-73
Same as above only came in Moonwind, Field Flowers Foaming Bath Oil. SSP $7. **CMV $8. no box, $11. MB.**

VICTORIANA POWDER SACHET 1972-74
1.5 oz. turquoise glass jar & lid. Came in Moonwind, Field Flowers. SSP $5. **CMV $6. BO, $8. MB.**

VICTORIANA DISH & SOAP 1972-73
Turquoise glass dish with white soap. SSP $4. **CMV $8. MB, dish only $3.**

SECRETAIRE 1972-75
7" high, pink paint over clear glass, gold cap. Holds 5 oz. of Foaming Bath Oil in Moonwind, Charisma, Brocade, Lilac & Lemon Velvet. OSP $6. **CMV $7. MB, $6. BO.**

ARMOIRE 1972-75
7" high, 5 oz. white glass bottle with gold cap. Choice of Field Flowers, Bird of Paradise, Elusive or Charisma bath oil. 1975 came in Field Flowers, Charisma & Bird of Paradise only. SSP $4. **CMV $5. MB, $4. BO.**

PRECIOUS HEARTS 1980
(Left) Heart embossed clear glass, 5 oz. gold tone cap. Comes in Here's My Heart, Unforgettable, Moonwind, Topaze or Sweet Honesty. SSP $1.29. **CMV $1. MB.**

FLUFFY CHICK 1980
(Center) 1 oz. clear glass yellow flock coated. Holds Hello Sunshine cologne. SSP $6. **CMV $4. MB.**

FLUTTERING FANCY 1980
(Right) 1 oz. clear glass with pink butterfly on yellow frosted plastic cap. Holds Sweet Honesty or Charisma cologne. SSP $5. **CMV $4. MB.**

CHRISTMAS BELLS 1979-80
1 oz. red glass. Silver cap. Holds Topaze or Sweet Honesty cologne. SSP $3. **CMV $3. MB.**

RED CARDINAL 1979-80
2 oz. clear glass painted red. Red cap. Holds Bird of Paradise or Charisma cologne. SSP $5. **CMV $4. MB.**

SILVER SWIRLS SALT SHAKER 1977-79
3 oz. silver plated over clear glass. Silver top. Came in Sweet Honesty or Topaze cologne. SSP $4. **CMV $3. MB, $2. BO.**

ISLAND PARAKEET 1977-78
1.5 oz. blue glass base & blue & yellow plastic top. Approx. 4 1/2" high. Came in Moonwind or Charisma Cologne. OSP $6. **CMV $4. MB, $3. BO.**

FLAMINGO 1971-72
5 oz. clear bird shaped bottle with gold cap. 10" tall. Came in Bird of Paradise, Elusive, Charisma, Brocade. SSP $4.50. **CMV $5. MB, $4. BO.**

SWAN LAKE 1972-76
8" high, 3 oz. white glass bottle with white cap. Came in Bird of Paradise, Charisma & Elusive. OSP $5. Moonwind SSP $5. **CMV $5. MB, $4. BO.**

BATH URN (CRUET) 1963-64
8 oz. white glass top & bottle. Perfume bath oil in Somewhere, Topaze, Cotillion. OSP $3.75 each. Here's My Heart, Persian Wood, To A Wild Rose. OSP $3.50 each. **CMV $10. MB, $6. bottle with label.**

LOVABLE SEAL 1976-77
1 oz. frosted glass, gold cap. Came in Cotillion or Here's My Heart. OSP $4. **CMV $3. MB, $2. BO.**

LOVE BIRD 1978
1 1/2 oz. milk glass bottle with gold cap. Came in Charisma or Moonwind cologne. SSP $4. **CMV $3. MB, $2. BO.**

REGAL PEACOCK 1973-74
4 oz. blue glass with gold cap. Came in Patchwork, Sonnet or Moonwind. SSP $6. **CMV $9. MB, $7. BO.**

COUNTRY STORE COFFEE MILL 1972-76
5 oz. ivory milk glass, white plastic cap & plastic handles on side with gold rim. Came in Sonnet, Moonwind, Bird of Paradise, Charisma cologne. SSP $6. **CMV $7. MB, $5. BO.** Came in 2 different size boxes.

LITTLE DUTCH KETTLE 1972-73
5 oz. orange painted clear glass with gold cap. Came in Cotillion, Honeysuckle Foaming Bath Oil or Lemon Velvet Bath Foam. SSP $5. **CMV $6. MB, $5. BO.**

SNOW OWL POWDER SACHET II 1979-80
(Left) 1.25 oz. frosted glass. Holds Moonwind or Timeless powder sachet. Blue Rhinestone eyes. Label in black lettering. SSP $7. **CMV $7. MB.**

CUTE COOKIE 1979-80
(Center) 1 oz. dark amber glass. Pink cap & point. Holds Hello Sunshine cologne. SSP $2.75. **CMV $2.75 MB.**

CHARMING CHIPMUNK 1979-80
(Right) 5 oz. clear glass painted frosted peach color. Holds Field Flowers or Sweet Honesty. SSP $4. **CMV $4. MB.**

SONG BIRD 1971-72
1.5 oz. clear glass with gold base cap. Came in Unforgettable, Topaze, Occur!, Here's My Heart & Cotillion. OSP $3. **CMV $5. MB, $4. BO.**

BIRD OF HAPPINESS 1975-76
1.5 oz. light blue glass, gold cap. Holds Charisma, Topaze, Occur!, or Unforgettable cologne. OSP $3. **CMV $5. MB, $4. BO.**

DR. HOOT 1977-79
(Left) 4 oz. white milk glass owl with blue plastic cap and white, gold or green tassel. Came in Sweet Honesty or Wild Country. OSP $7.50. **CMV $6. MB, $5. BO.**

DR. HOOT 1975-76
4 oz. opal white glass, black cap, gold tassel. Holds Wild Country After Shave or Sweet Honesty cologne. OSP $5. **CMV $6. MB, $5. BO.**

PRECIOUS OWL 1972-74
(Center) 1 1/2 oz. white bottle with gold eyes. Came in Moonwind, Field Flowers, Charisma, Roses Roses. OSP $3. **CMV $3. MB, $2. BO.**

SNOW OWL 1976-77
(Right) 1.25 oz. frosted glass base and frosted plastic head with blue eyes. Came in Moonwind or Sonnet. Label in blue lettering. SSP $4. **CMV $5. MB, $4. BO.**

SILVER DOVE ORNAMENT 1976
1/2 oz. bottle with gold or silver cap. Came in silver metal bird holder marked Christmas '76 on both sides & Avon on inside. Came in Bird of Paradise or Occur! cologne. SSP $4. **CMV $5. MB, $4. no box.**

ROYAL SWAN 1971-72
1 oz. white glass, gold crown cap. Came in Elusive, Charisma, Bird of Paradise, Topaze, Unforgettable, Cotillion. SSP $3. **CMV $6. MB, $4. BO.**

ROYAL SWAN 1974
1 oz. blue glass with gold crown cap. Came in Unforgettable, Topaze, Cotillion, Here's My Heart. SSP $2.50. **CMV $6. BO, $8. MB.**

CRYSTAL FACETS 1973-75
3 oz. clear glass. Choice of Roses Roses or Field Flowers. OSP $4. **CMV $4. MB, $3. BO.**

OWL FANCY 1974-76
4 oz. clear glass. Came in Raining Violets or Roses Roses. SSP $4. **CMV $4. MB, $3. BO.**

CRYSTALSONG 1975-76
4 oz. red glass with frosted bow and handle. Holds Timeless or Sonnet. OSP $6. **CMV $5. BO, $6. MB.**

CHRISTMAS BELLS 1974-75
1 oz. red painted glass with gold cap. Came in Topaze, Occur!, Cotillion To A Wild Rose or Sweet Honesty. OSP $2.25. **CMV $4. BO, $5. MB.**

GARDEN FRESH DECANTER 1979-80
10 oz. clear glass. Yellow & gold pump & cap. Green box. SSP $7. **CMV $4. MB.**

HEAVENLY CHERUB HOSTESS BELL 1979-80
3.75 oz. clear glass painted frosted tan. Gold plastic handle. 1979 embossed on bottom. Comes in Topaze or Bird of Paradise cologne. SSP $7. **CMV $6. MB.**

SNOW BIRD 1973-74
1.5 oz. white milk glass, white plastic cap. Came in Patchwork, Moonwind, Sonnet Cream Sachet. OSP $2.50. **CMV $4. MB, $3. BO.**

ROBIN RED-BREAST 1974-75
2 oz. red frosted glass with silver plastic top. Holds Charisma, Roses Roses, Bird of Paradise. OSP $4. **CMV $4. MB, $3. BO.**

FLIGHT TO BEAUTY 1975
5 oz. glass jar with white frosted top. Holds Rich Moisture or Vita-Moist Cream or SSS Skin Softener. OSP $5. **CMV $4. MB, $3. BO.**

PARTRIDGE 1973-75
5 oz. white milk glass with white plastic lid. Came in Unforgettable, Topaze, Occur!, Somewhere. OSP $5. **CMV $5. MB, $4. BO.**

MOONLIGHT GLOW ANNUAL BELL 1981-82
3 oz. glass bell, frosted top. Choice of Moonwind or Topaze. SSP $9. **CMV $7. MB.**

FRAGRANCE BELL 1968-69
(Left) 1 oz. gold handle. Bell actually rings. Came in Charisma, Brocade, Regence, Unforgettable, Rapture, Occur!, Somewhere, Topaze, Cotillion, Here's My Heart, To A Wild Rose, Wishing. OSP $3.50. **CMV bell with tag $15., $20. MB.**

FRAGRANCE BELL 1965-66
(Center) 4 oz. clear glass, plastic handle, neck tag. Came in Rapture, Occur!, Somewhere, Topaze, Cotillion, Here's My Heart, To A Wild Rose, Wishing. OSP $3.50. **CMV bell with tag $15., $20. MB.**

HOBNAIL BELL 1973-74
(Right) 2 oz. white milk glass with gold handle & gold bell underneath. Holds Unforgettable, Topaze, Here's My Heart, To A Wild Rose or Sweet Honesty. SSP $4. **CMV $5. MB, $4. BO.**

JOYOUS BELL 1978
Light blue frosted over clear glass. Silver cap. Came in Charisma or Topaze cologne. In blue & white box. SSP $3. **CMV $3. MB.**

SUNNY SHINE UP 1978-79
White plastic base with yellow screw on egg lid. SSP $3. **CMV $1. MB.**

ROYAL SIAMESE CAT 1978-79
Light gray paint over clear glass. 4.5 oz. gray plastic head has blue glass jewel eyes. Came in Cotillion or Moonwind cologne. SSP $7. **CMV $6. MB, $5. BO.**

EMERALD BELL 1978-79
3.75 oz. light green glass. Gold and green plastic cap. Bottom has "Avon 1978" embossed. Came in Sweet Honesty or Roses Roses cologne. SSP $6. **CMV $5. MB, $4. BO.**

ROSEPOINT BELL 1978
(Left) 4 oz. clear glass, clear plastic top. Came in Charisma or Roses Roses cologne. OSP $8.50. **CMV $6. MB, $5. BO.**

HOSPITALITY BELL 1976-77
(Right) Silver top, 3.75 oz. blue glass bottom. Came in Moonwind or Roses Roses cologne. Avon 1976 stamped in bottom. OSP $8. **CMV $6. MB, $5. BO.**

KITTEN PETITE 1973-74
1.5 oz. amber glass ball with white plastic cat for cap. Came in Sonnet or Moonwind. SSP $3. **CMV $4. BO, $5. MB.**

MING CAT 1971
6 oz. white glass & head, blue trim & neck ribbon. Came in Moonwind, Bird of Paradise, Elusive, Charisma. SSP $6. **CMV $9. MB, $7. BO.**

KITTEN LITTLE 1972-76
3 1/2" high, white glass bottle holds 1 1/2 oz. cologne in Occur!, Topaze, Unforgettable, Somewhere, Cotillion. SSP $2. **CMV $3. BO, $4. MB.**

COUNTRY KITCHEN 1974-79
10 oz. red glass with plastic top. Holds Moisturized Hand Lotion. OSP $6. **CMV $3. MB, $2. BO.** Reissued in 1979.

LADY SPANIEL 1974-76
1.5 oz. opal glass with plastic head. Holds Patchwork, Sonnet or Moonwind cologne. OSP $3. **CMV $4. MB, $3. BO.**

SITTING PRETTY 1976-77
1.5 oz. white milk glass base, white plastic top. Came in Charisma or Topaze. Pink ribbons painted on each corner. OSP $6. **CMV $6. MB, $5. BO.**

ROYAL ELEPHANT 1977-79
1/2 oz. white milk glass with gold snap on top. Came in Charisma or Topaze. OSP $6. **CMV $5. MB, $4. BO.**

KITTEN LITTLE 1975-76
1.5 oz. black glass with black head. Holds Sweet Honesty, Bird of Paradise or Roses Roses. OSP $4. **CMV $5. MB, $4. BO.**

TABATHA 1975-76
3 oz. black glass and plastic. Holds Imperial Garden, Bird of Paradise or Cotillion cologne. OSP $6. **CMV $5. MB, $4. BO.**

KITTEN'S HIDEAWAY 1974-76
1 oz. amber basket, white plastic kitten cap. Came in Field Flowers, Bird of Paradise or Charisma Cream Sachet. OSP $4. **CMV $5. MB, $4. BO.**

BLUE EYES 1975-76
1.5 oz. opal glass with blue rhinestone eyes. Available in Topaze or Sweet Honesty cologne. OSP $4. **CMV $5. BO, $6. MB.**

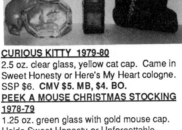

CURIOUS KITTY 1979-80
2.5 oz. clear glass, yellow cat cap. Came in Sweet Honesty or Here's My Heart cologne. SSP $6. **CMV $5. MB, $4. BO.**

PEEK A MOUSE CHRISTMAS STOCKING 1978-79
1.25 oz. green glass with gold mouse cap. Holds Sweet Honesty or Unforgettable cologne. Came with red velvet stocking with gold trim. SSP $5. **CMV $5. MB, $3. BO.**

MANSION LAMP 1975-76
6 oz. blue glass with white plastic top. Holds Bird of Paradise or Moonwind cologne. OSP $8. **CMV $8. MB, $7. BO.**

EMPIRE GREEN BUD VASE 1975
3 oz. green glass with silver base. Holds moonwind, Sonnet or Imperial Garden cologne. OSP $6. **CMV $5. MB, $3. BO.**

BUTTERFLY GARDEN BUD VASE 1975-76
6 oz. black glazed glass with gold stopper. Holds Roses Roses, Bird of Paradise or Topaze cologne. OSP $6. **CMV $6. MB, $4. BO.**

SEAGREEN BUD VASE 1972-73
5 oz. 9" high green glass bottle holds foaming bath oil in Field Flowers, Honeysuckle or Bird of Paradise. SSP $4. **CMV $4. MB, $2. BO.**

PRINCESS OF YORKSHIRE 1976-78
(Left) 1 oz. off white over milk glass. Came in Sweet Honesty or Topaze cologne. SSP $4. **CMV $4. MB, $3. BO.**

ROYAL PEKINESE 1974-75
(Center) 1.5 oz. white glass & white plastic head. Came in Unforgettable, Somewhere, Topaze. OSP $5. **CMV $5. MB, $3. BO.**

FUZZY BEAR 1977-79
(Right) Tan flock over clear glass base & head. Came in Sweet Honesty or Occur! OSP $6.50. **CMV $4.50 MB, $3. BO.**

SEA SPIRIT 1973-76
5 oz. light green glass with green plastic tail over cap. Holds Elusive, Topaze or Cotillion. OSP $5. **CMV $5. MB, $4. BO.**

SONG OF THE SEA 1974-75
80 bath pearls, aqua colored glass with plastic head. Holds Moonwind, Sonnet or Imperial Garden. OSP $7. **CMV $7. MB, $5. BO.**

SEA TREASURE 1971-72
5 oz. clear glass coated iridescent sea shell shaped bottle, gold cap. Came in Field Flowers, Charisma, Honeysuckle, Lilac. 7" long. SSP $5. **CMV $8. MB, $6. BO.**

BUTTERFLY 1972-73
1 1/2 oz. 3 1/2" high, gold cap with 2 prongs. Holds cologne in Occur!, Topaze, Unforgettable, Somewhere & Here's My Heart. SSP $3. CMV $5. MB, $3. BO. Reissued in 1976 in Field Flowers & Sweet Honesty. Same CMV.

DOLPHIN MINIATURE 1973-74
1.5 oz. clear glass, gold tail. Holds Charisma, Bird of Paradise or Field Flowers cologne. OSP $3. CMV $4. MB, $3. BO.

CRYSTAL POINT SALT SHAKER 1976-77
1.5 oz. blue glass. Holds Sonnet or Cotillion cologne. OSP $3. CMV $3. MB, $2. BO.

EUROPEAN DOLPHIN
(Right) Bath oil, 165 cc size, frosted glass, gold tail cap. Foreign Dolphin smaller than U.S. size. CMV $25.

DOLPHIN 1968-69
(Left) 8 oz. frosted glass with gold tail cap. Sold in U.S.A. SSP $4. CMV $7. MB, $5. BO.

DOLPHIN FROM MEXICO
(Center) About same size as American Dolphin, only bottle is clear glass, with gold tail. Also came in frosted glass. CMV $20. each.

QUEEN OF SCOTS 1973-76
1 oz. white milk glass, white plastic head. Came in Sweet Honesty, Unforgettable, Somewhere, Cotillion, Here's My Heart. SSP $3. CMV $5. MB, $4. BO.

DACHSUND 1973-74
1.5 oz. frosted glass, gold cap. Came in Unforgettable, Somewhere, Topaze, Cotillion. SSP $3. CMV $5. MB, $4. BO.

TIFFANY LAMP 1972-74
5 oz. brown glass base with pink shade, pink and orange flowers, green leaves on lavender background. Came in Sonnet, Moonwind, Field Flowers, Roses Roses. SSP $7. CMV $9. MB, $8. BO. Also came in pink and yellow flowers on shade, also all white flowers. CMV $11. MB.

HEARTH LAMP 1973-76
8 oz. black glass with gold handle, has daisies around neck with yellow & white shade. Holds Roses Roses, Bird of Paradise or Elusive. SSP $8. CMV $8. MB, $7. BO.

CHIMNEY LAMP 1973-74
2 oz. clear glass bottom with white plastic shade with pink flowers. Holds Patchwork Sonnet or Moonwind. SSP $4. CMV $6. MB, $5. BO.

PARISIAN GARDEN 1974-75
.33 oz. white milk glass with gold cap. Came in Sonnet, moonwind or Charisma perfume. OSP $5. CMV $5. MB, $4. BO.

EVENING GLOW 1974-75
.33 oz. white milk glass with green flowers, white and gold plastic cap. Came in Moonwind, Sonnet or Charisma. OSP $6. CMV $6. BO, $7. MB.

FRAGRANCE SPLENDOR 1971-74
4 1/2" high clear glass bottle with gold cap & frosted plastic handle. Holds perfume oil in Bird of Paradise, Elusive, Occur!, Charisma or Unforgettable. OSP $5. CMV $5. MB, $4. BO.

FLORAL BUD VASE 1973-75
5 oz. white milk glass. Holds Roses Roses, Lemon Velvet Bath Foam, Field Flowers or Honeysuckle Foaming Bath Oil. SSP $5. CMV $6. MB, $5. BO.

SUZETTE 1973-76
5 oz. cream colored milk glass with cream colored plastic head & a pink-lavender bow around neck. Holds Field Flowers, Bird of Paradise or Cotillion Foaming Bath Oil. SSP $5. CMV $6. MB, $5. BO.

BON BON "BLACK" 1973
1 oz. black milk glass with black plastic cap. Holds Field Flowers, Bird of Paradise, Roses Roses or Elusive. OSP $2. CMV $6. MB, $5. BO.

BON BON "WHITE" 1972-73
1 oz. white milk glass with white cap. Holds Unforgettable, Topaze, Occur!, Cotillion or Here's My Heart cologne. OSP $2. CMV $6. MB, $5. BO.

SEA HORSE 1970-72
Clear glass 6 oz. container holds Skin-So-Soft, gold cap. SSP $5. **CMV $7. MB, $6. BO.**

SEA HORSE MINIATURE COLOGNE 1973-76
1.5 oz. clear glass, gold cap. Came in Unforgettable, Here's My Heart, Cotillion. SSP $3. **CMV $5. MB, $4. BO.**

MING BLUE LAMP 1974-76
5 oz. blue glass lamp, white plastic shade with gold tip. Holds Charisma, Bird of Paradise or Field FLowers Foaming Bath Oil. OSP $6. CMV $6. MB, $5. BO.

CHARMLIGHT 1975-76
.88 oz. cream sachet in white shade and 2 oz. cologne in pink base. Holds Imperial Garden, Sonnet or Moonwind. OSP $7. **CMV $7. MB, $6. BO.**

PARLOR LAMP 1971-72
2 sections. Gold cap over 3 oz. cologne top section in light amber iridescent glass. Yellow frosted glass bottom with talc 6 1/2" high. Holds Bird of Paradise, Elusive, Charisma, Regence or Moonwind. OSP $7. **CMV $10. MB, $8. BO.**

COURTING LAMP 1970-71
5 oz. blue glass base with white milk glass shade & blue velvet ribbon. Holds Elusive, Brocade, Charisma, Hana Gasa or Regence. OSP $6. **CMV $11. MB, $9. BO.**

COUNTRY CHARM 1976-77
(Left) 4.8 oz. white milk glass, yellow stove window. Green & white plastic top. Came in Field Flowers or Sonnet. SSP $7. **CMV $7. BO, $8. MB.**

HURRICANE LAMP 1973-74
(Right) 6 oz. white milk glass bottom with clear glass shade, gold cap. Holds Roses Roses, Field Flowers, Bird of Paradise or Charisma cologne. SSP $8. **CMV $11. MB, $9. BO.**

AVONSHIRE DECANTER 1979
6 oz. clear glass painted blue and white. Holds Charisma or Somehwere cologne. R on bottom for Reissue and dated May, 1979. SSP $9. **CMV $6. MB.**

AVONSHIRE BATH OIL DECANTER
6 oz. clear glass painted blue and white. Holds Skin-So-Soft. R on bottom for reissue and dated May, 1979. SSP $10. **CMV $5. MB.**

AVONSHIRE HOSTESS SOAPS
Blue box holds 3 white bars. SSP $4. **CMV $5. MB.**

FLOWER FANCY 1979-80
1.25 oz. clear glass, gold flower cap. Holds Field Flowers or Roses Roses. SSP $4. **CMV $4. MB.**

SPRING SONG 1979-80
1.5 oz. clear glass. Comes with plastic frosted flower stopper. Came in Lily of the Valley or Sweet Honesty cologne. SSP $6. **CMV $4. MB.**

SKIN-SO-SOFT DECANTER 1965-66
10. oz. bottle with gold painted glass stopper. 1st issue came with solid painted gold around center & later issue not solid band as pictured. OSP $5. **CMV solid band $11. MB, $7. BO mint. Not solid band $9. MB, $5. BO mint.**

SKIN-SO-SOFT DECANTER 1966
(Left) 10 oz. bottle with glass & cork stopper. 10" high. OSP $5. **CMV $6. BO, $8. MB.**

SKIN-SO-SOFT DECANTER 1967
(Right) 8 oz. bottle with glass & cork stopper. 11" high. OSP $5. **CMV $6. BO, $8. MB.**

COLOGNE RONDELLE 1978-79
.5 oz. clear glass, gold cap. Came in Sweet Honesty, Charisma, Cotillion, Topaze, Unforgettable, Moonwind, Here's My Heart, Sonnet, Occur!, Bird of Paradise. Came in different color Christmas boxes. SSP $1. **CMV $1. MB.**

BERMUDA FRESH 1978-79
6 oz. purple plastic, green top. SSP $3. **CMV $1.50.**

COUNTRY CREAMERY "MILK CAN" 1978-79
10 oz. white painted over clear glass. Holds moisturized hand lotion. SSP $6. **CMV $6. MB.**

COUNTRY STYLE COFFEE POT 1979-80
Came in special color of box. 10 oz. clear glass painted red or green, blue or yellow. Holds moisturized hand lotion. Comes with matching hand pump. SSP $8. **CMV $5. MB.**

CREAMERY DECANTER 1973-75
8 oz. yellow painted over clear glass with brown basket of blue & orange flowers. Holds Roses Roses, Field Flowers, Bird of Paradise hand & body cream lotion. OSP $5. **CMV $6. MB, $5. BO.**

LIQUID MILK BATH 1975-76
6 oz. frosted glass bottle with gold cap. Holds Imperial Garden, Sonnet or Moonwind. OSP $5. **CMV $4. MB, $2. BO.**

SKIN-SO-SOFT DECANTER 1964
(Left) 6 oz. gold crown top, came with gold neck tag. OSP $3.50. **CMV $10. MB, $5. BO** with tag, mint.

SKIN-SO-SOFT DECANTER 1962-63
(Right) 5 3/4 oz. gold neck string with white label, pink & white box. OSP $3.50. **CMV $10. MB, BO $5. mint with tag.**

HUDSON MANOR COLLECTION 1978-79
SALTCELLAR CANDLE & SPOON
Silver plated. Comes with glass lined candle. Bottom says HMC Avon Silver Plate on both pieces. Silver and white box. SSP $19. **CMV $10. MB.**

SILVER PLATED DISH AND SATIN SACHET
6" silver plated dish with red satin sachet pillow. Bottom of dish says Avon Silver Plate HMC, Italy. SSP $19. **CMV $10. MB.**

SILVER PLATED HOSTESS BELL
5 1/2" high silver plated bell. Avon Silver Plate HMC on bottom. SSP $19. **CMV $10. MB.**

SILVER PLATED BUD VASE AND SCENTED ROSE
8" high silver plated bud vase. Came with long stemmed fabric rose and 2 Roses Roses pellets. SSP $19. **CMV $10. MB.**

LADY SKATER TALC 1979-80
3.75 oz. gold top can. Red cap. Choice of Ariane or Sweet Honesty talc. SSP $4. **CMV $1. mint, no box issued.**

GENTLEMAN SKATER TALC 1979-80
3.75 oz. gold top can. Blue cap. Choice of Clint or Trazarra talc. SSP $4. **CMV $1. mint. No box issued.**

BATH SEASONS 1969
(Left) 3 oz. bath oil. Came in Charisma & Brocade. Black milk glass with silver cap & base. OSP $4.50. **CMV $6. MB, $4. BO.**

EMOLLIENT FRESHENER FOR AFTER BATH 1972-74
(Center) 6 oz. clear glass with gold cap, holds Sonnet, Charisma, Imperial Garden or Moonwind pearlescent liquid. SSP $4. **CMV $3. MB, $1. BO.**

AMBER CRUET 1973-75
(Right) 6 oz. light amber ribbed glass. Holds Field Flowers, Bird of Paradise or Charisma foaming bath oil. SSP $5. **CMV $4. MB, $3. BO.** 1975 Came only in Field Flowers & Bird of Paradise.

OOPS COLOGNE DECANTER 1981
(Left) White glass, brown spots. Ice Cream bottle with tan plastic cone top. 1.5 oz. Sweet Honesty or Country Breeze. SSP $6. **CMV $3. MB.**

BIG SPENDER 1981-82
(Center) 1 oz. green glass, silver cap. Light Musk for men or Sweet Honesty cologne. SSP $4. **CMV $2. MB.**

ULTRA CRYSTAL COLOGNE 1981-82
(Right) Gray box holds 2 oz. clear glass & glass cap. Choice of Tasha, Foxfire, Timeless, Ariane. SSP $10. **CMV $3. MB.** See Soap Dish section & Candle section for other Ultra Crystal Collections.

ICE CREAM LIP POMADE 1974-76
.13 oz. white plastic bottom with light pink, dark pink, or red top for Cherry, Strawberry or Tutti-Frutti flavors. OSP $2. CMV $3. BO, $4. MB.

ICE CREAM CONE LIP POMADE 1974-76
Yellow cone with different color tops for Cherry, Strawberry, Tutti-Frutti, Mint, Chocolate. OSP $2. CMV $3. BO, $4. MB.

COLOGNE ELEGANTE 1973-74
3 oz. clear glass, gold cap with atomizer, also white plastic cap. Holds Imperial Garden, Patchwork, Sonnet or Moonwind. SSP $6. CMV $3. MB, $2. BO.

COURTING ROSE 1974
1.5 oz. red glass rose with gold cap & stem. Came in Moonwind, Sonnet or Imperial Garden. SSP $5. Later issue painted red over clear glass. CMV $6. MB each.

SWEET TREAT COLOGNE 1974-76
White & brown painted glass with red cap. Came in Pink & Pretty cologne. SSP $2.50. CMV $2.50.

COURTING ROSE 1977
(Right) 1.5 oz. amber coated over clear glass rose bottle with gold top. Came in Roses Roses or Moonwind cologne. SSP $5. CMV $5. MB, $4. BO.

PYRAMID OF FRAGRANCE 1969
Top is 1/8 oz. perfume, gold cap. Center is 2 oz. cologne. Bottom is 2-3 oz. cream sachet in black glass. 6" high, came in Charisma, Brocade or Regence. OSP $12.50. CMV $12.50, $17.50 MB.

FASHION BOOT PIN CUSHION 1972-76
5 1/2" tall, blue milk glass with lavender bow & velvet cushion that fits over cap. Holds 4 oz. cologne. Roses Roses or Charisma. Regular price $6. Sonnet or Moonwind SSP $6. CMV $7. MB, $6. BO.

PICTURE FRAME COLOGNE 1970-71
4 oz. gold paint on clear glass. Gold cap & gold plastic frame to hold bottle. Came in Elusive, Charisma, Brocade, Regence. SSP $8. CMV $10. mint, $12. MB.

ALADDIN'S LAMP 1971-73
7 1/2" long, 6 oz. green glass bottle with gold cap. Holds foaming bath oil in Charisma, Bird of Paradise, Elusive, Occurl or Unforgettable. SSP $7. CMV $8. MB, $6. BO.

VENETIAN BLUE 1974-76
Frosted turquoise glass with turquoise plastic lid & gold tip. Holds 75 bath pearls. Came in Moonwind, Sonnet or Imperial Garden. SSP $6. CMV $6. MB, $4. BO.

DOVECOTE 1974-76
4 oz. clear glass with gold roof & 2 white doves. Holds Field Flowers, Bird of Paradise, Charisma or Roses Roses cologne. SSP $3. CMV $3. MB, $2. BO.

ROYAL APPLE COLOGNE 1972-73
(Left) 3 oz. frosted red glass with gold cap. Came in 4 fragrances. SSP $4. CMV $5. MB, $4. BO.

GARNET BUD VASE 1973-76
(Right) 3 oz. garnet colored translucent glass bottle & stopper. Came in Occur!, Somewhere, Topaze or To A Wild Rose cologne. SSP $5. CMV $4. MB, $3. BO.

ROYAL VASE 1970
(Left) 3 oz. blue cologne bottle in Elusive, Charisma, Brocade or Regence. OSP $5. CMV $5. MB, $3. BO.

RUBY BUD VASE 1970-71
(Right) 3 oz. red box holds ruby glass vase filled with Unforgettable, Rapture, Occur!, Somewhere, Topaze or Cotillion. OSP $5. CMV $5. MB, $3. BO.

GRAPE BUD VASE 1973
(Left) 6 oz. grape frosted glass holds Skin-So-Soft. SSP $5. CMV $5. MB, $3. BO.

NILE BLUE BATH URN 1972-74
(Right) 6 oz. deep blue glass with gold trim. SSP $6. CMV $5. MB, $4. BO.

NILE GREEN BATH URN 1975
(Right) Same as above only green glass. CMV $4. MB, $3. BO.

CRYSTALIQUE COLOGNE 1975
(Left) 4 oz. clear glass with glass stopper. Holds Moonwind, Sonnet or Imperial Garden. OSP $5. CMV $4. MB, $3. BO.

BREATH FRESH APOTHECARY DECANTER 1974
(Center) 8 oz. clear glass with gold cap. Holds Breath Fresh Mouthwash. SSP $3. CMV $3. MB, $2. BO.

COUNTRY PUMP 1975
(Right) 10 oz. clear glass with plastic top. Holds Rich Moisture or Vita Moist body lotion. OSP $5. CMV $4. MB, $3. BO.

LOVELY TOUCH DECANTER 1971
(Left) 12 oz. clear glass, gold cap with dispenser cap. Holds Vita Moist or Rich Moisture body lotion. SSP $4. CMV $2. MB, $1. BO.

LOVELY TOUCH DECANTER 1972-73
(Inside Left) 12 oz. clear glass with dispenser cap. Holds Vita Moist or Rich Moisture body lotion. SSP $4. CMV $2. MB, $1. BO.

CLASSIC BEAUTY 1972-76
(Inside Right) 10 oz. clear glass. Holds Bird of Paradise or Field Flowers hand & body cream. SSP $5. CMV $3. MB, $2. BO.

PINEAPPLE 1973-74
(Right) 10 oz. clear glass with green plastic leaves, dispenser top. Holds Moisturized Hand Lotion. SSP $5. CMV $4. MB, $3. BO.

BELL JAR 1973-75
(Left) 5 oz. clear glass with bouquet of pink & white flowers. Had gold cap & base with pink ribbon. Holds Field Flowers, Bird of Paradise, Charisma or Brocade cologne. SSP $7. CMV $7. BO, $9. MB. 1976 sold only in Field Flowers, Bird of Paradise & Charisma. Same CMV.

CRUET COLOGNE 1973-74
(Right) 8 oz. clear glass with glass stopper & flat dish. Holds Imperial Garden, Patchwork, Sonnet or Moonwind cologne. SSP $13. CMV $10. BO & dish, $13. MB.

PERSIAN PITCHER 1974-76
(Left) 6 oz. blue glass. Holds Bird of Paradise, Charisma or Elusive foaming bath oil. OSP $5. CMV $3. MB, $2. BO.

COLOGNE ELEGANTE 1971-72
(Center) 4 oz. gold sprayed over clear glass & red rose on gold cap. 12" high. Came in Bird of Paradise, Hana Gasa, Elusive or Charisma. OSP $8.50. Moonwind OSP $10. CMV $10. MB, $7. BO.

EMERALD BUD VASE 1971
(Right) 3 oz. green glass & glass top, 9" high. Came in Topaze, Occur!, Unforgettable, Here's My Heart or To A Wild Rose. OSP $5. CMV $4. MB, $3. BO.

SAPPHIRE SWIRL 1973-74
(Left) 5 oz. blue glass with gold cap. Holds Charisma or Bird of Paradise perfumed skin softener. SSP $4. CMV $1. MB.

PERIOD PIECE 1972-73
(Right) 5 oz. frosted glass. Came in Moonwind, Bird of Paradise, Charisma or Elusive. 1976 came with Charisma & Bird of Paradise. SSP $6. CMV $5. MB, $4. BO.

APOTHECARY 1973-74
(Left) 8 oz. Spicy After Shave in light brown glass with gold cap.

APOTHECARY 1973-76
(Center) 8 oz. Lemon Velvet Moisturized Friction Lotion in light yellow glass with gold cap. Also came in light green or blue-green glass.

APOTHECARY 1973
(Right) 8 oz. Breath Fresh in dark green with gold cap.
SSP $3. each. **CMV $5. MB each, $4. BO each.**

BAROQUE CREAM SACHET 1974
(Left) 2 oz. white milk glass with gold top & bottom. Came in Imperial Garden, Sonnet or Moonwind. SSP $5. **CMV $5. MB, $4. BO.**

COUNTRY STORE MINERAL SPRING BATH CRYSTALS 1973-75
(Right) 12 oz. clear glass with gold cap. Holds green Mineral Springs Bath Crystals. SSP $5.50. **CMV $4. MB, $2. BO.**

CAMEO CREAM SACHET 1975-76
(Left) .66 oz. painted blue glass with blue & white plastic top. Came in Here's My Heart, Charisma, Topaze or To A Wild Rose. OSP $4. **CMV $2. MB, $1. BO.**

GATHER A GARDEN CREAM SACHET 1975-76
(Center) .66 pinted blue glass jar with floral design on plastic & metal lid. Came in Hawaiian White Ginger, Roses Roses, Lemon Velvet, Lily of the Valley. OSP $4. **CMV $2. MB, $1. BO.**

EMERALDESQUE CREAM SACHET 1975-76
(Right) 1 oz. green glass with green plastic top. Holds Here's My Heart, Occur! or Sweet Honesty. OSP $3. **CMV $2. MB, $1. BO.**

PETTI FLEUR COLOGNE 1969-70
(Left) 1 oz. gold cap. Shaped like flower. Came in Elusive, Brocade, Charisma or Regence. OSP $2.50. **CMV $5. MB, $3. BO.**

PURSE PETITE COLOGNE 1971
(Right) 1 1/2 oz. embossed bottle with gold trim and cap & chain. Elusive, Charisma, Bird of Paradise, Field Flowers or Hana Gasa. OSP $4. **CMV $7. MB, $5. BO.**

KEEPSAKE CREAM SACHET 1971-73
(Left) 6 1/2" high, gold lid on marbleized glass jar with flower in colors. Came in Moonwind. OSP $5. Bird of Paradise, Field Flowers, Elusive, Charisma. SSP $3. **CMV $4. - $5. MB.**

KEEPSAKE CREAM SACHET 1970-73
(Right) 5 1/2" high gold metal tree lid on .66 oz. frosted glass jar. Came in Bird of Paradise, Elusive, Charisma, Brocade or Regence. SSP $3.50. **CMV $4. - $5. MB.**

GOLDEN FLAMINGO 1975
(Left) 6 oz. clear glass with gold flamingo on front. Holds Bird of Paradise, Charisma or Field Flowers foaming bath oil. OSP $6. **CMV $3. MB, $2. BO.**

ATHENA BATH URN 1975-76
(Right) 6 oz. clear glass. Holds Field Flowers, Bird of Paradise foaming bath oil or Roses Roses cream bath foam. OSP $6. **CMV $3. MB, $2. BO.**

COUNTRY CHARM BUTTER CHURN 1973-74
(Left) 1.5 oz. clear glass, gold bands & cap. Came in Field Flowers, Elusive, Occur! or Somewhere cologne. SSP $3. **CMV $5. MB, $4. BO.**

GOLDEN THIMBLE 1972-74
(Right) 2 oz. clear glass with gold cap. Came in Bird of Paradise, Brocade, Charisma or Elusive cologne. SSP $2. **CMV $4. MB, $3. BO.**

DEW KISS DECANTER 1974-75
(Left) 4 oz. clear glass with pink lid. OSP $3.
CMV $2. MB, $1. BO.
SEA LEGEND DECANTER 1975-76
(Right) 6 oz. clear glass with white cap. Holds
Moonwind or Sonnet foaming bath oil or Roses
Roses creamy bath foam. OSP $5. CMV $4.,
$3. BO.

COUNTRY JUG 1976-78
(Left) 10 oz. gray painted over clear glass.
Blue & gray plastic pump. Came with almond
scented hand lotion. OSP $8. CMV $5. MB,
$4. BO.
SEA FANTASY BUD VASE 1978-79
(Right) 6 oz. bottle. Gold & white fish &
seaweed design on both sides. Holds Skin-
So-Soft bath oil, bubble bath & Smooth As Silk.
SSP $7. CMV $4. MB, $3. BO.

COUNTRY STYLE COFFEE POT 1975-76
(Left) 10 oz. yellow speckled paint over clear
glass. Came with yellow & white pump top.
Came with moisturized hand lotion. OSP $6.
CMV $7. MB, $6. BO.
GOLDEN HARVEST 1977-80
(Right) 10 oz. ear of corn shaped clear &
green glass bottle. Gold & plastic pump top.
Came with Avon almond scented hand lotion.
OSP $8.50. CMV $6. MB, $5. BO.

PORCELAIN FLORAL BOUQUET 1980
(Left) 4" high porcelain. Dated 1980 on
bottom. SSP $18. CMV $10. MB.
ULTRA MIST ATOMIZER 1980-81
(Right) 1.5 oz. clear swirl glass bottle with gold
top & atomizer bulb. Choice of Ariane,
Timeless, Tasha or Candid. SSP $11. CMV
$2. MB.

CRYSTALINE BOWL & FLOWERS 1982
Pink box holds 5" long glass bowl with plastic
insert to hold artificial flowers. Comes with
fragrance tablet. SSP $18. CMV $10. MB.

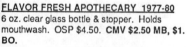

FLAVOR FRESH APOTHECARY 1977-80
6 oz. clear glass bottle & stopper. Holds
mouthwash. OSP $4.50. CMV $2.50 MB, $1.
BO.

FOAMING BATH OIL DECANTER 1975
6 oz. clear glass with gold cap. Came in
Cotillion, Field Flowers, Bird of Paradise,
Charisma, Sonnet, Imperial Garden, Moonwind
& Timeless. SSP $2.88. This sold C26 - 1975
only. Very short issue. CMV $8. MB. This is
the same bottle as the 1972-74 Emollient
Freshener for After Bath. Only label & box are
changed.

LOOKING GLASS 1970-72
6 1/2" high, clear glass mirror. Frame holds 1
1/2 oz. cologne in Bird of Paradise, Elusive,
Charisma, Brocade, Regence, Unforgettable,
Rapture, Occur!, Somewhere, Topaze,
Cotillion, Here's My Heart or To A Wild Rose.
With gold handle cap. OSP $3.50. CMV $7.
BO, $9. MB.

HONEY BEAR BABY 1974-76
4 oz. yellow painted glass with blue plastic
bear on lid. SSP $4. CMV $4. MB, $3. BO.

TREE MOUSE 1977-79
(Left) .66 oz. clear glass & clear plastic top. Gold mouse. Came in Sweet Honesty or Charisma. OSP $6. **CMV $3. MB, $2. BO.**
SILVER PEAR 1977
(Center) .66 oz. silver plated over clear glass. Silver top. Came in Sweet Honesty or Charisma. SSP $4. **CMV $3. BO, $4. MB.**
ENCHANTED APPLE 1976-78
(Right) .66 oz. gold plated over clear glass. Gold top. Came in Charisma or Sonnet. OSP $5.50. **CMV $3. BO, $4. MB.**

VICTORIAN SEWING BASKET 1974-76
(Left) 5 oz. white milk glass basket with lavender plastic, gold cord holds pink flower. Came in Roses Roses, Bird of Paradise or Charisma perfumed Skin-So-Soft. OSP $4. **CMV $4. MB, $2. BO.**
VANITY JAR 1975-76
(Right) 5 oz. clear glass with silver lid. Choice of Rich Moisture Cream or SSS skin conditioner. OSP $4. **CMV $1. MB.**

FUNBURGER LIP GLOSS 1977-78
(Left) Came in Frostlight Rose & Frostlight Coral lip gloss. Brown plastic. OSP $4.50. **CMV $2.50 - $4.50 MB.**
CHRISTMAS SURPRISE 1976
(Center) 1 oz. green glass boot. Came in Sweet Honesty, Moonwind, Charisma or Topaze cologne. Red cap or silver cap. SSP 99c. **CMV $2. MB, $1. BO.**
ORIENTAL PEONY VASE 1977
(Right) 1.5 oz. red paint over clear glass with gold design. Came in Sweet Honesty or Moonwind. OSP $6. **CMV $4. BO, $6. MB.**

WINTER GARDEN 1975-76
(Left) 6 oz. clear glass with gold cap. Holds Here's My Heart, Topaze or Occur! cologne. OSP $5. **CMV $3. MB, $2. BO.**
REGENCY DECANTER 1974-75
(Right) 6 oz. clear glass filled with Skin-So-Soft bath oil. OSP $5. **CMV $3. MB, $2. BO.**

CASTLEFORD COLLECTION EMOLLIENT BATH PEARLS 1974-76
(Left) Holds 60 bath pearls. Clear glass. Came in Imperial Garden, Sonnet or Moonwind. OSP $8. **CMV $9. MB, $6. BO.**
CASTLEFORD COLLECTION COLOGNE GELEE 1975-76
(Right) 4 oz. glass holds Raining Violets, Roses Roses or Apple Blossoms cologne gelee. OSP $8. **CMV $8. MB, $6. BO.**

HUMPTY DUMPTY BANK 1982
Box holds ceramic bank made in Korea for Avon. Dated 1982. Sold empty. 5" high. SSP $12. **CMV $7. MB.**
CRYSTAL CLEAR HOSTESS DECANTER 1980-81
Clear glass jar & glass lid, Avon stainless spoon. Comes in 5.5 oz. Strawberry Bubble Bath Gelee. SSP $11. **CMV $3. MB.**

PEAR LUMIERE 1975-76
(Left) 2 oz. clear glass & plastic with gold leaf. Holds Roses Roses, Charisma or Bird of Paradise cologne. OSP $5. **CMV $5. MB, $4. BO.**
SONG OF LOVE 1975-76
(Right) 2 oz. clear glass, clear plastic top with white bird. Holds Bird of Paradise, Charisma or Sweet Honesty. 1976 issued with blue base, blue top in Moonwind & Here's My Heart. OSP $4. **CMV $3. MB, $2. BO.**

SCENTIMENTS COLOGNE 1978-79
(Left) 2 oz. clear glass. Came with pink card on front to write your own message. Came in Sweet Honesty or Here's My Heart cologne. SSP $4.99. **CMV $4. MB, $2. BO.**
GOLDEN BAMBOO VASE 1978-79
(Right) 1 oz. yellow painted over clear glass, black cap, base. Came in Moonwind or Sweet Honesty cologne. SSP $3. **CMV $3. - $2. BO.**

VICTORIAN WASHSTAND 1973-74
(Left) 4 oz. buff painted with gray plastic simulated marble top with blue pitcher & bowl for cap. Came in Field Flowers, Bird of Paradise or Charisma foaming bath oil. SSP $5. **CMV $7. MB, $6. BO.**
REMEMBER WHEN SCHOOL DESK 1972-74
(Right) 4 oz. black glass with light brown plastic seat front & desk top, red apple for cap. Came in Rapture, Here's My Heart, Cotillion or Somewhere cologne. SSP $5. **CMV $7. MB, $5. BO.**

TEATIME POWDER SACHET 1974-75
1.25 oz. frosted white with gold cap. Holds Moonwind, Sonnet or Roses Roses. OSP $4. CMV $4. MB, $3. BO.

SCENT WITH LOVE 1975-76
.66 oz. gold toned glass base with amber plastic top that is a stamp dispenser. Holds Unforgettable, Topaze or Here's My Heart cream sachet. OSP $4. CMV $2. MB, $1. BO.

AMERICAN HEIRLOOM SHIPS DECANTER 1981-82
(Left) 6 oz. clear glass, glass top. Choice of Wild Country After Shave or Sweet Honesty Body Splash. SSP $9. CMV $5. MB.

SOFT SWIRLS BATH DECANTER 1981-82
(Right) 8 oz. clear glass, frosted cap. Choice of Smooth As Silk bath oil or Skin-So-Soft. SSP $10. CMV $4. MB.

NATURE'S BEST WOODEN DISPLAY SPOON HOLDER 1981-82
Made of wood, 3 1/2" x 7". Does not say Avon. Comes in Avon box. SSP $7. CMV $5. MB.

NATURE'S BEST COLLECTOR'S SPOONS 1981-82
4 different stainless spoons with Avon on them. 5" long in flannel pouch. porcelain inlaid with fruit - strawberry, orange, plum, raspberry. SSP $10. each. CMV $5. each MB.

VANITY COLLECTION TRAY 1980-81
10" x 12" metal tray made in England. SSP $8. CMV $3. MB.

ULTRA COLOGNE DECANTER
2 oz. beige painted over clear glass. Choice of Ariane, Candid or Timeless Ultra cologne. SSP $8. CMV $1. MB.

VANITY COLLECTION ULTRA SOFT BODY SATIN PUMP 1980-81
10 oz. beige over clear glass. Same choice as cologne. SSP $10. CMV $1. MB.

ULTRA BATH DECANTER
6.75 oz. beige plastic bottle. SSP $7. CMV $1. no box.

ULTRA BODY POWDER
(Right) 6 oz. plastic. OSP $10. CMV $2. MB.

TAPESTRY COLLECTION BELL 1981
5" high white porcelain bell. Dated 1981. Dove on top of bell. SSP $15. CMV $10. MB.

TAPESTRY COLLECTION PICTURE FRAME 1981
(Right) 5" high white porcelain picture frame. Dated 1981. SSP $13. CMV $8. MB.

BUTTERFLY FANTASY PORCELAIN TREASURE FAN 1980-81
Fan shaped porcelain box. Dated 1980 on botom. SSP $13. CMV $8. MB. Add $5. for backward printed bottom label.

CHRISTMAS REMEMBRANCE CERAMIC WREATH 1980
White ceramic, gold tassel. Dated 1980. 3" across. SSP $8. CMV $6. MB.

SWEET REMEMBRANCE 1982
(Left) 3 1/4" porcelain box. Valentines Day 1982 on bottom. "A Token of Love" on inside with a gold foil wrapped chocolate. Short issue. SSP $15. CMV $8. MB.

CHRISTMAS REMEMBRANCE DOVE 1981
(Right) Second in a series of tree ornaments from Avon. White ceramic dove, gold cord. SSP $8. CMV $6. MB.

ANNIVERSARY KEEPSAKE - MEN 1981-82
Replica of California Perfume Co. "Early Day Avon". Bay Rum After Shave. 3 oz. clear glass with glass top in plastic cork. SSP $7. CMV $4. MB.

ANNIVERSARY KEEPSAKE - WOMEN 1981-82
3 oz. clear glass CPC replica of 1908 design. Holds White Lilac cologne. Dated 1981. SSP $7. CMV $4. MB. Both came to Avon managers as a Demo empty and marked Not For Sale. CMV $10. each.

ANNIVERSARY KEEPSAKE C.P.C. FLACON 1979
.75 oz. clear glass. Silver cap has 1979 on top. Came with Sweet Honesty or Trailing Arbutus cologne. SSP $5. CMV $4. MB.

AMERICAN HEIRLOOM PORCELAIN BOWL 1981
6" across 4" high, white bowl. "Independence Day 1981" on bottom. Comes with black plastic base stand. SSP $20. **CMV $14. MB.**

ANNIVERSARY KEEPSAKE EAU DE TOILETTE 1979
Large 8 oz. clear glass bottle, CPC embossed on back side. Avon 1979 on bottom. Gold cap. Pink and green box. Came in Trailing Arbutus cologne. Pink neck ribbon. SSP $10. **CMV $4. MB.**

COUNTRY TALC SHAKER 1977-79
3 oz. gray and blue speckled metal can shaker top. Came in Sweet Honesty or Charisma perfumed talc. SSP $5. **CMV $3. MB, $2. BO.**

CALIFORNIA PERFUME CO. ANNIVER-SARY KEEPSAKE 1977078
3.75. oz. blue can sold to public with Avon 1977 on the bottom. SSP $3. **CMV $2. MB, $1. BO.** Was also given to Avon Reps during 91st Anniversary with "Anniversary Celebration Avon 1977" on the bottom. **CMV $4. MB.** Came in Roses Roses or Trailing Arbutus Talc.

CALIFORNIA PERFUME CO. ANNIVER-SARY KEEPSAKE COLOGNE 1975
(Left) Issued in honor of 89th Anniversary. 1.7 oz. bottle, pink ribbon & gold cap. Came in Charisma or Sweet Honesty cologne. Sold in 2 campaigns only. **CMV $4., $6. MB.** 1st issue Avon Presidents Club Reps received this bottle with 4A design under bottom label. Regular issue had Avon on bottom. **CMV for 4A deisgn & "M" for Managers.** Given to Managers only. **CMV $15. MB.**

CPC ANNIVERSARY KEEPSAKE COLOGNE 1976
(Right) 1.7 oz. clear glass bottle, gold cap. Bottle is embossed on back side (Avon 90th Anniversary Keepsake). Came in Moonwind or Cotillion cologne. Sold 2 campaigns only. OSP $6. **CMV $6. MB, $4. BO.**

DINGO BOOT 1978-79
6 oz. camel tan plastic bottle and cap. Choice of Sweet Honesty Body Splash or Wild Country After Shave. SSP $4. **CMV $2. MB.**

VINTAGE YEAR "CHAMPAIGN YEAR" 1978-79
2 oz. green glass, gold cap. 1979 embossed in bottom. Came in Sweet Honesty or Wild Country cologne. Green and gold box. SSP $4. **CMV $3. MB, $2. BO.**

ANNIVERSARY KEEPSAKE C.P.C. 1978-79
1.5 oz. clear glass. Old style C.P.C. label and design. Pink neck ribbon. Came in Trailing Arbutus, Sweet Honesty or Somewhere cologne. SSP $5. **CMV $3. MB, $2. BO.**

SILVER FAWN 1978-79
.5 oz. silver coated over clear glass. Choice of Sweet Honesty or Charisma cologne. SSP $2. **CMV $2. BO, $3. MB.**

AMERICAN FASHION THIMBLES 1982-86
Hand painted porcelain ladies from 1890s to 1940s design. 8 different. DP $6. each. **CMV $6. each MB.**

AMERICAN FASHION THIMBLE DISPLAY RACK 1983
12 1/2" long mahogany rack with 8 pegs. Can hang on wall or sit on shelf. SSP $13. **CMV $7. MB.**

LIP TOPPING LIP GLOSS 1982-83
Tin box holds choice of Chocolate Fudge or Butterscotch. SSP $1.50. each. **CMV $1. each.**

LAVENDER & LACE 1970-72
Lavender & white box holds 1.7 oz. white glass bottle of Lavender cologne with lavender ribbon. A lavender & white lace handkerchief came with it. OSP $4.50. **CMV $5. set, BO $2. MB.**

CAPE COD 1876 COLLECTION
(all are ruby red glass)

1876 HOSTESS BELL 1979-80
6 1/2" high "Christmas 1979" on bottom. SSP $10. **CMV $7. MB.** Also came clear glass coated red.

CAPE COD DESSERT PLATES 1980
Box of 2 red glass plates marked Avon. SSP $11. **CMV $8. MB.**

CAPE COD CRUET 1975-80
5 oz. red glass. Holds Skin-So-Soft. SSP $8. **CMV $6. MB.**

CAPE COD CANDLESTICK COLOGNE 1975-80
5 oz. red glass. Came in Charisma, patchwork or Bird of Paradise. SSP $8. **CMV $6. MB.**

CAPE COD WINE GOBLET 1976-80
Red glass candle. SSP $5. **CMV $5.** Also issued to Reps with Presidents Celebration 1976 embossed on bottom. **CMV $6.**

DESSERT BOWL & GUEST SOAPS 1978-80
SSP $9. **CMV $8. MB.**

SALT SHAKER 1978-80
May 1978 on bottom. SSP $4. **CMV $4. MB.** Latter issue not dated on bottom.

CAPE COD WATER GOBLET 1976-80
Red glass candle. SSP $9. **CMV $6., $7. MB.**

CAPE COD WINE DECANTER 1977-80
16 oz. red glass holds bubble bath. SSP $14. **CMV $9. MB.**

CAPE COD DINNER PLATE 1982-83
Full size ruby red glass dinner plate. SSP $14. **CMV $9. MB.**

CAPE COD SUGAR BOWL 1980-83
3 1/2" high red glass. Comes with 3 sachet tablets. SSP $10. **CMV $6. MB.**

CAPE COD CREAMER CANDLE 1981-84
4" high ruby red glass. holds candle, also came 1983 without candle. SSP $9. **CMV $6. MB.**

CAPE COD DESSERT SERVER 1981-84
8" long, ruby red plastic handle. Stainless blade made by Regent Sheffield for Avon. SSP $10. **CMV $6. MB.**

1876 CAPE COD PEDESTAL MUGS 1982-84
Box holds 2 ruby red glass mugs 5" high. SSP $16. set. **CMV $10. MB set.**

1876 CAPE COD COVERED BUTTER DISH 1983-84
7" long red glass. SSP $15. **CMV $10.**

CAPE COD CANDLE HOLDERS 1983-84
3 3/4" wide, 2 in a box. SSP $15. **CMV $10. MB.**

MOTHERS DAY FIGURINE "LITTLE THINGS" 1983-84
(Left) 3 3/4" high hand painted porcelain boy figurine. SSP $18. **CMV $12. MB.**

MOTHERS DAY FIGURINE "CHERISHED MOMENTS" 1983-84
(Right) 4" high hand painted porcelain girl figurine. SSP $18. **CMV $12. MB.**

McCONNELLS CORNER TOWN TREE 1982
6" high ceramic tree, green and white. Dated "Christmas 1982". SSP $12. **CMV $8. MB.**

NATIVITY "THREE WISE MEN" 1982
(Left to Right) All are white bisque porcelain. The Magi Kaspar, The Magi Melchior, The Magi Balthasar. SSP $19.50 each. **CMV $12. each MB.**

HEART STRINGS DECANTER 1983
.5 oz. red glass with gold cap. Choice of three fragrances. SSP $3. **CMV $1. MB.**

AUTUMN SCURRY "SQUIRREL" 1982-83
.5 oz. clear glass squirrel, gold cap. Choice of Moonwind, Topaze or Charisma cologne. SSP $2.25. **CMV $1. MB.**

BABY BASSETT DECANTER 1978-79
1.25 oz. amber glass and matching plastic head. Holds Topaze or Sweet Honesty Cologne. SSP $3. **CMV $2. BO, $3. MB.**

McCONNELLS CORNER GENERAL STORE 1982
5 1/2" ceramic box, roof lifts off. Dated "Christmas 1982". SSP $24. CMV $15. MB.

KEEPING THE CHRISTMAS TRADITION 1982
Hand painted porcelain figurine dated 1982. 2nd in Christmas Memories Series. SSP $49.50. CMV $25. MB.

MRS. CLAUS SUGAR BOWL & CREAMER 1983-84
Red, white and green ceramic sugar bowl & creamer. SSP $13. each. CMV $8. MB each.

NATIVITY COLLECTION 1983
All are white porcelain.
SHEPHERD - 6 1/2" high. SSP $22.50. CMV $14. MB.
SHEEP - 4" long. SSP $13.50. CMV $8.
SHEPHERD BOY - 4 3/4" high. SSP $19.50. CMV $12. MB.

NESTLED TOGETHER ORNAMENT 1982
(Left) Small nest with two blue birds and red and white hat. SSP $7. CMV $4. MB.
MELVIN P. MERRYMOUSE ORNAMENT 1982
(Center) Small plastic mouse Santa. Back of mirror says Avon Christmas, 1982. SSP $10. CMV $6. MB.
McCONNELLS CORNER TOWN SHOPPERS 1982
(Right) 3" high ceramic figurine. Bottom says Christmas, 1982. SSP $10. CMV $5. MB.

MELVIN P. MERRYMOUSE KEEPSAKE ORNAMENT 1983
2 3/4" high Santa mouse on sleigh. Dated 1983. Plastic, 2nd in a series. SSP $10. CMV $6. MB.

CHRISTMAS PORCELAIN FIGURINE 1983
5 1/2" high hand painted porcelain figurine. Called "Enjoying the Night Before Christmas." Dated Christmas 1983. SSP $52.50. CMV $25. MB.

CHRISTMAS REMEMBRANCE ANGEL 1982
White ceramic angel, gold tassel. Comes in white felt bag. SSP $9. CMV $6. MB.

HAPPY HOLIDAYS ORNAMENT 1983
Small brown, red and white plastic Kangaroo tree ornament. SSP $5. CMV $3. MB.

MOM'S PRIDE AND JOY PICTURE FRAME 1983
6 1/2" x 2" clear glass MOM frame. SSP $10.
CMV $6. MB.

SUMMER FANTASY COLLECTION 1983
TRAY
12" tin tray, red and green design. SSP $9.
CMV $3. MB.
GLASSES
Set of two 15 oz. drinking glasses. SSP $10.
CMV $3. MB set.
CANDLE
3 1/2" high white tin can. Refillable candle.
Green and red design. SSP $10. **CMV $6.
MB.**

**COUNTRY CHRISTMAS ORNAMENT &
CANDY SET 1982**
Box held three red, green and gold ornament
boxes with peppermint candy and candy sticks.
SSP $9. **CMV $4. MB.**

EMERALD ACCENT COLLECTION
DECANTER 1982-83
10" high, clear glass, green glass stopper.
SSP $15. **CMV $10. MB.**
CORDIAL GLASSES
Set of two clear glasses with green glass
stems, 4 1/2" high. SSP $13. **CMV $8. MB
set.**
SERVING TRAY
11 1/2" long green glass tray. SSP $15. **CMV
$8. MB.**

**SEASONAL SCENTS FRAGRANCE
ORNAMENTS 1982**
Three different scented plastic ornaments.
Snowflake, blue; sleigh, red; jingle bells,
amber. SSP $4. each. **CMV $2.50 each MB.**

**MEMORIES PORCELAIN MUSIC BOX 1983-
84**
White 4 1/4" long porcelain box with music box
in lid. SSP $27.50. **CMV $15. MB.**
IMAGE OF LOVE PAPERWEIGHT 1983
4" wide clear glass heart, red felt bottom. SSP
$10. **CMV $6. MB.**

**SANTA'S SEESAW TREE ORNAMENT
1983-84**
Small Santa and elves plastic ornament. SSP
$8. **CMV $5. MB.**
**WINTER FUN "IGLOO" TREE ORNAMENT
1983-84**
White plastic igloo with eskimo family around
tree. SSP $8. **CMV $5. MB.**

VICTORIAN COLLECTOR DOLL 1983-84
8" high 19th century doll with porcelain head,
arms and legs. Comes with metal stand.
Fancy box. SSP $24.50. **CMV $15. MB.**

**AMERICAN HEIRLOOM PORCELAIN BOWL
1983-84**
6" across, 4" high porcelain bowl. Plastic
stand. Flower design on bowl. SSP $17.50.
CMV $12. MB.

VICTORIANA PICTURE FRAME 1983-84
4 1/2" x 5 1/4" size metal frame. Fancy box.
SSP $16.50. **CMV $6. MB.**

SNOWFLAKE ORNAMENT 1983
(Left) White porcelain snowflake dated 1983.
2 1/2" wide on gold tassel. SSP $8. **CMV $5.
MB.**
**CAPTURED MOMENTS FRAME ORNAMENT
1983**
(Right) Green and red plastic wreath. Slide a
picture in center. 4" across. SSP $4. **CMV
$3. MB.**

**FLORAL EXPRESSIONS CERAMIC TILES
1983**
6" square ceramic tiles made in England.
Flower design and four different colors. Love,
Happiness, Friendship or Hospitality. SSP
$10. **CMV $2. MB each.**

**BUNNY MATES SALT & PEPPER SHAKERS
1983**
Bunny box holds two small ceramic white
rabbit shakers. SSP $12. **CMV $7. MB.**
**CLAUS & COMPANY SANTA'S HELPERS
SALT & PEPPER SHAKERS 1983**
Red box holds two small green and red
ceramic boy and girl salt & pepper shakers. 2
1/2" high. SSP $10. **CMV $6. MB.**

JOLLY JELLY BEANS 1983
4" high paper cartons with 1.5 oz. of jelly
beans. Choice of Rudolph or Santa carton.
SSP 90c each. **CMV $1. each mint.**

STYLISH LADY DECANTER 1982-83
8 oz. white glass pig with white and pink pump
top. Choice of Country Orchard Liquid
Cleanser or Moisturizer Hand Lotion. SSP $9.
CMV $5. MB.

CHRISTMAS THIMBLE 1982
(Left) White porcelain, dated 1982.
CHRISTMAS THIMBLE 1981
(Right) Issued in 1982, but dated 1981. SSP
$9. each. **CMV $5. each MB.**

SWEET DREAMS 1979-80
1.25 oz. blue frosted over clear glass. White
plastic boys head cap. Holds Zany or
Somewhere cologne. SSP $5. **CMV $5. MB.**

PEACE ON EARTH ANGELS ORNAMENT SET 1983
Box holds 5 porcelain angels to hang on Christmas tree. Each angel 2 1/2" wide. SSP $37.50. **CMV $25. set MB.**

IMAGES OF HOLLYWOOD 1983-84 - SCARLETT O'HARA
1st in a series porcelain figurine, 4 1/2" high. Vivian Leigh as Scarlett O'Hara. DP $18. **CMV $18. MB.**
RHETT BUTLER FIGURINE 1984-85
Clark Gable figurine, 5 3/4" high. DP $18. **CMV $18. MB.**

PIERRE DECANTER 1984
8 oz. white glass pig. Cloth apron on front. Holds Care Deeply Hand Lotion. SSP $10. **CMV $6. MB.**

FRAGRANCE KEEPSAKE 1983
.5 oz. fan shaped clear glass, with rose red cap. Choice of Somewhere, Here's My Heart, Regence, Rapture, Persian Wood, Brocade, Cotillion. SSP $2. **CMV $1. MB.**
GINGERBREAD COTTAGE 1983-84
.5 oz. dark amber glass, pink cap. Choice of Sweet Honesty or Charisma cologne. 2" high. SSP $3. **CMV $1. MB.**

FRED ASTAIRE FIGURINE 1984
6 3/4" high porcelain. 3rd in series. DP $18. **CMV $18. MB.**
GINGER ROGERS FIGURINE 1984
4th in series. 6" high porcelain. DP $18. **CMV $18. MB.**

WRITE TOUCH MOUSE 1982-83
(Left) 1 oz. green glass and white plastic mouse with stick on decals. Choice of Sweet Honesty or Charisma cologne. SSP$6. **CMV $3. MB.**
FRAGRANCE NOTABLES 1982
(Center) .5 oz. clear glass with ribbon design. Red cap and box. Choice of Wild Jasmine, Occurl, Moonwind, Charisma, Topaze or Sweet Honesty cologne. SSP $1.50. **CMV $1. MB.**
CRYSTALLIQUE TREE 1982
(Right) .5 oz. clear glass tree bottle with bronze color cap. Choice of Foxfire, Timeless or Odyssey cologne. SSP $3. **CMV $2. MB.**

SUMMER FUN FIGURINE 1986
(Right) 3 1/2" wide porcelain figurine by Jessie Wilcox Smith. DP $21. **CMV $21. MB.**
GIVING THANKS FIGURINE 1986
(Left) 3 1/4" wide porcelain figurine by Jessie Wilcox Smith. DP $21. **CMV $21. MB.**

JUDY GARLAND FIGURINE 1985
5 1/2" high porcelain. DP $20. **CMV $20. MB.**

CHRISTMAS FIGURINE 1984
6 3/8" high porcelain. Dated Christmas 1984.
DP $30. **CMV $30. MB.**

WE WISH YOU A MERRY CHRISTMAS FIGURINE 1986
(Left) 3 1/2" wide porcelain figurine with music box base. DP $12. **CMV $12. MB.**

A WINTER SNOW FIGURINE
(Right) Porcelain figurine by Jessie Wilcox Smith. DP $20. **CMV $20. MB.**

PORCELAIN CAT FIGURINES 1984
Choice of 4 porcelain cat figurines. Siamese Tabby, Calico, Persian. DP $2. each. **CMV $2. each MB.**

WINTER PALS ORNAMENT 1985
2 1/2" wide plastic. **CMV $3.**

CARDINAL FIGURINE 1985
Red porcelain bird.

BLUEBIRD FIGURINE 1986
Blue, orange & white porcelain bird. DP $24. on both birds. **CMV $24. each MB.**

PURRFECT CAT 1987
1.5 oz. cologne. Black glass. DP $3.25. **CMV $3.25 MB.**

COUNTRY CHICKEN 1987
9.5 oz. white ceramic bottle with pump. Holds hand loiton. DP $7.25. **CMV $7.25 MB.**

JOAN WALSH ANGLUND FIGURINE COLLECTION 1986-87
(Top) 3 1/2" high porcelain figurines is "School Days" & "My ABCs". 1986 "Magic Slippers" & "Home Run" is 3 3/4" high. DP. $8.50. **CMV $8.50 MB each.**

JESSIE WILCOX SMITH FIGURINES 1986
(Bottom) 3 1/2" wide porcelain figurines choice of "Be My Valentine", "Springtime", & "Helping Mom". DP $21. each. **CMV $21. MB each.**

BUNNY BUD VASE 1986
3 1/2" high porcelain. Comes empty. DP $6. **CMV $6. MB.**

BUNNY LUV CERAMIC BOX 1982
Ceramic top & bottom. Rabbit on lid. Sold empty. DP $8. **CMV $8. MB.**

JOY TO THE WORLD MUSICAL FIGURINE 1985
(Left to Right) Small porcelain figurine, music base. DP $14. **CMV $14. MB.**

EASTER CHARM FIGURINE 1985
4" high porcelain. Dated Easter 1985. DP $9. **CMV $9. MB.**

MOTHERS TOUCH FIGURINE 1984
Shiny glaze porcelain. Mother's Day figurine. DP $25. **CMV $25. MB.**

YOU'RE THE BERRIES CANDY JAR 1984
Clear glass 5" high fruit jar with berry cloth lid cover. Holds hard candy. DP $4. **CMV $4. MB.**

COUNTRY CHARM LOTION PUMP 1985
10 oz. jug bottle with pump. DP $5. **CMV $3. MB.**

CHRISTMAS BELL 1985
(Right) Wood handle, porcelain bell dated Xmas 1985. DP $9. **CMV $9. MB.**

AVON COUNTRY PORCELAIN BELL 1985
(Center) 3 1/4" high porcelain bell. DP $6. **CMV $6. MB.**

GOOD LUCK BELL 1983
(Left) 4 1/2" high porcelain elf on flower bell. DP $9. **CMV $9. MB.**

FOUR SEASONS EGG SERIES 1984
4 different porcelain eggs - wood base.
Winter, Spring, Summer, Autumn. DP. $9.
each. **CMV $9. MB.**

TREASURED MOMENTS BELL 1984
Fostoria glass bell. 5" high. DP $8. **CMV $8. MB.**

CHRSITMAS THIMBLE 1983
(Right) Small white porcelain thimble with
decal. 1983 Christmas in gold. SSP $9. **CMV $9. MB.**

FARM FRESH SALT & PEPPER SHAKERS 1986
2 piece white glass, yellow egg center on
bottom part. DP $4. **CMV $4. MB.**

BUTTERFLY TRINKET BOX 1984
Small 2 1/2" porcelain box with 2 butterfly
earrings. DP $8. **CMV $8. MB.**

GOLDEN DREAMS MUSIC BOX 1985
Blue porcelain box, music in lid. DP $15.
CMV $15. MB.

SHADES OF AUTUMN DISH 1984
Yellow & green ceramic dish. DP $8. **CMV $8. MB.**

SHADES OF AUTUMN SALT & PEPPER 1984
Yellow & green ceramic. DP $8. set. **CMV $8. MB.**

POINSETTIA SEASONS IN BLOOM 1986
(Right) Red porcelain flower. DP $21. **CMV $21. MB.**

MAGNOLIA SEASONS IN BLOOM 1986
(Left) Yellow, white and green porcelain
flower. Both have Avon label. DP $21. **CMV $21. MB.**

EUROPEAN TRADITION CUP & SAUCER'S COLLECTION

FRANCE 1985
2 1/4" cup & 4 1/2" saucer. Pink & white
porcelain.

GERMANY 1985
Yellow & white porcelain.

NETHERLANDS 1984
Blue & white porcelain.

FLORENCE 1984
Blue & white porcelain.
DP $15. each. **CMV $15. each MB.**

BUNNY CERAMIC TRINKET DISH 1985
Rabbit dish - DP $6. **CMV $6. MB.**

BUNNY BELL 1984
3" high ceramic rabbit bell. DP $6. **CMV $6. MB.**

KITTEN KITCHEN WALL HOOK 1985
White glass. DP $10. **CMV $6. MB.**

BEAR COOKIE JAR 1985
Brown ceramic cookie jar. DP $18. **CMV $18. MB.**

BABY BEAR BANK 1986
Ceramic blue & tan bank with small green &
white bear blanket. Comes with iron on letters.
DP $7. **CMV $7. MB**

BIRTHDAY BELL 1986
5 3/4" high clear lead crystal bells. Choice of
12 different flowers on bells. DP $9. **CMV $9. MB.**

CHEF ANDRE KITCHEN UTENSIL HOLDER 1987
6" high white ceramic, jar trimmed in black &
red. 4 wood untensils. Not marked Avon. DP $8. **CMV $8. MB.**

LOVE A BUNNY COLLECTION 1987
Small wood Easter eggs & rabbits, 2"-3" high.
4 different. Artist Bunny, Bunny with Crayon,
Lunchtime Bunny, Painting Bunny. DP $2.25
each. **CMV $2.25 each MB.**

STATUE OF LIBERTY CENTENNIAL BOWL 1985
6" porcelain white bowl. Wood base. DP $15.
CMV $15. MB.

HEARTS FROM THE HEART 1987
Heart shaped lead crystal dish & 8 pink heart shaped bath pearls. DP $5.50. **CMV $5.50.**
FLORAL HEART POMANDER 1987
White bisque porcelain heart. 3 1/2" across on pink nylon cord. DP $5. **CMV $5.**

COUNTRY VILLAGE CANISTER SET 1985
White pottery canisters by Plaltzgraff. Marked Avon on bottom. DP $39. set. **CMV $39. set MB.**

KITTEN CRACKER SERVER 1986
White & brown ceramic cracker bowl. 8 3/4" long. Not marked Avon on any piece shown, only on box. DP $7.80. **CMV $3. MB.**
If it's not marked Avon, we suggest you don't collect it. Little chance of future resale.
KITTEN CREAMER 1986
White ceramic. 5 1/4" high. DP $7.20. **CMV $3. MB.**
CERAMIC BASKET 1986
White ceramic 6" wide, 4 3/4" high. Not marked Avon. DP $12. **CMV $5. MB.**

FOREVER YOURS MUG 1987
White ceramic heart shaped mug. DP $3.85. **CMV $4. MB.**
MOM MUG 1987
White ceramic mug. Comes with silk yellow rose. DP $4.25. **CMV $4.25.**

MR. CLAUS MUG 1984
MRS. CLAUS MUG 1984
Both white porcelain, each came with 4 packets of cocoa. DP $6. each. **CMV $6. each MB.**

STATUE OF LIBERTY BRASS STAMP 1985
1886-1986 on wood base. DP $10. **CMV $10. MB.**
HOSPITALITY SPOON SERIES 1985
Wood rack with 4 spoons - Italian Grapes, German Maiden, Scottish Thistle, American Pineapple. DP $6. each piece. **CMV $25. set MB with rack.**

CHRISTMAS TREE MUG 1985
(Right) 4" high porcelain cup. DP $5. **CMV $3. MB.**
SANTA'S STORY MUG 1984
(Left) 3 5/8" high porcelain. DP $3. **CMV $3. MB.**
LOVE MUG JELLY BEANS 1983-84
3 1/2" high ceramic mug filled with 8 oz. of jelly beans. Some mugs came with Heart on bottom and no date or lettering and some came with heart on bottom and dated 1983 in red or black letters. DP $6. **CMV $6. MB.**
HAPPINESS MUG 1984
Ceramic mug cup with jelly beans. DP $6. **CMV $6. MB.**

CHRISTMAS THIMBLE 1984
Porcelain - Dated Christmas 1984. DP $5. **CMV $5. MB.**
CHRISTMAS LIGHTS MUG 1985
White mug cup. DP $3. **CMV $3. MB.**
SWEET SENTIMENTS MUG 1986
White ceramic mug, heart handles. DP $3. **CMV $3. MB.**

CAPE COD COLLECTION 1984-88
All red glass.
CONDIMENT DISH 1985
SSP $9. **CMV $9. MB.**
HURRICANE CANDLE HOLDER 1985
DP $9. **CMV $9. MB.**
COLLECTION FLOWER VASE 1985
8" tall. DP $9. **CMV $9. MB.**
WATER PITCHER 1984
8 1/4'" high. DP $15. **CMV $15. MB.**

CAPE COD SERVING PLATTER 1986
(Not Shown) Red glass, 10 3/4" x 13 1/2". DP $17.50. **CMV $17.50 MB.**
CAPE COD SERVING BOWL 1986
8 3/4" red glass bowl. DP $14. **CMV $14. MB.**

HUMMINGBIRD CRYSTAL BELL 1985
Each piece is clear glass & etched frosted design. DP $9. **CMV $9. MB.**
HUMMINGBIRD CHAMPAIGN GLASSES 1985
9" high box of 2 glasses. DP $21. **CMV $21. MB.**
HUMMINGBIRD CRYSTAL VASE 1986
7 1/2" high vase. DP $22.50. **CMV $22.50 MB.**
HUMMINGBIRD CRYSTAL CAKE PLATE 1985
12" glass cake plate on 3" glass stand. DP $22.50. **CMV $22.50 MB.**
HUMMINGBIRD CRYSTAL TREE ORNAMENT 1986
3 1/2" high glass. DP $6. **CMV $6. MB.**

WATER LILY PERFUME BOTTLE 1985
(Right) 1.5 oz. blue glass & frosted glass stopper. Sold empty. DP $6. **CMV $6. MB.**
TIMELESS TREASURE POTPOURRI
(Left) Glass jar, pewter top. 2 1/2" high. DP $10. **CMV $10. MB.**

CRYSTAL BUD VASE 1987
5" clear glass. Not marked Avon, only box. DP $3. **CMV $3. MB.** We suggest you don't collect products of this type not marked Avon. They will have little future value.
FROSTED BUD VASE 1986
4" high comes in frosted glass or blue-violet frosted glass. Not marked Avon, only box. DP $4.20. **CMV $4. MB.**

CERAMIC BUTTERFLY COLLECTION 1986
All white porcelain with butterflys on side. None marked Avon, only on boxes.
TUMBLER
DP $4.80.
DISPENSER PUMP
DP $6.
SOAP DISH
DP $5.50.
We suggest you don't collect this type of household product. It's not marked Avon & has no general appeal to collectors for future resale.

HOLY FAMILY NATIVITY FIGURINES 1986
Porcelain figurines 2 1/2" to 3 3/4" high. Mary, Joseph & Baby Jesus in manger. DP $12. **CMV $12. set MB.**
THE MAGI NATIVITY FIGURINES 1986
Porcelain figurines. Melchior, Balthasar & Kaspar. DP $6. each. **CMV $6. each.**

CAMEL & DONKEY FIGURINES 1984
Goes in Nativity set. White porcelain. DP $10. each. **CMV $10. each MB.**

NATIVITY ANGEL & STABLE 1985
White porcelain angel & plastic stable. DP $20. set. **CMV $20. set MB.**

FOSTORIA ORNAMENTS 1985
Christmas village, Christmas tree or Angel ornament. DP $5. **CMV $5. each.**

BABY'S FIRST CHRISTMAS ORNAMENT 1986
(Above) 4" high white porcelain by Joan Walsh Anglund.
DONKEY & CAMEL NATIVITY FIGURINES 1986
(Left) Heavenly Blessings Nativity collection. Both pastel porcelain. 3 1/2" long. DP $6. ea. **CMV $6. ea. MB.**

MERRY CHRISTMAS ORNAMENT CARD 1985
Xmas card holds 3" porcelain ornament. DP $5. **CMV $5. MB.**

NATIVITY ORNAMENT COLLECTION 1985
All white porcelain. The Shepherd, The Holy Family, The Three Magi. DP $5. each. **CMV $5. MB each.**

SANTA CHRISTMAS TREE ORNAMENTS 1986
Each in 2" high plastic. **CMV $1. each.**
SATIN & LACE SACHET ORNAMENTS 1986
4 1/2" tall, burgundy, green or ivory. DP $2.50 each. **CMV $2.50 MB each.**
TEDDY BEAR PHOTO ORNAMENT 1986
3" high wood bear tree ornaments with small picture frame. 3 different. Drummer, Nighttime Teddy or Artist. DP $2.50 each. **CMV $2.50 each MB,**

SANTA CLAUS & MRS. CLAUS SOFT ORNAMENTS 1986
5 1/2" high stuffed ornaments. DP $3. each. **CMV $3. each.**

CHRISTMAS BELL 1986
White porcelain bell 5" high dated 1986. Gold trim. DP $11. **CMV $11. MB.**
SNOW ANGEL TREE TOPPER DOLL 1986
10 1/2" high. Head & hands are porcelain. Blue lace dress. DP $7. **CMV $7. MB.**

SANTA'S HELPER ORNAMENT 1985
4" high plastic elf. DP $3. **CMV $3.**

SANTA & FRIENDS ACTION ORNAMENTS 1986
3 1/2" high porcelain Santa, Reindeer or Little Elf. DP $3. each. **CMV $3. each MB.**

ANGEL NATIVITY FIGURINES 1986
3" porcelain angel. DP $6. **CMV $6. MB.**
CHRISTMAS TREE POMANDER 1986
9" high green ceramic tree. Comes with wax chips. DP $12. **CMV $12. MB.**

SANTA ORNAMENTS WOODEN 1985
Trimming the Tree, Santa Hanging the Star & Santa with Ornament. DP $2. each. **CMV $2. each MB.**

CHRISTMAS GLASS LIGHT COVERS 1985
3 1/4" high. 5 different. **CMV $2. each.**

CHILDREN'S TOYS

All items are priced mint condition. See front of book for grading examples.

CIRCUS TROUPE WOODEN ORNAMENT COLLECTION 1985
6 different. Balancing Acrobats, Lion, Roly Poly Clown, Ballerina, Ring Master, Polka Dot Clown. DP $2. each. **CMV $2. each MB.**

TEDDY BEAR ORNAMENT COLLECTION 1986
Tiny white flocked bears on red metal high chair, piano, baby buggy or train. DP $2. each. **CMV $2. each MB.**

NOAH'S ARK ORNAMENTS 1986
1" to 2" wood ornaments. Mr. & Mrs. Noah, 2 lions, 2 sheep, 2 deer, 2 penguins. All different. DP $6. set. **CMV $6. set MB.**

MARCHING WOOD ORNAMENTS 1985
Choice of 5 wood painted Xmas tree ornaments. DP $1.50. **CMV $1.50 each MB.**

SNOOPY'S SKI TEAM 1974-75
7 oz. white plastic bottle, red skis, yellow "Woodstock". Holds bubble bath. OSP $5. **CMV $5. MB.**

WOODSTOCK BRUSH & COMB 1975-78
Yellow plastic brush, green comb. OSP $4. **CMV $1. BO, $2. MB.**

FUZZY TEDDY SKATING PIN 1986
Small bear pin. **CMV $1.**

SANTA AWAY PIN 1986
Red, white & green plastic pin. **CMV $1.**

CANDY CANE PIN 1986
Small ballpoint pen in red & white or green & white pin.

TEDDY BEAR ORNAMENT COLLECTION 1985
Teddy on Tricycle, Bench, Rocker, Wagon or Sledge. DP $2. **CMV $2. MB each.**

SNOOPY MUG 1969-72
5 oz. white glass, 5 inches high. Came 2 ways, red or blue top. Blue top is more rare. Also came with oval or round decal. OSP $3.50. **CMV $7. red top MB, $9. blue top MB, $2. less no box.**

PERRY THE PENGUIN 1966-67
Black and white penguin soap dish and white plastic soap dish. OSP $6., penguin $4., vest soap $5. Set $12. MB.

SNOOPY SOAP DISH 1968-76
White bar of Avon soap sets in black and white plastic soap dish. OSP $6. **CMV $6. MB,** Snoopy only $2.

TEDDY BEAR VALENTINE COLLECTION 1987
Red metal, white flocked bears. Mailbox, Heart or Music Stand. DP $1.75 each. **CMV $1.75 each.**

VICTORIAN STYLE CHRISTMAS LIGHTS 1985
Set of 7. DP $9. **CMV $9. set MB.**

JEWEL TONE ORNAMENTS 1985
Lyre, Mandolin or Horn. DP $1.50 each. **CMV $1.50 each.**

CHILDREN'S TOYS & COLLECTABLES

Children's toys and collectables continue to be popular with many collectors. Almost all children's toys are plastic which are about the only plastic items in the book truly collectable. All children's items must be in new mint condition. If they are not, I suggest you do not buy them. Be sure to read <u>What's Hot and What's Not</u> in the introduction section of this book.

SNOOPY COME HOME SOAP DISH AND SOAP 1973-74
6" long, brown raft with white sail, has 3 oz. brown soap. SSP $3. **CMV $6. MB.**

CHARLIE BROWN 1968-72
4 oz. red, white and black plastic bottle of Non Tear Shampoo. OSP $2.50. **CMV $5. MB, $3. BO.**
LUCY 1970-72
4 oz. red, white and black plastic bottle holds bubble bath. OSP $2.50. **CMV $5. MB, $3. BO.**

LUCY MUG 1969-70
5 oz. white glass, yellow top and label. White cap, Non Tear Shampoo. OSP $3.50. **CMV $8.**
CHARLIE BROWN MUG 1969-70
5 oz. white glass, blue top and label. White cap, bubble bath. OSP $3.50. **CMV $8.**

SNOOPY & DOG HOUSE 1969-72
8 oz. white plastic dog and red plastic 3" high dog house, holds Non Tear Shampoo. OSP $3. **CMV $3., $5. MB.**
LINUS 1968-74
Red, white and green plastic 4 oz. tube of Gel Bubble Bath with red, white and black plastic Linus, plastic holder. OSP $3.50. **CMV $5. MB, $3. Linus & tube only.**

SNOOPY COMB & BRUSH SET 1971-75
5 1/2" long black and brush and white comb. OSP $3.50. **CMV $5. MB.**

SNOOPY THE FLYING ACE 1969
4 oz. 6" high white plastic with blue hat, yellow glasses, holds bubble bath. OSP $3. **CMV $2., $5. MB.**
JUMPIN' JIMMINY 1969-73
8 oz. 6" high, green, red and yellow pull toy with yellow cap. Holds bubble bath. OSP $3.50. **CMV 45. MB, $3. BO.**

SIX SHOOTER 1962-63
6 oz. gray plastic and white gun with No Tears Shampoo. OSP $1.98. **CMV $18. BO mint, $24. MB.**

BO BO THE ELEPHANT 1973-74
6 oz. pink plastic with squeeze head. Filled with baby shampoo. SSP $3. **CMV $3. BO, $5. MB.**
SNOOPY'S SNOW FLYER 1973
10 oz. red, white and black. Holds bubble bath. SSP $4. **CMV $5. MB, $3. BO.**

CLEAN AS A WHISTLE 1960-61
8 oz. red & white plastic bottle, real whistle cap. Came in bubble bath. OSP $1.79. **CMV $15. MB, $10. BO**
E.T. FLOWERS FIGURINE 1984
2 1/2" high hand painted porcelain. SSP $8. **CMV $5. MB.**

CHARLIE BROWN COMB & BRUSH 1972
4 1/2" long, red, black and white with white comb. SSP $3. **CMV $5. MB.**

GRID KID BRUSH & COMB 1973-74
4 1/2" long, red, black and white with white comb. SSP $3. **CMV $5. MB.**

SNOOPY'S BUBBLE TUB 1971-72
5" long, 12 oz. blue and white plastic tub, bottle holds bubble bath. OSP $2. **CMV $3. BO, $5. MB.**

PEANUTS PALS SHAMPOO 1971-72
6 oz. plastic, white, red, and black bottle with yellow cap. 6" high. OSP $3.50. **CMV $5. MB, $3. BO.**

THREE LITTLE PIGS 1967-68
3 oz. each, 4 1/2" high. Blue pigs, yellow hat holds bubble bath, yellow pig, green hat holds baby shampoo, and pink pig with pink hat holds baby lotion. OSP $1.35. **CMV $6. each, $9. MB.**

LITTLE RED RIDING HOOD 1968
4 oz. yellow plastic bottle, red cap. Holds bubble bath. OSP $1.50. **CMV $2. BO, $6. with glasses MB.**

WOLF 1968
4 oz. yellow and blue plastic bottle, green cap, holds Non Tear Shampoo. OSP $1.50. **CMV $2. BO, $6. MB with white fang teeth.**

MR. MANY MOODS 1965-66
6 oz. white plastic bottle with blue and yellow hat, red nose and mouth, black eyes. Holds shampoo. OSP $1.98. **CMV $8., $10. MB.**

MR. PRESTO CHANGO 1968
6 oz. yellow plastic bottle with red hat, black eyes and pink lips. Holds No Tear Shampoo. OSP $2.25. **CMV $6., $8. MB.**

GOOD HABIT RABBIT 1967
3 oz., 4 1/2" high. White plastic rabbit, green hat and orange carrot. Came in Tot 'N Tyke Shampoo. OSP $1.50. **CMV $8., $12. MB.**

BUBBLE BUNNY 1964-65
Pink and white rabbit puppet with 6 oz. tube of bubble bath gel. OSP $1.98. **CMV $5. puppet only, $11. MB.**

BUGLE 1965
6 oz. blue plastic bugle with yellow cap. Holds Tot 'N Tyke Shampoo. OSP $1.79. **CMV $10. BO, $15. MB.**

FIFE 1965
6 oz. yellow plastic bottle with red cap. Came in hand lotion or hair trainer. OSP $1.49. **CMV $10. BO, $15. MB.**

THREE BEARS 1966-67
4 3/4" high each. 3 oz. each. White plastic bottles with blue caps. OSP $1.25 each. Papa Bear holds baby oil. **CMV $10. BO, $14. MB.** Mama Bear holds baby lotion, Baby Bear holds shampoo. **CMV $8. BO, $12. MB each.**

A WINNER 1960-62
4 oz. maroon plastic boxing gloves with white caps. Tied togehter with white plastic cord. Hand Guard and Hair Guard. OSP $1.98. **CMV $20. MB, $7. each bottle.**

LITTLE CHAMP 1967-68
1/2 oz. each with white caps. Blue boxing glove holds Non Tear Shampoo, yellow glove holds Hair Trainer. OSP $2.50. **CMV $17. MB. Each glove $5.**

CUCKOO CLOCK 1965-66
10 oz. red, white and blue plastic clock holds bubble bath. OSP $2.50. **CMV $8., $10. MB.**

WRIST WASH BUBBLE BATH 1969-70
2 oz. orange plastic clock with blue cap. OSP $3. **CMV $6. MB, $4. BO.**

RING 'EM UP CLEAN 1970-72
8 oz. orange plastic bottle with red or white cap holds Non Tear Shampoo. OSP $2.50. **CMV $3., $5. MB.**

SAFE SAM 1965
8 oz. red and black plastic safe holds bubble bath. OSP $1.98. **CMV $8., $11. MB.**

SPACE AGE 1968-69
4 oz. silver and yellow plastic rocket holds liquid hair trainer. OSP $1.50. **CMV $3. $5. MB.**

BO BO THE ELEPHANT 1970
5 oz. light or dark pink plastic bottle of Non Tear Shampoo. OSP $2.50. **CMV $3. BO, $5. MB.**

RED STREAK BOAT 1972-73
5 oz. red plastic boat, white cap. Holds bubble bath. OSP $2. **CMV $5. MB, $3. BO.**

WHISTLE TOTS 1966-67
6 3/4" high, 4 oz. white plastic bottle with whistle cap. Red cap fireman holds Tot 'N Tyke Shampoo. Blue cap policeman holds Hair Trainer and green clown holds bubble bath. OSP $1.50 each. **CMV $7. BO mint, $10. MB.**

GLOBE BANK 1966-67
10 oz. blue plastic globe holds bubble bath. Black base. Bank has 5 different colored sets of stick on countries. North America came in orange, blue, tan, pink or yellow. OSP $2.50. **CMV $16. MB, $10. BO.**

MAD HATTER 1970
6 oz. bronze plastic with pink hat and clock. Came in bubble bath. OSP $3. **CMV $4. BO, $6. MB.**

SPINNING TOP 1966-67
4 oz. red and white top holds bubble bath, yellow top spinner. OSP $1.75. **CMV $10. MB, $6. BO.**

SCHOOL DAYS 1966-67
8 oz. red and white plastic ruler holds Non Tear Shampoo. Yellow cap. OSP $1.98. **CMV $7., $10. MB.**

MILK BATH 1968-69
6 oz. pink plastic milk can holds powdered bubble bath. OSP $4. **CMV $3. BO, $5. MB.**

CONCERTINA 1970-72
8 oz. blue and yellow plastic squeeze bottle. Holds bubble bath. Musical cap with pink strap. OSP $2.50. **CMV $8. MB, $6. BO.**

CONCERTINA 1962-65
8 oz. red and yellow plastic squeeze bottle with musical cap. Holds bubble bath. OSP $1.98. **CMV $12., $15. MB.**

MR. LION 1967
4 oz. white plastic bottle with red bubble pipe over white cap. Holds bubble bath. OSP $1.50. **CMV $6. BO, $8. MB.**

TIN MAN 1967
4 oz. white plastic bottle with blue bubble pipe over white cap. Holds Non Tear Shampoo. OSP $1.50. **CMV $6. BO, $8. MB.**

STRAW MAN 1967
4 oz. white plastic bottle with yellow bubble pipe over white cap. Holds hand lotion. OSP $1.50. **CMV $6. BO, $8. MB.**

BIRD HOUSE 1969
7" high orange plastic bottom with tan roof. Holds 8 oz. of Powdered Bubble Bath. OSP $3.75. **CMV $7. BO, $9. MB.**

SANTA'S HELPER 1967-68
Red and white sponge with 6 oz. tube of Gel Bubble Bath. OSP $2.50. **CMV $8. MB.**

AVONVILLE SLUGGER 1961-62
6 oz. tan plastic bat holds shampoo. OSP $1.49. **CMV $12. BO, $17. MB.**

SURE WINNER SLUGGER DECANTER 1973
6 oz. yellow plastic bat. Holds Sure Winner Bracing Lotion or Liquid Hair Trainer or Avon Spicy After Shave. SSP $2. **CMV $4. mint, no box issued.**

TOPSY TURVEY CLOWN 1965 ONLY
10 oz. red, white and yellow plastic clown. Blue hat, black feet. Holds bubble bath. OSP $2.50. **CMV $16. MB, $12. BO mint.**

ONE TWO LACE MY SHOE 1968-69
8 oz. bubble bath. Pink plastic shoe with orange tie on and yellow cap. Green or yellow roof. OSP $2.98. **CMV $6. BO, $9. MB.**

TIC TOC TURTLE 1968-69
8 oz. 5 1/2" high. Green turtle, yellow clock face with pink hands. Bubble bath. OSP $2.50. **CMV $6. BO, $9. MB.**

LAND HO 1961-62
(Left) 8 oz. blue & white plastic telescope holds Hair Trainer. OSP $1.49. **CMV $17. MB, $12. BO mint.**

NAUGHTY-LESS 1961-62
(Right) 8 oz. red & white submarine with white & blue cap. Holds bubble bath. OSP $1.79. **CMV $15. BO mint, $20. MB.**

FIRST MATE SHAMPOO 1963-64
8 oz. blue and white plastic sailor with white hat. OSP $1.98. **CMV $15. MB, $11. BO.**

CAPTAIN'S BUBBLE BATH 1963-64
8 oz. white, yellow and black plastic bottle with blue hat. OSP $1.98. **CMV $15. MB, $11. BO.**

AQUA CAR 1964-65
(Left) 8 oz. red & white plastic bottle of bubble bath. OSP $1.98. **CMV $10. - $15. MB.**

S.S. SUDS 1970-71
(Right) 8 oz. blue & white plastic boat holds No Tear Shampoo. OSP $3. **CMV $5. - $7. MB.**

TUB CATCH 1968-69
2 ft. long yellow rod & reel holds 6 oz. bubble bath. Pink, green & blue plastic fish. OSP $3.50. **CMV $9. MB.**

LITTLE MISSY ROLLING PIN 1966-67
12" long, 8 oz. pink plastic center with orange ends. Holds Non Tear Shampoo. OSP $2.25. **CMV $9. BO mint, $13. MB.**

BIRD FEEDER 1967-68
11" high, black and white plastic center with red base and yellow top. Holds 7 1/2 oz. powdered bubble bath. OSP $3.50. **CMV $8. BO, $12. MB.**

PACKY THE ELEPHANT 1964-65
3 oz. each. OSP $1.10 each. Each has white hat. Blue holds baby oil, yellow holds baby shampoo, baby lotion in red. **CMV red & blue $10. BO each, $15. MB; yellow $15. BO, $20. MB.**

SMILEY THE WHALE 1967-68
(Left) 9" blue plastic whale holds 9 oz. bubble bath. OSP $1.98. **CMV $6. BO, $9. MB.**
WHITEY THE WHALE 1959-62
(Right) 8 oz. white plastic whale holds bubble bath. OSP $1.79. **CMV $15. MB, $10. BO.**

SANTA'S CHIMNEY 1964-65
Red & white box holds 5 oz. of powdered bubble bath. Top of box makes a puzzle game. OSP $1.98. **CMV $20. MB.**

TOOFIE TWOSOME 1963-64
This is the 1st issue of the Toofie series. 3 1/2 oz. green & blue tube & green cap. Choice of red, yellow, blue or green toothbrush. OSP $1.25. **CMV $8. MB, TO $3.**

EASTER DEC A DOO 1968-69
(Left) 8 oz. pink & yellow plastic egg holds bubble bath. Came with stick on decorations. OSP $2.50. **CMV $6. MB, $4. BO.**
HUMPTY DUMPTY 1963-65
(Right) 8 oz. plastic bottle of bubble bath. Blue bottom, white top, black belt. OSP $1.98. **CMV $9. MB, $6. BO.**

LIL FOLKS TIME 1961-64
(Left) 8 oz. yellow & white plastic clock with yellow cap & red time hands, holds bubble bath. OSP $1.75. **CMV $8. BO, $11. MB.**
TIC TOC TIGER 1967-69
(Right) 8 oz. orange & white plastic clock with yellow cap & hands, holds bubble bath. OSP $1.75. **CMV $6. BO, $8. MB.**

TOOFIE TOOTHPASTE 1967-68
3 1/2 oz. white tube with racoon & pink cap & toothbrush, pink & white box. OSP $1.25. **CMV $6. MB, $2. TO.**

MARY NON TEAR SHAMPOO 1968-69
(Left) 3 oz. pink plastic bottle. OSP $1.35.
CMV $6. BO, $8. MB.
LITTLE LAMB BABY LOTION 1968-69
(Center) 3 oz. white plastic lamb with blue
cap. OSP $1.35. CMV $5. BO, $7. MB.
LITTLE RED SCHOOLHOUSE 1968-69
(Right) 3 oz. red plastic school with yellow
cap. Contains bubble bath. OSP $1.35. CMV
$6. BO, $8. MB.

LITTLE HELPER IRON 1962-64
(Left) 8 oz. blue plastic iron with white handle.
Holds bubble bath. OSP $2. CMV $13. mint,
$17. MB.
WATERING CAN 1962-64
(Right) 8 oz. yellow plastic bottle holds bubble
bath. Blue cap. OSP $2. CMV $13. mint,
$17. MB.

TOOFIE TOOTHPASTE 1969-70
3 1/2 oz. blue & green tube with pink cap &
toothbrush in blue & green box. OSP $1.35.
CMV $5. MB, $2. TO.

CHIEF SCRUBBEM 1969-70
(Left) 4 oz. red & yellow plastic Indian holds
liquid soap. OSP $2.50. CMV $6. MB, $4.
BO.
SCRUB MUG 1968-69
(Right) 6 oz. blue plastic mug with blue brush
lid. Holds liquid soap. OSP $2.50. CMV $6.
MB, $4. BO.

LIL TOM TURTLES 1961-63
3 oz. plastic turtles. OSP $1.10 each. Each
has white hat. Yellow holds baby shampoo,,
blue has baby oil & baby lotion in red. CMV
$10. each, $15. MB.

TOY SOLDIERS 1964
4 oz. each. Red, white & blue plastic bottles,
black caps. Came in Hair Trainer, shampoo,
hand lotion, bubble bath. OSP $1.25 each.
CMV $10. each BO, $12. MB.

PADDLE 'N' BALL SET 1966-67
6 oz. tan plastic paddle with red cap. Holds
shampoo. Rubber ball hooked to paddle. 8"
long by 4 1/2" wide. OSP $1.75. CMV $12. -
$15. MB.

MICKEY MOUSE 1969-71
(Left) 4 1/2 oz. red pants, black & white palstic
Mickey with yellow feet. Holds bubble bath.
OSP $3.50. CMV $5. BO, $7. MB.
PLUTO 1970-71
(Right) 4 oz. yellow & black plastic dog with
red collar. Holds Non Tear shampoo. OSP
$3.50. CMV $5. BO, $7. MB.

JET PLANE 1965 ONLY
3 oz. red, white & blue plastic tube with white
plastic wings came in gel bubble bath,
children's gel shampoo or Hair Tainer. OSP
$1.50. CMV $10. mint, $15. MB.

TOPSY TURVEY 1970-72
(Left) 4 oz. green plastic bottle with white cap
holds bubble bath. OSP $2. CMV $3. MB, $1.
BO.
BALL & CUP 1972-73
(Right) 4 oz. blue bottom with green cup &
ball. Holds shampoo. OSP $2. CMV $4. MB,
$2. BO.

TUB TALK TELEPHONE 1969
(Blue) 6 oz. blue plastic telephone with yellow cap & holder. Holds No Tear Shampoo. OSP $2.25. **CMV $7. - $9. MB.**

VERY OWN TELEPHONE 1964-65
(Red) 6 oz. red plastic telephone & base. Holds Baby Shampoo. OSP $1.98. **CMV $9. BO, $13. MB.**

TUB TALK TELEPHONE 1967-68
(Yellow) 6 oz. yellow telephone with red cap & holder. Holds Tot 'N' Tyke shampoo. OSP $1.75. **CMV $8. BO, $11. MB.**

FRILLY DUCK 1960-62
(Left) 3 oz. yellow plastic duck with blue cap. Came in baby oil, baby lotion & Tot 'N' Tyke shampoo. OSP 98c. **CMV $10., $13. MB.**

PIG IN A POKE 1960-62
(Right) 8 oz. pink plastic pig holds bubble bath. Came in pink bag. OSP $1.79. **CMV $9. BO, $14. BO with bag., $18. MB.**

BUNNY FLUFF PUFF 1979-80
(Left) 3.5 oz. yellow plastic with fluff tail & pink eyes & ears. Holds children's talc. SSP $6. **CMV $3.50 MB.**

RED STREAK CAR 1979-80
(Right) 7 oz. red plastic with blue & silver stick on decals. Holds bubble bath for children. SSP $4. **CMV $3. MB.**

TOOTHBRUSH DUO (CHILDREN'S) 1979
(Left) Red & pink box holds 1 red & 1 white toothbrush for kids. SSP 89c. **CMV 50c. MB.**

PINK PANTHER TOOTHBRUSH HOLDER 1979
(Right) Pink plastic holder. Yellow & red toothbrushes. Blue & pink box. SSP $5. **CMV $3. MB.**

BARNEY BEAVER TOOTHBRUSHES & HOLDER 1973
(Left) 4" high, brown plastic with white & blue. Has pink & blue toothbrushes. Comes with a sticker to put on wall. SSP $2.50. **CMV $4. MB.**

'I LOVE TOOFIE' TOOTHBRUSHES & HOLDER 1973
(Right) 5" high, white & pink, holds red & blue toothbrushes. Comes with sticker to put on wall. SSP $2. **CMV $4. MB.**

BABY SHOE PIN CUSHION 1973-74
(Left) 7 oz. whie plastic with pink pin cushion & blue bow. Filled with baby lotion. SSP $4. **CMV $4. BO, $5. MB.**

SUNNY BUNNY BABY POMANDER 1973-76
(Center) Wax figurine with nursery fresh fragrance. SSP $5. **CMV $5. BO, $6. MB.**

SAFETY PIN DECANTER 1973-74
(Right) 8 oz. yellow plastic filled with baby lotion. SSP $3. **CMV $4. BO, $5. MB.**

TENNIS ANYONE? 1975-76
(Left) 5 oz. gray & black plastic. Holds Sweet Honesty after bath freshener or Avon Spicy after shave. OSP $3. **CMV $2.50.**

SLUGGER BRUSH 1974-75
(Right) 7" long brown & black plastic. OSP $3.50. **CMV $3.**

ON THE RUN "JOGGING SHOE" 1978-79
(Left) 6 oz. blue plastic with white stripes. Holds Wild Country after shave or Sweet Honesty body splash. SSP $4. **CMV $4. MB.**

CONAIR "HAIR DRYER" 1978-79
(Right) 6 oz. off-white plastic. Blue letters and cap. Holds Naturally Gentle shampoo. SSP $5. **CMV $4. MB.**

ACCUSING ALLIGATOR 1978-79
(Left) 6 oz. green, yellow & tan plastic. Holds bubble bath. SSP $5. **CMV $3.50 MB.**

SUPERMAN BUBBLE BATH 1978-79
(Right) 8 oz. blue, red & gray plastic. Holds bubble bath. Box came with 2 red and yellow plastic cut out capes. SSP $6. **CMV $5. MB.**

HANG TEN SKATEBOARD DECANTER 1978-79
(Left) 5.5 oz. yellow plastic with top stick on decal. Holds bubble bath for children. SSP $5. **CMV $2.50 MB.**

KARROT TAN DECANTER 1978-79
(Center) 4 oz. orange plastic with green leaf top. Holds Bronze Glory tanning lotion. SSP $5. **CMV $4. BO, no box issued.**

HEAVY HITTER DECANTER 1978-79
(Right) 4 oz. dark blue plastic. White letters. holds non tear shampoo. SSP $5. **CMV $3. MB.**

TOOFIE THE TIGER 1966-67
(Left) 3 1/2 oz. green & orange tube, green cap, toothbrush. OSP $1.35. **CMV $6. MB, $3. TO mint.**

TOOFIE ON GUARD 1968-69
(Right) 3 1/2 oz. red, white, & blue tube, blue cap. Avon toothbrush. OSP $1.25. **CMV TO $2. mint, $5. MB.**

MY PUPPY 1986
Brown stuffed pup 11" high. DP $12. **CMV $12.**

SPACE PATROLLER DECANTER 1979-80

(Left) 8 oz. gray plastic, black cap & stick on decals. SSP $5. **CMV $3.**

SPIDERMAN TOOTHBRUSH & HOLDER 1979-80
(Right) Red & blue plastic. Yellow & green Avon toothbrushes. SSP $5. **CMV $2.50 MB.**

SPOTTY TO THE RESCUE TOOTHBRUSH HOLDER 1976-77
Red, white & black plastic toothbrush holder holds 2 Avon toothbrushes. SSP $2.49. **CMV $2. MB.**

BATMOBILE 1978-79
(Left) 6 oz. blue & silver plastic with stick on decals. Came in bubble bath for children. SSP $5. **CMV $5. MB.**

LIP POP POMADE "PEPSI" 1978-79
(Right) Dark amber plastic. Gray cap. Looks like Pepsi Cola bottle. SSP $3. **CMV $3. MB.**

SWEET PICKLES FUN BOOK & RECORD 1978-79
Book & record issued by Avon Products. Came in an envelope. There are 4 different ones. SSP $2. **CMV $3. complete mint.**

GRID KID LIQUID HAIR TRAINER 1974-75
(Left) 8 oz. red, black & white plastic. OSP $2. **CMV $2. BO, $3. MB.**

ARCH E. BEAR BRUSH & COMB 1975-76
(Right) Red, white & blue brush with white comb. OSP $3. **CMV $2. - $3. MB.**

JACKKNIFE COMB & BRUSH 1974-76
(Left) Blue & silver plastic comb. Cub Scout gold label on top. OSP $5. **CMV $3. MB.**

ICE CREAM COMB 1977-78
(Center) Orange plastic comb with pink & brown ice cream & red cherry on top. OSP $3. **CMV $2. MB.**

REGGIE RACCOON HAIRBRUSH & COMB 1977
(Right) 6 1/4" long. Brown, white, pink & black brush & white comb. SSP $4. **CMV $2. MB.**

GIRAFFABATH BATH BRUSH 1977-79
(Left) Orange & beige plastic. Blue eyes. OSP $6. **CMV $3.50 MB.**

BATMAN STYLING BRUSH 1977-78
(Center) Blue, gray & black plastic brush. OSP $6. **CMV $5. MB.**

SUPERMAN STYLING BRUSH 1977
(Right) Red & blue plastic brush. OSP $6. **CMV $5. MB.**

WALLY WALRUS TOOTHBRUSH HOLDER & TOOTHBRUSH 1977-78
Adhesive back holder sticks to wall. Came with 2 child sized Avon toothbrushes in red & white. Plastic holder is blue & red with white hat & trim. SSP $2. **CMV $2. MB.**

HOT DOG! BRUSH & COMB 1975-76
(Left) Yellow & red plastic comb. OSP $3.
CMV $2. - $3. MB.
SUNANA BRONZE GLORY TANNING LOTION 1974-76
(Right) 6 oz. yellow plastic banana. OSP
$2.75. **CMV $3. BO, no box issued.**

TED E. BEAR TOOTHBRUSH HOLDER 1974-75
Box holds tan, pink & white plastic holder &
pink & white Avon toothbrushes. OSP $2.75.
CMV $3. MB.

TOOFIE THE CLOWN 1978
Orange, yellow & white plastic toothbrush
holder. Blue & pink toothbrushes. SSP $3.
CMV $2. MB.

PRECIOUS LAMB BABY LOTION 1975-76
6 oz. white plastic lamb with blue bow. Holds
baby lotion. SSP $3. **CMV $4. MB.**

SCRUBBO THE ELEPHANT BATH BRUSH 1975
White plastic, pink ears & cheeks. SSP $2.29.
CMV $2. MB. 1976 issue was all pink plastic.
Each is 8" long. SSP $2. **CMV $2. MB.**

SCHOOL DAYS RULER COMB 1976-79
Box holds yellow plastic 6" ruler comb. OSP
$3. **CMV $2. MB.**

TOOFIE TOOTHPASTE 1971-73
(Left) 3 1/2 oz. yellow & orange tube & box.
OSP 89c. **CMV $2. - $3. MB.**
TOOFIE TOOTHBRUSH DUO 1973-74
(Right) Pak of 2, green worm & yellow bird.
SSP $2. **CMV $2. MB.**

ELLA ELEPHANT SCENTED STUFFED ANIMAL 1979-80
Pink box holds pink scented elephant with
turquoise ears & pink ribbon. Has Avon tag.
Made in Taiwan. SSP $8. **CMV $6. MB.**

LOVING LION DECANTER 1978-79
(Left) 8 oz. plastic purple, yellow, pink &
orange. Holds Non Tear Shampoo. SSP $5.
CMV $3.50 MB.
THREE RING CIRCUS CHILDREN'S TALC 1978-79
(Center) 5 oz., 2 sections of center turn
around. SSP $2.49. CMV $2. MB.
OCTOPUS TOOTHBRUSH HOLDER 1978-79
(Right) Purple & orange plastic toothbrush
holder. Comes with orange & white Avon
toothbrushes. SSP $4. **CMV $2.50 MB.**

MOST VALUABLE GORILLA 1979-80
(Left) 4 oz. orange & blue plastic stick on front
& back decals in any letter. Holds bubble bath
for children. **CMV $3.50 MB.**
WILLIE WEATHERMAN 1979-80
(Center) 6 oz. tan plastic, pink cap. Blue
umbrella changes color with the weather.
Holds Non Tear Shampoo. SSP $5. **CMV $3. MB.**
IMP THE CHIMP BATH BRUSH 1980
(Right) Brown plastic, yellow, black & pink
trim. 10" long. SSP $7. **CMV $4. MB.**

TOOFIE TIGER TOOTHBRUSHES & HOLDER 1976
(Left) Yellow, black, white & pink. Has 1 pink
& 1 white toothbrush. OSP $2.50. **CMV 42. MB.**
TOOFIE TOOTHBRUSH DUO 1971-73
(Center) One yellow giraffe, 1 pink rabbit
brush. OSP $1. **CMV $2. MB.**
TORTOISE 'N' HARE TOOTHBRUSH DUO 1975-76
(Right) Green tortoise & yellow hare. OSP
$1.80. **CMV $1. MB.**

BRONTOSAURUS BUBBLE BATH 1975-76
(Left) 10 oz. blue gray plastic. OSP $3.50.
CMV $2. BO, $3. MB.
LOVABLE LEO 1974-76
(Right) 10 oz. yellow plastic, pink cap.
Children's shampoo. OSP $3. CMV $2. BO,
$3. MB.

SURE WINNER CATCHER'S MITT 1974-75
(Left) 6 oz. brown plastic with brown cap.
Holds Avon liquid hair trainer. OSP $2. CMV
$3.
WINKIE BLINK CLOCK BUBBLE BATH
1975-76
(Right) 8 oz. yellow with blue clock hands &
blue cap. OSP $4. CMV $3. BO, $4. MB.

TURN A WORD BUBBLE BATH 1972-74
8 oz. pink plastic bottle with white cap & green
lettered sides. OSP $3.50. CMV $3.
CLANCY THE CLOWN SOAP HOLDER &
SOAP 1973-74
Orange, pink and white clown holds green and
white, pink and orange 3 oz. soap. SSP $3.50.
CMV $6. MB.

MILLICENT MOUSE DEMI STICK 1977-78
(Left) Came with Pink & Pretty fragrance demi
stick. Colors are pink & white. OSP $3.75.
CMV $3.50 MB.
GLOW WORM 1977-79
(Inside Left) Came with Care Deeply lip balm.
White rubber top with purple spots. Demi stick
is blue & green. OSP $3.50. CMV $3.50 MB.
GILROY THE GHOST 1977-78
(Inside Right) Came with Care Deeply lip
balm. White & black rubber top with black,
green & white demi stick. OSP $3.50. CMV
$3.50 MB.
HUCK L. BERRY 1977-78
(Right) Came with Care Deeply lip balm.
Blue, yellow & white rubber top with yellow &
white demi stick. OSP $3.75. CMV $3.50 MB.

SCHOOL DAYS BARRETTE 1973-75
(Top Left) Brown & yellow pencil barrette.
SSP $1.50. CMV $1.50 MB.
COMB BARRETTE 1973
(Bottom Left) 2" long, white plastic with red,
pink & green design. SSP $1.50. CMV $2.
MB.
JENNY GIRAFFE 1973
(Right) Yellow & brown with coral cord. SSP
$1.50. CMV $2.50 MB.

JACK IN A BOX GLACE 1976
(Left) White plastic with pink & green trim.
SSP $2. CMV $3.50 MB.
CHICK A PEEK GLACE 1977
(Right) Yellow plastic back & chick with purple
egg. SSP $2. CMV $3.50 MB.

KISS 'N' MAKEUP LIP GLOSS COMPACT
1977-79
(Top) Came with Frostlight Peach & Frostlight
Pink lip gloss. Red plastic container. OSP $4.
CMV $1.
LOVE LOCKET GLACE 1972
(Bottom) CMV $6. MB, $4. CO.

TOOFIE TRAIN 1974-75
Red plastic train, yellow plastic cup. Red &
blue toofie toothbrushes & yellow with red cap
Toofie toothpaste. OSP $5. CMV $5. - $7.
MB.

RAPID RABBIT PIN PAL 1974-75
(Left) White plastic with pink & green. Feet swing. Filled with perfumed glace. SSP $2.
CMV $2. - $3. MB.
MYRTLE TURTLE PIN PAL 1974
(Right) Green plastic with pink & green. Filled with perfumed glace. SSP $2. **CMV $2. - $3. MB.**

CHILDREN'S FUN JEWELRY
LUV-A-DUCKY 1973
(Top Left) Yellow & orange. SSP $2. **CMV $3.50 - $5. MB.**
PANDY BEAR PIN 1973
(Bottom Left) Black & white. SSP $1.50.
CMV $3.50 - $5. MB.
FLY-A-KITE 1973
(Center) Red, white and blue. SSP $2. **CMV $3.50 - $5. MB.**

FUZZY BUG 1973-74
(Top Right) Blue with green fur. SSP $2.
CMV $3.50 - $5. MB.
PERKEY PARROT 1973
(Bottom Right) Red & green. SSP $1.50.
CMV $3.50 - $5. MB.

LOONEY LATHER BUBBLE BATH 1971
(Left) 6 oz. spray can, pink cap. OSP $2.
CMV $4.
LOONEY LATHER SHAMPOO 1971
(Right) 6 oz. size, green cap. OSP $2. **CMV $4.**

ROTO-BOAT FLOATING SOAP DISH & SOAP 1973-75
9" long blue & white boat with red rudder holds 3 oz. blue soap. SSP $3. **CMV $5.** Reissued with "R" on bottom.

BOBBIN' ROBIN PIN 1975-76
(Top Left) White cage, red bird (bird movable). OSP $2. **CMV $3. MB.**
MINUTE MOUSE PIN 1974-75
(Bottom Left) White with blue clock, orange hands & numbers. OSP $2. **CMV $3. MB.**
PEDAL PUSHER PIN 1975-76
(Top Center) Blue elephant with green jacket & pink bike. OSP $1.89. **CMV $3. MB.**

LICKETY STICK MOUSE PIN 1974-76
(Bottom Center) White plastic with green hat & pink striped stick. OSP $2. **CMV $3. MB.**
MAGIC RABBIT PIN 1975-76
(Top Right) White & pink rabbit with gray hat. OSP $2. **CMV $3. MB.**
COTTON TAIL GLACE 1976-78
(Bottom Right) Yellow & pink with white tail. OSP $2. **CMV $3. MB.**

BUMBLEY BEE PINS 1973-74
Yellow with black stripes. One with big stripes & 1 narrow stripes. OSP $2. **CMV $4. - $6. MB.**

CHILDREN'S TOYS

GREAT CATCH, CHARLIE BROWN, SOAP HOLDER & SOAP 1975-76
(Left) Red, white, black & brown plastic. OSP $4. **CMV $6. MB.**

QUACK & DOODLE FLOATING SOAP DISH & SOAP 1974-75
(Right) Yellow rubber with yellow soap. OSP $3.50. **CMV $5. MB.**

RING AROUND ROSIE 1966-67
Pink rubber elephant sticks on wall with blue bar of Avon soap. OSP $2.25. **CMV $15. MB, soap only $6., elephant only $4.**

CLEAN SHOT 1970-72
Orange net holds orange basketball sponge & 1 bar of Clean Shot soap. OSP $4.50. **CMV $6. MB. set.**

CHILDREN'S PERFUME GLACE PIN PALS
Add $1. each MB.

FUNNY BUNNY 1973-74
(Top Left) Pink & white. SSP $2. CMV $4.

CALICO CAT 1973
(Top Center) Red with white dots. Also came red & no dots. SSP $2. **CMV $4.**

CALICO CAT 1974-75
(Repeat Top Center) Blue with white dots. Also came blue with no dots on bottom half. OSP $2. **CMV $3. each.**

BLOUSE MOUSE 1972
(Top Right) Green & pink. Also came green with white trim. SSP $2. **CMV $4.**

BLUE MOO 1974
(Middle Left) Blue & pink. SSP $2. **CMV $3.**

SNIFFY PIN PAL 1972-75
(Middle Center) Black, white & pink. SSP $2. **CMV $3.**

ELPHIE THE ELEPHANT 1973
(Middle Right) Yellow & pink. SSP $2. **CMV $4.**

GINGERBREAD PIN PAL 1973
(Bottom Center) Brown & pink. Also came brown & white. SSP $2. **CMV $5. pink, $6. white.**

PUPPY LOVE PIN PAL GLACE 1975
(Top Left) Beige dog with black ears & pink pillow. OSP $2. **CMV $4. MB.**

WEE WILLY WINTER PIN PAL GLACE 1974-75
(Top Center) White snowman with pink hat, scarf & mittens. OSP $1.88. **CMV $4. MB.**

SUNNY FRESH ORANGE GLACE NECKLACE 1974-75
(Top Right) Orange & yellow with green cord. OSP $3. **CMV $4. MB.**

PETER PATCHES PIN PAL GLACE 1975-76
(Bottom Left) Yellow with red & blue trim. OSP $2. **CMV $4. MB.**

CHICKEN LITTLE PIN PAL GLACE 1975
(Bottom Inside Left) Yellow chicken with pink flower & green leaf. OSP $2.49. **CMV $4.**

WILLIE THE WORM PIN PAL GLACE 1974-75
(Bottom Inside Right) Red apple, green worm. OSP $2. **CMV $4. MB.**

ROCK-A-ROO PIN PAL GLACE 1975-77
(Bottom Right) Pink with dark pink rocking pouch. OSP $2. **CMV $3. MB.**

REGGIE RACOON HAIR BRUSH AND COMB 1973
6 1/2" long, tan and black with tan comb. SSP $3. **CMV $4. MB.**

FREDDIE THE FROG 1969-70
(Left) Green rubber frog soap dish & green vest soap. Pink lips & pink band around hat. OSP $1.75. **CMV frog only $2., with soap $6. MB.**
FREDDIE THE FROG 1965-66
(Right) Green rubber frog with yellow hat & eyes, pink lips, green soap. OSP $3. **CMV frog only $5., with soap $10. MB.**

FIRST DOWN 1965-67
Large box holds real junior size football & 6 oz. brown football soap on a rope. Rope comes out side of soap. OSP $3.95 Avon soap & ball. **CMV soap $9. MB, ball $15., set MB $27.50 .**

WASH AWEIGH SOAP & DISH 1966-67
Green plastic boat dish & yellow anchor soap on a rope. OSP $1.98. **CMV boat $6., anchor soap $9., set $18. MB.**

REGINALD G. RACOON III 1970-71
Black, brown and white rubber soap dish and 3 oz. pink vest soap. OSP $3.50. **CMV racoon only $2., $6. set MB.**
RANDY PANDY SOAP DISH 1972-74
Black, white & pink rubber soap dish & 3 oz. white soap. OSP $3.50. **CMV panda only $2., set $6. MB.**

BARNEY BEAVER SOAP DISH & SOAP 1971-72
10 1/2" long, brown soap dish and brown vest soap. OSP $3.50. **CMV $6. MB. Beaver only $2.**

PADDLEWOG FROG FLOATING SOAP DISH & SOAP 1975-76
Green plastic with pink propeller and yellow soap. OSP $4. **CMV $3. MB.**

ORIENTAL FAN PERFUME GLACE 1982-83
(Left) Red plastic fan, black tassel, choice of Timeless or Candid. Red & black box. SSP $4. **CMV $2. MB.**
STRAWBERRY CONE LIP GLOSS 1982-83
(Right) Yellow & pink plastic, yellow & lavender box. SSP $4. **CMV $2. MB.**

GAYLORD GATER 1967-69
10" long green and yellow rubber soap dish with yellow soap. OSP $2.25. **CMV gater only $2., $7. set MB.**
TOPSY TURTLE FLOATING SOAP DISH & SOAP 1973-74
7" long green rubber soap dish with 3 oz. pink soap. SSP $2. **CMV $3. MB.** Reissued 1979. Some came light green body and dark green head. Also came matching body and head.

SOAP BOAT, FLOATING SOAP DISH AND SOAP 1973-74
7 1/2" long blue and red boat with white sail and white soap. SSP $2. **CMV $5. MB.**

PINK PEARL SCRUB AWAY NAIL BRUSH AND SOAP 1977-78
3 oz. soap, pink brush shaped like pink pearl eraser. OSP $4. **CMV $4. MB.**

FREDDY THE FROG MUG 1970
5 oz. white glass with red or orange top and white cap. holds bubble bath. OSP $3.50. **CMV $5., $7. MB.**

GAYLORD GATOR MUG 1970-72
5 oz. white glass mug with yellow top and white cap. Holds Non Tear Shampoo. OSP $3.50. **CMV $5., $7. MB.**

TERRIBLE TUBBLES FLOATING SOAP DISH AND SOAP 1977-78
(Left) Blue plastic dish with 3 oz. soap. SSP $4. **CMV $5. MB.**

RANDY PANDY SOAP DISH AND SOAP 1976-77
(Right) Black, light blue and red rubber soap dish and 3 oz. blue and white soap. SSP $4. **CMV (Panda only) $1. Set $5. MB.**

MOON FLIGHT GAME 1970-72
4 oz. white Space Capsule holds Non Tear Shampoo. Comes with black game sheet. OSP $4. **CMV $5. MB, $1.50 BO.**

MR. ROBOTTLE 1971-72
8" high plastic bottle with blue body and red legs and arms. Silver and yellow cap. Holds bubble bath. Came with white plastic wrench to put together. OSP $3.50. **CMV $4. BO, $6. MB.**

KANGA WINKS 1971-72
7" high yellow and orange plastic bottle with pink hat, holds 8 oz. of bubble bath. Box also holds black and white plastic target and package of 16 plastic chips for tiddlywinks. OSP $4. **CMV $4. complete set, $1. Kangaroo only, $6. set MB.**

CHOO-CHOO TRAIN 1971-72
Soap coach is 4" long plastic soap dish with yellow bar of soap. OSP $1.50. **CMV $6. MB, with soap, $1. soap coach only.** Caboose is pink plastic bottle, 3" long with Non Tear Shampoo, OSP $2. **CMV $4. MB.** Puffer Chugger is 4" long green plastic bottle with yellow cap and nose. Holds bubble bath. OSP $2. **CMV $4. MB.**

SPOOL-A-DOO ROLLETTE 1972-73
.33 oz. Rollette with red cap. Came with yellow plastic spool, eight yards of pink yarn and blue and pink plastic needles. SSP $2. **CMV $4. MB.**

SPLASH DOWN BUBBLE BATH 1970-71
8 oz. white plastic bottle with red cap and yellow base ring. Came with 3 plastic toss rings. OSP $4. **CMV $3. BO, $5. MB.**

HICKORY DICKORY CLOCK 1971-72
5 1/2" high, 8 oz. yellow plastic cheese clock with orange face and pink hands, purple mouse cap. Contains Non Tear Shampoo. OSP $4.50. **CMV $4. BO, $6. MB.**

POP-A-DUCK GAME 1978
6 oz. blue plastic with red-orange cap. Came with 3 green balls. Pink, orange and yellow ducks and red-orange ball holder. Bottle holds bubble bath for children. SSP $4. **CMV $4. MB.**

ROCKABYE PONY DECANTER 1975-76
6 oz. yellow plastic, holds Clearly Gentle Baby Lotion. OSP $4. **CMV $3. BO, $4. MB.**
JACK-IN-THE-BOX 1975-76
4 oz. yellow and pink plastic, holds baby cream. OSP $4. **CMV $3. BO, $4. MB.**

EASTER DEC-A-DOO FOR CHILDREN 1978
(Left) 8 oz. plastic yellow base, pink top. Came with stick on decals. This is different from 68-69 issue. Old one does not say for children on label. Holds bubble bath. SSP $3.99. **CMV $3. MB, $2. BO.**
DUSTER D. DUCKLING FLUFF PUFF 1978-82
3.5 oz. yellow plastic and fluff top. Holds Delicate Daisies or Sweet Pickles perfumed talc. SSP $4.44. **CMV $3. MB, $2. BO.**

TYRANNOSAURUS REX 1976-78
4 oz. green plastic bottle, green rubber head. holds bubble bath for children. SSP $3. **CMV $2. BO, $3. MB.**
TUB SUB 1978-79
6 oz. yellow plastic, 10" long. Holds bubble bath for children. SSP $4. **CMV $2. BO, $3. MB.**

POP A DUCK 1971-72
6 oz. blue plastic bottle holds bubble bath. 3 plastic ducks and ball. OSP $3.50. **CMV $5. complete set MB.**

MAZE GAME 1971-72
6 oz. green plastic bottle, white cap. holds Non Tear Shampoo. OSP $2.50. **CMV $5. MB, $3. BO.**
HUGGY BEAR 1971-72
8 oz. brown plastic bottle with lace-up vest, holds bubble bath. OSP $3.50. **CMV $5. MB, $3. BO.**

LITTLE WIGGLY GAME & BUBBLE BATH 1973
8 oz. green with pink legs, red and yellow hoops. Holds bubble bath. SSP $3.50. **CMV $3.50 MB.**

CUSTOM CAR 1976-78
7 oz. blue plastic bottle with red tire cap. Filled with bubble bath for children. OSP $5. **CMV $2. BO, $3. MB.**
TRICERATOPS 1977-78
8 1/2 oz. green plastic bottle. Came with bubble bath for children. OSP $5.50. **CMV $2. BO, $3. MB.**

LOOP-A-MOOSE GAME AND SOAP 1972-75
7" high brown plastic moose, yellow antlers. has green, pink and yellow rings to toss. Comes with 3 oz. yellow soap. SSP $3. **CMV $3. - $4. MB.**

SCHROEDER 1970-72
6 oz. red, white, black and yellow plastic bottle holds bubble bath, in piano shaped box. OSP $3.50. **CMV $4., $9. MB in piano box.**
LINUS 1970-72
4 oz. red, white and black plastic bottle holds Non Tear Shampoo. OSP $3. **CMV $6. MB, $3. BO.**

CURLEY CATERPILLAR COMB 1974-75
6" long green and pink plastic. OSP $1.50. **CMV $1.50 MB.**
SHAGGY DOG COMB 1975-76
5" long white plastic. OSP $1.25. **CMV $1.50 MB.**
AL E. GATOR COMB & BRUSH 1974
5" long green plastic with green comb. OSP $3. **CMV $3. MB.**

ARISTOCAT 1971-72
4 oz. gray cat with pink collar holds Non Tear Shampoo. OSP $3. **CMV $4. BO, $5. MB.**

CLUCK A DOO 1971
8 oz. yellow bottle, pink hat. Came with stick on decals. holds bubble bath. OSP $3. **CMV $5. MB, $3. BO.**

SUNBONNET SUE DEMI STICK 1975-77
.19 oz. red and white plastic. Pink & Pretty fragrance. OSP $2.50. **CMV $3. MB, $2. BO.**

NUTSHELL COLOR MAGIC LIPSTICK 1974-75
Peanut shaped case came in Pink Sorcery (blue lipstick) or Peach Sorcery (green lipstick). OSP $2. **CMV $3. MB, $2. BO.**

SCHOOL DAYS PENCIL LIP POMADE 1975-76
.13 oz. red, white and yellow plastic. Choice of strawberry, cherry or tutti-frutti. OSP $2.50. **CMV $3. MB, $2. BO.**

SWEET LIPS LIP GLOSS COOKIE 1975-76
Brown plastic with 2 shades of lip gloss. OSP $3. **CMV $3. MB, $2. BO.**

COMBSICLE 1979-80
Popsicle box holds brown and beige Avon comb. SSP $2. **CMV $1. MB.**

CHOCOLATE CHIPLICK COMPACT 1979-80
Tan and brown plastic, holds lip gloss. SSP $3.50. **CMV $2. MB.**

POWDER DRILL 1979-80
5 oz. yellow plastic with silver plastic drill cap. Holds Wild Country or Electric Pre Shave. SSP $6. **CMV $4. MB.**

TUGGABLE TEDDY TOOTHBRUSH HOLDER 1980-81
Tan and blue plastic. Pink and green Avon toothbrushes. Orange ring on gold cord. SSP $5. **CMV $5. MB.**

SMILEY SNAIL TOOTHBRUSH HOLDER 1980-81
Yellow and green plastic. Orange and blue Avon toothbrushes. SSP $6. **CMV $6. MB.**

CLEAN-'EM-UP-PUMP 1981-82
8 oz. yellow plastic with white and yellow pump dispenser. Comes with card of stick on decals. Come in Liquid Cleanser. SSP $5. **CMV $3. MB.**

TED E. BEAR BABY LOTION DISPENSER 1981-82
10 oz. plastic in choice of pink or blue bear. Comes with matching pump dispenser. SSP $7. **CMV $2. MB.**

SPONGIE THE CLOWN 1981
6 oz. plastic bottle with green cap and comes with orange sponge for top. SSP $5. **CMV $1. MB.**

BED OF NAILS COMB 1978-79
5 1/2" comb, tan, white and red. SSP $2.49. **CMV $1. MB.**

WONDER WOMAN MIRROR 1978-79
7 1/2" long plastic mirror. SSP $6. **CMV $2. MB.**

SWEET PICKLES ZANY ZEBRA HAIR BRUSH 1978-79
White, black, pink and green plastic. SSP $5. **CMV $1. MB.**

TASTI MINT LIP GLOSS COMPACT 1978-79
Green and silver plastic. SSP $3. **CMV $2. MB.**

PLAYFUL PUPS LIGHT SWITCH COVER 1982
(Left & center) 3 1/2" x 4 1/2" plastic dog light switch covers. Both came with blue and yellow dot stick-on fragrance bows. Golden pup, and white and gray pup. SSP $4.50. **CMV $1. each MB.**

PLAY PUPS WALL HOOK 1982
(Right) Plastic wall hook, Avon back. SSP $3. **CMV $1. MB.**

AUTOGRAPH HOUND STUFFED ANIMAL & DIPLOMA LIP BALM 1980-81
8 1/2" high tan cotton. Blue plastic cap. White tassel, red satin ribbon on neck. Comes with Care Deeply lip balm Diploma. SSP $10. **CMV $7. MB.**

E.T. & ELLIOTT DECAL SOAP 1983
3 oz. blue bar with decal of E.T. on face. Back of bar says "I'll be right there". SSP $3. **CMV $3. MB.**

E.T. BATH DECANTER 1983-84
7 oz. blue plastic with tan plastic head. Holds Bubble Bath. SSP $9. **CMV $4. MB.**

E.T. MUG 1983-84
4 1/2" high white porcelain mug with E.T. for the handle. SSP $20. **CMV $15. MB.**

E.T. & GERTIE DECAL SOAP 1984
3 oz. pink bar. SSP $4. **CMV $3. MB.**

BOWLING PIN 1960-62
4 oz. white plastic trimmed in red. Came in Vigorate, Liquid Deodorant, Hand Guard, Hair Trainer, After Shaving Lotion, After Shower for Men, Liquid Hair Lotion, Shampoo, Cream Hair Lotion & Electric Pre-Shave. OSP $1.19. **CMV 10 different. $10. each BO, $15. MB. Vigorate $15. BO, $20. MB.**

WABBIT CAR 1983
5 oz. blue plastic car & white rabbit cap. Choice of Children's Bubble Bath or Non-Tear Shampoo. Comes with sheet of stick on decals to decorate. SSP $6. **CMV $4. MB.**

HERSHEY'S KISS CHOCOLATE LIP GLOSS 1983-84
(Left) Brown plastic, holds lip gloss. SSP $3. **CMV $2. MB.**

STARRY NIGHT TRINKET BOX 1983-84
(Center) Blue, white, red and yellow plastic box. Lid can be a pin or earrings. SSP $5. **CMV $3. MB.**

GINGERBREAD MAN SCENTED PIN 1983-84
(Right) Brown gingerbread man pin on cane card. SSP $4. **CMV $2.50.**

SUPER SHOE 1974-76
6 oz. white plastic shoe with blue plastic toe section cap. holds Sure Winner Liquid Hair Trainer or Sure Winner Bracing Lotion. OSP $3. **CMV $3. MB, $2. BO.**

JUST FOR KICKS 1974-75
7 oz. black & white plastic shoe with black plastic cap. Holds Avon Spicy or Avon Sure Winner Bracing Lotion. OSP $4. **CMV $4. MB, $3. BO.**

BUBBA LEE BUNNY 1982-83
6 oz. white plastic rabbit, yellow cap. Choice of Bubble Bath or Non-Tear Shampoo. SSP $5.50. **CMV $3. MB.**

TWEETHOUSE PAPER CUP TOOTHBRUSH HOLDER 1982-83
(Left) White plastic cup holder with stick on decals & 2 child toothbrushes. SSP $7.50. **CMV $4. MB.**

FELIX FOX WALL HOOK 1982-83
(Right) White & tan plastic. SSP $3.50. **CMV $1. MB.**

ORANGATAN 1976
6 oz. orange shaped and colored plastic bottle. Holds suntan lotion. OSP $4. **CMV $2., no box issued.**

AVON IN SPACE 1981
Liquid Cleanser, blue and white, 1 oz. tube.
Non Tear Shampoo, blue 1 oz. plastic robot
bottle, gold cap.
Lip Balm, blue and green. No boxes. SSP $1.
each. **CMV $1. each.**

I.M. CLEAN II "ROBOT" 1980-81
Blue plastic robot with pump dispenser.
Comes with card of stick-on decals. holds 8
oz. of Liquid Cleanser. SSP $7. **CMV $4. MB.**
TUB TUG 1980-81
5 oz. plastic. Comes in yellow and green cap
with Non Tear Shampoo, red and lavender cap
with bubble bath, and blue and red cap with
Liquid Cleanser. SSP $3. each. **CMV $1.
each. No boxes.**

PLAY PUPS TOOTHBRUSH HOLDER 1981-82
Blue and orange shoe, brown ears, holds
green and pink Avon toothbrushes. Dated
1981 on back. SSP $6. **CMV $3. MB.**
CLEAN FLIGHT DECANTER 1982
6 oz. plastic sea plane shaped. Choice of Non
Tear Shampoo in yellow plastic with blue cap
or Liquid CLeanser in orange with yellow cap.
SSP $3. **CMV $1. No box issued.**

CRAYOLA LIP GLOSS SET 1980-81
Crayola box holds 3 plastic crayon shaped
Avon lip gloss in chocolate, grape and
strawberry. SSP $5. **CMV $2. MB.**

MARIA MAKEOVER BATH DECANTER 1982
6 oz. plastic face bottle and sheet of stick-on
decals. Choice of Non Tear Shampoo or
Children's Liquid Cleanser. SSP $5. **CMV $2.
MB.**

NESTLE CRUNCH LIP GLOSS COMPACT 1980-81
2 3/4" long white, blue and red plastic. SSP
$3. **CMV $1. MB.**
REFLECTOR PROTECTOR LIP GLOSS COMPACT 1980-81
Gray with red reflector top. SSP $5. **CMV $1.
MB.**

TOOFY THE TOOTH CLOWN 1983-84
Yellow plastic tube holds 1 Avon toothbrush.
SSP $5. **CMV $3. MB.**
CUTE CHICK PIN & EARRINGS 1983-84
Yellow plastic egg holds yellow chick pin. Blue
egg holds small yellow chick earrings. SSP
$4. each. **CMV $1. each mint.**
LIP SHADES LIP GLOSS 1983-84
Red plastic sunglasses with lip gloss. SSP $5.
CMV $2. MB.

SWEET PICKLES PUZZLES 1978
Set of 3 cardboard puzzles 8" x 6 1/2" size.
Sold set for 25c with $3.50 purchase. **CMV $3.
each puzzle.**

COUNTRY KITCHEN SPICE ANGEL DOLL 1982-83
Box holds spice fragrance doll 7 1/2" high. DP
$8. **CMV $8. MB.**

LITTLE RAG DOLL 1982-83
4" high doll, red dress, yellow hair, green hair
ribbons, black shoes. Comes with Demi Stick
in moonwind or Sweet Honesty. SSP $7.
CMV $7. MB.

SCOOTER SEAL PUPPET 1983
13" long white puppet. Blue sweater & knit hat.
SSP $18. **CMV $10.**

ROBOT BANK 1985
Blue, yellow & orange plastic bank. DP $6.
CMV $3. MB.

BABY ELEPHANT PUMP 1985
8 oz. blue plastic, holds baby lotion. **CMV $2.
MB.**

MUPPET BABIES - MISS PIGGY & KERMIT
4 oz. each plastic, rubber finger puppet tops.
Non Tear Shampoo & Bubble Bath. **CMV $1.
each MB.**

ALLSTAR LEAGUE "BASEBALL BAT" 1987
9 1/2"long tan plastic bottle. Holds shampoo.
DP $2.75. **CMV $2.75 MB.**

TOOL KIT SCREWDRIVER 1986
6 3/4" yellow plastic. Holds 3.5 oz. Bubble
bath. DP $2.25. **CMV $2.25 MB.**

TOOL KIT WRENCH 1986
6 1/2" green plastic. Holds 3.5 oz. Non Tear
Shampoo. DP $2.20. **CMV $2.20 MB.**

E.T. ZIPPER PULL 1984
2" plastic. **CMV $1.**

BABY'S KEEPSAKE BEAR 1982
5" high white stuffed bear. Red hat, green
ribbon dated 1982. SSP $7. **CMV $7. MB.**

FUN IN SPACE SOAPS 1986
Box holds yellow & blue soaps. DP $2. **CMV
$2. MB.**

SUDSVILLE TRUCK & SOAP 1986
Box holds yellow, blue & red plastic dump truck
& bar of yellow Sudsville soap. DP $4.50.
CMV $4.50 MB.

SOMERSAULTS PAL DOLLS 1985
(Top) 6" to 10" stuffed toys. Miss Pear,
Fergus, Charlie Barley, Zappy & Zippy. All
have Avon Tags. DP $10. **CMV $10. each.**

SOMERSAULTS STUFFED TOYS 1986
(Bottom) Each about 10" long. Tabina
Banana, One Two Sweetpeas, Herby Derby
Cucumber & Tallulah Tomato. DP $8. each.
CMV $8. each.

BY THE JUG 1974-75
All 3 - 10 oz. beige plastic. Strawberry Bath
Foam, Astringent, Balsam Shampoo. Brown
caps look like corks. SSP $3. each. No boxes
issued. **CMV $1. each.**

SOMERSAULTS PRODUCTS 1985-86
TABINA & HERBY DERBY
2 oz. plastic cologne green & yellow & yellow &
pink. DP $2. **CMV $2. each.**
MINI DOLLS
Mini plastic - Zippy, Herby Derby, Charley
Barley, Miss Pear & Tallulah. DP $2. each.
CMV $2. each MB.

**SOMERSAULTS MINI PALS WITH MUGS
1986**
9 different plastic mugs & stuffed mini top.
Tabina, One Two, Tallulah, Herby Derby, Miss
Pear, Fergus, Zippy, Charlie Barley, Zappy.
DP $4.50 each. **CMV $4.50 each MB.**

CHICK N. MUG 1987
White ceramic mug & small stuffed yellow
chick. Neither says Avon. Only on box. DP
$5.50. **CMV $5.50 MB.**

TEDDY BEAR HUG MUG 1986
White ceramic mugs, Avon on bottom. 3
different mugs with small brown stuffed bears.
DP $6. **CMV $6. MB.**

BEARIFF THE SHERIFF BEAR. 1986
9" tall brown stuffed bear & brown cowboy hat. Star says Beariff. Blue bandana. DP $8. **CMV $8 MB.**

PUFF THE MAGIC DRAGON 1986
9" tall turquoise & yellow stuffed dragon with 2 oz. dragon talc to put inside. DP $8.50. **CMV $8.50 MB.**

LITTLE BLOSSOM DOLL 1986
11" tall doll.
DAISY DREAMER DOLL 1986
11" high doll.
SCAMPER LILY DOLL 1986
10 1/2" high doll. DP $5.50 each. **CMV $5.50 each.**

LITTLE RED RIDING HOOD DOLL 1985
(Left) 8 1/4" high, porcelain face, hands & feet. Red cape on metal stand. DP $18. **CMV $18 MB.**
CINDERELLA FAIRY TALE DOLL 1984
(Center) 9 1/4" high, porcelain head, hands & feet. Blue dress. Blonde hair. On Stand. DP $18. **CMV $18. MB.**
VICTORIAN COLLECTOR DOLL 1984
(Right) 8" high, porcelain face, hands & legs. DP $16. **CMV $16. MB.**

CARMICHAEL COLLECTABLES 1985
Calendar-**CMV $1**
Plastic Clip-**CMV .50 each.**
Book of Nursey Rhymes-**CMV $1 MB.**
Stuffed Toy-Large-**CMV $15.**
Stuffed Toy Mini-**CMV $2. MB.**

PLUSH PUPPY 1985
Brown & white stuffed dog with red scarf & red & black shirt. Removable coat. DP $7. **CMV $7. MB.**
HUGGIE BEAR 1985
Tan colored stuffed bear. Red bow tie, came with record or tape. DP $11. **CMV $11.**
KIRBY BEAR 1984
Light brown stuffed bear with red night shirt & hat. Came with iron on personal letters. **CMV $10.**
HERBERT THE HEDGE HOG PUPPET 1984
Small hairy plush puppet. DP $9. **CMV $9.**

SUMMER BRIDE FIGURINE 1986
(Left) 6" high white porclain. DP $18. **CMV $18. MB.**
RAPUNZEL FAIRY TALE DOLL 1986
(Center) 8" tall doll with porcelain head, feet & hands. Lavender dress, gold trim. Blonde hair. DP $19.50. **CMV $19.50. MB.**
EARLY AMERICAN DOLL 1987
(Right) 18 1/2" doll with porcelain head, feet & hands. Burgandy top, green skirt, white apron. DP $13. **CMV $13. MB.**

BALLERINA KITTEN & GOLDEN SLIPPER NECKLACE 1986
(Right) 6" white stuffed kitten with pink clothes. Gold tone slipper necklace. DP $6. **CMV $6. MB.**
SPECIAL LOVE SACHET
(Left) Fabric sachet dolls-choice of boy or girl. DP $3. **CMV $2. each MB.**

CLASS OF 85 FROG 1985
Box & sleeve holds green & orange bean bag. DP $3. **CMV $3. MB.**
BUNNY PLUSH TOY 1985
5" stuffed gray & white rabbit. DP $2.50. **CMV $2.50 MB.**

SPRING BUNNY COLLECTION 1986
Fuzzy bunnies in Metal Wagon, Baby Carriage, High Chair, Cradle, or Rocker. DP $1.75 each. **CMV $1.75 each. MB.**

DAYTIME-NIGHTTIME DOLL 1985
Reversible cloth doll. 8" high. Blue on one side. DP $4. **CMV $4.**

PERCIVAL PENGUIN & SOAP 1986
7" stuffed penguin & penguin wrapped bar of soap. DP $4. **CMV $4.**
CHRISTMAS MINI ROLL A SOAP 1986
1 oz. each. One red, one green. **CMV .50 each.**

LULLABY BUNNY 1987
8 1/2" yellow plush movable rabbit with music box. DP $9.50. **CMV $9.50. MB.**
HORATIO HARE 1987
7" high stuffed toy rabbit. Blue, pink, white & yellow. DP $4. **CMV $4. MB.**

HOLIDAY SLEIGH & TEDDY BEAR 1986
Red wicker sleigh 12" long brown bear & red cap & neck scarf. DP $11. **CMV $11. MB.**
CUDDLE BUNNY 1987
Light brown wicker basket with white stuffed rabbit. Pink & lavender ribbon. DP $6.75. **CMV $6.75 MB.**

BRIGHT'N UP MAGNET FRAMES 1987
Not marked Avon. Choice of "You Brighten Every Day", Love Makes A House A Home" & "You're So Special". Fabric cover on mini frames. DP $2. each. **CMV $1. each. MB.**
FLOWER POT FLORAL MAGNETS 1987
Brown plastic. Pansies, Geraniums, or Violets. Not marked Avon. DP $1.50 each. **CMV $1. each. MB.**

VERONICA VALENTINE FINGER PUPPET 1987
Pink plastic says "Hug Me". DP $2.75. **CMV $2. MB.**
GARDEN FRESH MAGNET PEN 1986
Choice of carrot or leak not shown. Orange & green. Not marked Avon, only box. DP $1.75. **CMV $1.75 MB each.**
SWEET SEA SALTWATER TAFFY LIP BALM 1986
Choice of 3-yellow, blue or pink caps. DP .50. **CMV .50 each.**
TOOTSIE ROLL LIP BALM 1987
Brown & white. DP .50. **CMV .50.**

EASTER SWEETKINS 1984
Choice of Rabbit, Chicken or Duck boxes full of candy. DP $1.70. **CMV $2. each. MB.**

FOOTBALL ZIPPER PULL 1984
2 1/4" long plastic football with thermometer. **CMV $2.**
PANDA ZIPER PULL 1984
Black & white plastic bear. **CMV $1.**

SOMERSAULTS ZIPPER PULLS 1985
5 different-Zappy, Fergus, Charley Barley, Herby Derby or Tallulah. DP $2. **CMV $1. ea.**

ON THE FARM BANK 1985
(Right) Stick on stickers & packets of bubble bath inside. DP $3. **CMV $3.**
CHRISTMAS TOYLAND CANDY 1984
(Center) 8 1/4" high tin can full of candy. DP $4. **CMV $4. MB.**
PLUSH LAMB BANK 1984
(Left) 8" long, 6" high. Fabric covered plastic bank. DP $8. **CMV $8. MB.**

MUPPET BABIES ROLL A SOAP 1985
3 oz. plastic green, pink, or blue. **CMV .50 each.**
ROLL A SOAP 1985
3 oz. plastic. Blue or green. **CMV .50 each.**

HALLOWEEN MAKE-UP SET 1985
Box holds jar of make-up base, 6 lipsticks & booklet. DP $3. **CMV $3. MB.**

LITTLE BLOSSOM-DAISY DREAMER, SCAMPER LILY HAND CREAMS 1984
1.5 oz. tubes. CMV .50 each.
LITTLE BLOSSOM LIP TINT 1984
CMV .50 each.
EASTERTIME HAIR & BODY SHAMPOO 1986
(Left) 2 oz. tubes with Chick Pink, Duck Lavender, Rabbit Blue. CMV .50 each.
HALLOWEEN HAIR COLOR GEL 1986
1.5 oz. tubes in green, red, orange & blue. **CMV .50 each.**

SWEET SEA GIFT SET 1986
Box holds 2 oz. Sweet Sea Talc & 10 pockets of bubble bath. **CMV $2.**
SWEET SEA COLOGNE-SHAMPOO & PEN 1986
CMV .50 each.

CLOWNING AROUND BODY SOAP 1984
Red, black or yellow. 1.5 oz. tubes. **CMV 50c each.**
FRUIT BUNCH DECORATNG SOAP 1984
Orange, Strawberry & Lemon 1.5 oz. tubes. **CMV .50 each.**
SOAP WRITERS 1985
3 different plastic bottles in blue, pink, & yellow. **CMV .50 each.**
LIP BALMS CHEFS TREAT 1984
Chocolate, Peppermint, Santa's Helper & Gingerbread. **CMV .50 each.**

COLOGNE PALS SET 1985
Small stuffed kangaroo or clown with .5oz. bottle of Apple Blossom or Sweet Honesty cologne. DP $4. **CMV $4. each MB.**

CHRISTMAS BEAR PIN 1984
Tiny Bear in red stocking.
ROCKING HORSE ORNAMENT PIN 1985
LET IT SNOWMAN PIN 1985
Snowman on skis. **CMV $1. each pin on card.**
LITTLEST ANGEL STORYBOOK & DOLL 1984
Box holds story book & small 4 3/4" blue stuffed angel doll. DP $7. **CMV $7. MB.**

FOREIGN AVONS

PONY POST IMPERATOR FOREIGN 1972
Green glass pony post 9" tall. 2-7/16" wide across the base. Came with gold cap and nose ring. **CMV $25.**
UNICORN - FOREIGN 1974
Emerald green glass, silver cap. Held cologne. Rare. Same size as Canada, clear. **CMV $150. green glass.**

CHATEAU D'AVON, CHAMPAGNE - EUROPE 1978
30 ml size green glass bottle. Came in green box. **CMV $7.**
ARIETE PONY POST - MEXICO 1979
5 1/4" high dark amber glass, gold cap. Brass ring. Brown box. **CMV $6.**

STANLEY STEAMER - MEXICO 1976
(Left) 158 ml, light green glass. Black seats and caps. **CMV $12.50.**
PACKARD ROADSTER - EUROPE 1975
(Right) 175 ml. medium amber glass, as the U.S. Porsche car only different.

BUGATTI, 1927, EUROPE 1979-80
195 ml. black glass, cream colored plastic top. **CMV $10. MB.**
BUGATTI, FATHER'S DAY CARD 1979
Gray, Avon marked card. **CMV $4.**

FOREIGN AVONS

We are showing only Decanters, Figurines, Soaps, Sets & Awards from Canada & all countries outside of the United States. All other products have been dropped due to mass production & lack of interest from most Avon collectors.

PONY DECANTER SHORT - GERMAN
120 cc After Shave, emerald green glass.
CMV $16. MB. More common issue is
greenish brown. **CMV $12. MB.**

SHORT PONY AFTER SHAVE - CANADA
Emerald green. **CMV $10.** 1973 Light amber -
Canada. **CMV $6.** Dark amber - Australian.
CMV $100.
UNICORN COLOGNE
Canada. **CMV $10.** Mexico is Her Prettiness.
CMV $20.

DUNE BUGGY - MEXICO 1975
148 ml size. Green glass, black cap. Came in
after shave. **CMV $12.**

PONY DECANTER - JAPAN 1976-77
118 ml size light amber glass. Appears green
when full of after shave. **CMV $13.** Pony also
came in dark green glass from Japan. **CMV
$14.** Light green glass from Mexico. **CMV
$11.** Light amber from Australia. **CMV $11.**
And light green from Australia. **CMV $10.**
BUTTERFLY POMANDER - EUROPE 1976
Pink plastic. **CMV $6. MB.**

ELECTRIC CHARGER - MEXICO 1972
Clear glass, red cap & red bottom label. Came
in After Shave. **CMV $32.**

PONY POST - MEXICO 1973
Shiny gold, painted over clear glass bottle.
bottle is same as American clear glass Pony
Post only Mexican bottle has mold number on
bottom. Mexico came both with & without
Avon on bottom where U.S. clear Pony Post
never has Avon on bottom. **CMV $25. MB,
$20. BO mint.**

MG CAR DECANTER 1975
England, Spain & Germany. Green glass.
CMV $14. MB.

RALLY CAR - EUROPE 1977
60 ml size cobalt blue color. Same as the U.S.
Porsche car only different color. **CMV $11.**

VOLKSWAGEN - MEXICO 1977
(Left) 120 ml black painted over clear glass.
Holds after shave. **CMV $8.**
RADIO - CANADA 1973
(Center) 5 oz. amber glass, gold cap. Holds
after shave. Gold front decal has 600 on
station number. **CMV $5.**
**CAPE COD WINE GOBLET & CANDLE -
EUROPE 1977**
(Right) Light purple glass, Avon on bottom.
CMV $8.

COUPE AFTER SHAVE - MEXICO 1975
(Left) Same as the Sterling 6 in U.S. **CMV
$12. MB.**
SKITTLE BOWLING PIN - GERMAN 1970
(Right) 120 cc whtie glass bottle holds after
shave. Red neck stripes & label. **CMV $12.
MB.**

MINI BIKE - SPAIN 1974-75
(Left) 120 cc green glass holds after shave.
CMV $13.
BOOK END COLOGNE FOREIGN 1974-75
(Center) 2 oz. dark amber glass, paper label.
Sold in Europe, Australia. **CMV $11.** Mexico
issued in green glass, paper label. **CMV $14.**
1st EDITION BOOK - FOREIGN 1974-75
(Right) 60 ml size, amber glass. Painted
label. **CMV $10.**

CRYSTALSONG BELL - MEXICO & EUROPE 1977
(Left) 118 ml. light green glass, clear plastic handle. CMV $12.
SUPER CYCLE - MEXICO 1977
(Right) 118 ml. light green glass and cap. CMV $12.50.

SEIGE CANNON - EUROPE 1976
(Left) 60 ml. size amber glass. After shave. CMV $10. MB.
ROCKET 022 - EUROPE 1976
(Right) 120 ml. size black glass. Gold cap. CMV $12. MB.

(Left to Right)
BLOOD HOUND PIPE - ENGLAND 1977
150 ml. white milk glass, black cap, silver band, came in after shave. CMV $10.
PONY EXPRESS RIDER PIPE - MEXICO 1978
88 ml. dark amber glass, white and gold handle. CMV $10.
CORN COB PIPE - MEXICO 1976
90 cc dark amber glass, black and gold cap. CMV $10.
PIPE FULL PIPE - MEXICO 1975
60 ml. light green glass, black and silver cap. CMV $10.

(Left to Right)
SOCCER PLAYER DECANTER - MEXICO 1980
90 ml. green glass with light green plastic top. CMV $12.50 MB.
1973 FORD PICKUP - MEXICO 1980
148 ml. emerald green glass with green plastic pickup bed & decals. CMV $10. MB.
PONY POST MINIATURES - MEXICO 1980
45 ml. dark amber glass. CMV $6. MB.
EL TORO BULL - MEXICO 1980
130 ml. dark amber glass with white plastic horns. CMV $8.50 MB.

PIPE DREAM - EUROPE 1969
177 cc size dark amber glss. Came in gold & maroon box without the plastic base stand. Avon cosmetics label on bottom. Same size as U.S. CMV $32.50 MB.

PERFUME AWARD - GERMAN 1970
(Left) Falconette Perfume given to German Avon ladies in red Avon box. CMV $25. MB.
FALCON AFTER SHAVE - GERMANY 1970
(Right) 150 cc amber glass bottle, gold falcon head cap. CMV $32. MB.

WINE SERVER 1972
After Shave - Mexican green. CMV $25. After Shave - Mexican clear. CMV $30. (flat caps). Cologne - Canadian green. CMV $20. (round cap).

RACING MOTORBIKE - EUROPE 1976-77
100 ml. size black glass, black cap. Looks purple next to bright light. CMV $18. MB.

CAPTAINS CHOICE AFTER SHAVE - CANADA
(Left) Emerald green glass. CMV $10.
TOUCH-DOWN AFTER SHAVE - MEXICO
(Right) Dull silver on blue glass. This bottle is easy to duplicate with silver paint. Use caution. CMV $15. mint.

ANGLER DECANTER - CANADIAN 1976
Darker blue glass than American. CMV $8.

NEW WORLD - EUROPE 1976
180 ml. size clear glass. Silver cap. Blue letters on cap. After shave. CMV $4. MB.
HAWK - EUROPE 1976
150 ml. size clear glass, gold cap. After shave. CMV $10. MB.
HAWK - JAPAN 1980
Same size & shape as Europe Hawk only has Japanese writing on bottle. CMV $15. MB.

HIGH SOCIETY ORB - EUROPE 1966
237 cc clear glass, red letters & gold crown cap. Red felt neck band. bottle same as our Royal Orb, only painted letters on front say "Avon High Society 237 ccm". **CMV $75. mint.**

VIKING HORN - EUROPE 1960s
205 cc dark amber glass. Foreign label on bottom. Goldtone top & horn tip.
CMV $22.50.

OIL LANTERN - MEXICO, FOREIGN 1975
(Left) Green glass, silver cap. After shave.
CMV $8.
SUPER SHAVER - FOREIGN 1976
(Center) 112 ml. size green glass, gray plastic top. After shave. **CMV $8.**
VIOLIN - MEXICO, SPAIN 1976
(Right) 88 ml. size clear glass, gold cap. Cologne. **CMV $15.**

ELEY GRAND PRIX - EUROPE 1978
(Left) 60 ml. red plastic, gold cap. **CMV $5.** Holds after shave.
SOCCER FOOTBALL - MEXICO 1978
(Center) Yellowish tan plastic bottle. **CMV $5.** Issued in Europe 1979 rust color. **CMV $5.**
SPICY AFTER SHAVE LOTION 1978
(Right) 15 ml. clear glass, black cap. **CMV $5.**

CRUZEIRO - BRAZIL 1976
115 ml. size clear glass bottle. Gold cap. Brazil on one side and 1949-1 Cruzeiro on the other side. Came in after shave. **CMV $17.**

(Left to Right)
BARBER POLE - CANADA 1976
3 oz. white glass and red painted stripes. Came in after shave. White cap. **CMV $6.**
BARBER POLE - MEXICO 1976
88 ml. size clear glass painted gray or white with paper stripe label. White cap. **CMV $8. each.**
CPC ANNIVERSARY KEEPSAKE - EUROPE 1977
15 ml. clear glass, black cap. **CMV $5.** Back of bottle is embossed "Avon Anniversary Keepsake" U.S. issue says 90th on back. **CMV $8. MB.** Rare issue with clear plastic cap. **CMV $10.**
COLOGNE - CANADA 1976
(Far Right) .5 oz. clear glass, white cap. **CMV $3.**

FOREIGN CHESS PIECE SHAVE LOTION 1971-72
150 cc gold cap, white painted bottle over clear glass. **CMV $11. MB, $9. BO.**

STRUCTURED COLOGNE - MEXICO
(Left) Clear glass, clear plastic top. **CMV $5.**
EDICION DE LUJO BOOK - MEXICO
(Right) Same as 1st Edition Book. **CMV $10.**

(Left to Right)
NOBLE PRINCE DECANTER - EUROPE 1979
90 ml. dark amber glass shown with American issue on left for size comparison. **CMV $10. MB.**
CHAMPAGNE DECANTER - MEXICO 1979-80
58 ml. green glass with gold plastic top. **CMV $6. MB.**
CHAMPAGNE DECANTER - EUROPE 1978
30 ml. green glass with plastic gold top. **CMV $5. MB.**
CHAMPAGNE DECANTER - AUSTRALIA 1978
30 ml. green glass with gold plastic cap. **CMV $5. MB.**

(Left to Right)
ZODIAC HOROSCOPE - MEXICO 1977
Cobalt blue glass, gold caps. blue and gold labels. Came in all 12 zodiac signs in choice of Charisma or Wild Country. **CMV $8. each.**
CHRISTMAS SURPRISE BOTT - CANADA 1977
1 oz. green glass, red cap. Different from U.S. issue. **CMV $3.**
AFTER SHAVE - EUROPE 1975
30 ml. clear glass with yucky green cap. **CMV $5.**
1/2 OZ. COLOGNE - CANADA 1975
Clear glass, black cap. **CMV $3.**

ST. BERNARD - SPAIN 1979
(Left) 150 ml. dark amber glass. Brown plastic neck strap with beige plastic keg around neck. Bottle is same size issued in U.S. keg & strap are different. **CMV $15. MB.**
ST. BERNARD - GERMANY 1972
(Right) 100 ml. dark amber glass. Silver keg and neck strap. Smaller than U.S. & Spain bottle. **CMV $18.**

EXCALIBUR - MEXICO 1976
(Left) Clear glass, gold cap. Blue painted label on front of bottle and black and gold neck label. **CMV $10.**
LEATHER BOOT - MEXICO 1975
(Center) Dark amber glass and cream color cap, plastic. Cologne for men. **CMV $10.**
LEATHER BOOT - MEXICO 1977
(Right) Dark amber glass and gold plastic cap. Cologne for men. **CMV $8.**

BOOT - MEXICO 1973
Dark brown amber boot on left pictured with American boot on right which is much lighter. Gold cap and bottom Spanish label. **CMV $15.**

BOOT - SPAIN 1972
(Left) 236 cc amber bottle, gold cap. Leather Cologne. **CMV $10.**
ELECTRIC PRE-SHAVE - SPAIN 1972-76
120 cc clear glass bottle with white cap & label. **CMV $5.**

VICTORIAN FASHION FIGURINE - BRAZIL 1976
Base is white milk glass with white plastic top. **CMV $35.**

COLONIA - MEXICO
(Left) 4A design on black cap. **CMV $9.**
COLONIA - MEXICO 1974-76
(Right) **CMV $5.**

EMPERATOR SHAVE LOTION - ENGLAND 1971
(Left) 150 cc size, clear ribbed bottle blue & silver neck band & cap. **CMV $10. - $14. MB.**
TALC DEODORANT - EUROPE 1970s
(Right) 85 g. white and blue paper container with plastic top and bottom. **CMV $2.**

ENCHANTED ISLES DECANTER - AUSTRALIA, MEXICO 1980
(Left) 60 ml. clear glass with gold top. **CMV $7. MB.**
SPANISH SENORITA - AUSTRALIA, MEXICO 1980
(Center) 115 ml. clear glass painted red & white with pink plastic top. **CMV $12.**
LITTLE BURRO - AUSTRALIA 1980
(Right) 25 ml. light smoked glass with plastic cap, straw hat & red flower. **CMV $7.**

COURTING LAMP - MEXICO 1976
Blue paint over clear glass base. Blue ribbon, white shade top. Lighter blue than one from England. CMV $16.

PINK COURTING LAMP - BRAZIL 1976
Pink painted glass bottom. Pink ribbon on white glass top. 140 ml. CMV $50.

NOVIA BRIDAL MOMENTS - MEXICO 1977
(Right) 147 ml. dull white paint over clear glass, white plastic top. Came all white. CMV $12. Some are showing up with painted flowers on cap. It is very easy to paint this so don't pay a big price for one that someone has probably painted the flowers to get more money out of. CMV $14. with painted flowers. Pictured in Mexican Avon catalog all white.

TRAVEL KIT - JAPAN 1979
(Left) White plastic case, Avon on clasp & 4A design on lid holds Avon comb, brush, 3 plastic jars & 3 plastic bottles. All are marked Avon. CMV $20.

PRECIOS RABBIT - EUROPE 1980
(Right) 30 ml. size goldtone over clear glass. CMV $10. MB.

LA BELLE TELEPHONE - BRAZIL 1978-79
Small white milk glass base with gold toned plastic top. CMV $30. MB.

PRECIOUS RABBIT - MEXICO 1976
30 ml. size. Smaller than U.S. gold plastic head. CMV $10. MB.

PETITE TELEPHONE - EUROPE 1975
30 ml. clear glass. One plastic cap is ivory and one is peach ivory color. CMV $10. each MB.

COFFEE MILL COLOGNE - CANADA 1974
(Left) Cream color milk glass, 5 oz. size. Same as U.S. issue only no gold trim. CMV $7.

SECRETAIRE - SPAIN 1976
(Center) Light pink milk glass, gold cap. Holds cologne. CMV $10.

FLOWER MAIDEN - CANADA 1974
(Right) 4 oz. dull yellow frosted paint over clear glass. Plain white plastic cap. U.S. issue has painted flower on cap. CMV $10.

KEEPSAKE CREAM SACHET - ENGLAND 1971
(Left) Lavender frosted glass bottom gold tree top. CMV $11.

FRAGRANCE LANTERN - ENGLAND 1971
(Right) 30cc Lantern shaped colognes bottle, gold cap. CMV $12. MB. Also came in 30 cc Skin So Soft, gold cap. CMV $10. MB.

FRAGRANT KEY - EUROPE 1979
(Left) Same as U.S. issue of 1967 only does not have 4A design on cap. Different label on box. CMV $8. MB.

ROSE POINT BELL - AUSTRALIA 1979
(Center) 115 ml. size clear glass coated light pink. No date on bottom. CMV $10.

LADY'S GLOVE POMANDER - EUROPE 1980
(Right) Lavender plastic, smaller in size than U.S. issue. CMV $5. MB.

COLOGNE BELLS - FOREIGN
15 cc each. One has gold & clear plastic handle. CMV $30. Right - gold cap & neck tassel. CMV $35.

CHIMNEY LAMP - CANADA 1975
2 oz. clear glass, plain frosted top shade. Holds cologne. CMV $6. MB.

PRECIOUS BELLS - EUROPE 1976
(Left) 30 ml. clear glass, gold cap. Cologne.
CMV $8. MB.
ROYAL SWAN - EUROPE 1976
(Right) 30 ml. size clear glass, gold cap.
Cologne. **CMV $12.50 MB.**

KEYNOTE - EUROPE 1968
7 cc clear glass key, gold cap. bottle is same
as U.S. only has foreign label on box & bottle.
Different from 1979 Fragrant Key. **CMV $25.
MB.**

RECOLLECTIONS CRUET - EUROPE 1976
(Left) Amethyst color glass cruet and stopper.
CMV $10.
**RECOLLECTION CANDLE STICK COL-
OGNE - EUROPE 1976**
(Center) 150 ml. size amethyst color glass.
CMV $10.
**FRAGRANCE HOURS CLOCK - EUROPE
1976**
(Right) 180 cc size olive color glass. Cologne.
CMV $12.

**COURTING LAMP-YELLOW - GERMAN
1972**
(Left) 150 ml yellow glass bottom with white
glass top. Holds cologne. Yellow box. **CMV
$20. MB.** Also came in blue as U.S. Also in
green - Mexico. **CMV $25. in green glass.**
**SKIN-SO-SOFT MINIATURE - GERMAN
1972**
(Right) 30 ml crown shaped bottle, gold cap.
CMV $5. MB.

PLUMIERE (INK WELL) - MEXICO 1977
(Left) 175 ml. dark amber glass, tan plastic
feather pen, black cap. **CMV $10.**
INKWELL - EUROPE 1978
(Right) 180 ml. dark amber glass, black cap,
gold feathered pen. **CMV $10.**

FUNNY FLOWER POT - ENGLAND 1973
120 ml yellow painted glass bottle with green
plastic flower pot lid with green, pink, blue &
yellow plastic flowers. Holds cologne. **CMV
$15. MB.**

**COMMEMORATION CROWN - EUROPE
1977**
(Left) 30 ml. size clear glass different from
U.S. crown. Gold cap. Came in cologne. Sold
from Queens Coronation Celebration. **CMV
$7. MB.**
SUN BURST COLOGNE - MEXICO 1976
(Right) 14.5 ml. size clear glass gold cap.
Came in cologne. **CMV $7.**

(Left to Right)
**1886 PERFUME ON ROLLETTE - GERMANY
1978**
Clear glass, red cap. **CMV $5.**
1886 EAU DE COLOGNE - EUROPE 1977
1886 embossed on clear bottle, red cap. **CMV
$8.**
**1886 EAU DE COLOGNE SPRAY -
GERMANY 1978**
50 g. clear glass, red cap. **CMV $11.**
1886 EAU DE COLOGNE - EUROPE 1976
100 ml. 1886 embossed on clear glass, red
cap. **CMV $9.**

TREE MOUSE DECANTER - MEXICO 1980
(Left) 18 g. dark amber glass with gold mouse.
CMV $5. MB.
**BOSTONIAN GLASS 1876 CANDLE -
MEXICO 1980**
(Center) Dark cobalt blue glass. **CMV $10.
MB.**
LITTLE BURRO - MEXICO 1980
(Right) Dark amber glass with straw hat and
pink flower. 28 ml. **CMV $5.50 MB.**

**SEA TREASURE DECANTER - MEXICO
1972**
Clear glass bottle with gold cap. **CMV $12.
MB.**

CHURCH MOUSE DECANTER - EUROPE 1980
(Left) White milk glass with pink and white plastic head & cloth veil. **CMV $10. MB.**
CHURCH MOUSE DECANTER - MEXICO 1980
Same as above only clear glass painted white. **CMV $7. MB.**
SEASON SONG BIRDBATH - EUROPE 1980
(Center) 30 ml. frosted glass with plastic top & blue bird. **CMV $7. MB.**
PETITE TELEPHONE - EUROPE 1980
(Right) 30 ml. clear glass painted gold with gold plastic top. **CMV $10. MB.**

BLUE EYED CAT - MEXICO 1980
(Left) 45 ml. white milk glass. **CMV $6. MB.**
CHRISTMAS ANGEL - MEXICO 1980
(Center) 2.8 ml. clear glass with white plastic head. **CMV $5. MB.**
LOVE BIRD - MEXICO 1980
(Right) Frosted glass with gold cap. 43 ml. **CMV $7. MB.**

(Left to Right)
FROSTED COLOGNE - JAPAN 1977
59 ml. frosted glass. Clear top same as our just two bottles in 1965. **CMV $10.**
HOBNAIL BELL - MEXICO 1974
58 ml frosted glass, gold handle. Belt on bottom. **CMV $11.**
ANGEL - EUROPE 1977
30 ml clear glass, gold cap. **CMV $6.50.**
BELL COLOGNE - EUROPE 1974
25 cc size. Same as our 1968 U.S. Bell on right only smaller in size. **CMV $8.**

BATH SEASONS - ENGLAND, SPAIN 1973-76
(Left) 90 ml white glass bottle with pink ribbon. Red & green strawberry design. Holds strawberry cream bath foam. **CMV $7. MB.**
FLORAL DEMI CUPS - ENGLAND 1973
(Right) 90 ml white glass cup, white metal lid with pink cap. Red & green flower design. Holds bath oil. **CMV $11. MB.**

(Left to Right)
FIGA FIST - BRAZIL 1977
55 cm. dark amber glass and matching plastic fist cap. **CMV $32.50.**
HEARTH LAMP COLOGNE DECANTER - BRAZIL 1980
Light green glass with green & white plastic shade & cloth daisies. 235 cm. **CMV $25. MB.**
LITTLE DUTCH KETTLE - BRAZIL 1980
150 cm. clear glass painted gray. Blue flowers & blue cap. **CMV $20. MB.**
PRECIOUS RABBIT - BRAZIL 1980
Clear glass with white plastic head. **CMV $20. MB.**

HOSPITALITY BELLS - MEXICO, EUROPE 1979
Mexico came in dark blue glass with silver handle. **CMV $8.50 MB.** European came in deep cobalt blue glass with silver handle. **CMV $10. MB.**
ANNIVERSARY KEEPSAKE - EUROPE 1979
Came with pink atomizer. **CMV $12.50 MB.**

FRAGRANCE HOURS FOREIGN 1975-77
(Left) 180 cc light amber glass, gold cap. Holds cologne. **CMV $12.50.**
SPANISH FIGURINE 1977
(Right) Pink plastic cap. Red & wite frosted painted base over clear glass. **CMV $12. each MB.** Spanish figurine pictured is from Spain. Also came from Mexico with dull red paint and Australia with shiny red paint. **CMV $10.**

ROCKER COLOGNE - EUROPE 1972
1/2 oz. gold indented top, pink or white label. 2 different labels. **CMV $9. each MB.**

(Left to Right)
SANTA CLAUS - MEXICO 1979
(Left) 29 ml all clear glass with red cap. U.S. had painted face. **CMV $5. MB.**
BIRD OF SPLENDOUR - EUROPE 1980
(Center) 75 ml. clear glass with gold plastic top. **CMV $10. MB.**
BIRD OF PARADISE - MEXICO 1980
(Right) 43 ml dark blue glass with darker blue plastic head. **CMV $6.50 MB.** Also issued in Spain with lighter blue plastic head. **CMV $8.50 MB.**

<u>SNOWMAN DECANTER - CANADA,
AUSTRALIA 1975</u>
(Left) 1 oz. white glass, pink cap. holds cologne. **CMV $5. MB.**
<u>CIRCUS TALC - CANADA 1975</u>
(Center) Cardboard sides, white plastic top & bottom. **CMV $2.**
<u>SPRING PROMISE COLOGNE MIST - CANADA 1975</u>
(Right) 3 oz. lavender plastic coated over clear glass bottle, matching plastic top. **CMV $5.**

(Left to Right)
<u>TIMELESS PUMP SPRAY COLOGNE - EUROPE 1980</u>
50 ml clear glass with gold top & decal. **CMV $6. MB.**
<u>FRAGRANCE BELLE - EUROPE 1980</u>
15 ml. clear glass with gold top. **CMV $5. MB.**
<u>ROSE BOTTLE - MEXICO 1980</u>
Clear glass with gold top. **CMV $7. MB.**
<u>V.S.O.P. DECANTER - EUROPE 1980</u>
30 ml. green glass with black top. **CMV $6. MB.**

<u>BATH TREASURE SNAIL - EUROPE 1976</u>
90 ml. size. Clear glass, gold cap. Shown next to the larger U.S. snail. **CMV $11.**

(Left to Right)
<u>FLIGHT TO BEAUTY - MEXICO 1977</u>
Pale blue painted over clear glass, white plastic dove top. **CMV $7.**
<u>GOOD LUCK ELEPHANT - MEXICO 1978</u>
43 ml. clear glass, silver cap. **CMV $8.50.**
<u>MINIATURE LOCION - MEXICO 1977</u>
57 g. clear glass, gold flowered cap. **CMV $6.**
<u>KOFFEE KLATCH - MEXICO 1978</u>
148 g. blue painted over clear glass. Yellow plastic cap. **CMV $8.50.**

<u>SERENADE IN BLUE DEMI-CUP - MEXICO 1974</u>
(Left) White glass, blue decal and cap. **CMV $11.**
<u>PERFUMED SKIN SOFTENER - JAPAN 1978</u>
(Center) White glass and gold cap. **CMV $8.**
<u>COCKER SPANIEL - MEXICO 1978</u>
(Right) 42 ml white glass and cap. **CMV $8.**

<u>BATH SEASONS - ENGLAND</u>
(Left) 90 mm white glass with dark flowers. **CMV $10.**
<u>LANTERN COLOGNE - ENGLAND 1978</u>
(Center Left) 15 mm clear glass, gold cap. **CMV $8.** Also issued in Canada. **CMV $3.**
<u>LAVENDER BATH OIL - ENGLAND</u>
(Center Right) 150 mm white plastic, lavender ribbon and label. **CMV $8.**
<u>BLUE NILE DECANTER - CANADA 1974-75</u>
(Right) 6 oz. blue glass and cap. Gold neck band. Holds foaming bath oil. OSP $4.75. **CMV $8.**

<u>GIVING DECANTER - EUROPE 1979</u>
(Left) 60 ml clear glass, flower gift card on front of box. **CMV $6.50 MB.**
<u>CARD, MOTHERS DAY - EUROPE 1979</u>
(Right) Pink flowered card in envelope. **CMV $3.**

(Left to Right)
<u>SCREW DRIVER - MEXICO 1977</u>
Clear glass, silver top on left. U.S. issue on right. **CMV $8.**
<u>STRAWBERRIES & CREAM BATH FOAM - EUROPE 1974</u>
120 cc white milk glass, red top. Strawberries are smaller that the U.S. issue on right. **CMV $6.50.**
<u>GIFT COLOGNE FOR MEN - EUROPE 1977</u>
30 ml clear glass, blue cap. Smaller than U.S. issue on right. **CMV $5.**

<u>MINUETTE - MEXICO 1978</u>
(Left) 88 g. size white glass, green painted neck band. **CMV $7.**
<u>RENAISSANCE CANDLE - AUSTRALIA 1977</u>
(Center) Blue glass with Cameo lady on side. **CMV $20.**
<u>JARRA PERSA - MEXICO 1978</u>
180 g. clear glass cream lotion. Blue and pink and green front label. **CMV $9.**

(Left to Right)
TEDDY BEARS - EUROPE 1977
22 ml. clear glass, gold cap. **CMV $6.** U.S. issue frosted glass. Mexico - 50 ml. frosted glass, frosted head. **CMV $15.** Mexico - 50 ml. dark brown frosted glass and matching head. **CMV $18.** Spain - 50 ml. lighter brown frosted glass and matching head. **CMV $20.**

LOOKING GLASS - FOREIGN, MEXICO 1977
(Left) Gold handle, dark amber glass. Mirror in center. 43 ml size. **CMV $8.50 MB.**
KITTEN PETITE - MEXICO 1976
(Right) Green glass ball, white cat cap. **CMV $8.50 MB.**

BOW BOTTLE - JAPAN, EUROPE & AUSTRALIA 1978
(Left) 30 ml. clear glass, gold cap. Cologne. **CMV $7.**
PRECIOUS SWAN - CANADA 1976
(Center) 4 ml. clear glass, gold cap. **CMV $8.**
PRECIOUS DOE - MEXICO 1977
(Right) 13 ml. frosted glass, frosted head cap. **CMV $8.**

EVENING LIGHT PERFUME - GERMAN 1972
Box holds small perfume bottle in pink hang on carton. **CMV $16. MB.**
FALCONETTE PERFUME - GERMAN 1970
1 dram bottle in gold and white box. **CMV $8. MB.**

ROYAL CROWN - MEXICO 1980
28 ml. clear glass, gold cap. Glass design different from others issued. **CMV $5.50 MB.**
COLOGNE BODY SILK - MEXICO 1976
Clear glass with gold top. 77g. **CMV $6. MB.**
POPLOVE LIPSTICKS - MEXICO 1980
Plastic tube came in 3 shades. **CMV $2.50 each MB.**

COLOGNE PETITE - CANADA 1975
1/2 oz. clear glass, gold cap. Came in all fragrances. **CMV $4. MB.**
PINEAPPLE COLOGNE DECANTER - CANADA
3 oz. clear glass, comes in Field Flowers, Hana Gasa, Bird of Paradise, Elusive and Charisma cologne. **CMV $5. MB.** Also sold in Mexico under name of Colonia Magnifiscents. **CMV $10. MB.**

CREAM LOTION - CANADA
5 1/4 oz. clear glass bottle with gold cap. **CMV $10.**
SKIN-SO-SOFT BATH CAPSULES - CANADA
Blue glass jar and lid. Made in Belgium on bottom of jar. Blue and silver neck label. **CMV $12.**
SKIN-SO-SOFT DECANTER - CANADA
6 oz. clear glass bottle holds bath oil. Silver top fits over white cap. **CMV $10.**

FRAGRANCE ORNAMENT - CANADA 1972
5/8 dram bullet perfume bottle, gold cap. In paper ornament. **CMV $14.**
CHRISTMAS ORNAMENT - ENGLAND 1973
Paper ornament holds small bottle of perfume, frosted cap. **CMV $15. MB.**

GRAPE BUD VASE - EUROPE 1974
(Left) 180 ml. purple glass holds perfumed bath oil. **CMV $8.**
EMERALD BUD VASE - AUSTRALIA 1977
(Center Left) 85 ml. emerald green glass holds cologne. **CMV $8.**
CREAM LOTION - JAPAN 1978
(Center Right) 150 ml. clear glass, gold cap. **CMV $10.**
EAU DE COLOGNE - EUROPE 1976
(Right) 50 ml. clear glass with white cap. Came in many fragrances. **CMV $8.**

LOTION LUXURY - FOREIGN 1969
Clear glass bottle and stopper. **CMV $10., $12. MB.**

LOTION LUXURY - AUSTRALIA 1974
Came in all fragrances. CMV $8.
BATH SEASONS - GERMAN 1971
90 cc white glass bottles trimmed in green (Honeysuckle), blue (Lily of the Valley), red (Strawberry), lavender (Lilac). Each holds bath foam. CMV $11.

NOVA BUD VASE - SPAIN 1976
(Left) 100 cc green glass and top. CMV $12.
NOVA BUD VASE - ENGLAND 1973
(Center) 100cc purple glass and cap. CMV $12.
U.S. ISSUE
(Right) was called Sea Green Bud Vase. It is shown to show size.

SKIN SO SOFT BATH CAPSULES - GERMAN 1973
Blue box holds glass jar of gold bath capsules, blue neck tag on gold cord. CMV $15. MB.
CREAM BODY LOTION - EUROPE 1968
177 cc bottle with gold cap. Same as U.S. 1964 Skin So Soft. CMV $12., $15. MB.

BATH SEASONS - EUROPE 1976
90 ml. white glass. Bubble bath. White cap. Blue painted band around neck. CMV $7. MB.
SWIRL PITCHER - EUROPE 1976
150 ml. clear glass swirl bottle and cap. CMV $7. MB.

SKIN SO SOFT CAPSULES - CANADA 1964
Tall glass jar, green, red and yellow capsules. CMV $22.50 MB.

ANDY CAPP - ENGLAND 1970
Black and white plastic with green hat. Holds body powder. CMV $125. BO mint, $185. MB.

THE RACERS SPORTS TALC - EUROPE 1972
Orange plastic bottle, white cap. CMV $8. MB.

MR. BUNNY - EUROPE 1975
(Left) 90 ml. white plastic, blue hat. CMV $6. It has an orange and green carrot.
MR. BUNNY - SPAIN 1976
(Center Left) 90 cc size, all white plastic, blue hat. CMV $7.
PINK ELEPHANT - EUROPE 1977
(Center Right) 150 ml pink plastic, dark pink cap. CMV $6.
ELFY THE ELEPHANT - MEXICO 1976
(Right) 150 g. pink plastic and cap. CMV $7.

CHESHIRE CAT SOAP AND SPONGE - AUSTRALIA 1977
Cat soap and sponge in pink and white. CMV $8. MB.
TUB TALK - AUSTRALIA 1974
Yellow box holds red plastic telephone with light blue base and cap. Holds shampoo for children. CMV $9. MB. Reissued 1979 in yellow bottle with blue cap and handle. CMV $7. MB.
RING RING PHONE - MEXICO 1979
Same as Tub Talk only in blue plastic with yellow cap and holder. CMV $6. MB.
RULER COMB -EUROPE 1977
Yellow plastic comb in metrics. CMV $4. MB.

PACKY THE ELEPHANT - MEXICO 1976
90 ml yellow plastic white cap. CMV $6.
PIGS - EUROPE 1975
150 ml. pink plastic bottle and cap. CMV $7.
LEO THE LION - MEXICO 1978
290 ml. yellow plastic, pink hat. CMV $6.50.

RABBIT - MEXICO 1976
(Left) 68 g. size. White plastic green hat,
lotion. **CMV $6. MB.**
PERFUMED TALC - MEXICO 1976
(Right) Tin can, gold and white. **CMV $4.**

SHAMPOO FOR CHILDREN - MEXICO
1979-80
90 ml. white, orange and red plastic with
orange whistle top. **CMV $5. MB.**
MADAME GUS PERFUME GLACE - MEXICO
1979-80
.7 g. green and purple plastic pin and perfume
glace. **CMV $4.50 MB.**
LOVE LOCKET - MEXICO 1979-80
Green, yellow and pink plastic. Solid perfume
container. Comes with pink necklace. **CMV**
$5. MB.
PRETTY PEACH SOLID PERFUME -
MEXICO 1979-80
.7 g. peach and green colored plastic solid
perfume container. **CMV $5. MB.**
ICE CREAM COMB FOR CHILDREN -
MEXICO 1979-80
Tan plastic with vanilla colored ice cream and
red cherry. **CMV $4. MB.**

WILD COUNTRY AFTER SHAVE - BRAZIL
1973
(Left) 105 cm. Red palstic, green cap. **CMV**
$10.
ELEPHANT IN A TUB 1976
(Center) Box holds pink elephant soap and
blue plastic tub brush. **CMV $6. MB.**
FOOTBALL BOOT - BRAZIL 1974
(Right) 85 cm. Black and white plastic boot
after shave. **CMV $12.**

WORLD BANK - EUROPE 1976
300 ml size blue plastic globe with stick-on
colored countries. It is larger than the U.S.
issue on right. **CMV $11. MB.**

CANDLE, RED GLASS - ENGLAND 1968
Dark red glass candle on left not coated as in
American red candle on right. Both same size.
Avon on bottom of glass. **CMV for red glass**
only $50.

CLOWN BUBBLE BATH - EUROPE 1972
120 ml plastic bottles, pink whistle cap. **CMV**
$7. MB.
FIREMAN SHAMPOO - EUROPE 1972
120 ml plastic bottles. Orange whistle cap.
CMV $7. MB.
BROTHER & SISTER BUBBLE BATH -
EUROPE 1972
120 ml plastic bottle with blue flower cap and
came with paper doll cut-outs and color
booklet. **CMV $7. MB.**

HIGHWAY BRUSH & COMB - AUSTRALIA
1976
(Left) Brown plastic. **CMV $5. MB.**
AUSSIE BEAR - AUSTRALIA 1976
(Center Left) Red, white and blue brush and
comb. **CMV $5. MB.**
VALET BRUSH & COMB - CANADA 1976
(Center Right) Brown plastic, gold leaf on top.
CMV $3.50 MB.
FOREST LORD BRUSH & COMB - AUSTRA-
LIA 1977
(Right) Brown and gold plastic. **CMV $3.50**
MB.

LITTLE PIGGY NON TEAR SHAMPOO -
CANADA 1973
150 cc pink plastic. **CMV $6.**
MAZE GAME-AMAZING CLOWN - CANADA
1973
6 oz. green plastic, pink lid. Clown on face.
CMV $6.

MOISTURE SECRET SET - EUROPE 1980
White vinyl contains skin care products in light
tan packaging. Same set in U.S. was pink
packaging. **CMV $8. MB.**
FISH BUBBLE BATH - EUROPE 1980
400 ml, plastic fish container with whtie top.
Holds pink bubble bath. **CMV $6.**
GOLF BALL - EUROPE 1980
45 ml. green, yellow and white plastic. 1/2 size
of U.S. issue. **CMV $6.50 MB.**

SMALL WORLD HAND CREAM - CANADA
1972-73
2.25 oz. green and white tube, pink cap. OSP $1.10. **CMV $7. MB.**

FLOWER TALK HAND CREAM - CANADA
1975-76
60 ml (2.25 oz.) white flowered tube and cap. Canada. OSP $2. **CMV $2.50 MB.**

CANDLE SET - CANADA
Red box holds wood candle holder with red scented candle. **CMV $9. MB.**

WEATHER OR NOT - CANADA
5 oz. dark amber glass, plain gold cap. **CMV $10. MB.**

FROSTED CANDLE - FOREIGN 1969
Frosted glass. **CMV $22.50.**

FESTIVE CANDLE - ENGLAND, AUSTRALIA, GERMAN 1972
Wooden candle holder does not say Avon. Perfumed candle not marked. Must be in box. **CMV $9.**

MODERNE CANDLE - ENGLAND 1973
Silver based candle holder marked Avon. Red candle wrapped in Avon paper. **CMV $8. MB.**

PERFUMED PAIR - EUROPE 1972
Matching talc and soap. All fragrances. **CMV $12. MB.**

SNOW DRIPS SET - CANADA 1973
Box holds cologne and soap. **CMV $10. MB.**

GIFTABLES SET - CANADA 1972
Box holds cologne and soap. **CMV $10. MB.**

PERFUMED PAIR SETS - EUROPE 1979
Box holds talc and soap. Container and product different color and design for each fragrance. Timeless, Ariane, Lily of the Valley, Honeysuckle, Unspoken, Moonwind. Moonwind and Unspoken have two different package designs. **CMV $9. each MB.**

DOUBLETTE SET - EUROPE 1973
Yellow box holds yellow flower shaped soap and 25c cologne. **CMV $14. MB.**

ELEGANCE GIFT SET - SOUTH AMERICA 1975
Light green and white box with clear lid holds cologne spray and perfumed talc. **CMV $25. MB.**

PERFUMED PAIR SET - EUROPE 1976
Different color boxes hold matching perfumed talc can and soap. **CMV $11. each set.**

FRAGRANCE FANCY SET - CANADA 1975
Box holds perfumed talc and perfume rollette. **CMV $6.**

SIDE BY SIDE SET - CANADA 1975
Box holds bar of soap and 1/2 oz. cologne. **CMV $8.**

PERFUMED PAIR - CANADA 1975
Box holds can of perfumed talc and bar of matching soap. Came in all fragrances. CMV $9. MB.

SIDE BY SIDE SET - GERMAN 1972
Blue box holds soap and 15 ml cologne bottle. CMV $13. MB.

SIDE BY SIDE BAMBOO SET - GERMAN 1971
Blue and green box holds green bar of soap and frosted 15 cc cologne with silver cap. CMV $15. MB.

FRAGRANCE TWINS - EUROPE 1976
Box holds cream sachet and bar of soap. CMV $9.

(Left to Right)
PERFUMED PAIR - EUROPE 1974
Came in 4 fragrances with different color on each one. Box holds bar of soap and perfumed talc in metal can. CMV $12. each MB.

PERFUMED PAIR - EUROPE 1975
4 differet fragrances in different colors with matching talc and bar of soap. CMV $12. each MB.

PERFUMED PAIR - EUROPE 1977
4 different fragrances in different colors with matching metal talc and bar of soap. CMV $10. each MB.

PERFUMED TALC SET - CANADA 1974
Box holds 3 metal talc cans. CMV $12. MB.

FLOWER TALK GIFT SET - SOUTH AMERICA 1975
Blue, gold and white box with clear lid. Holds perfumed talc and cream sachet. CMV $22.50 MB.

MERRY TINTS SET - EUROPE 1976
Box holds nail enamel and 1 blue lipstick. CMV $10.

SKIN SO SOFT SMOOTHIES - AUSTRALIA 1977
(Left) Gold and blue box holds 85 g. Satin talc and 100 ml plastic bottle of Skin So Soft bath oil. CMV $8. MB.

SKIN SO SOFT SMOOTHIES - AUSTRALIA 1976
(Right) Blue and gold box holds 85g. Satin talc and 100 ml plastic bottle of Skin So Soft bath oil. CMV $10. MB.

FRAGRANCE FLING SET - FOREIGN 1969
15 cc cologne and green soap. CMV $17. MB.

SIDE BY SIDE - ENGLAND 1973
Light green box holds yellow soap and bottle of cologne, gold cap. CMV $12. MB.

SIDE BY SIDE SET - FOREIGN 1976
Box holds 15 ml clear glass bottle cologne, gold cap, 1 bar of soap. CMV $9. MB.

ELEGANTE SET - MEXICO 1974
Yellow and gold box holds cologne and perfume rollette. CMV $20. MB.

FRAGRANCE FANCY-CANADA 1975
Box holds perfumed talc and perfume rollette.
CMV $7.50 MB.

PRETTY PEACH PRINCESS GIFT SET-AUSTRALIA 1978
Pink box holds 100 g. white plastic Pretty Peach Talc and yellow glass cream sachet.
CMV $12. MB.

SWEET VIOLETS GIFT SET 1978
Box holds Sweet Violets Talc and cream sachet. **CMV $10. MB.**

FRAGRANCE FAVORITES-CANADA 1975
Box holds cream sachet and perfumed talc.
CMV $7.50 MB.

RICH MOISTURE DOUBLE CANADA 1975
Pink and white box holds 2 pink and white tubes of rich moisture hand cream in French and English. **CMV $7.**

PERFUMED PAIR-MEXICO 1977
Pink and white box holds matching 48 g. metal talc and 13 ml. bottle of cologne. Came in Elegante pictured and Somewhere and Charisma. **CMV $8. MB.**

DELMONICO DUET-JAPAN 1979
Blue box holds blue compact and blue lipstick.
CMV 17. MB.

DELMONICO COMPACT AND LIPSTICK-JAPAN 1979
Blue plastic compact and lipstick holder.
Came with blue velvet pouch. **CMV $14. MB.**

EMPRESS DELUXE GIFT SET-JAPAN, AUSTRALIA 1979
Box holds bone type, flower embossed lipstick and compact, with brass trim. **CMV $18. MB Japan, CMV $12. MB Australia.**

MOONWIND GIFT SET-JAPAN 1979
Blue box holds 4 bars Moonwind soap and 70 ml. bottle Moonwind cologne. **CMV $25. MB.**

CHIC SELECTED SUMMER FRUIT SET-EUROPE 1980
Box holds nail polish, lipstick and wand style eye shadow. **CMV $12. MB.**

FASHION MAKE-UP GROUP SET-EUROPE 1980
Box holds eye shadow, 60 ml. cremelucent foundation, mascara and lipstick. **CMV $16. MB.**

(Left to Right)
PERFUMED PAIR-CANADA 1976
Box holds perfumed soap and metal talc in choice of fragrances. **CMV $8. MB.**

BOUQUET OF PANSIES SOAP-AUSTRALIA 1977
Blue box holds white bar with flowered decal.
CMV $4.50. MB.

PERFUMED SOAP BARS-EUROPE 1978
Large bars in Lavender, Lilac and Lily of The Valley. **CMV $4. each, mint.**

GIFT SET FOR MEN-MEXICO 1979
(Left) 48 g. plastic talc, brown and white, and 45 ml. clear glass cologne with brown cap.
CMV $10. MB.

PERFUMED PAIR-MEXICO 1979
(Right) Clear glass petite perfume with red top and 48 g. talc in flowered cardboard container.
CMV $8. MB.

FRAGRANCE DUET SETS-EUROPE 1979
Box holds soap and perfume rolette. Each fragrance has different color design and bottle. Elegance, green; Arlane, pink; Timeless, tan; Unspoken, blue; Moonwind, blue; Charisma, ed. **CMV $8. MB.**

PRETTY PEACH GIFT SET-SOUTH AMERICA 1975
Pink box with clear top holds Pretty Peach Talc and Cream Sachet. **CMV $22.50 MB.**

SONNET SOAP-JAPAN 1978
White box holds 6 pink soaps. **CMV $14. MB.**
Also came in Moonwind, 6 to a box. **CMV $15. MB.**

EMPRISE GIFT SET-AUSTRALIA 1980
Black, gold and the box holds 18 g. Ultra creme perfume, 100 g. perfumed talc, and 50 ml. Ultra cologne spray. CMV $20. MB.

GENESIS GIFT SET-AUSTRALIA 1980
Brown and gold box holds 50 ml. Ultra cologne spray, same as U.S. Timeless, and 9 ml. Ultra perfume concentrate. CMV $20. MB.

LAVENDER SOAPS-EUROPE 1976
(Left) Red Christmas box holds 3 lavender soaps. CMV $12. MB.

OCCUR! SOAPS-SPAIN 1975
(Center) Black box holds 3 yucky colored bars. CMV $12. MB.

AVONSHIRE BLUE SOAPS-AUSTRALIA 1975
(Right) Blue box holds 3 bars, blue, in angel shape. CMV $12. MB.

DECORATOR SOAP EGGS-CANADA 1972
(Left) 6 eggs shaped soaps, 2 blue, 2 yellow, 2 pink. MB $7. MB.

HAWAIIAN WHITE GINGER SOAP CANADA 1973
(Right) 3 white soaps. CMV $6. MB.

STERLING SIX SOAP-MEXICO 1974
Box holds 2 yellow car embossed bars. CMV $16. MB.

LAVENDER COLOGNE-SPAIN 1975
50 cc white milk glass, purple painted flowers, white cap. Came without neck ribbon. CMV $5. MB.

LAVENDER PERFUMED SOAPS-SPAIN 1975
Box of 3 long lavender bars. CMV $12. MB.

LAVENDER DUO SET-EUROPE 1974
Box holds 1 lavender bar of soap and 50 ml. milk glass lavender cologne with neck ribbon. CMV $14.

LAVENDER PERFUMED SOAPS-AUSTRALIA 1976
Box holds 3 square lavender soaps. CMV $10. MB.

BATH FLOWER SOAP & SPONGE-ENGLAND 1969
Box holds bar of soap & flowered sponge. CMV $20. MB.

SNOWBIRDS SOAP-CANADA 1973
3 blue soaps. CMV $7. MB.

QUACK A. DOODLE-CANADA 1975
Bar of soap with white and orange rubber duck. CMV $6.50 MB.

TIMOTHY TIGER-GERMANY 1973
Yellow plastic soap dish. CMV $13. MB.

RECOLLECTIONS SOAP-EUROPE 1975
(Left) Yellow girl soap in green box. CMV $7. MB.

CHILDRENS NOVELTY SOAP SET-EUROPE 1976
(Right) Box holds 3 small hippo soaps in green, pink, and orange. CMV $7. MB.

ORCHARD FLOWERS SOAPS-EUROPE 1978
(Left) Yellow and gray box holds 3 yellow soaps. CMV $8.50 MB.

JUMBO SOAP TRIO-CANADA 1973
3 blue elephant soaps. CMV $10. MB.

NATURE BEAUTIFUL SOAPS-CANADA 1979
(Left) Box holds 2 bars with fruit decals only.
CMV $5. MB.
NATURE BOUNTIFUL SOAP-CANADA 1979
(Center) Holds 1 decal soap. CMV $3. MB.
WINTER SCAPE SOAP-CANADA 1979
(Right) Holds 1 Currier & Ives decal soap.
CMV $3. MB.

OSIDOS BEAR SOAPS-MEXICO 1976
(Left) Box hold 3 yellow bears. CMV $12.50 MB.
TEDDY BEAR COLOGNE-BRAZIL 1978
(Right) 20 cm. dark amber glass gold ring around neck. CMV $20. MB.

SHUT OUT SOAP & SPONGE CANADA 1975
Box holds orange Avon sponge & white hockey puck soap. CMV $7.50. MB.

PHINIA T. FROG SOAP & SPONGE-CANADA 1974
Green frog sponge and yellow-green and orange wrapped soap. CMV $7. MB.

SUMMER BUTTERFLIES SOAPS-JAPAN 1979
(Left) Holds 3 butterfly bars. CMV $18. MB.
TOUCH OF BEAUTY SOAPS-JAPAN 1979
(Right) Holds 2 pink flower embossed bars.
CMV $10. MB.

LITTLE PRO SOAP & SPONGE-CANADA 1972-73
Left hand sponge light orange & white ball soap. Green box from Canada. OSP $4.,
CMV $9. MB.

GARDEN GIRL SOAP-CANADA 1977
4 oz. bar. Garden Girl-1 was light yellow in Field Flowers and one was lilac and lavender in color. CMV $5. each, MB.

HER PRETTINESS SPONGE MITT & SOAP-CANADA 1972
Pink & yellow sponge & bar of soap. CMV $8. MB.

HAWAIIAN WHITE GINGER-CANADA PERFUMED TALC 1975
(Left) 2.75 oz. can, pink cap. CMV $2.
PERFUMED SOAPS 1975
(Right) Box holds 3 bars. CMV $6.50.

HIGH BUTTON SHOE-ENGLAND & EUROPE 1976
Pink boot soap. CMV $10. MB.

TUBBY TIGERS SOAP SET CANADA 1975
2 small orange tiger soaps. CMV $7. MB.

GRAND TOURER SOAPS-EUROPE 1975
Silver & black box in 2 different sizes. Holds 2 car embossed bars of the same size. CMV $13. MB. each set.

PERFUMED SOAPS-EUROPE 1980
Single bars, boxed. Came in Timeless, Ariane, Emprise, and Unspoken. CMV $3. each. MB.

PANSY SOAP SET-JAPAN 1979
(Left) Blue box holds 3 decaled bars. **CMV $18. MB.**

LOVE BIRD SOAPS-JAPAN 1979
(Right) Pink & white box holds 6 pink heart shaped bars. **CMV $18. MB.**

SOCCER FOOTBALL SOAP ON A ROPE-EUROPE 1976
White soap and rope. **CMV $7. MB.**

HARVEY THE RABBIT SOAP ON A ROPE-EUROPE 1977
Yellow rabbit soap, white rope. **CMV $7. MB.**

BIG SHOT SOAP ON A ROPE-EUROPE, AUSTRALIA 1978
Brownish gray soap on white rope. **CMV $7. MB.**

HAPPY HIPPO SOAP ON A ROPE-CANADA 1978
Hippo on white rope. **CMV 45. MB.**

LORD LEO SOAP ON A ROPE-EUROPE, AUSTRALIA 1978
Tanish grey lion soap on white rope. **CMV $7. MB.**

(Left to Right)
ERIC THE BRAVE SOAP-EUROPE 1976
Blue soap. **CMV $8.**

HUGGY BEAR SOAP-EUROPE 1976
Tan color soap. **CMV $8. MB.**

WINTER RIDE SOAP-EUROPE 1976,
Pink soap. **CMV $8. MB.**

BIG IN A BONNET SOAP-EUROPE 1976
4.9 oz. pink pig soap. **CMV $8. MB.**

SOAPS-EUROPE 1972
Came in all fragrances. **CMV $5. each MB.**

PEEK A BOO SOAP-EUROPE 1977
Yellow chick soap. **CMV $6. MB.**

FRAGRANCE BELL SOAP-FOREIGN 1978
Pink bell soap from Canada-**CMV $4. MB.**

CHILDREN'S NOVELTY WALRUS SOAP-EUROPE 1977
Green walrus soap. **CMV $6. MB.**

CHEERFUL CHIMP SOAP-EUROPE 1977
Orange monkey soap. **CMV $6. MB.**

GOLDEN CARRIAGE SOAP-EUROPE 1977
Yellow carriage soap. **CMV $6. MB.**

WYNKEN, BLYNKEN & NOD SOAP-CANADA 1976
Box holds pink, yellow & blue soaps. **CMV $5. MB.**

OLAND SOAP ON A ROPE-AUSTRALIA 1976
(Left) Tan soap on white rope. **CMV $6. MB.**

IMPERIAL GARDENS SOAP ON A ROPE-CANADA 1974
(Inside Left) White soap on orange rope. **CMV $5. MB.**

SURE WINNER SKI BOOT SOAP ON A ROPE-CANADA 1976
(Inside Right) Blue soap, white rope. **CMV $6. MB.**

PARISIENNE BELL SOAP-SPAIN 1977
(Right) Pink Lady bust soap. **CMV $8. MB.**

A TOKEN OF LOVE SOAP-AUSTRALIA 1979
(Left) White bar with pink center. **CMV $6.50. MB.**

ORCHARD FLOWERS SOAPS-EUROPE 1979
(Center) Gray box holds 3 yellow flower embossed soaps. **CMV $7. MB.**

PIRATE PETE SOAP ON A ROPE-EUROPE 1978
(Right) Yellow soap with orange rope. **CMV $5. MB.**

PERSIAN KITTEN SOAP-CANADA 1977
White soap in purple box. OSP $4., **CMV $4. MB.**

SOAPS ON A ROPE-FOREIGN 1969-70
Each yellow soap, left to right.
HARRY THE HOUND, HAPPY COW, RUFUS THE SQUIRREL. **CMV $16. each MB.**

SOUTH SEAS SOAPS-EUROPE 1979
(Left) Box holds 3 green fish shaped soaps. **CMV $6. MB.**

LEMON SOAP TRIO-EUROPE 1979
(Right) Holds 4 yellow lemon shaped soaps. **CMV $6. MB.**

(Left to Right)

ST. BERNARD SOAP-EUROPE 1975
White soap. Blue & green box. CMV $10. MB.
$8. soap only.

BO BO SOAP-EUROPE 1975
Yellow elephant soap. Blue & yellow soap.
CMV $10. MB. $8. soap only.

HIGH FLYER SOAP ON A ROPE -EUROPE 1975
Yellow soap. White rope. Yellow soap & box.
CMV $10. MB. $8. soap only.

PERSIAN KITTEN SOAP-EUROPE 1975
White cat soap, blue box. CMV $10. MB. $8.
soap only.

MOLLY MOUSE SOAP-EUROPE 1972
(Left) Blue mouse soap on white rope. CMV
$12. MB.

MR. FROG SOAP-EUROPE 1972
(Right) Green soap on pink or white rope.
CMV $12. MB.

FRAGRANCE BELL SOAP-EUROPE 1975
Dark pink soap and box. CMV $11. MB.

LITTLE GIRL BLUE SOAP-EUROPE 1975
Blue soap, white and blue box. CMV $12. MB.

KNIGHT IN ARMOR-EUROPE 1975
White soap, black and yellow box. CMV $17.
MB.

CHEEKY CHAPPIE SOAP ON A ROPE-EUROPE 1974
Light green soap on white rope. CMV $11. MB.
Reissued 1979 in Australia under the name of
Cheeky Charlie. CMV $7. MB.

REGENCE-CANADA 1974
PERFUMED TALC
2.75 oz. green metal can, gold cap. CMV $2.
SAVON PERFUMED SOAP
Box holds 3 green bars. CMV $6.
PERFUME SOAP
3 oz. plain wrapper. 3 oz. green floral wrapper.
CMV $3. each.

CAMEO SOAP ON A ROPE-CANADA 1972
Pink soap, white rope. CMV $5. MB.

MINERAL SPRINGS SOAP ON A ROPE-CANADA 1973
Beige soap, white soap. CMV $5. MB.

AVON SOAP GEMS-FOREIGN 1974
Orange, yellow and green soaps. CMV $12.
MB.

DUTCH SHOE SOAP-SPAIN 1974
Blue soap and box. CMV $12. MB, $10. soap
only. Also sold in Canada.

LADY SLIPPER SOAP-SPAIN. ENGLAND 1974
Lavender soap and box. CMV $12. MB, $10.
soap only.

TOUCH OF BEAUTY SOAPS-SPAIN 1974
Gold and pink box holds 2 white bars. CMV
$11. MB.

FOUR SEASONS SOAP SET-EUROPE 1974
Box holds 4 bars of orange, blue, yellow, and
green soap. CMV $11. MB.

ELEGANTE PERFUMED SOAPS-EUROPE 1974
Green box holds 3 embossed aqua bars. CMV
$13. MB.

LILAC SOAP-EUROPE 1972
Blue box holds lilac soap with blue ribbon.
CMV $10. MB.

STRAWBERRY FAIR SOAP-EUROPE 1972
Strawberry soap in yellow basket and ribbon.
CMV $9. MB.

FIELD FLOWERS SOAPS - JAPAN 1979
Green box holds 2 pink, 2 green and 2 yellow soaps. **CMV $18. MB.**
TOUCH OF ROSES SOAPS - JAPAN 1979-80
Red box holds 6 pink rose shaped bars. **CMV $18. MB.**

WHITE GINGER SOAP FOREIGN 1969
Beige soap came in fancy box. **CMV $12. MB.**

SOAPS - SINGLE BARS
FROM EUROPE
Aqua soap, Elegance, Nearness and Dr. Zabriskies soap. **CMV $3. each bar.**
FROM CANADA
Clear Skin, Regence, Moonwind, Scent of Roses, Hawaiian White Ginger, Charisma, Rich Moisture Soap, and Blue Lotus. **CMV $2. each bar.**
FROM SPAIN
Perfumed Deodorant Soap, Deluxe Toilette Soap, Charisma, Topaze, Regence in Brocade package. **CMV $4. each bar.**
FROM AUSTRALIA
Occur! **CMV $4.**

JUMBO SOAP SET - EUROPE 1972
Blue, tan and pink elephant soap. **CMV $11. MB.**
TOP DOG SOAP - EUROPE 1972
Tan colored soap on white rope. **CMV $11. MB.**

WINTER SONG SOAPS - EUROPE & CANADA 1979-80
Cardinal box holds 2 white bird decal bars. **CMV $6. MB Europe. CMV $5. MB Canada.**
LADY SLIPPER SOAPS - EUROPE 1979-80
Box holds 2 white, 2 pink slipper bars. **CMV $8. MB.**

FASHION BOOT HOSTESS SOAP - ENGLAND 1973
Soap is blue with lavender bow. **CMV $9. MB.**
CANADA
Soap is same only no bow. Boxes are different labels. **CMV $7. MB.**

DECORATOR SOAP 1972
(Left) Gold box holds 5 oz. white bar. **CMV $4. MB.**
SKIN-SO-SOFT SOAP-ON-A-ROPE - CANADA 1976
(Center) Turquoise soap with white rope. **CMV $5. MB.**
CAMEO SOAP SET 1975
(Right) Blue box holds 4 white cameo soaps. **CMV $6.50 MB.** Also came in white box with blue trim. **CMV $11.**

BOUTIQUE SOAP SET - EUROPE 1973
Box holds 2 green bars and 2 lavender bars. **CMV $8. MB.**
ROSE BLOSSOMS SOAP - EUROPE & SPAIN 1973
Box is pink, holds 4 flower embossed bars. **CMV $8. MB.**

ROSE BLOSSOMS SOAPS - MEXICO 1975
Pink box holds 4 white bars. **CMV $10. MB.**
FLEUR D'AVON - SPAIN 1975
Pink, white and green box holds 3 flower soaps. **CMV $12. MB.**
PERFUMED FLOWER SOAPS - MEXICO 1976
Green box holds 4 gray flower soaps. **CMV $12.50 MB.**

PERFUMED SOAPS - JAPAN 1978
Three different colored bars in own box in Bird of Paradise, Charisma and Unforgettable. **CMV $7. each.**

463

FOREIGN AVONS

UNFORGETTABLE SOAPS - SPAIN 1975
Orange box holds 3 orange bars. 4A design embossed in center of soaps. **CMV $10. MB.**
CHRISTMAS ORNAMENT - MEXICO 1977
Pink and green hang-up card holds eye shadow wand. **CMV $10. mint.**
CHRISTMAS ORNAMENT - EUROPE 1974
Small diamond shaped bottle, gold cap. Came in green and gold hang-on holder. **CMV $10. MB.**

SKIN SO SOFT SOAPS - CANADA 1977
(Left) Gray box holds three SSS white bars. **CMV $5. MB.**
SKIN SO SOFT SOAPS - CANADA 1976
(Center) Winter scene box holds 3 white bars of SSS soap. **CMV $5. MB.**
PINE TREE GIFT SOAPS - CANADA 1976
(Right) Green box holds 3 green tree soaps. **CMV $6.50 MB.**

BUTTERFLY SOAP SET - SPAIN 1975
(Left) Box holds 4 bars in yellow, orange, turquoise and lavender butterflies. **CMV $12. MB.**
AVONS PERFUMED SOAPS - CANADA 1975
(Center) Matching boxes came with 3 bars of Lavender, Lily of the Valley, green, Honey-suckles, yellow, and Apple Blossom in pink. **CMV $5. each set.**
BUTTERFLY SOAPS - CANADA 1976
(Right) Box holds 3 yellow bars. **CMV $7. MB.**

LOVE SOAPS - MEXICO 1974
Love box holds 4 yellow bars. **CMV $22.50 MB.**

APPLE BLOSSOMS SOAP SET - CANADA 1975
Green and white box holds 4 flower shaped soaps. **CMV $6. MB.**
HOSTESS SOAP SET - CANADA 1975
Green and pink box holds 2 pink bars and 2 green bars. **CMV $6. MB.**

HONEYSUCKLE PERFUMED SOAPS - AUSTRALIA 1976
(Left) Box holds 3 yellow bars. Also came in Lilac with 3 pink bars. **CMV $8. each MB.**
TOPAZE SOAP - AUSTRALIA 1978
(Center) Yellow box holds 3 topaze yellow bars. **CMV $8. MB.**
TOPAZE SOAP COLUMN - SPAIN 1975
(Right) Yellow box holds 3 yellow column bars in plastic holder. **CMV $13. MB.**

GIFT OF THE SEA - CANADA 1975
Peralessen soap dish and 4 pink sea shell soaps. **CMV $9. MB.**

COUNTRY PEACH SOAPS - EUROPE 1978
Box holds 3 long bars. Also came in strawberry. **CMV $7. each MB.**
COUNTRY CUPBOARD SOAPS - AUSTRALIA 1977
Box holds 3 square bars in peach in pink, or strawberry in red soaps. **CMV $9. each MB.**
COUNTRY CUPBOARD SOAPS - CANADA 1976
Box holds 3 long bars. Came in strawberry and peach. **CMV $7. MB.**

CAMEO SOAP SET - CANADA 1975
Brown box, 3 bars. **CMV $6. MB.**
TOUCH OF ROSES SOAP-ON-A-ROPE 1975
Pink rose soap, white rope. **CMV $5. MB.**

PERFUMED SOAPS - SPAIN 1975
Flowered boxes came with 3 bars in Lilac, Hyacinth, Magnolia. **CMV $11. each MB.**

SOMEWHERE SOAP - SPAIN 1975
Box holds 3 pink S soaps. **CMV $11. MB.**
NEARNESS PERFUMED SOAPS - SPAIN 1975
White and gold box holds 3 pink ribbed soaps.
CMV $12. MB.
LOVEBIRDS SOAP SET - AUSTRALIA 1977
Box holds 3 pink bird embossed soaps. **CMV $9. MB.**

IMPERIAL GARDEN SOAP-ON-A-ROPE - CANADA 1977
Orange rope, white bar. **CMV $4.**

GENTLEMAN'S COLLECTION - FOREIGN 1969
Red and silver box holds bar of soap and 6cc bottle of shave lotion with copper cap. **CMV $16. MB.**

GENTLEMEN'S COLLECTION SET - ENGLAND 1972
Box holds 50cc bottle, brown cap, bar of soap.
CMV $13. MB.

WILD COUNTRY SADDLE KIT - CANADA 1975
Box holds all brown plastic kit with box containing 6 oz. Wild Country After Shave and 7 oz. Spray Talc. **CMV $20.**

INTERNATIONAL MEN'S SET - ENGLAND 1973
Green and white box holds 50 ml size bottle with green cap. Holds After Shave Lotion and 1 white bar World embossed soap. **CMV $13. MB.**

CARTE BLANCHE MEN'S GIFT SET - CANADA 1972
Box holds Carte Blanche After Shave and Soap-On-A-Rope. **CMV $16.**

STACK PACK SET - FOREIGN
Bronze box holds bar of soap and 50cc bottle of shave lotion. **CMV $16. MB.**

THE TRAVELLER SET - AUSTRALIA 1979
Brown box holds one 100 ml light brown plastic Tai Winds after shave and one dark brown 75 ml squeeze spray deodorant. **CMV $6.50 MB.**
LEATHER AFTER SHAVE - MEXICO 1979-80
118 ml clear glass with brown top and label.
CMV $5. MB.
LEATHER TALC - MEXICO 1979-80
100 g. cardboard container. **CMV $3. MB.**

DAILY DOUBLE SET - AUSTRALIA 1976
(Left) Brown and white box holds choice of mens fragrance with 100 g. talc and 150 ml plastic after shave. Blend 7 pictured. **CMV $12. MB.**
GENTLEMAN'S COLLECTION SET - AUSTRALIA 1977
(Right) Box holds choice of mens fragrance in 100 g. talc and 150 ml plastic bottle of after shave. Windjammer pictured. **CMV $12.**

ESTUCHE VIA JERO SET - MEXICO 1977
Blue box holds 90 ml size blue plastic bottle, gold caps in after shave and deodorant or brown box with brown bottles and gold caps.
CMV $10. each set.

DAYLIGHT SAVING TIME - FOREIGN 1969
Gold clock. 150 cc size. CMV $15. BO, $20. MB.

OLD BARREL - FOREIGN 1969
6 oz. brown & silver with brown cap. CMV $15. BO, $20. MB.

FIRST CLASS MALE - CANADA 1971-72
From Canada. Clear glass bottle painted red with red cap. Remove paint & is same as factory test bottle. CMV $7. BO, $8. MB.

DECISIONS - FOREIGN 1968
Smaller than American Decisions. CMV $15. BO, $20. MB.

DANCER DECANTER - CANADA 1986
(Left) 50 ml white glass & white plastic top. CMV $8. MB.

CLASSICAL FIGURINE DECANTER - ENGLAND
(Right) 50 ml size white glass bottle & white plastic cap. Same thing sold in Canada & called "Sarah Decanter". CMV $10. MB both.

E.T. & ELLIOTT PLATE - EUROPE 1983
5" blue face plate. Blue box. Comes with plate stand. CMV $15. MB.

CHRISTMAS ON THE FARM CHRISTMAS GIFT - CANADA 1975
Same as 1973 American Christmas Plate only front says 1975 - Avon on front. French & English label on back. Only given to Team Leader Avon Reps at Christmas. CMV $50. Also a plate was given in 1974 thru 1978 marked the same way. Different plates. All same CMV.

ANTISEPTIC - CANADA 1940s
6 oz. bottles with turquoise caps & boxes. Same labels but 2 different size bottles. Short one rare. OSP 62¢. CMV $20., $25. short. Add $5. for box.

ART NOUVEAU SOAP SET - CANADA 1986
Pink tin box, lady & flower tin lid. Holds 2 Avon Soaps. CMV $10. MB.

TEDDY BEAR HIG MUG - CANADA 1987
White coffee mug. Red heart design, with white stuffed bear. CMV $6. MB.

LIGHTER DECANTER - CANADA 1986
40 ml blue plastic, silver plastic top. CMV 44. MB.

SEVILLA FLAMENCO DANCER - ENGLAND 1986
50 ml black glass, white plastic top, red fan. CMV $10.

AWARDS & REPRESENTATIVES GIFTS

What's Hot & What's Not in Awards

Avon Representative Awards continue to be one of the hottest areas of Avon Collecting. California Perfume products are the single best investment followed closely by Avon Rep Awards in the Avon Collection.

What's Hot in Awards is all jewelry type awards that are marked Avon or the Avon symbols on them. Most all glass awards, figurines, clocks, watches, ceramic items such as cups, dishes, plates, etc. Metal trays, plates, boxes. Anything with sterling silver or real gold in it. Paper weights, lucite items, perfume bottles, pen & pencil sets, buttons. Sets in boxes, key chains, stuffed toys marked Avon, Order Book covers, radios, telephones & Avon umbrellas. All of the above must be marked Avon on the Award. If it's not marked Avon, don't buy it. These are the main items most award collectors are looking for & pay a fair price for.

What's Not Hot

Plaques - picture frames or pictures, tropheys, cloth material items, clothes, bags, anything that is too big or hard to display. Paper items, purses, sets of silverware, display banners, guide books, portfolios. Only things that are very old "1940s" or older of this type award will bring a fair price. Most collectors do not want these items as they don't display well. T-shirts and jackets with Avon logos are popular items and an exception to collecting clothes. All of the above items should be bought with caution. I have a lot of this type of collectables in this book but some may be removed in future issues due to low collector interest.

1961 MANAGERS DIAMOND 4A PIN
4A diamond pin with diamond crown guard. Given to managers reaching a special quota in 1961. **CMV $175.**

1968 MANAGERS DIAMOND RING
1/4 carat art carved 58 faceted diamond set in a gold 4A design mounting. Given to managers for achievement of sales goals for several quarters. **CMV $500.** mint

1978 PRESIDENT'S CLUB RING "LADY'S"
(Left) Gold plated sterling 4A ring with red simulated ruby. Stone comes in several different shades. Given to all female Presien'ts Club Reps. **CMV $35. MB.**
1978 MANAGERS 4A RING
(Right) Silver 4A ring with high grade ruby stone given to 4 managers in Atanta branch for best planning.
CMV price not etablished.

1900 CPC I.D. PIN
 Brass I.D. pin given to early day Reps. to show they worked for the CPC company. This is the 1st I.D. pin ever given by the CPC.
CMV $125.00

1961 MANAGERS DIAMOND PIN
Gold 4A pin same as Representatives except has an "M" made of 11 diamonds. CMV $125. MB.

1961-76 DIAMOND 4A PIN
Larger than other 4A pins; set with diamond. Given for selling $3,000. at customer price in an 18 campaign period. In 1974-76 you had to sell $4,500. in 13 campaigns. CMV $50. MB.

1963-76 SAPPHIRE 4A PIN
Set with a genuine sapphire. Awarded for reaching $2,000. in customer sales price in a 9 campaigne period. In 1974-76 you had to sell $5,500. in 13 campaigns. CMV $30. MB.

1963-70 PEARL 4A PIN
10 kt. gold in a 4A design with a pearl in center. Awarded for reaching $1,000 in customer price sales in a 9 campaign period. 5/8" diameter. CMV $20. MB

1973-76 RUBY 4A PIN
10 kt. gold with ruby in center. Awarded for selling $2,500. in customer price sales in 6 month period to become eligible for President's Club Membership. CMV $15.

1971 CIRCLE OF EXCELLENCE RING
Same as pin only ring. CMV $275. mint.

1969 CIRCLE OF EXCELLENCE PIN
4A gold pin circled with pearls and diamonds in center. Managers only pin has a logo on back and can also be worn as a pendant. CMV $250.

1956-61 JEWELED PIN - DIAMOND
Same as pearl jeweled pin except has five diamonds instead of pearls. Came with black and gold star guard also containing five diamonds. This was the top award and was given after attaining the 4 diamond star guard. A minimum of $25,000 in sales were required for this award. CMV $175. mint.

1910-25 CPC IDENTIFICATION PIN
Given to all Representatives to identify them as official company Representatives. Says CPC 1886 on face. also came with blue enamel center. CMV $90. mint

1910-15 CPC IDENTIFICATION HONOR PIN
Given to Representatives for selling $250. in merchandise. CMV $90. mint. Both pins are brass.

1929-38 CPC AVON I.D. PIN
(Top) Given to all Reps to show they work for Avon and the CPC. Silver pin with blue enamel. "California Perfume Co., Inc., "Avon" on face of pin. This pin is larger in size than the 1938-45 I.D. pins. This pin came in two different ways. The A and V on Avon is close together on one and wide apart on the others. CMV $45.

1929-38 I.D.HONOR AWARD PIN
(Bottom) Gold tone with dark blue enamel. Given to Reps for $250. in sales. "CPC - AVON - HONOR" on face of pin. CMV $55. mint.

1945-61 CITY MANAGERS I.D. PIN & PEARL GUARD
Given to all City Managers. Pin has 5 pearls. Guard is set with 11 seed pearls. CMV $75. mint.

1964 QUEENS AWARD PIN
Gold colored metal 11/4" across. Given to each member of the winning team during the 78th Anniversary for top sales. CMV $20.

1938-45 IDENTIFICATION PIN
Silver with aqua enamel. Given to all Representatives for identification. "Avon Products, Inc., Avon" on face of pin. CMV $30 mint.

1938-45 HONOR I.D. PIN "GOLD"
Gold plated with aqua enamel Given for $250. in sales. "Avon Products, Inc., Avon Honor" on face of pin. CMV $35. mint.

1945-61 JEWELED PIN PEARL - HIGHEST HONOR CASE
10K gold with black enamel background. 5 oriental pearls are set in the A. Came in black highest award case above. Given for sales of $1000. CMV $30. pin, $40 in cae.

1945-51 IDENTIFICATION PIN
Gold pin with black background. "A" has scroll design rather than jewels. Edges are plain, no writing. Given to Representatives for $1,000. in sales. CMV $20.

1938-45 I.D. HONOR PIN & CASE "SILVER"

(Left) Silver with aqua enamel. Given to all Representatives for identification. "Avon Products, Inc., Avon Honor on face of pin. CMV $30.

1945-61 FIELD MANAGER'S I.D. PIN & GUARD

(Right) Same design as the jeweled pin but has no printing. The "M" guard is smooth gold. CMV $55.

1936 50th ANNIVERSARY PIN

Red circle with gold feather. Given to every representative who made a house to house sales trip of her area. CMV $55. mint.

1945-61 JEWELED PIN - HIGHEST HONOR - "PEARL"

10K gold with black enamel background, 5 oriental pearls are set in the A. Given for sales of $1,000. CMV $30.

1956-61 STAR GUARDS

Raised star on round gold metal pin. Given for each $5,000. in sales in any 12 month period. Four guards could be won, each had an additional diamond. Made to wear with the jeweled pin. CMV $15. one diamond. Add $12.50 for each additional diamond.

1945-56 JEWEL PIN NUMERAL GUARDS

Smooth gold numerals given for additional sales in multiples of $1,000. starting with No. 2. There was no No. 1. These are made to attach to the jewel pin. Highest numeral known is 115. The higher the number the more valuable. CMV $8. on numbers 2 to 10. $12. on 11 to 20. $14. on 21 to 30. $18. on 31 to 40 $20. on 41 to 75. $25. each on 76 up.

1977 HEART DIAMOND A PIN

14k gold heart shape pin with 12 small diamonds. Can also be used as a pendant on chain. Came in gray felt box with white outer box. Only 1 given in each division for top Rep. Rare. CMV $400. mint

1969 CHARM BRACELET AWARD

22 kt. gold finish, double-link bracelet with safety chain & 5 charms. Each charm given for progressively higher sales. CMV $7. ea. charm, plus bracelet.

1976-78 A PIN AWARD

Given to Reps. for selling $1,500. in Avon in a 13 campaign period. Came in blue lined box. CMV $5. MB or red lined box CMV $7. MB

1971-76 GOLDEN ACHIEVEMENT AWARD

Bracelet & 1st charm awarded for $5,500. total sales in 6 month period. Each succeeding charm awarded for $5,500. within each subsequent 6 month period. First charm - 2 joined 4A design with green stone. Second charm - Avon Rose with red stone. Third charm - The First Lady with a genuine topaze. Fourth charm - The "World of Avon" set with a genuine aquamarine. Fifth charm - "The Doorknocker" with a genuine amethyst. Sixth charm - jeweled "A" with a genuine sapphire. Seventh charm - the "Key" with a genuine garnet. Eighth charm - Great Oak. (Above order of charms correct) CMV $35. each charm. Charm No. 8 $50.

1963-65 MANAGERS CHARM BRACELET

One charm was given each quarter for 3 years making a total of 12 charms possible. These were won by attaining certain sales increases which increased with each quarter making the later charms very difficult to get. For this reason past the eighth quarter are very hard to find. The bracelet charms are 10 kt. gold. Only four bracelets were won with all 12 charms. A total of 6191 individual charms were given to 1445 managers. The last four charms are like the one pictured in center of bracelet. No. 9 has Rubys, No. 10 Sapphire, No. 11, Emerald & No. 12 Diamond. Each one had 4 stones. CMV 1st 8 charms $45. ea. plus bracelet No. 9 & 10 $60. each. No. 11, 12, $75. ea. CMV all 12 charms $800. mint.

1959 CHARM BRACELET - SILVER
Only 2 districts won in each branch. This was a test bracelet & very few were given for sales achievement. **CMV $200. mint with all 6 charms.**

1965 GOLDEN CIRCLE CHARM BRACELET AWARD
22 kt. gold finish double-link bracelet with safety chain and 5 gold charms. Each charm given for progressively higher sales. **CMV $7.** each charm, plus bracelet $7. Came in an Avon box.

1972-79 CIRCLE OF EXCELLENCE CHARM BRACELET
10K gold bracelet & gold charm with 3 diamonds & 4A design. Black & gold Avon box. Green inside. Given to managers only. **CMV $300. MB.** Also came charm with 4 diamonds last charm. **CMV $350. MB.**

1978 PRESIDENT'S CLUB RING FOR MEN
Gold plated sterling silver 4A ring with ruby stone. Given to male Avon Reps. for selling $6000 worth of Avon in 1 year period. Came in plain blue velvet ring box. **CMV $150. MB.**

1982 ALBEE RING AWARD
Gold plated sterling silver. Given to Reps for meeting sales goals. **CMV $15. MB.**

1977 PRESIDENT'S CELEBRATION DIAMOND RING AWARD
14K gold ring with 8 small diamond in center. Given to managers in Pasadena branch for largest increase in sales. Only 20 rings given in this branch. Does not say Avon. **CMV $100.**

1981 BUTTERFLY PIN AWARD
Gold tone enameled stick pin given to Reps. Does not say Avon. **CMV $5.**

1978 SMOKY QUARTZ RING - MANAGERS
Smoky quartz stone, 14K gold mounting marked Avon. Given to managers in C26-78 for best activity event in Atlanta branch. **CMV $40.**

1977 PRESIDENT'S CELEBRATION STAR AWARD
Sterling silver star & chain with small diamond made by Tiffany. Was given to winning district manager in division. **CMV $35.**

1974 MANAGERS ACHIEVEMENT AWARD PIN & CHARM BRACELET
1 given to top sales manager in each division. Brush sterling silver with blue sapphire in center of Avon Door Knocker. **CMV $70. - $75. MB each.**

1974 DIVISION MANAGERS ACHIEVEMENT CUFF LINKS AWARD
Same as awards pin on left, only are cuff links. Given to male Division Managers - **CMV $85. set. Mint.**

1964 SILVER DOOR KNOCKER PIN
Given to all managers in conjunction with the door knocker award program. **CMV $25., $30 MB.**

1964-83 GOLD DOOR KNOCKER PIN
Came on green or white cards. **CMV $10 on card. CMV pin only $7.** Also came in bue box with white sleeve. Same CMV.

1981 DON'T KNOCK ME DOOR-KNOCKER NECKLACE AWARD
Gold tone door knocker with simulated diamond. Given to Reps. Comes in "Jo Anne Jewels" box. Made only for Avon. CMV $15. MB.

1980 IDENTIFICATION PIN AUSTRALIA
Gold toned door knocker pin. CMV $10.
1980 AVON REPRESENTATIVE STICK PIN
Blue & gold. (Says Avon Representative) CMV $20.

1981 DOOR KNOCKER DIAMOND PIN
Gold with small diamond. Given to managers. Came in Tan box. CMV $60. MB.

1966 DOOR KNOCKER EARRINGS
Gold tone earring. Avon Calling on them. CMV $32.50 pr. MB.

1978 HEART STICK PIN AWARD
Sterling silver heart pin made by Tiffany & Co. with Avon products slip. Given to managers only, during President's Celebration. Does not say Avon. Must be in box with Tiffany & Co. Avon card. CMV $30. MB.

1979 ACORN STICK PIN AWARD
Sterling silver acorn pin from Tiffany & Co. given to managers. Came with small card with great oak & Tiffany card for Avon products. CMV $35. MB.

1978 PRESIDENT'S CELEBRATION "A" PIN AWARD
White box holds "A" sterling silver pin given to President's Club Reps. only. CMV $12.50 MB.

1980-81 PRESIDENT'S CLUB PIN AWARD
Gold tone pin given to President's Club Members only. Comes in Blue Avon box. Given in 1980 & 1981. CMV $15 MB.

1977 APPLE STICK PIN
Red apple with 4A design 1977 & P.C. for President's Club on green Leaf. Pin is gold tone color. Given to winning team in each district for highest sales. CMV $15.
1978 LIVE-LOVE-LAUGH DIAMOND PIN AWARD
14K gold with 2 point diamond. Given to Avon managers for reaching appointment goal for August conference. CMV $30. MB.

1971 EMPLOYEES GIFT KEY CHAIN
Blue box with gray flannel bag holds gold horseshoe with Avon on one side and You're in Demand on back side of charm. CMV $20. MB.

AN OPEN LETTER TO ALL AVON REPS.

Do you want to increase the number of Avon collectors in the world? This would greatly increase your sales, too, you know! Try to find out your customer's various interests and those of her children and husband, too! For example:

Mrs. Smith loves animals - bring every animal decanter to her attention as they appear on the market. Sell her the first one and she'll likely buy more, or all, that come! Mr. Smith is a sports fan! Point out what a smart collection he could have on a neat shelf in his den. Young Johnny would love the majestic elephant, or that dinosaur decanter and teenager Sue really "digs" the "Fried Egg" or "Hamburger" compacts.

All these people have a good chance of ending up being a collector! So what does that really mean? Well it means that your collectables will maintain their value and the market will grow steadily. Avon Reps. will have good steady sales. Collectors will have a wider and wider circle of ever growing and interested folk to swap and shop with.

Show your own collection to friends, help to stir the interest of others. Believe me, it will pay off in the end!!

Most important of all, don't forget to carry a copy of Hastin's Avon Collectors Encyclopedia to show your customers. "By showing this book to your customers, you can help create new collectors and you will profit 10 fold, as collectors will buy many more Avon products from you. Be sure to point out information on the Avon Times - Avon Club which they can enjoy right from their own living room. Tell them about the free advertising to over 2000 members to buy, sell or trade Avons. Remember, if you help educate your customers on Avon Collecting you will profit greatly in larger future sales.

For more information on the Avon Times, write or send $15.00 for 1 full year subscription in U.S. or $18.00 U.S. Funds in Canada to: Avon Times - Box 9868 - Kansas City, Missouri 64134.

1980 PRESIDENT'S CELEBRATION MEN'S AWARD KEY CHAIN
Sterling silver with oak tree on one side & inscribed on other. Given to men Reps. only for top sales. CMV $100. MB.

1970'S 5 YEAR SERVICE AWARD KEY RING
Sterling silver - 4A design on front comes in Blue felt Tiffany bag & box. CMV $25.

1976-77 SALES ACHIEVEMENT KEY CHAIN
Silver tone key chain. 4A emblem on front & back market "Avon Sales Achievement Award C/23/76, C/9/77." In special Sales Achievement Award Avon box. CMV $11. MB.

1968 ANNIVERSARY CAMPAIGN KEY CHAIN
(Left) Silver charm and key chain. **CMV $22.50**

1972 CIRCLE OF EXCELLENCE KEY CHAIN
(Right) Silver charm and chain with 4A design on one side and Mexico 1972. This was given by Mexico Avon branch to Circle of Excellence Award winning managers for the year 1971. Trip was made in 1972 for approximately 185 winning managers. **CMV $55. mint.**

1968 ANNIVERSARY CAMPAIGN HONOR AWARD KEY CHAIN
White Avon box holds gold & silver double key ring. Made by Swank. **CMV $17.50 MB.**

1980 -10 YEAR SERVICE AWARDS
5 different gifts. All of sterling silver. All marked with 4A design. Each comes in Tiffany & Co. box. Given to Avon managers & all Avon Employees for 10 years service. They had their choice of Pen & Pencil set with T clips, 3 inch purse mirror, Cuff Links 7/8" diameter, & Small 1 1/4" high silver flask that opens, on sterling silver chain 23 1/2" long. **CMV each item or set. $40 MB. Flask $60, pen set $50 MB.**

1975 BOCA OR BUST MANAGERS KEY CHAIN
Silver 4A design, **CMV $15. MB.**

1973-75 4A KEY RING AWARD
Gold lucite key ring in green or red lined box. **CMV $10. MB each.**

1967 DISTINGUISHED MANAGEMENT AWARD
Sterling silver key chain with raised 4A design set in brushed finish area. Given to top manager in each division. **CMV $35. MB, $27.50 chain only.**

1978 "KEY CHAIN" DISTRICT MANAGER SAFE DRIVER AWARD
Large brass key chain has "4A" on one side & "Avon District Manager Safe Driver Award 1978" on other side. Came in white & green box. 4A on box lid. Came also with Avon card shown. **CMV $10. MB.**

1979 KEY CHAIN "THANKS AMERICA" AWARD
Team leader white box holds silver tone heart key chain "Thanks America for making us number one" Back side says "Avon loves team leaders." **CMV $12.50 MB.**

1964 LUCKY 7 PIN
Gold tone pin with simulated pearl in center. Given to each representative who sent in a certain size order. **CMV $10., $13. MB.**

1966 GOOD LUCK BRACELET
Gold double link bracelet with gold charm. Good luck four leaf clover on the front. Back is plain. Not marked Avon. **CMV $12., $15. MB.**

1953 AWARD BRACELET
1953 on back of sterling silver heart shaped charm. **CMV $40 MB**

1969-70 AVON ATTENDANCE CHARM
1969 AD on one round charm & 1970 Heart shape AD on the other. Both gold tone & chain. **CMV $17 ea.**

1951 FIGURE 8 CHARM BRACELET
Sterling silver bracelet with 2 skates attached. Given to representatives for interviewing 120 Avon customers during the figure 8 campaign 3-1951. Made only for Avon. **CMV$50.**

1956 MANAGERS BRACELET
Bracelet given to top selling city & district managers during President's campaign 1956. **CMV $100 MB.**

1961 BELL BRACELET AWARD
Silver bracelet & bell that rings. Avon not on bell. **CMV $30.**

1964 BELL AWARDS
Gold bell earrings. Christmas sales award. **CMV $20.** Gold bell charm bracelet. Christmas sales award. **CMV $30.**

1979 DREAM CHARM MANAGERS NECKLACE
Gold tone necklace & 3 charms of orchid, butterfly & sea shell. Given to Avon managers at 1979 Dream Conference. Does not say Avon on charms. Came in maroon satin bag with pink tie string. **CMV $25. mint in bag.**

1977 TLC NECKLACE AWARD
Given to Team Leaders. 14K gold. **CMV $25.**

1960 MANAGERS CHRISTMAS GIFT
Pearl bracelet with small diamonds & matching earrings. Given to Avon managers at Chritmas about 1960. Does not say Avon. Made by Majestic. **CMV $300. MB.**

1974 PRESIDENTS CELEBRATION AWARD
14 kt. gold necklace with 3 point diamond. Given to 10 top representatives in each of the 81 winning districts for outstanding sales during this presidents celebration. **CMV $60. MB.**

1975 FIRST AVON LADY PENDANT AWARD
Siver toned with scroll 'A' design around glass insert. On the presentation card it starts "Congratulations! We're happy to present you with this exclusive award. Designed especially for you. It's symbolic of the personal service upon which Avon was founded and which has guided us throughout the years" **CMV $25. - $30. MB.**

1977 MANAGERS GIFT DIAMOND LOOP
Diamond Loop necklace given to managers in special gold bar type box, on introduction of Avons new 14K gold filled jewelry. **CMV $40. MB as pictured.**

1978 SMILE PENDANT AWARD
Red and gold pendant, given to all Avon Team Leaders. Back side says Avon, Team Leader, March 1978. **CMV $10. MB.** Also given to District Managers with D.M. on back. **CMV $15.** Both came in red box with Avon sleeve. Smile Pendant also given to Division managers at conference. Back says "N.Y. March, 78, Avon". Red box comes with plain white sleeve. **CMV $30. MB.**

1966 HONOR AWARD CAMEO PERFUME GLACE NECKLACE
Blue & white set trimmed in gold. **CMV $18., $22.50 MB.**

1975 SUNNY STAR AWARD NECKLACE
Given to managers on introduction to Sunny Star necklace. This is the same one that sold only it has Aug. 1975 engraved on it. It can easily be duplicated so a price above the cost from Avon should not be paid. Brass star & chain. **CMV $10. MB.**

1969 PRESIDENT'S CELEBRATION DIAMOND HEART LOCKET AWARD
Given to top 20 Reps. in each district during President's Celebration. Inscribed on back "President's Club 1979" **CMV $20. MB.** Same given to district managers only has DM Inscribed on back also. **CMV $30. MB.**

1979 CHRISTMAS GIFT - REPS.
Sterling silver goldtone chain with 10K gold charm with 2 small diamonds. Came in black felt box. Back is marked District managers 1979 - **CMV $65.**, Team Leaders 1979 - **CMV $50.**

1978 VALENTINE HEART PENDANT AWARD
14K gold heart. Does not say Avon. Only 2500 were given to Reps. at sales meetings. Must have C3-78 brochure with heart to prove it's from Avon. **CMV $25. with brochure.**

1978 EARRINGS - TEAM LEADER CHRISTMAS GIFT
10K solid gold with small diamond chip. Given to team leaders at Christmas, 1978. Came in Avon box. **CMV $40. MB.**

1982 TEAM LEADER TEDDY BEAR AWARD
Sterling silver bear with movable arms & sterling silver chain. From Tiffany. Approx. 1/2 inch high. Marked T.L. on back of bear. **CMV $30. MB.**

1979 HEART NO. 1 PENDANT AWARD
14K gold heart with small diamond given to 1 top Rep. in each division. In Avon blue velvet box. **CMV $125. MB**

1982 SILVER CIRCLE CELEBRATION-NECKLACE AWARD. ENGLAND
Blue box holds clear crystal pendant on sterling silver chain. Marked Avon. Given to Silver Circle Reps. **CMV $40. MB.** Also shown with silver Circle Celebration Banquet Menu. **CMV $5.**

1980 ACORN NECKLACE AWARD
Sterling Silver acorn Pendant & necklace. Comes with great oak card & Tiffany Box in velvet pouch. Given to managers only. **CMV $60. MB with card.**

1978 "YOU'RE PRECIOUS TO US" PENDANT MANAGERS GIFT
14K gold filled with real pearl & small diamond. Gold box says "You're Precious to Us" on lid. Given to Avon managers. Must be in box as described. Came with card signed by S.M. Kent. **CMV $50. MB.**

1971 - 85th ANNIVERSARY AWARD JEWELRY
22 Kt. gold plated sterling silver necklace, ring & earrings. Each shaped like a rose with diamond in center. Necklace was for representatives not in the presidents club, and the earrings for the presidents club members only. Two diamond rings were given in each district by a drawing. One was given to a presidents club member the other to a non-member. Ring also available in prize catalog for 2400 points. **CMV necklace $35. - $40. MB, Ring $80. - $85. MB, Earrings $35. - $40. MB.**

1971 85th ANNIVERSARY PINS
22 Kt. gold plated sterling silver pin with diamond. Small pin for representative not in president club, representatives only. Given for meeting sales goal in C-12-71. **CMV small pin $15. - $20. MB. Large pin $20. - $25. MB.**

1967 - 81st ANNIVERSARY PINS
Sterling silver pins came in 12 different flowers. Representatives who met their personal prize goal for this anniversary campaign had their choice of one of these 12 flowers. Carnation, Violet, Daffodil, Daisy, Lily of the Valley, Rose, Lily, Gladiolus, Aster, Calendula. Chrysanthemum and Jonquil. **CMV Rose $15., $25. MB. Calendula $30., $40. MB; all others $20., $30. MB.**

1968 ANNIVERSARY AWARD ROSE PIN
Victory luncheon July 9, 1968. Gold rose pin with ruby stone in Avon box. **CMV $27.50 MB only.**

1968 "G" CLEF MANAGERS PIN
Gold in color. Awarded to managers. **CMV $15. pin only, $20. MB.**

1969 SALES ACHIEVEMENT AWARD
Large gold Charisma design pin came in black Avon box. **CMV $20. MB.**

1971 MOONWIND AWARD PIN
Sterling silver pin given to Reps. for meeting sales goals. **CMV $22.50.**

1965 AWARD PIN
White plastic on blue background with silver or gold frame. **CMV $25. in box. $15. pin only.**

1979 SHELL SALES LEADER AWARD
Sterling silver shell comes in Tiffany felt bag & box. Given to managers. **CMV $125. MB.**

1968 SHELL JEWELRY
(Left) Given for recommending someone as a representative. For each name representatives could choose either the pin or earrings. For 2 or more names you got the set. **CMV $12. Set.**

155 NEARNESS MANAGERS PIN
(Right) Gold shell pin with pearl. **CMV $35.**

1962 KEY PIN AWARD
(Top) Gold key, surprise gift for activity. **CMV $10.**

1961 AWARD EARRINGS
(Bottom) Gold star design. Avon is not on them. **CMV $15. MB pair.**

1944 Only - AWARD PIN
Hand made sterling silver pin with roses & lilies, given to Reps. for selling $300. to $400. during Christmas campaign. **CMV $50, $60 MB.**

1943 MANAGERS AWARD PIN
Gold plated lapel pin with hand set stones, cost Avon $25. in 1943. Only 2 were given to the 2 top selling managers in U.S. during loyalty campaign, March 2-22, 1943. **CMV $125.**

1951 CLOVER TIME PIN
Given to representatives for calling on 120 customers in one campaign. Made by Coro. Pin is outlined with imitation seed pearls & dotted with aquamarine stones for color. Does not say avon. Came with certificate from Avon in Coro box. **CMV $40. MB - $25. Pin only.**

1942 VICTORY PIN AWARD
Sterling silver wing pin with red, white and blue center. Given to Reps. during Acres of Diamonds campaign 1942 for getting new customers. **CMV $70. $80 MB.**

1944 BOW PIN AWARD
Lapel pin is gold plate with center stone of synthetic aquamarine. Given to Reps. for selling over $300. in 1 campaign. **CMV $30, $45 MB.**

1942 BOWKNOT AWARD PIN
Gold pin with sequins shaped like bow. Given to representatives for selling $100. to $150. in one campaign. **CMV $40, $50 MB.**

1970 - 5 YEAR SERVICE PIN
For Avon plant employees, not Reps. Gold circle with 4A emblem & blue stone. **CMV $30. - MB $25. pin only.**

1955 RED ROBIN PIN
Sterling silver pins made by Cora Company. does not say Avon on it. Given in pairs for getting 12 new customers. **CMV $25. - $30. MB.**

1979 EIFFEL TOWER MANAGERS PIN
Small gold tone tie tack type pin given to
managers on Paris trip. Does not say Avon.
In plain blue box. Pin is 1 1/8" high. **CMV
$15.**

1977 TOP FIFTY PIN AWARD
Gold tone pin has top 50 & 4A design with red
backgound. Given to top 50 Reps. in division
for sales. **CMV $16.**
1978 TOP FIFTY PIN AWARD
Same as 1977 pin only has red rose with green
leaves. **CMV $12.50.**

**1980 SHOOTING STAR PIN -
MANAGERS**
Gold tone pin in brown box with outer sleeve.
Given to managers. **CMV $25. MB.** Also
came as tie tack for men. **CMV $30. MB.**

1980 ROYAL RIBBON TAC PIN AWARD
Sterling silver with yellow, red, white, or blue
enamel. Given to managers for recruiting new
Reps. **CMV - Yellow $15. Red $20.
White $25. Blue $30. MB each.**

1979 FLAG PIN AWARD
Gold tone red, white and blue enamel lapel pin.
Given to Circle of Excellence winners in Paris
trip. Came in red velvet Avon ring box. **CMV
$50. MB.**
1976 MANAGERS PANELIST PIN
Gold tone name pin. Marked "Nat. District
Managers Panelist" **CMV $15.** Given each
year.

1981 TELEPHONE TIE TAC AWARD
Gold tone telephone Tie Tac. Given to Reps.
CMV $10.

1982 AVON'S BEST PIN AWARD
Small brass pin says "Avon's Best, Morton
Grove." With 4A design. Given to managers
for Atlanta conference. **CMV $20.**
1981 UNICORN PIN AWARD
Brass unicorn lapel pin given to managers at
August conference 1981. Back inscribed
Conference 81. Avon box says For Display
Only - not for resale. **CMV $20. MB.** Same
pin given to Team Leaders. **CMV with TL
on back $10.** Pin also sold to public only
plain no marking on back. No CMV also came
with SC on back. **CMV $20. MB.**

1970 - 25 YEAR SERVICE AWARD PIN
1/10 yellow 10K gold 4A pin with 25 on it. Was
for 25 years service. Was never issued. Very
Rare. **CMV $150.**

1979 AVON PIN - DIVISION MANAGER
Gold tone pin with red enamel filled heart
shaped O given to division managers only.
CMV $25. MB - in red box.
1979 AVON PIN - REPS
Gold tone pin same as above only does not
have red heart. **CMV $10. MB - in white
box.**
**1979 AVON PIN - DISTRICT
MANAGERS**
Same gold tone pin as reps. above only DM
inscribed on back. **CMV $15. MB - in
white box.**

1979 AVON NO. 1 PIN - HOLLAND
Gold tone pin given to Zone Avon Managers in
Holland. **CMV $50.**

1980 C OF E PIN
Small pin says C of E 1980. **CMV $10.**
1979 C OF E WINNERS PIN
Blue Enamel on gold tone pin. **CMV $20.**
1981 SELL A THON TIE TAC
Red, white & blue tie tac pin. Given to all Reps. at sales meeting. **CMV $2.**
1980 CABLE CAR STICK PIN
Gold tone, sterling silver cable car stick pin given t o Avon managers on trip to San Francisco. Does not say Avon. **CMV $15.**

1969 MONEY CLIP TEAM LEADER AWARD
Green & white lined black & brass box holds 12K gold filled money clip with solid 10K gold emblem with 2 small diamonds on top. Awarded to male team leaders. Rare. "Team Leader 1979" on back. **CMV $125. MB.** Also given to male managers with D.M. on back. **CMV $150. MB.**

AVON STAR PIN
(left) **CMV $60.** If you have any information on what year or what this pin was given for, please write Bud Hastin and tell him.
1938 SERVICE AWARD
(Right) Bronze medallion hangs from aqua colored bar with Avon in gold. Given to representatives for outstanding improvement in sales. **CMV $50. mint.**

1963 - 1500 PIN
(Top) Given to reps. for $1,500. in sales in one campaign. **CMV $20.**
1969-70 TEAM CAPTAIN PIN
(Bottom) Torch pin says T C -69-70. **CMV $20.**

1945 MEDALLION OF HONOR
Made of solid gold, it is 7/8 inches long & 1 3/8 inches wide. Woman on the front is raised. Back side is engraved to person & date. Came with award scroll. Medal can be worn on a ribbon or brooch. This medal was given to women only in 1945 during World War II both military & civilian for service to their country above and beyond the call of duty. Very few medals were given out. **CMV medal $500., Scroll $50.**

1963 MONEY CLIP
(Left) 10K gold filled. Back says Pathways of Achievement 1963. 4A design on front and initials. **CMV $75. MB.**
1969 MONEY CLIP
(Center) Black and gold box holds 10K gold filled 4A design on front with initials. Back says Management Conference Atlanta, Georgia November 1969, **CMV $75 MB.**
1960 MONEY CLIP
(Right) 10K gold filled. Small 4A design on face and initials. Nothing on back. **CMV $75.**

1931-37 STAR REPRESENATIVE GOLD MEDALLION
10 kt. gold filled medal. Given to representatives for selling $1,000. worth of Avon in any 12 month period. **CMV $150. - $165. MB.**

1930-31 GOLD STAR REPRESENTA-TIVE MEDAL - CPC
Highest honor given to Representatives that achieved the goal of $1000. in sales from January to January. If goal reached second year a second gold star is engraved, and so on. Made of gold. **CMV $275. MB.**

1937-45 STAR REPRESENTATIVE GOLD MEDALLION
10kt. gold filled medal, given to representatives for selling $1,000. worth of Avon in any 12 month period. **CMV $50. - $60.** in Black Highest Award box shown.

1960 ANNIVERSARY PRINCESS BRACELET
Awarded for increased sales. Bracelet with diamond. Bracelet with emerald, Bracelet with ruby or topaze. 14K gold. **CMV $260. each MB.**

LOYAL SERVICE AWARD - 15 YEAR
Solid 10K gold. 4A emblem on front. Avon 15 years loyal service on back. Given to employees of Avon. Came on 10K gold wrist chain. **CMV $150.**

1970's 4A TIE CLIP SERVICE AWARD
Gold tone with 4A design. Given to Avon employees. **CMV $25.**

1978 KEY RING 5 YEAR SERVICE AWARD
1/10 10K gold 4A symbol key ring given to Avon plant employees for 5 years service. Started in 1978. **CMV $17.50.**

1968 SWEATER GUARD AWARD
6" gold chain with 4A design clips on each end. Given as general managers honor award to each representative of the winning team in each district. **CMV $25. - $30. MB**

1962 SERVICE AWARD CHARM
22 kt. gold finish slightly larger than a quarter, given to all representatives who sold 50 or more customers during campaign 6. **CMV $18.**

1969 PRESIDENTS COURT CHARM
22 kt. gold finish charm. Given to all representatives of the team in each district. **CMV $20.**

1978 - 4A BLUE ENAMEL PIN
Gold tone & blue enamel pin. Comes in Avon box. No information on what it's for. **CMV $12. MB.**

1975 TOP SALES MEDALLION

Gold colored metal medallion. Avon lady carrying case. Italy at bottom of foot. No Avon on it. Given to Avon Reps. for top sales and touring Springdale plant. 2 different designs. One star & one round. **CMV $17, $22.50 MB each.**

1969 TIE TAC AWARD

Small 1/10 10K gold tie tac given to Avon Male Executive with blue sapphire in center. Came in Avon Box. **CMV $50 MB.**

1962 DEDICATED TO SERVICE AWARD

1886-1962 4A deisgn - gold tone. **CMV $20.**

1980 GREAT OAK NO. 1 MEDALLION AWARD.

Small medal - Avon Oak Tree on one side, Pasadena No. 1 - 1980 4A deisgn on other side. **CMV $12.**

1970'S CIRCLE OF EXCELLENCE PIN

Brass - 4A design and C of E Managers only. **CMV $20.**

1966 TOUR GUIDE JACKET GUARDS

Silver color aluminum with 4A design. Used by Avon plant tour guides. **CMV $32.50.**

15 YEAR SERVICE CUFF LINKS

4A design on face and Avon 15 years Loyal Service on back with persons initials. Given to Avon male executives after 15 years service with Avon. Made of solid 10K gold. **CMV $300. pair mint.** Also came 30 year service. Same cuff links. **Same CMV.**

1973 TOUR GUIDE JACKET GUARDS

Gold metal with pressed flower in center of 4A. Used by Avon plant tour guides. **CMV $25.**

1967 RETIREMENT PIN

Gold disk with raised 4A design hanging from a golden bow. Given to retiring representatives with 10 years or more of service. **CMV $50.**

1960'S - 1970'S 4A DOUBLE STICK PIN AWARD

10K gold double 4A stick pin. We have no information on what it is. Please contact Bud Hastin if you know. Comes in Avon box. **CMV $75. MB.**

1979-80 PRESIDENT'S CLUB LADY'S PINS

Gold colored 4A pin - 79 in middle is 1st of an annual 4A year pin given to President's Club Reps. for meeting sales goal for that year. **CMV $10. each year.**

1966 4A MENS CUFF LINKS

Silver links with 4A design. Given to plant & office employees only. **CMV $35. pr.**

1965-68 DISTINGUISHED MANAGEMENT AWARD EARRINGS

4A design clip-on earrings. **CMV $35. pair MB.**

1980-81 PRESIDENT'S CLUB MEN'S TIE TAC
Small gold tone 4A - 81 on face. Given to male President's Club members. CMV $15., $20. MB.

1979-80 PRESIDENT'S CLUB MEN'S PIN AWARD
Gold tone 4A design & 79 on one & 80 on the other. Given to all male President's Club members. Smaller than lady's pin. CMV $20. MB.ea.

1965 AVON HAWAIIAN HOLIDAY CHARM AWARD
14K gold given to 7 avon managers in Hawaii in 1965. Each manager had their initials put on back. CMV $150.

1976 CHARM "DAY TO REMEMBER" AWARD
Small gold tone charm marked "A Day to Remember - C21-76" Came in blue Avon box. CMV $15. MB.

1980 PRESIDENT'S CELEBRATION GREAT OAK MANAGER CHARM AWARD
Sterling silver cut out great oak tree charm. Comes with oak tree card in Avon box. Given to top managers in each district. CMV $100. MB. 1 top manager in each division won a cut out silver oak charm with sapphire around edge. CMV $150. MB. 1 top manager in each branch won same charm only with Ruby's around edge. CMV $200. MB. The top manager in the U.S. won same cut out oak charm with a diamond. Very Rare. CMV not established.

1980 DISTRICT MANAGERS CHARM BRACELET
Sterling silver chain & heart shaped charm says "DM 1980". Came in Tiffany & Co. Box. Given to District Managers at September conference. CMV $75.

1980 PRESIDENT'S CELEBRATION NECKLACE
Gold tone charm with Great Oak on one side & The President's Celebration 1980 on other side. Given to top Reps. in each district. CMV $20. MB. Same charm in silver tone given to 10 top winning district Reps. CMV $30. MD.

1980 SALES LEADERSHIP AWARD
Gold tone & black face. Says "Outstanding Sales Leadership" 5th Qtr. 1979-80 Avon. Came with red neck velvet ribbon. CMV $40.

1981 PRESIDENT'S CELEBRATION SALES ACHIEVEMENT MEDAL
(Left) Dated Dec. 11, 1981 on back side. Only 1 given to each branch. Put on red, white and blue ribbon. CMV $150.

1976 PRESIDENT'S CAMPAIGN KEY CHAIN
(Right) Chrome & white with red letters. Given to President's Club Reps. CMV $10.

CIRCLE OF EXCELLENCE PIN 1987
Small pin C of E 1987 4A design. CMV $25.

ALBEE KEY CHAIN 1987
Blue & gold tone. For sponsorship of new Reps. CMV $15.

SPONSORSHIP PIN 1986
Gold tone pin for sponsorship. CMV $10.

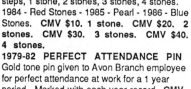

1976 - 90th ANNIVERSARY BICENTENNIAL PENDANT AWARD
Brass coin & chain given to Reps. for selling $285. worth of Avon in 2 campaigns. Front & back view shown. **CMV $15. MB.**

1978-82 INTERNATIONAL RUNNING CIRCUIT MEDALION & NECKLACE
Silver tone medalion given to winners in each city in each age group for running in Avon races. Came in black & gold box. Rare. **CMV $125. MB.**

1984-85-86 PRESIDENT'S CLUB ACHIEVEMENT PINS AWARD
Brass pin with stones for sales increase. 4 steps, 1 stone, 2 stones, 3 stones, 4 stones. 1984 - Red Stones - 1985 - Pearl - 1986 - Blue Stones. **CMV $10. 1 stone. CMV $20. 2 stones. CMV $30. 3 stones. CMV $40. 4 stones.**

1979-82 PERFECT ATTENDANCE PIN
Gold tone pin given to Avon Branch employee for perfect attendance at work for a 1 year period. Marked with each year record. **CMV $35.**

1984 PRESIDENT'S CLUB KEY RING AWARD
Gray box says Avon Tribute 1984. Gold tone with Albee charm. **CMV $15.**

1986 BLUE HEART AVON AWARD PIN
Silver tone pin with blue heart stone. Given to Reps in Newark branch for 3 orders. **CMV $10. MB.**

1985 ROYAL AVON PIN
Blue, white & green enamel lapel pin. Given to Managers. **CMV $10.00**

1986 AVON 86 ROSE PIN
Gold tone Rose-Avon 86 lapel pin given to Avon Reps. **CMV $5.**

1987 GOLD DIGGER PIN
Small gold tone pick ax. Not marked Avon. Given for signing new avon Reps. **CMV $5.**

1985 I LOVE AVON PIN AWARD
Gold tone - red heart. **CMV $5.**

1985 LIBERTY PIN AWARD
Avon on front. **CMV $5.**

1985 GOLD FEVER AWARD
Small walnut plaque imprinted in wood says "Avon Gold Fever Additions Achievement Sept. 1985" with winners name on brass plaque. 1 oz. 999 fine pure gold "Avon 4A Pasadena" gold coin. Coin is loose but must be with plaque. **CMV $50.** plus current value of 1 oz. of gold.

1984 SPONSORSHIP AWARDS
1/10 10K gold pin with 2 hands. Given to Reps for signing up 10 new Avon Reps. Came in gray & gold box. **CMV $10. MB.**

CHARM BRACELET
1/10 10K gold charm & bracelet in gray & gold box. Back says 25 Sponsorships Avon. Came with Ruby stone. 2 hands on front. **CMV $25.**

AVON 5000 PIN 1985
(Left) Red, black & gold pin says Avon 5000. Given to Reps for top sales. **CMV $25.**

THOUSANDAIR CLUB 5000 PIN 1986
(Center) White & gold and red pin with "TC 1886-1986 $5,000.00" on face. **CMV $25.**

THOUSANDAIR CLUB PIN 1986
(Right) White, gold & red pin 1886-1986. **CMV $10.**

1980 4A STICK PIN AWARD
1" 4A design in silver tone, gold outer trim. **CMV $15.**

1987 AVON PIN AWARD
Gold tone Avon pin. **CMV $15.**
1987 PRESIDENT'S CLUB PIN AWARD
Gold tone with hanging rose. **CMV $25.**
1986 ALBEE AVON 100 PIN - ENGLAND
Gold tone. Blue enamel. **CMV $65.**

1984 PRESIDENT'S CLUB PIN "MENS"
Brush gold tone stick pin or tie tac. Given to male Reps for meeting sales goals. 4A design on each. **1st goal 1 red ruby. CMV $35. 2 Rubys $50. 3 Rubys $75. 4 Rubys $100. all MB.** In black velvet box. Maroon liner.

1980 CHARM BRACELET AWARD
Sterling silver charm & heart pendant. Both dated 1980 & "S.C." for Sales Coordinator & "TL" for Team Leader.
Comes in blue bag & blue Tiffany box, with white bow ribbon. **CMV "SC" $90. MB. CMV "TL" $40. MB.**

1983 GROUP SALES LEADER PIN AWARD
Gold tone - 4A design. **CMV $8.**
1981 MORTON GROVE 25 YEAR PIN
Silver tone pin - not sterling. **CMV $8.**

1985 SPONSORSHIP MEDALLION AWARD
Gold tone pendant on white ribbon. **CMV $10.**
1981 CIRCLE OF EXCELLENCE MEDALLION AWARD
Gold tone 4A design, 1981 on back. Red ribbon. **CMV $10.**

1983 GREAT OAK CUFF LINK AWARD
Sterling Silver - not marked Avon. Plain black box. Given to male Div. Managers. **CMV $100.**
1981 GREAT OAK COIN AWARD
Sterling Silver coin says Kansas City #1 - 1981 with great oak tree. Given to Managers in Tiffany bag & box. **CMV $40.**

1980s 5 YEAR HEART KEY RING AWARD
In Tiffany box. Sterling silver. For 5 year Avon service. **CMV $20.**
1976 OAK TREE ATLANTA BRANCH PENDANT
(Right) Gray pewter on neck chain. **CMV $15.**

HONOR SOCIETY PIN 1987
HS on gold tone pin.
Level 1 - Has a Ruby. **CMV $20.**
Level 2 - Has a Sapphire. **CMV $25.**
Level 3 - Has a Diamond. **CMV $30.**
PRESIDENT'S CLUB PIN 1987
Gold tone pin with "PC" on face.
Level 1 - Has a Pearl. **CMV $10.**
Level 2 - Has a Topaz. **CMV $15.**

1984 GROUP SALES LEADER I.D. PIN
Gold tone stick pin comes in red velvet box. Pin says GSL - Avon. Comes with outer sleeve with Lang all over it. **CMV $15. MB.**

1975 AVON SALES ACHIEVEMENT AWARD BRACELET
Given for sales. Avon on one side and sales achievement on the other. Sterling. **CMV $15. - $20. MB.**

1979 #1 DIAMOND HEART PENDANT AWARD
Given to top Manager for top sales. 7 diamond on gold heart & chain. **CMV $50.**
1976 #1 PENDANT AWARD
Given for top sales in Morton Grove Branch. Gold tone pendant. **CMV $15.**

1964 HAPPY ANNIVERSARY NECKLACE
For 38 years as a representative. October 1964. **CMV $35.**

1974 TEAM LEADER PIN
(Right) Gold raised letters & rim. Given to team leaders. **CMV $7. - $9. MB.**

1975 TEAM LEADER PIN
(Left) Gold with indented letters. Given to team leaders. **CMV $7., $9. MB.**

1977 SALES ACHIEVEMENT AWARD PENDANT
1" gold pendant with 18" chain. Says 1977 Avon Sales Achievement Award & 4A design on other side. Came in white Avon box. Given to top 10% of sales Reps. in each division. **CMV $20. MB.** Same pendant slightly larger - came in blue box. **CMV $25. MB.**

1979 SALES ACHIEVEMENT AWARD
Solid bronze with Oak Tree on front with "District Manager Quarterly Sales Achievement Award - Avon" 4A symbol on back. Given to managers only. **CMV $50.**

1980 RUNNING CIRCUIT AVON MEDAL
2 1/4" medal has red, white and blue ribbon & medal says "Avon International Running Circuit." Given to people who ran in Avon Running Circuit. **CMV $40.**

1968 FIELD OPERATIONS AWARD
Solid brass, Avon 4A emblem on front. Field operations seminar on back. Given to managers in Pasadena branch in Better Way program. **CMV $55.**

1960 GOLF LEAGUE CHARM
1960 on back. Front has Avon League with 4A design & golfer. Solid brass. Given to Avon plant employees, Pasadena branch, for playing golf tournament. **CMV $40.**

1981 PRESIDENT'S CLUB MEN'S POCKET WATCH AWARD
Gold tone Swiss made 17 jewel watch. Avon on face of watch, metal face cover. Given to male President's Club members. **CMV $150 MB.**

1982 PRESIDENT'S SALES CHALLENGE AWARD WATCH
Black face, Avon Quartz & small diamond on 12 on face. Gold tone case. Black lizard strap. 1 top rep in each district won. Came in Avon gray felt case & outer sleeve. **CMV $100 MB & sleeve.**
Same watch only gold face watch & no diamond & black lizard look leather strap in tan felt Avon case & outer sleeve. 20 given in each district to Presidents Club reps only. **CMV $50 MB sleeve.**

CLOCK 20 YEAR AWARD 1978
(left) Small brass Tiffany & Co. Quartz clock. Top engraved "Avon 20 years & winners initials". Given to Avon managers for 20 years service. **CMV $75.**

CLOCK AUGUST CONFERENCE AWARD 1978
(right) Brass Relide 400 electronic clock. Given to managers for going to August Conference 1978, bottom engraved. **CMV $50.**

CIRCLE OF EXCELLENCE AWARD CLOCK 1982
Clear lucite digital clock with engraved name of winning Avon manager. Is not marked Avon. **CMV $50.**

PRESIDENTS CLUB CARD CASE AWARD 1982
Silver plated card case in Tiffany box & felt bag. Engraved on case "Presidents Club & 4A design". **CMV $35 MB.**

NEWARK FIRST AWARD CLOCK 1973
Alfry electric clock, black face, white painted over brass. Back side says "Newark First 1973" plus owners initials. Given to district supervisors. **CMV $40.**

1986 HONOR SOCIETY CLOCK
Small Lucite quartz clock given for selling $15,000 in Avon. **CMV $20.**

CIRCLE OF EXCELLENCE HOUR GLASS AWARD 1981
Tall brass hour glass C of E. 1981 on top. **CMV $50.**

40th AVON ANNIVERSARY CLOCK AWARD 1981
Hamilton Quartz clock, glass dome, Avon 40th name plate on base for 40 years of service. **CMV $175.**

CUSTOMER SERVICE AWARD CLOCK 1980
(left) Brass Tiffany & Co. clock given to Avon managers. Engraved on top "Avon Customer Service Award Conference 1980". Comes in Tiffany box & felt bag. **CMV $100.**

MILLION DOLLAR INCREASE AWARD CLOCK 1981
(right) Gold tone round Seth Thomas alarm clock. Given to managers for 1 million dollar increase in sales. Engraved on back side "Our First Million $ Increase". **CMV $65.**

CLOCK - FIELD OPERATION SEMINAR 1970
(Left) Brass Relide 7 jewel clock. **CMV $50.**

CLOCK - SUMMER SHAPE UP AWARD 1970
(Right) Brass Linder clock - top inscribed "Summer Shape Up Award." **CMV $75.**

SELLATHON CLOCK AWARD 1981
Mirrow Clock. **CMV $20.**

CLOCK SPEEDWAY DIVISION AWARD 1978
For outstanding sales. **CMV $35.**
SALES CLUB AWARD 1977
$100,000 sales increase plaque. Atlanta Branch. **CMV $15.**

HEAT CLOCK AWARD 1981
(Left) Clear lucite - red face - Avon on front.
CMV $25.
CLOCK PICTURE FRAME AWARD 1983
(Right) Clear lucite, purple & red clock face.
Avon on front. **CMV $25.**

CLOCK "WE'RE HOT" AWARD 1982
White plastic Isis quartz battery clock. **CMV $75.**
CLOCK "AVON" AWARD 1982
White plastic Isis electric clock. Face is red & marked Avon. **CMV $75.**

25 YEAR WATCH BAUME & MERCIER AWARD
Gold case watch. Given for 25 year Avon service. Back inscribed "Avon - 25 years."
CMV $75. plus value of used watch.

MEN'S PRESIDENTS SALES CHALLENGE WATCH AWARD 1982
(Left) Gold tone case & face marked Avon. Black strap. Avon box. **CMV $125. MB.**
WINNING IS BEAUTIFUL WATCH AWARD
(Right) Ladies quartz watch. Avon on face & on box. **CMV $25. MB.**

THE PRESIDENT'S CLUB

1974 PRESIDENT'S CLUB MEMBERS WATCH
Awarded to club members. Gold watch & hands with black strap. Box blue & white.
CMV $42.50 MB.

PRESIDENT'S CLUB 1981 WATCH WOMEN'S 1980
(left) gold tone 17 jewel watch on chain. Back says "President's Club 81". **CMV $50. MB.**
PRESIDENT'S CLUB 1981 MEN'S WATCH 1980
(right) gold tone pocket watch on chain given to male President's Club Reps. Inscribed on back "President's Club 1981". **CMV $125 MB.** No face cover, **CMV $125 MB.**

COLOR UP WATCH AWARD 1979
Le Jour Time Co. watch in gold tone case, white strap. Back side says "For the most colorful time of your life". Came in white box, sleeve & blue felt wrap. Given to Reps for customers served. **CMV $35 MB.**

PENDANT WATCH AWARD 1970
Gold tone watch on neck chain given to 6 Reps. in each district for top sales. Made by Sheffield. Also sold in stores. 9,000 watches given by Avon. **CMV $20.**

DIVISION MANAGERS AWARD CLOCK 1969
Sterling silver Seth Thomas electric clock. 4" square face, bottom says, "Divisional Managers Tribute 1969". **CMV $125 mint.**

Color never looked so good!

AVON MANAGERS ACHIEVEMENT CLOCK 1968
Box with 4A design & outer Avon sleeve. Clock set in top of brushed gold hour glass inscribed on bottom "1968 Avon Managers Achievement". **CMV $100 clock only. $135 MB with outer sleeve.**

TEAM LEADER WATCH 1977
Given to all Avon team leaders for Christmas 1977. 2 different. (left) for women, (right) for men. The cases are different and the difference in size of winding stem. Very few of the mens watches given. **CMV for womens $40 MB. CMV for mens $125 MB.**
MANAGERS WATCH 1977
Avon watch same as team leader watch only face says Avon in place of Team Leader & 4A symbol that rotates instead of Avon. Came in male & female size watch as above. **CMV $75 MB.**

OUTSTANDING SALES MANAGEMENT CLOCK AWARD 1977
Relide 15 jewel Swiss solid brass clock. Inscribed on top "In Recognition of Outstanding Sales Management - Third Quarter 1977". Given to No. 1 Avon manager in each division. **CMV $125.**

WATCH STICK PIN. MANAGERS 1979
(left) Gold tone 4A design on face. Given to managers. **CMV $75.**
FIELD SUPPORT PENDANT AWARD 1978
(right) 1/20 12K gold filled. Back is dated "1978 Field Support Manager". Given to managers. **CMV $30.**
NAT. DISTRICT MANAGER PANELIST PIN 1978
(bottom) Gold tone. Given to managers. **CMV $10.**

PRESIDENT'S CELEBRATION CLOCK AWARD 1974
Solid brass clock with "President's Celebration 1974" on face. Clock made by Relide, 15 jewels. Given to Avon managers. Came in plain box & pink felt bag. **CMV $150. mint.**

LIBERTY CLOCK AWARD 1977
Given to managers for 1 million dollar sales increase. Gold tone clock by Bulova. Inside slide clock cover says "To a Million Dollar Baby (name of manager) Division $1,000,000 Sales Increase 1977". Came in Bulova Americana Collection. **CMV $125.**

PRESIDENT'S CELEBRATION AWARD CLOCK 1976
Gold plastic & metal Westclock. 4 red roses on face. Was not made only for Avon. **CMV $12.**

ANTIQUE CAR GLASSES 1971
Eight different glasses picturing Stanley Steamer, Silver Duesenberg, Gold Cadillac, Sterling Six, Electric Charger, Packard Roadster, Touring T & Straight Eight. Selling 10 Avon cars won a set of 4 glasses. Selling 15 Avon cars won a set of 8 glasses. **CMV set of 4 $12, set of 8 $27.50 MB.**
ANTIQUE CAR PITCHER 1971
Reps. won this by having one person they recommended appointed as a representative. Also available in prize catalog for 1,400 points. 2 different pitchers. Rare one has silver Duesenberg & Stanley Steamer on it. **CMV $35, $40 MB.** Most of them have Straight Eight & Packard Roadster decal on it. **CMV $25, $30 MB.**

HOURS FOR EXCELLENCE CLOCK AWARD 1977
Gold label on top of Bulova travel alarm. Does not say Avon. Given to Reps. **CMV $15 MB.**

PIN "WATCH US GROW" AWARD 1981
(left) Green & white tie tac type pin . Says "Newark - Watch us Grow". Given to managers. **CMV $5.**

NEWARK NO. 1 1982 PENDANT AWARD 1982
(right) Gold tone 1/2" size pendant. Given to managers No. 1 in sales. Brown box. **CMV $20 MB.**

DIARY CLOCK 1968
Made by Seth Thomas. Gold, back opens & says "Avon Award", **CMV $40.**

KEY CHAIN SERVICE AWARD 10 YEARS 1970's
Gold tone key chain with blue stone in center of 4A design. Comes in Avon white & green lined box. Given to managers. **CMV $15 MB.**

ROSE ANNIVERSARY PITCHER AWARD 1980
9" tall clear glass with engraved rose. Given to Reps. for selling $800 in C14-15 1980. **CMV $25 MB.**

20 YEAR SERVICE AWARDS 1980's
Given for 20 years service. All are marked Avon or has 4A emblem on it. All from Tiffany. Choice of
STERLING SILVER PICTURE FRAME
9" high x 7" wide. **CMV $100.**
QUARTZ POLISHED BRASS CLOCK
2 1/2" square. **CMV $75.**
CRYSTAL CANDLESTICKS - TALL
9 1/4" high, 4 1/8" wide base. **CMV $75 set.**
CRYSTAL CANDLESTICKS - SHORT
4 1/2" high x 4 1/8" wide base. **CMV $75 set.**

HOP SKIP & JUMP MEDAL AWARD 1982
Gold tone medal with 4A design on one side & Hop, Skip & Jump Order Count Growth 1982 on back. Hangs on blue & yellow ribbon. **CMV $25.**

ROSE ANNIVERSARY GOBLETS AWARD 1980
6 1/2" high with engraved rose. Set of 4 for selling $400 in C14-15 1980. **CMV $15 set of 4.**

20 YEAR SERVICE AWARDS 1980's
Given for 20 years service. All are marked Avon or has 4A design. All come from Tiffany & Co. Choice of
CRYSTAL PITCHER
5 3/4" high. **CMV $60.**
CRYSTAL VASE
7 1/2" wide. **CMV $60.**
CRYSTAL TULIP WINE GLASSES
Set of 6, 8" high. **CMV $75 set.**

HEART PRESIDENTS SALES CHALLENGE AWARD 1982
Small clear crystal heart on gold tone ribbon pin. Maroon velvet Avon box & outer sleeve. **CMV $10 MB with sleeve.**

PENDANT - PRESIDENTS CELEBRATION 1980
Sterling silver chain & pendant with 25 blue saphires around edge. Oak tree in center. Back says "The Presidents Celebration 1980 Avon". Given to 250 top managers in US, 1 per division. **CMV $200.**

ROSE STICK PIN AWARD 1981
Small Sterling silver rose. No markings in Tiffany & Co. turquoise box. Given to Avon reps for recruiting & sales goals. **CMV $25 MB.**

CIRCLE OF EXCELLENCE TRINKET BOX 1982
Small leaded glass box with Rose embossed on lid. Comes with 4A brass coin. Back says "Roman Holiday C of E 1982". Only given to Pasadena Branch managers. **CMV $35 box & coin.**

PRESIDENTS SALES COMPETITION JEWELRY AWARDS 1983
3 levels, all Sterling Silver made by Tiffany.
BRACELET
Given 10 to a district. **CMV $25 MB.**
PENDANT NECKLACE
Given 2 to a district. **CMV $35 MB.**
LAPEL PIN
Given to each rep in top sales group who met individual sales goals. **CMV $15 MB.**
Each comes in Tiffany box & Avon card.

20 YEAR SERVICE CLOCK AWARD 1980's
7" wide x 4 1/2" high Tiffany brass clock. Avon on top. Given for 30 years service at Avon. **CMV $75.**

30 YEAR SERVICE PEARL NECKLACE AWARD 1980's
17" long cultured pearl necklace with 14K gold Avon marked clasp. Given for 30 years service. Comes in blue holder from Tiffany. **CMV $100 mint.**

PRESIDENTS CLUB PIN AWARD 1981
Gold tone pin with 81 in center of 4A design cut out. **CMV $5 MB.**

DOOR KNOCKER TIE TAC AWARD 1970's
10K gold. Given to male executives at Avon. **CMV $60.**

TIE TAC MEN'S PRESIDENTS CLUB AWARD 1981-82
Gold tone 4A design Tie Tac given to men's Presidents Club. Comes in Avon box with 2 different backs as shown. **CMV $20 MB.**

FASHION HISTORY GLASSES AWARD 1980
Set of 6, 12 oz. glasses marked 1890's, 1920's, 1940's, 1950's, 1960's & 1970's. Given as set to Avon reps for signing up new Avon reps. **CMV $30 set.**

TEST DIVISION HEART PENDANT AWARD 1981
(left) Sterling silver & gold heart pendant & silver chain. Given to managers only in Tiffany & Co. box. **CMV $150 MB.**

ANNIE PENDANT MANAGERS 1982
(right) 14K gold filled pendant & chain. Back marked "I love you" & marked DM on side. Given to district managers. Came in gray Avon box with special card from Avon. **CMV $60 MB.**

15 YEAR SERVICE AWARDS 1980's
All are marked Avon or has 4A design. Each comes from Tiffany & design. Each comes from Tiffany & Co. Given for 15 years service at Avon. Choice of

STERLING SILVER PERPETUAL CALENDAR
6" wide, 4 1/4" high. **CMV $75.**

CRYSTAL DECANTER WITH STERLING SILVER TAG
11" high. **CMV $75.**

STERLING SILVER SALT & PEPPER SET
2 1/4" high. **CMV $75 set.**

STERLING SILVER PIN BOX
3" diameter. **CMV $75.**

ALBEE AWARDS GOLD & SILVER 1985
Gold tone Albee given 2 in each district. **CMV $100.**

SILVER TONE ALBEE
4 given in each district. Both have black bases & came in red felt bags. **CMV $75.**

ALBEE AWARDS - GOLD & SILVER 1986
Same as 1985 Albee's only base has "Avon 100 1886-1986" to match the gold tone or silver tone. **CMV $100 gold - $75 silver MB.**

ALBEE AWARD - 1987 GOLD & SILVER
Gold tone Albee only 2 given in each district. Comes with "PC 1987 Sales Excellence" plaque across base on both gold & silver. **CMV $100.**

SILVER TONE ALBEE
Only 4 given in each district. **CMV $75.**

ALBEE AWARD 1987
Porcelain figurine given to Presidents Club Reps. Green dress. **CMV $85.**

ALBEE FIGURINE AWARD 1985
Hand painted porcelain. **CMV $75.**

ALBEE FIGURINE AWARD 1986
Fine porcelain. Special designed for Avon 100 Anniversary. For top reps only. **CMV $85.**

LEFT TO RIGHT
ALBEE AWARD NO. 1 1978
Porcelain figurine 8 1/2" high in honor of the 1st Avon lady of 1886, Mrs. P.F.E. Albee. Given to top Reps. in sales in each district. Pink umbrella is also porcelain. **CMV $125 MB.**
ALBEE AWARD NO. 2 1979
Hand painted porcelain figurine of the 1st Avon Rep. of 1886. 2nd in a series. Given to President's Club Reps. for outstanding sales. Colors are blue and pink. **CMV $100 MB.**
ALBEE AWARD - CANADA 1979
Is the same as 1978 Albee issued in U.S. only the bottom printing is in French & English & dated 1979. **CMV $125 mint.**
ALBEE AWARD NO. 3 1980
3rd in the Albee series. Given to President's Club Reps. only. **CMV $100 MB.**
ALBEE AWARD NO. 4 1981
4th in the Albee series. Given to President's Club Reps. only. **CMV $50 MB.**

ALBEE AWARD 1982
5th in a series given to President's Club members for sales of $7,000 in 1 year. **CMV $50.**

ALBEE FIGURINE AWARD 1984
Hand painted porcelain. Given to P.C. Reps. **CMV $65.**

WOMEN OF ACHIEVEMENT AWARD 1961
(Left) Painted ceramic figure of 1886 sales lady. One given in each district for highest sales. Came with stained walnut base & gold plaque inscribed "Avon Woman of Achievement Award". Printed on bottom of figure "Imported Expressly for Avon Products, Inc. Made in West Germany". **CMV $300. $325 MB.**

WOMEN OF ACHIEVEMENT AWARD 1969
(Right) White ceramic figure much the same as 1961 model. Base is tall & of white wood with gold trim. Printed on bottom of figure "Imported Expressly for Avon Products, Inc. Made in Western Germany Dresden Art". Brass plaque on base (not shown) says "Presented to. . .for Outstanding Contribution to the Better Way". **CMV $275. $325 MB.**

ALBEE FIGURINE AWARD 1983
Purple dress lady given to all Presidents Club reps for top sales. **CMV $70 MB.**

LADY OF ACHIEVEMENT TEST 1961
(Right) Pictured on right is smaller size original artwork test figurine for 1961 Lady of Achievement Award. Stands 7" high. Rare. Was not sold or given out by Avon. No price established. Used by factory only.

FIGURINE AWARD 1973

Awarded to each representative in district with greatest total sales increase. Made by Hummel, numbered & says "Made for Avon" on bottom. "Figurine 8" sits on white marble base with glass dome. **CMV $200. $225 MB.**

PRECIOUS MOMENTS CHRISTMAS MOUSE 1980

(Right) Given to Avon Reps. for signing up 2 new Avon Reps. **CMV $55 MB.**

PRECIOUS MOMENTS DISPLAY POSTER 1980

(Left) Used by managers C18-80. **CMV $5 mint.**

GOING AVON CALLING AWARD 1982

Yellow ceramic car with rabbit in pink, green base. Given to reps for Recommendation prize. **CMV $50 MB.**

FIRST LADY PORCELAIN FIGURINE 1976

Blue, white & pink porcelain made in Spain. Given to President's Club members only for outstanding sales in 90th Anniversary celebration. **CMV $45 MB.**

COLLECTORS CORNER FIGURINE AWARD 1982

Cherished Moments Collection mouse figurine. Given to 25 Reps. for top sales in Campaign 8, 1982 in each district. **CMV $40 MB.**

COME RAIN OR SHINE AWARD 1983

Ceramic Cherished Moments Rabbit with screw on ceramic umbrella. Given to reps for sales goals. 1st of 3 levels. **CMV $35 MB.**

LLADRO PORCELAIN LADY DIVISION MANAGER AWARD 1975

12 1/2" lady figurine made by Lladro in Spain. Comes with detachable porcelain umbrella. Given to division managers only. Dose not say Avon. Same figurine can also be purchased in fine stores. **CMV not eatablished**

PRECIOUS MOMENTS AWARD 1980

Rabbit figurine marked on bottom "President's Club Luncheon 1980". Given to Reps. at President's Club Luncheon only. **CMV $20 MB.**

PRECIOUS MOMENTS AWARD SET 1980

Set of 3 rabbit figurines given to Reps. for top sales. No. 1 is "Ready for an Avon Day". **CMV $25.**
No. 2 is "My first call". **CMV $35.**
No. 3 is "Which shade do you prefer". **CMV $60.**
Set of 3 CMV $110. Made in Japan only for Avon.

SMALL TREASURE CHERISHED MOMENTS MINIS AWARD 1982
Pink box holds 3 mini rabbit ceramic figurines. Given to reps for Step 4 sales goals. **CMV $30 MB set.**

WE DID IT TOGETHER AWARD 1985
2 rabbit ceramic figurine in Cherished Moments Award series to Reps. **CMV $80. MB.**

PRESIDENT'S AWARD PERFUME 1963
Clear glass with stopper, silver 4A tag & string. Given to national winners in each division for President's Campaign, 1963. Box silver & white base with clear plastic lid. Bottom label on bottle says "Occur! Perfume Avon Products, Inc. N.Y., N.Y. contains 1 fl. oz.". **CMV $200 bottle only. $250 MB with label & tag.** Also came in 1/2 oz. size with gold neck 4A tag. Please write Bud Hastin if you know when and for what the 1/2 oz. size was given for.

SMALL TREASURES CURRIER & IVES MINIS AWARDS 1982
Pink box holds mini ceramic Tea Set. Given to reps for Step 2 of sales goal. Made in Japan. **CMV $25 MB set.**

SMALL TREASURES ALBEE MINIATURES 1982
Pink box holds mini Albee figurines of number 2,3 & 4 Albee Awards. Given to Avon reps for 5th Step sales goal. **CMV $35 MB set.**

PERFUME - CIRCLE OF EXCELLENCE 1978
1 oz. glass stopper bottle, made in France. Paper neck tag says "Made Exclusively For You. Circle of Excellence 1978". **CMV $100 mint.**

OCTOBER 8 AWARD 1951
1 dram Forever Spring Perfume, smooth gold cap & bottle. Given to each representative sending an order in campaign 12, 1951. **CMV $40 MB.**

REPRESENTATIVE CHRISTMAS GIFT 1975
Clear glass in blue box. Reproduction of Trailing Arbutus Powder Sachet. **CMV $15 MB.**

SMALL TREASURE MINI ROSE AWARD 1982
Pink box holds small green leaf & pink ceramic rose. "The Avon Rose" on base, made in Taiwan. Given to reps for Step 1 of sales goal. **CMV $5 MB.**

CHRISTMAS GIFT PERFUME 1963
Given to Avon sales ladies for Christmas. The bottle at left is same as the one sealed in gold plastic container with green tassel & red ribbon. 4-10 oz. Christmas gift given to all representatives submitting an order in Dec. 1963. **CMV $40 complete. Bottle only $15.**

AVON 100 THOUSANDAIRE CLUB PIN 1986
Red, white & gold lapel pin. Came with numbers to hang below. Marked 1886-1986. **CMV $10.** No numbers.
1985 - Same pin only blue border design. **CMV $10.**

TASHA TEAM LEADER COLOGNE AWARD 1979
1.8 oz. spray cologne. Says "Team Leader 1979" in gold letters on front. Came in gold wrapped box with maroon color ribbon. **CMV $12.50 MB.**
TASHA "GO AHEAD AND DREAM" MANAGERS GIFT
Same bottle as above only "Go Ahead & Dream" in gold letters on face of bottle for managers at Christmas Conference. **CMV $25. MB.**

GOLDEN SLIPPER AWARD 1959
All gold metal slipper with red stone in toe & clear plastic heel. 1/2 oz. glass stoppered perfume bottle fits in slipper toe . No Avon name on shoe but has paper label on bottom of bottle saying "73rd Anniversary. Avon Products, Inc." Given to each representative in the winning group of each branch for top sales. **CMV $200 slipper & bottle with label. $250 MB.**

MANAGERS GIFT PERFUME 1950
(Left) 1/2 oz. glass stoppered bottle in plastic case. Given to managers to help introduce To A Wild Rose. Paper label on bottom reads "Perfume Avon Products, Inc., Distributor, New York, Montreal, Vol. 1/2 oz.". Came with neck tassel. **CMV $250 mint, in plastic case.**
PRESIDENT'S AWARD CELEBRATION PERFUME 1955
(Right) 1/2 oz. perfume, glass stopper. Given to the winning team members for top sales. **CMV $100 BO mint. $140 MB.**

GREAT OAK CARD CASE 1987
(Left) Brass. **CMV $5.**
HONOR SOCIETY CARD CASE 1985
(Right) Brass card case. **CMV $10.**

AVON 100 AWARD PINS 1986
Small gold tone on left with black letters. **CMV $10.**
Small silver tone with black letters. **CMV $10.**
TRENDSETTER PIN AWARD 1984
Gold tone pin. **CMV $10.**

AVON 100 WATCH AWARD 1986
Black face quartz watch with Avon 100 on face - brown leather grain strap. Given to managers in Newark Branch. **CMV $65.**
AVON 100 PRESIDENT'S CLUB PIN 1986
Gold tone pin. Given to Reps. in black velvet Avon box. **CMV $15. MB.**
HONOR SOCIETY PIN 1986-87
Same as President's Club only came with Honor Society on bottom. **CMV $24.**

G.S.L. #1 PIN 1983
Red Pin. **CMV $10.**
AVON 100 TRENDSETTER PIN 1986
Blue, white & gold. **CMV $15.**
NIGHT MAGIC PIN 1987
CMV $2.
THOUSANDAIRE CLUB PIN 1985
Blue & white enamel. CMV with numbers up to 4. **CMV $10.** Add $5 for each number up to 4.
PEACH TREE PIN 1985
CMV $25.
AVON $1000 CLUB PIN 1986
CMV $15.
AVON LOVES ORDERS HEART PIN 1981
CMV $15.

PURSE OF GOLD AWARD 1948
Cardboard tube contained 8 samples of Golden Promise. CMV in packages shown. Given to each representative sending in an order at the close of campaign 3. **CMV $30.**

AVON 100 GLASSES 1986
Set of 4 drinking glasses. Embossed Avon 100. **CMV $15. Set.**

AVON 100 DESK CADDY
Clear plastic with Avon 100 1886 - 1986 or caddy - white pen & note paper. Given to Managers. **CMV $15.**

AVON 100 ALBEE MIRROR 1986
13" x 17" gold tone frame mirror. 1886 - 1986 & 1st Avon Rep embossed on mirror. Given to managers at August Conference & also given for sponsorship. **CMV $60.**

AVON 100 MANAGERS COMPACT AWARD 1986
Gold tone. Inscribed on back "Avon Centennial 1986 Dist. Sales Managers Conference." **CMV $40.**

AVON 100 BINOCULARS AWARD 1986
7 x 35 Binolux - Black. Given to Reps. Case says Avon 100. **CMV $75.**
AVON 100 TOTE BAG AWARD 1986
White canvas bag trimmed in blue & red. Given to people on trip to New York for 100 year celebration. **CMV $25.**
AVON 100 COFFEE CUP AWARD 1986
Blue ceramic cup. Avon 100 1886 - 1986 in gold letters. Given to representatives. **CMV $8.**

AVON 100 COFFEE MUG PASADENA 1986
White glass cup. Avon 100 on front. **CMV $10.**
AVON 100 PASADENA #1 AWARD 1986
Wood base, clear lucite Avon 100 plaque. **CMV $15.**

AVON 100 CLOCK AWARD 1986
Clear lucite clock. Black face & letters. Given to Managers. **CMV $35.**

AVON 100 CALCULATOR 1986
Gold tone face Avon 1886 - 1986. Given to Managers. **CMV $10.**
AVON 100 BELL 1986
Clear glass bell, 5 3/4" high. Avon 100 embossed. **CMV $25.**

CENTENNIAL ARCH WATCH 1986
Enamelled arch stand with Avon face quartz pocket watch. Can be hung on chain around neck. Given to 10 top reps in each division for 100th anniversary. Comes in Avon 100 pink box & white Avon sleeve. **CMV $100.**

AVON 100 LEMONADE SET 1986
White plastic pitcher & 4 plastic Avon 100 glasses. **CMV $20.**

AVON 100 LIBERTY APRON 1986
Small red apron. White design from N.Y. Liberty Weekend. **CMV $25.**

AVON 100 HEAD BAND 1986
White head band. 100 years of beauty. **CMV $10.**

AVON 100 YEARS BAG CLOSER 1986
White plastic strip bag fastener. **CMV $1.**

AVON 100 CUP 1986
Plastic coffee cup. Look how good we look now. **CMV $1.**

AVON 100 LIBERTY WEEKEND T-SHIRT 1986
White T-shirt with collar. Given to workers on 4th of July Celebration in N.Y. **CMV $15.**

CENTENNIAL JEWELRY CASE AWARD 1986
8 3/4" square brass box. Given to Reps. **CMV $25.**

CENTENNIAL JEWELRY COLLECTION AWARDS 1986
All gold tone & rhinestones. Given to Reps.
Pin **CMV $20.**
Earrings **CMV $25.**
Bracelet **CMV $30.**
Necklace **CMV $40.**

AVON NAME PLATE 1986
Gray & white plastic cork board. **CMV $2.**

100 YEAR ZIP LOCK FOR BAGS 1986
White & red letters. **CMV $2.**

PENS 1986
2 different. Both white, 1 Parker, 1 Shaffer. **CMV $15. ea.**

AVON 100 PLATE AWARD 1986
White porcelain plate. Back says C26 - 1985 Limited Edition. Pasadena Branch only. **CMV $25.**

AVON 100 LICENSE PLATE 1986
1886 - 1986

AVON LICENSE PLATE 1986
White & red letters. **CMV both $2.**

I LOVE AVON LICENSE PLATE FRAME
White frame given to Reps. **CMV $5.**

CHECK BOOK COVER 1986
White plastic 1886 - 1986. Given to Avon Reps. **CMV $3.**

AVON 100 T-SHIRT AWARD 1986
White shirt, black letters, red trim. **CMV $10.**

NEWARK AVON FAMILY T-SHIRT AWARD 1987
White shirt, red design for Newark branch employees. **CMV $10.**

PRESIDENTS CLUB BIRTHDAY GIFT 1986
Chrome picture from "Avon 100" & note from James Preston Avon President. **CMV $8.**

MEDAL - 4A PENDANT AWARD 1980
Silver tone & black 4A design about 2 1/2" on red, white & blue neck ribbon. Given to managers only. Back says "You are a winner 1980" & name. **CMV $20.**

AVON 100 ROSE KEY CHAIN PENDANT 1986
Pink or gray Avon 100 box & sleeve has gold tone key chain & chain to use as necklace. Back says "Avon 1886-1986". Given to top 10 Reps. **CMV $15.**

"AVON 100" PILL BOX AWARD 1986
Small chrome box "Avon 100" on lid. Given at Presidents Club luncheon. **CMV $15.**

AVON 100 GOLD PIN AWARD 1986
14K gold. Small diamond. Given to Division Managers. **CMV $100.**

LIBERTY DIVISION PIN 1986
Blue & gold tone lapel pin. Status of liberty on face. Given to reps. **CMV $10.**

AVON 100 AWARD PINS 1986
Left is Newark branch Managers pins 14K gold. Has hook on back to wear as necklace. Back says Newark 1886-1986 14 K. **CMV $75. MB.**
Center is Newark branch. Gold tone. Larger in size. Very thin. **CMV $20.**
Right is Morton Grove Pin. Thicker gold tone. Design is different on all 3. **CMV $10.**

AWARD PINS MISC. 1986
AVON 2000 PIN
Black, white & gold. **CMV $20.**
AVON 100 PIN LARGE
1886-1986 - Black, red & gold. **CMV $25.**
AVON MEMBER PIN
Blue, black & gold. **CMV $10.**
AVON PIN
Black, red & gold. **CMV $10.**
AVON 100 PIN
Small black, red & gold. **CMV $10.**
AVON 100 PIN
Blue, white & red. **CMV $10.**
I LOVE AVON PIN
Black, red & gold. **CMV $10.**

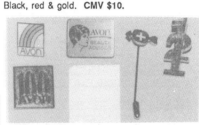

AVON RAINBOW PIN 1986
CMV $20.
AVON BEAUTY ADVISOR PIN 1970s
CMV $15.
ARROW. APPLE PIN 1986
Red apple, white cross stick pin. **CMV $10.**
1-2 PIN 1970s
Gold tone. **CMV $25.**
AVON 100 PIN
Gold tone. **CMV $10.**

AVON 100 DIVISION SALES MEDALLIONS 1986
Gold tone, siver tone & bronze tone medallions. Each say PC-Avon 100. Given in each division, 1 gold, 4 silver & 5 bronze.
CMV $100. gold
CMV $85. silver
CMV $70. bronze

PAPERWEIGHT CHRISTMAS IS FOR CHILDREN 1986
Avon - 1986 embossed clear glass. Given to Managers only at 6 places in U.S. **CMV $25.**

PAPERWEIGHT - GREAT OAK - AWARD 1981
Clear glass Avon, Kansas City #1-1981 etched on bottom. **CMV $50.**

GIVE N GAIN PRIZE 1970
10 3/4" high, 4" in diameter. A rose, butterfly and lady bug are etched in glass. Given to Avon ladies as prize. This was also sold in stores to public. Came in plain box with Avon stamped on it. Made by Abilities. **CMV $20 MB.**

RENAULT CAR GLASS 1971
(Right) Some sets ca--me with this Renault car in set. Rare. **CMV $15.**

AVON 100 MIRROR 1986
Red plastic holder & Avon printed on mirror. **CMV $2.**

AVON 100 MATCHES 1986
Silver box. **CMV $1.**

RECOGNITION AWARD PIN 1974
About 1" size gold tone. Given to branch employees, rare. **CMV $35.**

REPRESENTATIVE OF THE MONTH PIN 1983-84
(Right) gold tone pin given to reps each month for meeting goals for the month. 2 in each district. Passed on to new rep each month. **CMV $10.**

45TH ANNIVERSARY VASE AWARD 1970'S
9 3/4" high x 4" across. Atlantis engraved "45th Avon Anniversary". Given for 45 years of Avon service. **CMV $200.**

PRESIDENTS DAY BOWL "LARGE" AWARD 1964
12 1/4" Oneida silver plate bowl. Center of bowl engraved with big 4A design & says "Presidents Day 1964 - Low Net." **CMV $45.**

PRESIDENTS DAY BOWL "SMALL" AWARD 1964
9 1/8" Oneida bowl as above. Center says "Presidents Day 1964 - Closest to Pin", 4A design. **CMV $40.**

SUBTLE REFLECTIONS HEART FLOWER VASE & FLOWERS 1982
Small heart shape lucite vase & silk flowers with Avon tag. Given to Presidents Club reps. Does not say Avon. **CMV $8.**

GOLDEN BELL COLLECTION AWARDS 1983
4 small brass bells given for meeting sales goals for C23, C24, C25, 1983. 1st bell has 4A design on top. 2nd bell has Acorn on top, 3rd bell has Avon door knocker. 4th bell was given if all 3 bells were won in all 3 campaigns as a bonus. 4th bell has a rose on top. **CMV 1st bell $10, 2nd bell $10, 3rd bell $15, 4th bell $20. MB.** Add $5. to set if in plain boxes. For managers.

CIRCLE OF EXCELLENCE CUP AWARD 1976
Polished pewter cup says "C of E 1976" engraved on side. Given to Circle managers only. **CMV $35.**

VALENTINE ATOMIZER AWARD 1980
Small clear crystal bottle, chrome top & red squeeze bulb. Given to team leaders & district manager. TL on bottom & DM. **CMV $10, TL bottle MB. CMV $20, DM bottle MB.**

ROSE ANNIVERSARY LUNCHEON PLATES AWARD 1980
Set of 4 clear glass 8" plates with engraved rose in center. Given to Reps. for selling $600 in C14-15 1980. **CMV $20 set of 4 plates.**

AVON LADY STEMWARE GLASSES AWARDS 1975
C-20 1975. Set of 6, 10 oz. & 6, 6 oz. glasses with 1st Avon Lady design. 1 set given to all Reps. in the winning district for top sales. **CMV set $50 MB.**

GREAT AMERICAN SELLATHON CHAMPAGNE GLASS 1981
Given to team leaders and managers. December 1981 on trip to Hawaii. **CMV $15.**

INITIAL GLASS AWARD 1970

Campaign 12 & 13, 1970. Reps. won the glasses and President's Club members won the goblets with initial of their choice for reaching sales of their choice or reaching sales goals in each campaign. The coasters were won by both for reaching sales goals both campaigns. **CMV on coasters $3, glasses $3, goblets $4 each.**

ULTRA CRYSTAL EVENT GLASS AWARD 1981

Tiffany & Co. box holds 2 engraved glasses. Given to Reps. who met sales goal by drawing for winner at sales meeting. **CMV $50 set MB.**

SALES ACHIEVEMENT AWARD 1979

Small gold tone trophy with wood base. Says "Avon Sales Achievement Award." **CMV $10.**

HONOR SOCIETY GOBLET 1987

Clear glass with black 4A design. Given to top reps. **CMV $15.**

1st DIVISION GLASS AWARD 1977

Lead crystal champagne glass given to No. 1 division Avon managers. **CMV $30.**

WINE GLASS FOR MANAGERS 1975

Yellow painted letters say "Avon Espana 1975". Came in 1975 Osborne Cream Sherry. Managers Gift Set on trip to Spain. **CMV $37.50.**

CIRCLE OF EXCELLENCE WINE GLASS 1979

Given to managers. Glass embossed "C of E 1979". Came in sets of 2 glasses. **CMV $25 each glass.**

CIRCLE OF EXCELLENCE CHAMPAGNE GLASS 1980

"C of E 1980" embossed on glass. Given to managers only in sets of 2 glasses. **CMV $25 each glass.**

GOLD PANNER TROPHY 1981

Metal gold panner. Plaque says "Sierra Division Achievement Break the Bank" 4A - 1981. Given to managers. **CMV $50.**

PASADENA BRANCH WINE GLASS 1974

No. 1 in sales. 429 given. "19 Avon 74 Pasadena Branch" on glasses. **CMV $15.**

CIRCLE OF EXCELLENCE GLASS 1974

Pasadena Branch No. 1 in sales C of E. Made by Fostoria, very thin glass. Only 30 given to managers. "C of E 1974" on side of glass. **CMV $30.** Same glass also came in 1973. Same CMV.

TEAM ACHIEVEMENT AWARD 1977

Goblet given in 1st and 3rd quarters to top team in each district. Came in white embossed Avon box. **CMV $15. each quarter. MB.**

$100,000 TROPHY AWARD 1982

Glass dome holds $100,000 of chopped up U.S. money. Says $100,000 on dome. Wood base. Brass plaque from Avon 4A design given to 1 manager in Pasadena Branch. **CMV $50.**

PICTURE FRAME RETIREMENT 1970s - 1980s

Sterling silver picture frame 8 x 10. Given to managers for retirement. Not marked Avon. Came with letters from Avon. **CMV $75.**

TRIBUTE VASE 1987

8" high clear glass vase. Embossed "Tribute 1987." Given to P.C. Reps only. **CMV $10.**

PRESIDENTS CLUB SILVER BASKET 1987

5 1/2" high silver plated basket. Has "PC Avon Presidents Club" tag attached. Given only to P.C. Reps only. **CMV $15.**

FOSTERIA COIN GLASS BUD VASE AWARD 1970s

8" high in Avon box. **CMV $30. MB**

FOSTERIA COIN GLASSES SALT & PEPPER SHAKER AWARDS 1970s

Came with Avon literature. **CMV $15. set.**

NEWARK #1 CRYSTAL BOX AWARD 1985-86

Lead crystal box with Newark with a heart 1985-1986 #1 embossed on glass lid. Given to managers in blue box. **CMV $25.**

CHRISTMAS GIFT TO REPS 1986

Lead crystal dish from France given to all reps at Christmas in green box. **CMV $10. MB** Given to Presidents Club Members in red P.C. box. **CMV $15. MB**

AVON 100 CHAMPAGNE AWARD 1986

1886-1986 Avon 100 label. Given to Honor Society Reps. **CMV $25.**

GLASS CASTLE AWARD 1984

Blown glass castle. **CMV $18.**

ALL YOU CAN BE CANDY DISH AWARD 1984

Clear glass full of candy. Given to managers 1984. **CMV $15.**

COMBOURG CRYSTAL AWARDS 1985

Each given to P.C. Reps for sales goals. Crystal made in France not just for Avon.
CMV Decanter $25.
Set of 6 Champagne Glasses $20.
Set of 6 Wine Glasses $20.
Crystal & Chrome Ice Bucket $20.

PRESIDENTS SALES CHALLENGE FLOWER AWARD 1983

Glass & brass box holds orchid. Label on top. Given to Reps for trip to Hawaii. **CMV $45.**

CIRCLE OF EXCELLENCE WINE AWARD 1981

Bottle of Abbey Chenin Blanc wine. Special black & gold label for Circle of Excellence 1981. **CMV $40. unopened.**

REPRESENTATIVE X-MAS GIFT 1983

(Left) 3" ceramic box with dove on top. Bottom says "Holiday Greetings Avon 1983". Given to all avon Reps. **CMV $10. MB.**

REPRESENTATIVE X-MAS GIFT 1984

Heavy clear glass vase with snowflakes etching. Bottom says "Happy Holidays Avon 1984." Came in nice silver box & outter sleeve. **CMV $20. MB.**

FRESH FLOWER STONEWARE AWARDS 1987

White stoneware dishes, blue design. Won for sales in C1-2-3-87.
Step 1 - 4 coffee cups. **CMV $12.**
Step 2 - 4 salad plates 8 1/8" diameter. **CMV $15.**
Step 3 - 4 bowls 7" across. **CMV $18.**
Step 4 - 4 dinner plates 10 1/2". **CMV $20.**
Step 5 - Coffee pot, sugar & creamer. **CMV $30.**

CERAMIC SAC AWARD 1986

White ceramic bag. Given to reps in U.S. & Canada. **CMV $20.**

SALES EXCELLENCE AWARD 1983

Lead crystal glass box. Inscribed "Sales Excellence Award 1983 Avon President's Sales Competition." **CMV $50.**

AVON 100 CERAMIC BOX 1986

White porcelain. Avon 100 front & back. 4A on top in red. **CMV $35.**

FRONT PAGE TUMBLERS 1971

14 oz. tumblers with Reps. name printed on "front page" of glass. Given for having a person reccommended as a Rep. appointed. **CMV $25 set of 8 MB.**

YOU MAKE ME SMILE GLASSES AWARDS 1978

Set of 6 glasses made only for Avon given to Avon Reps. for signing up a new Avon lady. **CMV $12 set MB.**

SPIRIT OF '76 CROCK SET AWARDS 1974

(Left) Multipurpose Pitcher - earned for $150 in sales. **CMV $7 MB.**
(Center) Bean Pot Casserole - earned for $200 in sales. **CMV $14 MB.**
(Right) Goodies Jar - earned for $300 in sales. **CMV $18 MB.**

CRYSTAL SALAD BOWL AWARD 1956

7 1/2" cut glass with silverplate edge. Comes with serving fork & spoon & card from Avon. Given to Reps. during 70th Anniversary Celebration in 1956. Made by Fina. **CMV $55 complete.**

SUGAR & CREAMER AWARD 1952

Sterling silver base and glass tops. Given to Avon Reps. in 1952. White and silver stiped box. Made by Fina. **CMV $55 set MB.**

CANDY DISH SET AWARD 1952

Sterling silver base by Fina. Glass screw on tops. Given to Avon Reps. in 1952. Came in plain white box. **CMV $55.**

PEOPLE WHO LIKE PEOPLE PRIZE PROGRAM AWARDS 1972

3rd level prize is a set of 8 10 oz. crystal and silver glasses. Won by Reps. for meeting 3rd level sales goals. Was not made only for Avon. **CMV $25 set MB.**

CRYSTAL CANDLE HOLDERS 1980

10" high clear crystal. Given to Reps. for 30 years continuous service. Base is inscribed "30th Avon Anniversary". **CMV $125 pair.**

PEOPLE WHO LIKE PEOPLE PRIZE PROGRAM AWARDS 1972
4th level prize is a 9" diameter & 6" high silver base and trim crystal footed fruit bow. Won by Reps. for meeting 4th & final level sales goals. Was not made only for Avon. **CMV $25 MB.**

PEOPLE WHO LIKE PEOPLE PRIZE PROGRAM AWARDS 1972
1st level prize. Walnut base with silver handle holds 3 crystal with silver trim 6 oz. bowls. Won by Reps. for meeting sales goals. Was not made only for Avon. **CMV $15 MB.**

PYRAMID PAPERWEIGHT AWARD 1981
Clear lucite with gold 4A design on bottom & 2 sides on top. Given to district managers only. **CMV $50.**

PEOPLE WHO LIKE PEOPLE PRIZE PROGRAM AWARDS 1972
2nd level prize is a 12 3/4" chip 'n dip serving set of crystal & silver trimmed. It comes with a 5" matching dip bowl in the center. Won by Reps. for meeting 2nd level sales goals. Was not made only for Avon. **CMV $15 MB.**

TIC TAC TOE APPLE SALAD SET AWARD 1973
(Left) 3 piece set, 10" clear glass apple bowl with William Rogers silver plated fork & spoon. Won for prize goal. Must be in Avon box with card. **CMV $10 MB.**

DIVIDED APPLE RELISH SET 1973
(Right) 3 piece set, 6" divided clear glass bowl with William Rogers silver plated fork & spoon. This bowl won by President's Club members only for prize goal. These items must be in the box with outlook and card, as they were not made only for Avon. **CMV $15 MB.**

CHRISTMAS CUP 1969
White glass mug. Avon on bottom. Given to district managers for Christmas. **CMV $30.**

CPC SALES MANAGERS GIFT 1909 - 1912
4" x 4" size, pressed crystal glass jar with Rogers Silver Plate lid. Given to each Rep. selling $50 in sales in December 1909 & 1912. The silver lid has an embossed floral design. **CMV $200 mint.**

AMERICAN HERITAGE AWARDS 1973
Set of glass crystal edged with silver. Given to Reps. in C-11, 1973. Consists of 10 7/8" relish dish. **CMV $20 MB.** Fruit bowl 7 1/8" high and 7 7/8" across. **CMV $20 MB.** Products were not made ony for Avon.

SCALLOPED SERVING DISH & SPOON PRIZE 1971
Pressed glass nut dish given to Reps. for meeting sales goals. Also available in local stores. **CMV $7 MB.**

SALES EXCELLENCE AWARD CUP 1977
6 1/2" high pewter cup. "4A design, Avon Sales Excellence Award 1977" on side of cup. Given to top 2% of sales Reps. in each division. **CMV $30 MB.**

MILLION DOLLAR INCREASE GOBLET
1978
(Left) Silver plated goblet given to all managers in top division for 1 million dollar increase in sales. **CMV $25.**

PORT O'CALL CANDY DISH & BAR
1977
(Right) China dish by IImoges - France & bar of French candy given to managers for meeting appointment goal. Box has gold label "Meet me at the lamp post, Port O'Call Pasadena". **CMV $10 MB.**

REPRESENTATIVE CHRISTMAS GIFT
1982
Small 4" porcelain dish made by Royal Worcester for Avon. Given to all Avon reps at Christmas 1982. Comes in green box with Avon card. **CMV $10 MB.**

WILD VIOLETS COLLECTION DESSERT BOWLS AWARDS 1984
Set of 6, 13.5 oz. dessert bowls. Clear glass with Violet flower design. Given to Avon reps for reaching level 3 of 4 sales goal levels. **CMV $15 MB set.**

ASH TRAY 1982
Used at Avon plants. **CMV $2.50.**

SMALL TREASURES FRAGRANCE BOTTLES IN MINIATURE AWARDS 1982
Pink box holds 3 mini size CPC reproductions with gold caps. Given to reps for Step 3 of sales goals. **CMV $15 MB.**

WILD VIOLETS COLLECTION PITCHER AWARDS 1984
Clear glass, Violet flower design. Given to Avon reps for level 1 of 4 levels. **CMV $12 MB.**

WILD VIOLETS COLLECTION WATER GLASSES 1984
Set of 6, 12 oz. clear glasss Violet flower design. Given to Avon reps for reaching level 2 of 4 levels. **CMV $12 MB set.**

WILD VIOLETS COLLECTION TRAY & SALAD PLATES 1984
11" x 17 1/2" white plastic tray & set of 6 clear glass salad plates with Violet flower design. Given to Avon reps for reaching level 4 of 4 sales goal levels. **CMV $20 set MB.**

TOWNHOUSE CANNISTER & COOKIE JAR SET AWARDS 1983
Given to reps for sales quota. 1st level, small, **CMV $10.** 2nd level, **CMV $20.** 3rd level, **CMV $30.** 4th level, Cookie Jar (right), **CMV $50,** or **CMV $90** entire set.

JOLLY SANTA AWARDS 1986
All white & red ceramic.
Level 1 - Candy jar 7 1/2" high. **CMV $10.**
Level 2 - Set of 4 Santa mugs. **CMV $15.**
Level 3 - Santa Plate. **CMV $20.**

CHRISTMAS GLASSES & TRAY AWARD 1985
Set of 6 12 oz. glasses with red & green X-mas tree design. CMV $20.00 MB set. Matching white ceramic 2 tier serving tray with brass handle. **CMV $15.00 MB.**

OSBORNE CREAM SHERRY MANAGERS GIFT SET 1975
Wine cask on box lid. Box holds 2 wine glasses with "Avon Espana 1975" painted in yellow, bottle of Osborne Cream Sherry with special label "Especially bottled for the 1974 members of the Circle of Excellence". This set was given to each manager on their C of E trip to Madrid, Spain. Only 200 sets given out. **CMV $130 set mint full.**

SALES ACHIEVEMENT MUG AWARD 1977
Pink rose on side and Sales Achievement 4th Quarter 1977 on other side. **CMV $10.**

ACHIEVEMENT AWARD MUG 1978
"1st Quarter 1978" on white ceramic mug given to team getting most new Avon ladies to sign up. **CMV $10.**

SPRINGDALE FOUNDERS CLUB COFFEE CUP AWARD 1979
(top) White glass cup given to all Plant employees who had worked from 1965 to 1979. Red letters. **CMV $15.**
COLOR UP AMERICA PEN 1979
(bottom) White, black & silver pen on brown leather neck cord. Given to managers. **CMV $10.**

PROSPECT COFFEE JAR & CUP AWARD 1977
Clear glass jar with green painted design on fromt says " 1886-Avon 1977". Filled with coffee beans. **CMV $20 jar only.** Coffee cup-came with jar in white box as set. Has Avon district manager 1977 on cup & other writings. **CMV $15 cup only.** Both given to Avon managers only.

MERRY CHRISTMAS MUG 1977
Short glass mug with green lettering on front. **CMV $8.**
CIRCLE OF EXCELLENCE MUG 1970'S
Pewter mug inscribed C of E Avon on front. **CMV $25.**

GOBLET-CIRCLE OF EXCELLENCE AWARD 1975
(left) 7 1/2" high sterling silver goblet. Given to C of E managers who went to Madrid, Spain 1975. Base says "Circle of Excellence, Madrid, 1975" **CMV $60.**
TEAM LEADER MUG AWARD 1976
(right) White glass mug. **CMV $17.50**

CIRCLE OF EXCELLENCE MUG AWARD 1978
Avon C of E District No. 1978 in red letters. Given to Reps. In winning districts. **CMV $25.**

QUEEN ELIZABETH CUP & SAUCER 1953
Avon 67th Anniversary celebration coincided with Queen Elizabeth Coronation. Awarded at a banquet for top organization. **CMV $80 mint.**

CURRIER & IVES SUGAR & CREAMER AWARD 1982
set given to Avon Reps. for signing up 1 new Avon Rep. **CMV $15 set.**

AWARD COMPACT 1966
(left) Sterling silver compact. Engraved on back "National Champion, President's Campaign, 1966". **CMV $17.**

AVON SUGAR BOWL CLUB 1960
(right) Awarded to sales ladies for getting new customers. **CMV $60.**

CURRIER & IVES 5 PIECES PLACE SETTING AWARD 1981-82
Each set has dinner plate, salad plate, cup & saucer, and soup bowl. Given to Avon Reps. for signing up 1 new Avon Rep. **CMV $25 set of 5 pieces.**
1977-81 Same set only marked **1977-81** on bottom of each piece in set. Only 300 sets got out in Newark Branch. **CMV with 77-81 bottom date $100 MB set.**

CURRIER & IVES TEA SET 1977-78
Set consists of plate, tea pot, sugar bowl & creamer. Avon Products, Inc. on bottom of each piece. Awarded to Avon Reps. for Distinquished Sales Achievement 1977. Plate-1st step. **CMV $6.50.** Sugar bowl & creamer-2nd step. **CMV $12.** Tea pot-3rd step. **CMV $17.50.** Cup& saucer-4th step. Saucer 1st issue marked 1977 on bottom 1978 issue has no date. Add $2 each piece for 1977 date. **CMV $35 set of 4.** Add $10 if writing on bottom is printed backwards for each piece.

MIKASA CHINA SET 1972
Candle holders & sugar/creamer set for reaching first prize goal. **CMV $5 each MB.** Beverage server for reaching second goal. **CMV $10 MB.** Eight cups & saucers for reaching third goal (to be won by President's Club members only). **CMV $4.** For each cup & saucer set. These items must be in Avon boxes with card or outlook as this set was not made just for Avon.

FOSTORIA SUGAR & CREAM SET AWARD 1970
From Fostoria glass, box says "Avon Cosmetics". Given to Reps for sales achievement. Design is from the Henry Ford Collection. **CMV $30 MB only.**

SILVER CANDLELIGHT SET GIFT 1972
Given to Reps. as a gift. Does not say Avon on set & was not made only for Avon. Can be bought in stores. Set has punch bowl & 2 goblets with silver rim. Box has Avon mailing label. **CMV $35 in Avon box.**

CURRIER & IVES COLLECTION AWARD 1977-78
Made only for Avon & stamped on bottom. Given to Avon. Reps. for meeting sales goals.
1st step - Dinner bell, **CMV $6.50 MB.**
2nd step - Butter dish, **CMV $12 MB.**
3rd step - Water pitcher 6 1/2" high. **CMV #17.50 MB.**
4th step - Cake plate 9 1/2" diam. **CMV $32.50 MB.** Add $10 each piece for bottom writing printed backwards.

PLATE AWARD "CPC" 1930'S
China plate about 9" has 2 deer on face, gold trim - "CPC Avon" on back. No information. **CMV $100.**

5 YEAR ANNIVERSARY PLATE
8 1/2" porcelian plate, "The Great Oak" for 5 year service to Avon. 1st issued 1987. **CMV $10 MB.**

10 YEAR ANNIVSERARY PLATE 1987 ON
8 1/2" porcelian plate. "The California Perfume Co." for 10 years service to Avon. 4 different plates issued starting in 1987. **CMV $15.**

15 YEAR ANNIVERSARY PLATE
8 1/2" porcelian plate. "The Avon Rose" on plate. Given for 15 years service. 1st issued 1987. **CMV $30 MB.**

20 YEAR ANNIVERSARY PLATE
8 1/2" porcelian plate. "The 1st Avon Representative" on plate. Given for 20 years service. Ist issued 1987. **CMV $40 MB.**

SPIRIT AVON AWARD PLATE 1986
7 1/4" clear glass plate. White lettering. 1 to a district. **CMV $35.**

25 YEAR SERVICE PLATE AWARD 1985 UP
8" Sterling Silver Plate. Inscribed "In Grateful Appreciation of Twenty Five Years of Loyal Service to Avon Customers. James Preston - President Avon Division." **CMV $75 in Tiffany bag & box.**

POSSET POT AWARD 1976
(left) 9" high stoneware. Bottom reads "Made in Brazil Exclusively for Avon Products, Inc.". **CMV $25.**

PITCHER & BOWL RECOMMENDATION PRIZE 1975-77
(right) Given for recommending someone, if appointed as a Rep. Has Avon on bottom of both pieces. **CMV $50 set.**

DECORATORS CHOICE PITCHER AND BOWL PRIZE 1977
Ceramic pitcher 10" high & bowl 15 1/4" across. Made only for Avon. Given to Reps. for signing up 1 new Avon Rep. **CMV $50.**

SALAD SET GIFT 1972
Given to Reps. as gifts. Does not say Avon and was not made only for Avon. Can be bought in stores. Came in plain box with Avon mailing label. Set has large salad bowl & 4 small ones & silver plated spoon & fork. **CMV $35 in Avon box.**

DISTINGUISHED MANAGEMENT AWARD 1967
Glass plate with 4A design on bottom. Came in white box lined in red velvet. **CMV $45 plate only. $55 MB.**

BICENTENNIAL PLATES 1976
Blue & white. Given to Reps. that sent in order for campaign 1, 2, 3 totaling $100 or more.
(left) Independence Hall.
(right) Liberty Bell. Made in England. Has Inscription on back. **CMV $20 Independence Hall; $30 Liberty Bell.**

RECOMMENDATION GIFT SNACK SET 1973
Fostoria lead crystal dish & bowl. Came in set of 4 each. Given to Avon. Reps. for signing up new Avon ladies. **CMV $15 each setting. $60 for all 8 pieces.**

TENDERNESS COMMEMORATIVE PLATE 1974
9" diameter ceramic plate, pastel blue and greens. Awarded to Reps. for sending in orders for campaign 1, 2, and 3,, 1974. Inscription on back in blue letters "Tenderness Commemorative Plate Special Edition, awarded to Reps. in January, 1974". Plate is made by Pontessa Ironstone of Spain. Award plate has Pontessa in blue letters. Plate also sold with no inscription on back. **CMV $22MB.** Red letter plate only.

77TH ANNIVERSARY QUEEN AWARD 1963
Awarded to 10 Reps. in each district that had greatest dollar increase in sales, were crowned Queen & also received Fostoria Crystal serving dish with Avon 4A in bottom. Tiara not marked Avon. Came with Avon Queen certificate - 2 different certificates were given. Also came with 1963 Queen Ribbon. 11 1/4" bowl. **CMV bowl only $50. CMV Tiara with ceritficate & ribbon $50. CMV complete set MB $100.**

CHRISTMAS BELLS-MANAGERS GIFT 1971
Red strap with 5 bells given to Avon managers at Christmas. Came with card with bells on it & "For you from Avon". Must have Avon card. **CMV $15 MB.**

BIRD PLATE AWARDS 1975

Campaign 10, 1975. Available to Reps. for meeting product goals; serving specified number of customers and meeting goals at suggested customer prices. Bluebird was lowest goal, Yellow Breasted Chat second and Baltimore Oriole last. If total goals attained, Rep. received all three plates. **CMV Bluebird, $20 MB, Yellow Breasted Chat $20 MB, Baltimore Oriole $30 MB.**

WILD FLOWERS AWARD PLATES 1976-78

Each is 8 3/4". Southern Wild Flower plate for $195 in sales. Southern & Eastern given for $245 in sales & Southern, Eastern, Nothern & Western flower plates for $330 in slaes. C-11, 1976. **CMV Southern $10 MB. Eastern $15 MB. All 4 plates MB $60 set. Northern & Western $20 each MB.** These same plates were reissued by Geni Products, a division of Avon in March, 1978, as awards to their sales reps.

FOSTORIA COIN PLATE AWARD 1970

Does not say Avon. Must be in Avon box. **CMV $25 MB.**

LENOX CHINA PRESIDENT'S CLUB BOWL AWARD 1979

White box with gold trim & burgundy inside holds 4A inscribed china bowl. Bottom inscribed "For Avon's Very Best" given to all President's Club members for 1980. Box has Avon outer sleeve. **CMV $40 MB, bowl only $30.**

FOSTORIA LEAD CRYSTAL PLATES AWARD 1978

Given for top sales. 1st four plates won by Reps: Jeweled A, 1st Rep., Door Knocker, great oak tree. **CMV $30 set of 4 or $7 each.**
President's Club Reps. & District Managers could win 1st 4 plus 4 more: 4A Avon Key, World of Avon Globe, Avon Rose Last. President's Club set had P.C. marked on Rose plate & D.M. marked Jeweled a plate for managers set. **CMV $100 D.M. set of 8, CMV $75 P.C. set of 8.**

COIN GLASS 1961-72

Coin glass in Avon boxes only are collectable. The same pieces are available in local stores with both 1886 and 1887 at low prices so get the box. Many pieces available at many different prices starting at **$10 up to $100 in Avon box.** 1st issue 1961.

REPRESENTATIVES SERVICE AWARD PLATES 1979-86

Awarded for years of service. 1st issued in 1973 and some design changes in 1979. 1st 5 are white porcelian with decals. All are the same CMV as 1973 to 79 plates except the 25 year plate which is silver tone only and **CMV $40. CMV complete set $140 MB.**

CHRISTMAS GIFT PLATE 1971

(Top Left) Sent to Reps. at Christmas. Clear glass with frosted First Avon Lady. **CMV $17 MB. $12 no box.**

CHRISTMAS GIFT PLATE 1972

(Top Right) Sent to every Rep. at Christmas. Clear glass frosted rose. **CMV $15 MB. $10 no box.**

CHRISTMAS GIFT PLATE 1973

(Bottom Left) Sent to Reps. who had been with company less than 2 years. Clear glass frosted 4A. **CMV $15 MB. $10 no box.**

CHRISTMAS GIFT PLATE 1974

(Bottom Right) Sent to Reps. at Christmas. Clear glass with frosted Door Knocker. **CMV $12 MB. $8 no box.**

FRAGRANCE JAR AWARD 1924

American Beauty fragrance jar hand painted design in blue & gold. Pink & green flowers on lid. Pink ribbon. Given to Reps. for top sales. **CMV $350.**

REPRESENTATIVES AWARD PLATES 1973-79

Awarded for years of service. First 5, white with colored decals. Two years-Doorknockers **CMV $10.** Five years-Oak Tree with pink or brown acorns, **CMV $15.** 5 year "Factory Mistake Plate" marked as normal 5th Anniversary plate on back but same as 10th year plate on front. Rare.

Add $25 to 5 year plate. Ten years-California Perfume Co. **CMV $20.** Fifteen years-Rose **CMV $25.** Twenty years-First Avon Lady **CMV $30.** Twenty-five years-Sterling silver with message from Avon President. **CMV $100.** All Prices are mint & boxed. **CMV complete set $200 MB.**

SILVER SERVICE AWARD TRAY 1957
Silver tray 13 1/2" long, "Avon-Wm. Rogers" on bottom. Awarded to Avon ladies in Anniversary Campaign. **CMV $30.**

NATIONAL CHAMPION AWARD 1966
Glass bowl with 4A design on bottom. **CMV $50 MB.**

CAKE STAND AWARD 1978
(Front) Given to top 50 Reps. in state. "Avon Division Top 50" inscribed in center. Silver plated. **CMV $25.**

IMPERIAL DIVISION AWARD TRAY 1979
(Back) Silver plated, inscribed "Avon Imperial Division Top 50, 1979 #29". **CMV $25.**

HIGHEST SALES AWARD BOWL 1976
Silver plated fruit bowl was awarded to 10 different Reps. for highest sales in their category. Each bowl is engraved different from the other. The one is engraved with "4A" design. "Highest Percentage Increase Christmas 1976". **CMV $25, $30 MB.** Not awarded in all branches.

GRAVY BOAT AWARD 1930'S
CPC Avon on bottom. Given to Reps. for sales award in 1930's. Blue & green flowers on both sides. Gold trim. **CMV $75.**

50 YEAR SERVICE PLATE 1976
Gold plated plate given to the late Mrs. Bessie O'Neal on July 27, 1976, by David Mitchell, President of Avon Products, for 50 continous years as an Avon lady. A letter from Avon & Mr. Mitchell came with the plate. The plate is 1 of a kind & priceless. The plate is made by Dirilyte. No value established.

COVERED DISH AWARD 1930'S
White ceramic bowl & lid. Gold trim with green & pink flowers. Bottom is stamped CPCo. Avon under glazing. Given to Avon Reps. for sales. **CMV $110 mint.**

PRESIDENT'S CELEBRATION AWARD BOWL 1977
Over 40,000 were given as awards. 6 7/8" silver plated bowl given to Avon Reps. in 2 winning districts in each division for top sales. Inscription in center of bowl "President's Celebration 1977"; on bottom of bowl, "Awarded exclusively to Avon Reps." F.B. Rogers. Came in white box as shown. Red silk rose also given at same time with name tag. **CMV Rose only with tag, $5. CMV bowl $25 MB.** Bowl did not come with rose.

GREAT SCENT EVENT TRAY AWARD 1980
9 1/2"x 17 3/4" gold tone mirror tray given to 15 Reps. In each district for selling the most Ultra colognes. Does not say Avon on tray. Came with & must have Great Scent Event card from division manager. **CMV$20 with card.**

SILVER SERVER AWARD 1977
(top) 11 3/4"x 18 3/4: silver plated tray & cover. Marked Avon Wm. Rogers on bottom. No information on why it was given to Reps. **CMV $45 mint.**

SILVER CREAMER AWARD 1950'S
(bottom) Avon Wm. Rogers on bottom. Silver-plate creamer. **No information on this as Avon award CMV $35.**

PRESIDENT'S AWARD SILVER BOWLS 1962
3 sizes silver bowls. 4A emblem and writing on outside. **CMV (left to right) $27.50, $32.50, $37.50.**

75TH ANNIVERSARY SALES CHAMPION SILVER TRAY 1961

Awarded to the top Avon district managers for best sales in campaign 9 & 10, 1961. **CMV $40.**

SILVER SERVER AWARD 1963

12 5/16"x2" given to the top 4 established Reps. In each district for sale improvement over the previous year. 4A design engraved in the bottom. Small 9" servers were given to 3 newer Reps. for highest sale & 3 for outstanding sales ability. **CMV 9" $40, 12" $45.**

ACHIEVEMENT AWARD SILVER TRAY 1961

4A design in center of silver tray. **CMV $35.**

PRESIDENT'S CELEBRATION TRAY AWARD 1978

12" silverplated tray marked 'Awarded Exclusively to Avon Reps." on back side. Given to 1 winning team Rep. In each division. **CMV $35 MB.**

DIVISION SALES WINNER TRAY AWARD 1975

17 3/4" longx 13" wide silver tray. Inscribed in center 'Awarded to (name of manager) President's Program Best Wishes, David S. Mitchell'. Given to top district managers in sales. Came in blue felt bag & white box. **CMV $150 MB in bag.**

EL CAMINO DIVISION SUGAR & CREAMER SET AWARD 1977

Silverplated creamer & sugar bowl. Tray is engraved 'Top 10 Sales-El Camino Division Campaigns 10-22, 1977'. Made by Sheridan. **CMV $35 set mint.**

SILVER SERVER 1964

9" diameter. Same as 1963 server except no 12" bowls given and all are gold lined on the inside. **CMV $40.**

SILVER TRAY 1965

9 7/8"x1" given to each Rep. from the winning group in each branch during the General Manager's Campaign, engraved "Honor Award-General Manager's Campaign 1965". **CMV $35.**

88TH ANNIVERSARY AWARD BOWL 1974

6" across and 3" high silverplated by Oneida. Paul Revere Silver. Given to top 5 sales Reps. in each district. **CMV $22.50** Same bowl given to top 5 President's Club Sales Reps. and their award bowl says "President's Club" over 4A ensigna. **CMV $22.50.**

SALES EXCELLENCE AWARD 1977

Paul Revere, Jostens Pewter 5" bowl C26-76-C9-77. Awarded to top sales Reps. **CMV $22.50 MB.**

SILVER AWARD BOWL 1969

Silverplate bowl by Fina. Has 4A symbol and Avon in center of bowl. 2 3/4" high and 5" wide at top. Awarded to Avon Reps. **CMV $20.**

CHINA BELL REP. GIFT 1973

Christmas present to all Reps. that had been with Avon over 2 years. White China with pink roses. **CMV $10 MB.**

CHRISTMAS ORNAMENTS MUSICAL GIFT SET 1974

Given to Reps. for getting new Reps. Red & gold bell & green & gold ball. Both have music boxes inside. Made by Heinz Deichett, West Germany. Both came in red box as set. **CMV $30 each no box; $75 set MB.**

THE GREAT AMERICAN SELLATHON CHRISTMAS TREE AWARD 1981

Approximately 600 given out at Hawaiian President's Celebration in Hawaii. Has bottom Avon label & green & white gift box. **CMV $45.**

MANAGERS CHRISTMAS TREE GIFT 1977

(Left) Hand blown glass Christmas tree in clear, green, red & yellow. Given to Avon managers at Christmas 1977. Does not say Avon. **CMV $25.**

MANAGERS CHRISTMAS TREE GIFT 1978

(Right) Brass Christmas tree ornament signed by "Bi Jan" on back. Given to Avon managers at Christmas 1978. Came in green box. **CMV $20 MB.**

"PICTURE FRAME" DREAM AWARD SEPTEMBER CONFERENCE 1979

Ceramic picture frame. White, pink & green flowers with white doves. Center is pink, says "Hold fast to your dreams, For if you do . . .Tomorrow you'll see More dreams can come true". **CMV $15.**

MANAGERS CHRISTMAS GIFT 1979

Blown glass in green leaves & red holly with red velvet ribbon. 2 pieces. Holly leaves ornament & candle holder. Given to managers for Christmas 1979. Does not say Avon. **CMV $15 set.**

REPRESENTATIVE CHRISTMAS GIFT 1979

Ceramic tile picture frame made in Japan. Box says "Happy Holidays Avon 1979". Given to all Avon Reps. at Christmas. **CMV $10 MB.**

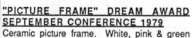

FLOWER BASKET AWARD 1981

Small white ceramic flower basket. **CMV $40.**

REPRESENTATIVE AWARD BOWL 1956

Sterling silver Paul Revere Bowl was given to each Rep. in the top selling district in each division during President's Campaign 1956. **CMV $45.**

COMPOTE TALL 1960'S

Fostoria coin glass award. Must be in Avon box. Given to Reps for sales award. **CMV $45.**

91ST ANNIVERSARY COIN GLASS AWARD 1977

Footed compote on right won by Reps. for selling $270 in C8-9-1977. **CMV $7 MB.** Centerpiece bowl and footed compote won for selling $540 in C8-9-1977. **CMV $12 MB.** Centerpiece bowl. A pair of candle holders won by President's Club members only with P.C. embossed on bottom. This coin glass was made only for Avon, using Avon emblems in coins and 1886-1977 and the name Avon. Came with card on each piece from Avon and in Avon box. **CMV$17 candle holders, MB.** District managers received a full set of Coin Glass with D.M. embossed in center of each piece. **CMV $75 MB for complete D.M. set.**

CAKE PLATE FOSTORIA COIN GLASS AWARD 1960'S

Fostoria glass cake plate given to Reps. for sales award. Comes in Avon box. Same piece was sold in local stores. Must be in Avon box as shown. **CMV $75 MB.**

APPLE PAPER WEIGHT AWARD 1978

Given to divisional managers for top sales. Clear crystal glass apple is engraved "You Made New York Smile", Avon, March 1978, on front side. **CMV $100.**

HEART TREASURE BOX AWARD 1976

Top sales teams in 252 winning districts won ceramic heart shaped box given in President's Celebration of 1976. Bottom says "Avon President's Celebration 1976". Made in Spain **CMV $20 MB.**

PRESIDENT'S CELEBRATION HEART AWARD 1979

Lucite heart marked "You're our number one-Avon 1979 President's Celebration". Made in Taiwan. Comes in white Avon box. **CMV $20 MB.**

MANAGER'S HEART "YOU'RE NO. 1"

(Right) Clear lucite, has smaller hole on top & heart is about 1/2" smaller. Came in red velvet bag. This one was given to managers only. **CMV $30 mint in bag.**

HEART PORCELAIN BOX AWARD 1980

Given to managers. Came in Tiffany & Co. box. Small porcelain heart box says "Bernardaud Limoges Made in France. Does not say Avon. **CMV $25 in box with card.**

TEAM LEADER BELL AWARD 1980

Fostoria bell inscribed "Avon Team Leader Recruit A Thon 1980". Only 1 in each district given. **CMV $30.**

LIMOGES FLORAL BOX AWARD 1980

Small white ceramic heart box with blue painted flowers. Given to managers. Does not say Avon. Must have Tiffany card for Avon Products. Was not made only for Avon. **CMV $25 MB with card.**

78TH ANNIVERSARY FOSTORIA AWARD SET 1964

Box marked Avon Cosmetics holds Fostoria salt & pepper, cruet & glass holding tray. Given to Reps. **CMV $45 in Avon box.**

LIMOGES FLORAL HEART BOX AWARD 1979

Small heart shaped ceramic box made by Limoge of France. Given to Avon managers. Must have Tiffany & Co. card as shown for Avon Products. 2 different designs as shown. **CMV $25 with card.**

MERRY MOODS OF CHRISTMAS ORNAMENT 1960'S

Dark blue ornament for managers only. Other side says "Avon Presents" with 4A design. **CMV $35 mint.**

50TH ANNIVERSARY AWARD LAMP 1936

Made only for Avon "Lalique reproduction" lamp. 22" high, 19" wide shade. Frosted carved glass base. Pink ribbon on shade, clear beads around edge of shade. White painted base. Given only to 50 Reps. for top sales in nation. **CMV $300.**

SILVER FLOWER BASKET AUGUST CONFERENCE AWARD 1978

Sterling silver basket made by Cartier, hand made. "August Conference 1978" on top of handle. Yellow silk flowers, green leaves. Given to managers only. **CMV $100 mint.**

CANDLESTICK AWARDS 1952

Sterling silver candlesticks 2 1/2" tall and 2 3/4" wide at the base. They were given to Reps. for calling on 120 customers during the 66th Avon Anniversary campaign, 1952. Came in nice gift box. The candlesticks were not made just for Avon. Must be in box with Avon card as shown. **CMV $60 MB.**

ROSE PERFUME LAMP AWARD 1926

Rose colored frosted glass, rose shaped electric lamp with antique green metal base. Top of rose has a small hole to put perfume to scent the air when lamp was burning. Given to only 8 Reps. for top sales. **CMV $160.**

TEAM LEADER JEWELRY BOX 1980

Silver tone box with blue felt interior. Mirror inside tray says "Team Leader-President's Celebration 1980". **CMV $20 mint.**

CIRCLE OF EXCELLENCE STEUBEN VASE AWARD 1970

9" high Steuben Vase, sits on Black wood base. Brass name plate says "Circle of Excellence Repeat Member-1970" plus name of winner. Comes in Steuben felt bag & box. Given to top C. of E. Managers only. **CMV $400 MB.**

GREAT OAK LAMP AWARD 1980

Electric light in wood base with solid hunk of clear glass with great oak engraved. Given to district managers at yearly conference. **CMV $100 mint.**

NATIONAL DISTRICT SALES MANAGER PANEL AWARD 1980

Silverplated card case. Given to top managers only. Made by Reed & Barton. In box & blue bag. **CMV $50.**

CARTIER CRYSTAL BELL AWARD 1968

Crystal bell in Cartier bag & box. Signed Val Lambert. Is not marked Avon. Given to one Rep. per district for most recommendations. **CMV $65 MB. Bell only $50.**

PRESIDENT'S CELEBRATION SILVER CHEST 1974

Silverplated, red lined. Embossed rose on lid. **CMV $47.50 MB.**

WE DID IT TOGETHER TRAY 1983
7 1/4" x 12" silver plated server tray. Given to Managers. **CMV $25.**

$1,000,000 DESK SET AWARD 1978
(Left) Wood base. Brass plaque. **CMV $50.**
DESK SET NATIONAL G.M. CHAMPIONS AWARD 1973
(Right) Marble base. **CMV $20.**

TOP RECRUITER PEN AWARD 1979
(Left) Sterling silver pen set. Engraved "Top Recruiter May 1979". **CMV $100.**
CIRCLE OF EXCELLENCE 8 YEAR PEN AWARD 1980
(Center) Engraved sterling silver pen set. **CMV $125.**
AVON TENNIS PAPER WEIGHT 1982
(Right) Heavy sterling silver paper weight engraved "1982 Avon Tennis". All are made by Tiffany & Co. **CMV $150.**

OPPORTUNITY UNLIMITED MUG AWARD 1981
Brass mug inscribed on side. **CMV $20.**
OPPORTUNITY UNLIMITED GLASS AWARD 1981
Champagne glass inscribed on side. **CMV $10.**

WINTER RECRUITING EVENT AWARD BOWL 1977
8" International silver plate. Side inscribed name - Gateway Division Winner 1977 - Winter Recruiting Event. **CMV $20.**
GATEWAY APPOINTMENT GOBLET AWARD 1975
Poole silver plate. Inscribed on side. **CMV 20.**

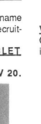

PAPER WEIGHT AWARD 1983
Square lucite with gold 4A center. Marked The Answer is Avon. **CMV $20.**
PAPER WEIGHT AWARD NEWARK 1983
Small round lucite, with 1979 Susan B. Anthony Dollar inside. **CMV $15.**

(LEFT) PAPER WEIGHT LOS ANGELES - 1983
Clear & red lucite marked "Road to the Gold." **CMV $25.**
(CENTER) PAPER WEIGHT - SAN FRANCISCO 1982
Small clear lucite. Gold inner base. **CMV $30.**
(RIGHT) PAPER WEIGHT - LONDON 1980
Clear & red lucite. Avon Marathon. **CMV $35.**

OAK TREE PAPER WEIGHT AWARD 1978
(Left) Lucite case holds oak tree coin with 4A design. Atlanta #1 - 1978. **CMV $20.**
READ LISTEN FOLLOW UP PLAQUE 1981
(Right) 4A design on sign. **CMV $10.**

VISION AWARD 1985
Clear lucite paper weight. Says "Avon Our Vision is Clear 1985". **CMV $15.**

MANAGER'S CONFERENCE CORSAGE 1960'S
Green & gold with red holly has Avon 7 dollar bill attached. Bill says "United States of Avon". Given to managers. **CMV $22.**

JEWELRY BOX AWARD 1968
10" long x 5" wide brocade & brass music box. Red lined. Given to Reps. for top sales. Does not say Avon. **CMV $60 mint.**

WOMEN'S INTERNATIONAL AVON "RUNNING" MARATHON AWARD 1979
Gold tone medallion in clear lucite with red background. Came on marble base with 22/9/79 plaque. **CMV $50.**
INTERNATIONAL WOMEN'S CHAMPIONSHIP MARATHON AWARD 1978 ATLANTA
Same as above only silver tone medallion with black background. **CMV $50.**

ARIANE NECKLACE & BOUQUET 1977
Wood basket & plastic flowers holds sterling silver necklace with August Conference 1977 on side. Given to Avon managers at August Conference Banquet. Necklace holds sample vial of Ariane perfume. **CMV $65 mint.**

HUDSON MANOR BUD VASE GIFT 1978
Avon silverplated bud vase & red rose in silver box. Bottom says "Team Leader, August 1978". Made in Italy. Same as regular issue only regular issue does not say Team Leader 1978 on bottom. **CMV $25.**
MANAGERS BUD VASE GIFT 1978
Same as above only says "August Conference 1978" on bottom instead of Team Leader. **CMV $35 MB.**

MANAGER'S FLOWER BASKET 1979
Basket of silk flowers with Avon tag to managers. In Avon box. **CMV $25 MB with tag.**
TEAM LEADER FLOWER BASKET 1979
Same flower basket only different box and different tag given to team leaders. **CMV $15 MB.**

SOUNDS OF SEASONS MUSIC BOX 1966
Given to managers only. Box holds green & gold Christmas Tree Pin, gold Key & Bell. Came from Cartier in New York. **CMV Music box only $65. Complete set $85 MB.**

SALES LEADERSHIP AWARD 1980
Large clear glass emerald diamond shaped paper weight. Engraved "Avon Sales Leadership Award Conference 1980". Tiffany & Co. on bottom. Comes in Tiffany box. Given to mangers only. **CMV $150 MB.**

OAK TREE PAPER WEIGHT AWARD 1980
Clear lucite with siver tone 4A design & oak tree. "Pasadena No. 1 - 1980" inscribed inside. Given to managers. **CMV $25.**

NO. 1 PAPER WEIGHT AWARD - CANADA
Chrome-plated No. 1, gold tone plaque says "You're Number One With Us". Given to Avon managers in Canada. **CMV $30.**

95th ANNIVERSARY CELEBRATION AWARD MUG 1981
(Left) White - Red letters. **CMV $20.**
WE'RE HOT MUG AWARD 1984
(Right) White mug - red & black letters. **CMV $10.**

PRESIDENT'S CLUB CUP 1986
Pinkish orange coffee cup. "Avon President's Club 86" on side in blue letters. **CMV $5.**
PEN "LOOK HOW GOOD YOU LOOK NOW" 1987
White pen. **CMV $2.**
PHYLLIS DAVIS ACHIEVEMENT AWARD 1985
Clear lucite 3" square with black background. C-26-85. **CMV $25.**

LIBERTY DIVISION PAPER WEIGHT 1978
Clear lucite has 4A design. "Liberty Division - Two Million Dollar Increase 1978". Given to top managers. **CMV $15.**
CIRCLE OF EXCELLENCE PINS 1979
(lower left) Small blue & gold tone pin says "C of E Winners 1979". Given to top managers. **CMV $10.**

OUTSTANDING IN FIELD CUP AWARD 1981
Ceramic cup with cow on other side. **CMV $10.**

CUSTOMER SERVICE AWARD MEASURING CUP 1982
By Fire King - Avon inscribed. **CMV $10.**

WE LOVE YOU MUG AWARD 1986
White ceramic cup. **CMV $5.**

AVON MARATHON AWARD, OTTAWA 1981
Clear lucite with white back. Dated 23 August 1981. Given in women's running circuit. **CMV $35.**

P.C. COFFEE CUP GIFT 1987
Ceramic coffee cup given to President's Club members on birthdays. White, blue, orange & pink. Has ceramic lid. **CMV $6. MB.**

SALES ACHIEVEMENT MUG 1977
White coffee cup, pink rose. Back says "Avon Sales Achievement Highest Percentage Increase Third Quarter 1977". **CMV $10.**

COFFEE CUP AWARDS 1984
Left to right.
WHITE GLASS - red letters, gold trim. **CMV $5.**
WHITE MUG - Avon in red letters all over. **CMV $5.**
SAY YES TO AVON MUG - White plastic, red letters. **CMV $5.**

WONDER MUG AWARD 1987
White plastic mug. **CMV $5 MB.**

HOLIDAY GREETINGS GLASS AWARD 1971
Clear glass, red letters. **CMV $12.**

GOBLET 1971
Ruby coated glass says Lena - Avon 1971. **CMV $10.**

P.C. X-MAS PREVIEW CUP 1985
White plastic, red letters. **CMV $2.**

CHRISTMAS ORNAMENT AWARD 1984
White plastic, green letters. Teddy bear on back side. **CMV $5.**

TELEPHONE HONOR SOCIETY AWARD 1986
Red telephone given for $50,000 in sales. Engraved on top "PC Avon Honor Society". Comes in Unisonic box. **CMV $75.**

AVON TELEPHONE 1986 AWARD
White phone, wall or desk mount. Avon in black letters - red slash. Given to reps. **CMV $25.**

#1 TREND SETTERS WALL TILE AWARD - 1985
White tile given in Morton Grove branch. **CMV $25.**

TELEPHONE AWARD 1986
Red wall mount or can sit on table. Says Avon in white letters. Given to reps. **CMV $20.**

SHAWNEE DOOR KNOCKER IN LUCITE AWARD 1970's
Gold tone door knocker sealed in lucite - has Shawnee in blue. **CMV $25.**

TELEPHONE PRESIDENT'S CLUB AWARD 1983
Red plastic Touch Tone, given to top sales reps only. Made by Webcor. Outer sleeve says "Avon Calling" & Avon Calling on telephone. **CMV $35.**

DIVISION COMPETITION AWARD 1973
Clear lucite paper weight given in Springdale branch. **CMV $10.**

HEAT THERMOMETER AWARD 1981
Clear lucite, black letters & trim given to managers in 4 test areas only. **CMV $25.**

REP. CHRISTMAS GIFT BOWL 1978
Fostoria bowl with 4A design & 1978 on bottom. Given to all Avon Reps. for Christmas 1979. Box shown with red ribbon & gold tag & white & gold plastic bell given to managers. **CMV $10 Reps. MB, CMV $15 managers with ribbon.**

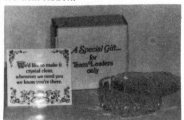

VALENTINE TEAM LEADER GIFT 1979
3 1/2" across crystal heart shaped glass dish given to all team leaders for Valentine's. **CMV $12.50 MB.**

CIRCLE OF EXCELLENCE CRYSTAL VASE 1980
Given to managers on trip to Spain. Box has "Avon Vase Soliflor". Was not made only for Avon. **CMV $40 in Avon box.**

SEASONS GREETINGS AVON REPS. 1977
5 1/2" high vase marked on bottom has 4A symbol. Given to all Avon Reps. at Christmas 1977 in special box. **CMV $12 MB.**

DIVISION MANAGER'S TROPHY 1966
Large pewter trophy given to winning manager in each division. **CMV $100.**

PRESIDENT'S CUP AWARD 1949
Sterling silver trophy engraved with top selling team in city & district in each division during President's Campaign during the late 40's & early 50's. Given to managers. **CMV $200 mint.**

JUBILEE ANNIVERSARY QUEEN AWARD 1977
Small wood base, gold top for division manager. **CMV $10.**

HOOSIER CUSTOMER SERVICE TROPHY 1975-76
(Left) Given to managers for most customers served. **CMV $22.50.**

PRESIDENT'S CELEBRATION TROPHY 1978
(Right) Marble base. **CMV $15.**

TRAVELING TROPHY 1972
Gold 4A with first Avon Lady over emblem on walnut base with engraved plate Team Honor Award. **CMV $30.**

35th ANNIVERSARY AWARD 1980's
Silver plate pitcher engraved on front. Given to Reps. for 35 years service as an Avon Rep. Comes with Avon card. In Avon box from Tiffany & Co. Engraved on side of pitcher "35th Avon Anniversary". **CMV $125 MB.**

ADDITION'S AWARD 1978
Black & clear plastic picture cube for recruiting new Reps. **CMV $25 MB.**

OBELISK COMMUNITY SERVICE AWARD 1979
8 1/4" clear lucite. 1 given to managers in each division. Has 4A design & message of Ralph Waldo Emerson in center. Came in 2 sizes - 1 is 2" shorter. **CMV $50 ea.**

KANSAS CITY BRANCH TROPHY 1969
"Number One" national sales increase. **CMV $17.**

LOVING CUP TROPHY 1961
Gold cup on white base. **CMV $20.**

TOP SALES TROPHY 1966
(Left) Small 5" high gold trophy, wood base. C-11-13-1966. **CMV $15.**

ACHIEVEMENT AWARD TROPHY 1954
(Right) Avon in raised letters on the base of the metal figure. Given to top Reps. in each district. **CMV $20.**

PRESIDENT'S CLUB TROPHY 1977
Gold tone top. **CMV $8.**

BUD VASE AWARD 1954
(Left) 8" tall sterling silver vase awarded to each Rep. in winning district during President's Campaign. **CMV $45.**

PRESIDENT'S TROPHY 1954-56
(Right) 13 5/8" high, sterling silver trophy was given to top selling city & district managers in each division during President's Campaign each year. Trophy sits on black base. **CMV $125.**

PRESIDENT'S CELEBRATION TROPHY 1977
Inscribed to Top Selling Rep. for President's Celebration. **CMV $20.**

PRESIDENT'S CELEBRATION TROPHY 1978
Given to Reps. for best increase over sales goal. Came with certificate. Marble with wood base. **CMV $20.**

ROYAL RIBBON TEAM LEADER AWARD TROPHY 1982
Wood base & silver toned cup. 1 given per district. **CMV $15.**

AVON CALLING PEN 1976
(Left) 14K gold filled. Made by Cross. In grey bag and red leather pen holder with rose design in gold. Pen is 5 1/4" long. Given to Reps. for recommendation prize. **CMV $20 MB.**

TOP 6 TEAM LEADER TROPHY 1977
(Right) Given for Top 6 Sales in Anniversary Celebration 1977. White marble base, gold statue. Blue plaque. **CMV $10.**

3 YEAR WINNER TROPHY 1971
Small wood base, brass plaque that says
"Avon 3 Year Winner". Given to Reps. **CMV**
$15.

DIVISIONAL SALES CAMPAIGN
AWARD 1954-56
Only 20 black plaques with solid sterling silver
rose, were given each year to managers in top
selling district in each of the 20 divisions in
U.S. **CMV $250.**

BEST SUPPORTING PERFORMANCE
TROPHY 1965
(Left) This type trophy should not get too high
in price as you can still buy the trophies & have
brass name plate put on them. **CMV $15.**
ACHIEVEMENT AWARD TROPHY
1958-59
(Right) This type has Avon in raised letters on
the base of the metal figure. These cannot be
purchased & should be worth more. **CMV**
$25.

KEY TO SUCCESS TROPHY AWARD
1978
Trophy floated to each winning manager in
division till final winning manager won & kept it.
CMV $60.

PRESIDENT'S TROPHY 1959-60
Sterling silver trophy given to managers in top
selling district in each division. Given late 50's
to early 60's. Trophy is inscribed with winning
team & year. **CMV $125.**

NATIONAL DISTRICT PANEL PLAQUE
1974
Picture frame plaque-Sara Fleming. Gold &
brown. **CMV $15.**

ANNIVERSARY QUEEN TROPHY 1978
Marble Base, Given to top Rep. in each
division for top sales. **CMV $15.**
QUEEN'S TIARA 1978
Came with Queen's Trophy. Is not marked
Avon. **No price established.**

STAR SPANGLED MANAGER PLAQUE
1970
Avon-Star Spangled Manager Summer 1970
on face plate. **CMV $14.**

DISTINGUISHED SALES MANAGE-
MENT PLAQUE AWARD 1977
Solid walnut base holds white ceramic tile
center plaque & brass name tag on bottom.
Given to top 10 managers in each division.
CMV $30.

PRESIDENT'S CELEBRATION PLAQUE
1977
Engraved wood plaque with Cape Cod Water
Goblet attached. Given to team leaders with
highest sales. **CMV $15 mint.**

OUTSTANDING MANAGERS PLAQUE 1971
Wood base with gold plaque. Outstanding managers first quarter. **CMV $20.**

TEAM LEADER PLAQUE AWARD 1979
Given to team leaders in C of E winning division. **CMV $30.**

MILLION DOLLAR CLUB PLAQUE PASADENA BRANCH 1978
Walnut base with red front & gold trim. Presented to district managers for outstanding sales increase. **CMV $75.**

PRESIDENT'S CELEBRATION GREAT OAK PLAQUE AWARD 1980
Scrimshaw great oak on white plastic center, wood frame. Comes with Avon card. Given to managers only. **CMV $35.**

BLUE RIBBON SOCIETY AWARD 1981
Wood & brass plaque. **CMV $25.**

MILLION DOLLAR SELECT GROUP AWARD 1977
(Left) Plaque with bag of money on front from Sovereign Divison. **CMV $75.**

OUTSTANDING ACHIEVEMENT AWARD 1975
(Right) Blue velvet on wood plaque, metal wreath with red, white & blue ribbon with 4A pendant with green stone in center. **CMV $100.**

AWARD PLAQUE 1971
Presented in campaign 1-26, 1971 for increased sales. **CMV $10.**

TOP 10 DIVISION TROPHY 1977
4 1/2" high 4A design inside lucite top on wood base & brass plaque. Given to top 10 sales Reps. in each division. Came in plain white box. **CMV $40.**

HONORABLE MENTION PLAQUE 1960'S
Green pearlessence plastic base with wood and brass plaque. **CMV $12,50.**

PICTURE GLASS FRAME PRIZE 1943
Etched glass frame holds 8x10 size picture. Given to Reps. for selling over $75 during campaign. **CMV $150.**

20 YEAR SILVER PICTURE FRAME AWARD 1981
Sterling silver picture frame from Tiffany & Co. given to Avon Reps. for 20 years service. Bottom of frame engraved "Avon 20 Years", & the initial of person winning frame. Comes in Tiffany felt bag. **CMV $100.**

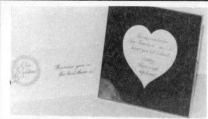

CIRCLE OF EXCELLENCE HEART PICTURE FRAME 1981
Silver tone small picture frame with C of E card. Given to C of E managers. **CMV $25.**

MANAGERS DIPLOMA 1963
Certificate given to new Avon managers during the 1960's. Did not come in frame. **CMV $10.**

TEAM LEADER PICTURE FRAME AWARD 1978
Chrome picture frame marked on top of frame "Made Exclusively for Avon Team Leaders". Given for meeting sales goals. **CMV $10 mint.**

ACHIEVEMENT AWARD 1950
Pink & white with gold. Given for high sales during 64th Anniversary Celebration. This was celebrating new packaging & redesign of Cotillion. This matches packaging for this era. Approx. 10 x 14 inches. **CMV $25.**

PAUL GREGORY PLAQUE 1964
Silver plaque on black wood. Given to each manager in the winning division. **CMV $35.**

PAUL GREGORY PLAQUE 1965-67
Black & silver plaque given to winning division of Avon's Paul Gregory Trophy. **CMV $30.**

DIVISION CHAMPION PLAQUE 1965
Given for highest sales during general managers campaign 1965. **CMV $30.**

PENN VALLEY DIVISION PLAQUE 1980
Wood base plaque. 4A design on bottom. **CMV $20.**

ORDER PLAQUE $1000.00 1978
Small plaque. **CMV $10.**
DIVISION WINNER PLAQUE 1976
Wabash Speedway Competition. **CMV $15.**

CHRISTMAS CONFERENCE AWARD 1985
2" deep wood frame with brass inscribed plaque with rose & 4A design & dated 1985. Given to managers only. **CMV $35.**

CIRCLE OF EXCELLENCE PLAQUE 1980
Wood board with list of managers. Circle of Excellence 1980 on brass plate. **CMV $50.**

LIBERTY DIVISION PLAQUE AWARD 1980
(Left) Small wood & brass plaque. 4A design #1 customer service. **CMV $10.**
$1,000,000 INCREASE PLAQUE 1978
Wood & brass plaque in Sovereign Division. **CMV $15.**

NATIONAL DISTRICT MANAGERS PANEL AWARD 1975
Chrome & brass picture frame. **CMV $20.**

GARDEN OF LILIES AWARDS 1985
Each item marked Avon & Avon boxes.
Flowers. **CMV $10 MB.**
Picture & Frame - 16" x 20". **CMV $20.**
Lamp - white ceramic. **CMV $25.**

MANAGERS PICTURE FRAME AWARD 1986
Small oval brass tone frame with 4A design.
Given at August conference. **CMV $15.**

WHITE HOUSE PICTURE FRAME AWARD 1986
100th year signed by Ronald Reagan. **CMV $10.**

OPPORTUNITY UNLIMITED PLAQUE AWARD 1983
Chrome & glass picture frame. Given to Managers. **CMV $10.**

MIRROR MAKE UP AWARD 1980
6" x 8" mirror, dull gold frame. Avon on front of mirror. Used by managers. **CMV $10.**

PICTURE FRAME "CERAMIC" AWARD 1984
Blue box holds small white ceramic picture frame with blue, green & yellow flowers. Given to Reps. for Sales Quota. **CMV $8.**

HONORED AVON SPONSOR AWARD PLAQUE 1984
8" x 10" picture frame. Given to reps. for signing 5 new Avon Reps. **CMV $5.**

BEAUTY VANITY AWARD 1984
White plastic cosmetic case in Avon Box.
Given to Reps. **CMV $15 MB.**

TIFFANY MONEY 1982
Tiffany box holds Tiffany $25. silver credit coin.
Given to Managers. Does not say Avon.
CMV $25. in felt bag & box.

THIS IS FOR YOU PEN & NOTE PAD AWARD 1984
White Avon Box holds note pads. CMV $7. White Avon light pen. CMV $10. $20. for set MB.

I LOVE NEW YORK GIFTS 1985
Note pad - blue plastic, apple rubber stamp & button. CMV $5. all.

SAN FRANCISCO RECORD 1980
Circle of Excellence envelope with Tony Bennet record. "I Left My Heart in San Francisco." CMV $5.

STICK WITH IT SOAP HOLDER 1973
Rubber soap holder given to Reps. Rare. CMV $3.

CARDS - PASADENA #1 1980s
Deck of cards. CMV $8.
CARDS - NEW YORK - LAS VEGAS - AWARD 1980
Deck of cards. CMV $10.
ICE SCRAPER AWARD 1984
White plastic - says "You're #1 with me - Avon" CMV $1.
FLASHLIGHT AWARD 1985
White plastic. Avon marked. Given to Reps. CMV $8.
KEY CHAIN AWARD 1983
Tan leather. Metal Avon tag. Given to Reps. CMV $5.

Left to Right
CIRCLE OF EXCELLENCE AWARDS 1977
NEW YORK - BERMUDA TRAVEL ITINERARY
Beige plastic cover & itinerary inside. CMV $5.
CANDY CUP
White plastic with gold covering. Rhinestone on front. CMV $7.
NAME TAG
White & blue plastic. CMV $5.

ORDER BOOK COVERS 1980s
Misc. order book covers used by Avon Reps. CMV $1-$5 each.

AVON 100 BOOK MARK 1986
Pocono Division leather book mark. Given to Reps. CMV $5.

SMALL TREASURE CABINET AWARD 1982
Small wood cabinet made in Brazil for small treasure figurines. CMV $10.

JEWELRY BOX MALE AWARD 1981
Fine wood box made by Buxton given to Male District Managers or Male Team Leaders. Brass label on front is only difference in both boxes. Same box can be bought in stores. Must have brass Avon name plate. CMV $90 D.M. CMV $75 T.L.

CIRCLE OF EXCELLENCE BUTTON 1979
2 1/4" brown & white button. CMV $2.
CALCULATOR 1986
Pocket calculator, in Avon box. Brass & green face. CMV $15.
"YO YO AVON" 1986
White Avon yo yo. CMV $5.

LEFT- CALCULATOR AWARD 1983
Red canvas holds small Novus solar calculator. CMV $20.
CALCULATOR AWARD 1982
Black vinyl with 4A holds Casio battery calculator. CMV $15.

DIRECTOR CHAIR AWARD 1985
White fold up chair, red canvas. 5 given in each district. **CMV $35.**

DOOR MAT AWARD 1980s
Red door mat, white letters. Black rubber back.
Botom mat is 2" smaller and is red with black letters. **CMV $15. ea.**

PRESIDENT'S DAY FRISBEE BAG AWARD 1984
White nylon zipper bag given to Reps. **CMV $20.**

BLAZER JACKETS 1982-83
Blue blazer with 4A brass buttons & gold 4A ensignia or jacket for Reps. **CMV $75.**
Also came for Managers with M in center of 4A ensignia. **CMV $100.**

BASEBALL HAT 1978
White & black Avon cap. **CMV $5.**

TRAVEL BAG AWARDS 1985
Each is tax nylon & vinyl.
Flight Bag. **CMV $25.**
Overnight Bag. **CMV $20.**
Garment Bag. **CMV $25.**

PRESIDENT'S CLUB SCARF X-MAS GIFT 1985
White silk scarf with red & gold P.C. design in red box. **CMV $5.**

PRESIDENT'S CLUB BIRTHDAY PICTURE FRAME GIFT 1985
Red front paper frame with floral back. **CMV $5.**

SANTA'S SACK BY AVON 1986
Red canvas bag. White letters. Given to Reps. **CMV $5.**

AVON MENU SCARF 1976
White silk scarf with Circle of Excellence dinner menu in L.A. Calif. 1976 printed in blue letters. **CMV $25.**

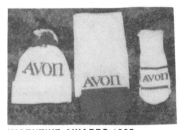

INCENTIVE AWARDS 1985
Stocking hat, mittens & neck scarf. White knit with red letters. Given to Reps. **CMV $25 set.**

FUN SHIRT AWARD 1985
White sweat shirt. Red & blue design. Given to Reps. **CMV $10.**

AWARDS & REPRESENTATIVES GIFTS

SWITCH TO AVON TOTE BAG AWARD 1987
Beige canvas bag. Orange letters. Also came larger in size from Newark branch. **CMV $5.**

T-SHIRT AVON SUNSET AWARD
Light blue shirt - yellow sun. **CMV $10.**

T SHIRTS AWARDS MISC. 1970s-1980s
AVON WOMENS RUN - GREEN
AVON RUNNING CANADA - WHITE & RED
AVON MARATHON INT. WOMEN'S CHAMPIONSHIP - RED & WHITE
AVON INTERNATIONAL MARATHON TRAINNG 1983
White - red design - 2 girls running. L.A.
AVON RUNNING
White - red letters.
CMV $10. each.

T-SHIRTS AWARDS MISC. 1970s - 80s
ROSE BOWL SWEATSHIRT 84
Red - **CMV $20.**
FUTURES CIRCUIT TENNIS
Red t-shirt.
AVON CHAMIONSHIP TENNIS
Red t-shirt.
AVON T-SHIRT
Blue shirt.

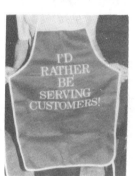

CUSTOMER SERVING APRON 1987
Red apron - white letters & trim. Given to Reps. **CMV $5.**

CHRISTMAS IS FOR CHILDREN APRON 1986
White apron - green & red design. Given to workers only at 6 parties in U.S. **CMV $15.**

APRON AWARD 1979
Fruit on apron with red or yellow border & straps. Given at representatives meetings. **CMV $8. ea.**

T-SHIRT AWARDS 1985-86
I'M SO EXCITED
Avon on back. White - red trim. **CMV $10.**
AVON BELT
Red canvas - white letters. **CMV $5.**
AVON - SAME FAMILY - NEW ADDRESS
Red sweatshirt. **CMV $10.**
NIGHT SHIRT - AVON
Red - white letters. CMV $10.
"I SURVIVED THE AVON BRANCH CLOSING KANSAS CITY 1985"
Yellow shirt. **CMV $10.**

APRON AWARDS 1986
"AVON". **CMV $5.**
"I LOVE AVON". **CMV $5.**
I LOVE SUMMER WITH AVON. **CMV $7.**
All are white - red & black letters & trim.

WE'RE HOT T-SHIRT & SWEATSHIRT & BUTTON 1984
Red T-Shirt & Sweatshirt & We're Hot button. Given to Reps - **CMV button $5.** T-Shirt **$10.** Sweatshirt **$12.**

T-SHIRT AWARD - "WE CAN DO IT TOGETHER" 1984
Red T-shirt given to Reps. **CMV $10.**
YOU'RE HOT - HOT PAD AWARD 1982
Red & white glove hot pad. Given to Reps. **CMV $3.**

CIRCLE OF EXCELLENCE BEACH ROBE & BAG 1977
White terry cloth robe trimmed in light blue with C of E on pocket. White canvas bag C of E 1977. **CMV $15. - Bag. $35. - Robe.**

SPORTS BAG AWARDS - 1980s
AVON SPORTS
Silver & black bag. Avon sports red patch on both sides. **CMV $30.**
GIRL SCOUT AVON BAG
Silver & black bag. Girl Scouts Leadership today & tomorrow on back side. Avon on other. **CMV $30.**
AVON CHAMPIONSHIPS OF WASHINGTON TENNIS RACKET COVER
White, red trim. **CMV $25.**
AVON CORPORATE PRESIDENT'S DAY 1984
Frisbee shape blue & white bag unzips to make tote bag. **CMV $25.**

TOTE BAGS 1985 - 1986
AVON HAWAII
White. **CMV $12.**
AVON
White. **CMV $5.**
AVON LIFE
Red. **CMV $12.**
HAT AVON
White Avon Hat. **CMV $5**

TOTE BAG "AVON SPORTS" 1982
White canvas, red & lavender letters. Given to staff members of Avon Running Circuit. **CMV $10.**

TOTE BAG "HAWAIIAN" 1983
Turquoise canvas bag given to Top Reps on 1983 Hawaiian trip. **CMV $15.**

AVON RUNNING BAG 1983
White canvas bag with red & fushia color lettering. **CMV $20.**

ROSE PARADE AVON SEAT CUSHION 1984
Reddish orange plastic - white letters. Only 150 made & given to people at Rose Bowl game 1984. **CMV $50.**

LICENSE PLATE FRAME AWARD 1980s
White plastic, marked Avon. **CMV $4.**
MANAGER'S TAMBORINE 1970's
Wood frame, skin marked Avon. Made in China. **CMV $30.**

AWARDS & REPRESENTATIVES GIFTS

TOTE BAG 1987
Canvas bag with red handle & letters. **CMV $10.**
BEACH TOWEL 1987
29" x 60 " white beach towel. Red letters. **CMV $15.**

CIRCLE OF EXCELLENCE LOVE CAMERA 1985
Coke can size love container with top & side C of E labels. Holds small black & red love plastic camera in felt bag. Given to Managers for Hawaii trip. **CMV $10 MB.**

EMPRISE T-SHIRT 1977
Black t-shirt given to Avon managers to introduce Emprise line. **CMV $15.**

HORIZONS CLOTHES BAG GIFT 1977
Given to Avon managers. White plastic bag. **CMV $15.**

TRAVEL BAG - CIRCLE OF EXCELLENCE 1978
White leatherette bag given to 250 district managers. **CMV $50.**

SELLATHON VISOR CAP 1981
(Left) Blue or red. **CMV $7.**
AVON TENNIS VISOR CAP 1981
(Right) White cap. **CMV $7.**

CIRCLE OF EXCELLENCE AWARDS 1979
Each item given to managers on C of E trip to Paris 1979.
TRAVEL ALARM CLOCK
(Lower right) Plaque on top says "Circle of Excellence 1979". **CMV $25.**
TOTE BAG
(Upper right) Dark navy blue. Circle of Excellence on front. **CMV $15.**
CIRCLE OF EXCELLENCE YEAR BOOK
(Center) Blue & gold cover shows all C of E winners. **CMV $10.**
FRAGRANCE & FASHION BINDER
White plastic. **CMV $25 with contents.**

TIME OF YOUR LIFE BAG AWARD 1978
Beige canvas bag with red letters given to Reps. on trip to New York. **CMV $10.**

ENVIRA VISOR HAT - AUSTRALIA 1980
Light pink visor hat given to Reps. at the introduction of Envira in Australia. **CMV $10.**

COLOR UP AMERICA NECK TIE 1979
(Top left) Given to male managers only. **CMV $10.**
COLOR UP FLAG
(Center) **CMV $2.**
COLOR UP HAT
(Bottom) **CMV $4.**

H-E-A-T BAG AWARD 1981
Canvas bag. **CMV $10.**
H-E-A-T HAT
White hat. **CMV $8.**

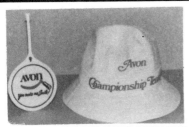

YOU MAKE ME SMILE LUGGAGE TAG 1978
White plastic. CMV$3.

AVON CHAMPIONSHIP TENNIS HAT 1978
White hat, red letters. **CMV $7.**

HARD HAT - CIRCLE OF EXCELLENCE 1979
White plastic hard hat with decal on front saying "Circle of Excellence". Given to managers in Pasadena branch. Hat was not made just for Avon. **CMV $10.**

BASEBALL CAP 1978
Blue & white Avon Products Inc. hat. Used by plant employees. **CMV $12.50**
NECKTIE - AVON 4A 1970's
Used by Avon management. Tie has 4A design & is dark blue. Made of Dacron Polyester. **CMV $12.50.**

PRESIDENT'S CLUB LUNCHEON BANNER 1978
White canvas, red & gold letters. **CMV $20.**

MANAGERS BANNER 1976
White silk banner about 8 ft. long, gold braid, pink letters. Used by managers to encourage Reps. to call on new customers. **CMV $15.**

PRESIDENT'S AWARD PENNANT 1951-52
Royal blue pennant with gold trim & letters. Given to top selling city & district division managers during early 50's. **CMV $45.**

PRESIDENT'S CELEBRATION BANNER 1974
Small dark blue felt banner about 18" long, yellow letters & cord. Used by managers. **CMV $15.**

AVON CHRISTMAS TABLE CLOTH 1977
4x4 ft. blue satin, white letters, used at Christmas dinner 1977 for Avon Reps. in Atlanta branch. **CMV $15.**

PRESIDENT'S AWARD BANNER 1961
Small banner given to top sales team in each division. Each winning division had their name on banner. **CMV $25.**

OUR BANNER YEAR 1966
Used during district sales meetings. **CMV $20.** There are many different banners of this type. **CMV will range $15 to $20 on most.**

COLOR UP AWARDS 1979
Blue & red backdrop used at sales meetings "Color Up America". **CMV $5.**
Color Up Plastic Bag-**CMV .50.**
Color Sale Paper Bat-**CMV .25.**
Color Never Looked So Good On Glasses-set of 6-**CMV $10 set of 6.**
Color Up Scarf-**CMV $2.**
Clutch Bag-**CMV $3.**
Make Up Bag-**CMV $6.**
File Folder-**CMV $6.**
Table Cloth & 4 matching napkins-**CMV $15 set.**
Colors are red, white & blue striped.

GREAT AMERICAN SELLATHON AWARDS 1981
Given to Avon Reps. for meeting top sales goals in C18-81.
T-Shirt-**CMV $5.**
Calculator-**CMV $20.**
Coffee Mugs, set of 2-**CMV $15 set.**
Drinking glasses, set of 4-**CMV $15.**
Hot Plate-**CMV $20.**
Telephone, antique-**CMV $100.**
Travel beach bag-**CMV $15.**
Clock-**CMV $35.**
Directors chair-**CMV $35.**
Umbrella-**CMV $25.**
Poncho in bag. **CMV $10.** All are red, white & blue decoration.

KEY CHAIN "RECORD BREAKER" 1979
Yellow, green, white or pink plastic. Has 4A design & says "I'm an Avon Record Breaker". Given to reps for getting new reps. **CMV $5.**

MATCHES-PRESIDENT'S CELEBRATION 1979
Blue foil top box. **CMV $2**
LUGGAGE TAG 1970'S
White plastic with gold 4A emblem & The Better Way. **CMV $5.**

MOISTURE SECRET MANAGERS GIFT SET 1975
Pink box holds pink plastic jars of creme gel 4oz., enriched freshened 5oz., and night concentrate 3 oz. C-8-75. **CMV $15 set MB.**

WHAT'S COOKING RECIPE BOX 1975
Given to Reps. for drawing their name at sales meetings. Avon on the bottom. **CMV $5.**
NAME TAGS LATE 1970'S
3 different stick on name tags used by Reps. **CMV .50 each.**

AVON SMILE SALES PROMOTION ITEMS 1978
Are all red and white.
SILK SCARF-$6
BALLOONS-2 different, .25 each
HAT-paper, $1
THE SMILE LIPS-red paperlips, .50.
RECORD-Avon Smile-red, small record, $2.

VALENTINE-PRESIDENT'S CLUB 1980
Given to President's Club Reps. Red valentine and white, red and green lace hankercheif, **CMV $5** mint in envelope.
KEY CHAIN HEART 1978
Red plastic heart given to managers. **CMV $2.**

TEDDY BEAR CANDLE AWARD 1980
Small plastic bear candle holder. Given to Avon Team Leaders. Neck tag says "From Avon with Love". Red candle. **CMV $20.**

DISTINGUISHED MANAGEMENT AWARD LUGGAGE TAG 1966
Plastic name tag for luggage on white strap. **CMV $7.50.**
POCKET ADDRESS MEMORANDUM 1966
2"x3" white w/gold lettering. **CMV $8.**

TRAVEL SURVIVAL KIT 1982
(Top) Given to managers March, 1982. **CMV $7.**
AVON CALLING KEYCHAIN AWARD 1980
(Bottom) Clear lucite with blue letters. Given to Avon Reps. **CMV $7.50**

MOISTURE SECRET PRESIDENT'S CLUB GIFT 1975
Sent to President's Club members to introduce Moisture Secret. **CMV $6 MB.**
I KNOW A SECRET PIN 1975
For President's Club members. Pink pin. **CMV $1. $2 on card.**

TEDDY BEAR TEAM LEADER GIFT 1981
White ceramic heart shaped box. Given to Team Leaders for 1981 year end party. Can also be bought in Hallmark stores. Does not say Avon . CMV $10 MB

TEDDY AWARD 1979
Black base with plaque. Brown top & bear has red shirt with Avon in white. Given to one Team Leader for recommendation support in each district. CMV $55.

TEDDY BEAR COOKIE JAR AWARD 1979
Tan & red ceramic bear cookie jar. Given to Team Leaders at Christmas. CMV $25.

POLLY PROSPECTING BIRD AWARD 1977
Stuffed toy by Possem Trot. Tag has Avon Products on it. Given to Avon managers for recruiting new reps. Came with 2 large cards as shown. CMV $25 with Avon tag. Add $1 each card. Came in Avon mailer tube & letter. CMV $35 MB all.

SALES AWARD SACHET 1962
Cream sachet in blue glass with blue, gold & white lid. Gold metal stand. $12 jar only. $15 in box.

AWARD BANK 1980
Black & gold tin bank. Given to Avon managers in Springdale branch. Special hold label on front says "Fifth National Bank & Trust Co. Springdale Branch. Assets 367 Managers, R. Manning President". Bottom marked "Made in England for Avon". CMV $30.

CABLE CAR MUSIC BOX AWARD 1981
Only 100 given to Circle of Excellence Managers at San Francisco C of E meeting. Was not made for Avon. CMV $35.

TED. E. BEAR TEAM LEADER GIFT 1978
Tan teddy bear with red shirt was given to all team leaders at end of year party Nov. 1978. Fold out Teddy Bear card was on each table at party. CMV $4 card, CMV $25 bear mint.

MONTE CARLO BRASS BOX AWARD 1981
Brass box with burgundy velvet lining. Lid inscribed Casino Monte Carlo. Given to Avon managers eligible to win a free trip to Monte Carlo. CMV $40.

TEMPO MANAGERS GIFT 1978
(Left) .33 oz. splash cologne. Given to district sales managers at August Conference 1978. Came with red felt belt. CMV $15 in bag.

TEMPO SPRAY ATOMIZER GIFT 1978
(Right) Given to avon Reps. for advanced orders of Tempo fragrance. Silver color container red letters. "Tempo Fall 1978" printed on bottom of case. Came in beige velvet bag, red pull string in special issue box. CMV $10 MB.

PRESIDENT'S CAMPAIGN COMPACT AWARD 1966
Case marked sterling silver & back marked "Branch Champions President's Campaign 1966". Came in white & gold Avon box in felt bag. CMV $35 in silver case MB.

ANNIVERSARY HONOR AWARD PURSE 1966
Red leatherette purse given to Reps. for high sales. 4A design on snap & Avon Anniversary Honor Award in gold letters on purse. Came in Avon box. **CMV $15 purse only. $20 MB.**

SURPRISE GIFT 1960
Silver and Gold box contained one Deluxe Lipstick. Given as a Christmas Gift to all representatives **CMV $22.50 MB.**

CIRCLE OF EXCELLENCE TOTE BAG 1976
Tan & brown tote bag with C of E on front. Given to Avon managers on Hawaii C of E front. Given to Avon managers on Hawaii C of E trip. **CMV $16.**

AWARD PURSE 1960'S
Avon marked box holds beige vinyl clutch purse trimmed in brass. Made by St. Thomas. Given to Reps. during President's Campaign. Purse does not say Avon. **CMV $9 mint in Avon box.**

PURSE AWARD 1951
Egg shell off white purse with clear plastic closure. Given to Avon Reps. for best sales. Came in Avon box. Purse not marked Avon. Must be in Avon box. **CMV $27.50 MB.**

ANNIVERSARY CAMPAIGN AWARD PURSE 1961
Same purse with deluxe lipstick & compact as Champagne Mood Set. In Avon award box. **CMV $20 MB.**

TRENDSETTER CARRY ALL BAG 1975
Made of tan burlap & brown leatherette. Given to managers only. **CMV $45.**

CIRCLE OF EXCELLENCE TOTEBAG 1972
About 18" across, black plastic. For trip to Mexico. Aztec calendar design. Given to C of E managers on Mexico trip. **CMV $30.**

FOAMING BATH OIL SAMPLE GIFT 1975
Given to President's Club members. 1/2 oz. bottle, white cap. President's CLub label on bottom. Came in introductory envelope. **CMV $3.50 in envelope.**

PORTFOLIO BAG AWARD 1935
Red two tone brown leather bag with suede inside. CMV with matching key case, billfold, change purse, 2 way mirror. Given to top 77 Reps in U.S. for top sales during Mr. McConnell birthday celebration. **CMV $75 complete.**

CIRCLE OF EXCELLENCE BAG 1981
White canvas bag, red line around bottom. Given to managers in San Francisco C of E trip. **CMV $15 mint.**

CIRCLE OF EXCELLENCE MAP 1981
Map of San Fraancisco given to C of E managers on trip. **CMV $3.**

FASHION PRIZES 1974
Given to Reps. for meeting sales goals. Blue & white in color. Made only for Avon.
(Bottom) Christian Dior Scarf, 14" x 44". **CMV $8.**
(Top Right) Sport Tote Bag 10" high 14" wide. **CMV $10.**
(Top Left) Kadin Hand Bag, blue sail cloth with white vinyl trim. Given to President's Club members only. 8" high, 10" wide. **CMV $12.**

CIRCLE OF EXCELLENCE TOTEBAG 1979
Khaki color bag. Says "Circle of Excellence'. Given to top 250 managers. **CMV $15.**

ATTACHE CASE AWARD 1981
Maroon case with brass corners & black leather handles. Does not say Avon but comes in Avon plastic bag. **CMV $10 in Avon bag.**

COOLER SEAT AWARD 1981
Yellow nylon insulated cooler seat given to Reps. for selling Avon vitamins in Springdale branch. Has Avon on seat. **CMV $15.**

MONEY ORGANIZER & BALL POINT PEN AWARD 1980
Tan canvas & brown trim, 4A design on side holds "President's Club" insignia pen. Given to President's Club Reps. for selling $325 of products in C16-17 1980. **CMV $10.**

GREAT OAK BAG AWARD 1980
Canvas bag. **CMV $10.**

PRESIDENT'S CAMPAIGN AWARD PURSE 1965
Bone beige coin & bill purse with 4A design on flap. Given to each Rep. in 2 top sales teams in each branch for greatest sales increase over year before period. **CMV $15.**

AVON CART AWARD 1980
Canvas wheeled cart collapses to make a hand bag. Given to Reps. for selling $525 in C16-17 1980. **CMV $25.**

S.M KENT COLLECTION AWARDS 1975
Given to Reps. for reaching 4 different levels of selling certain amounts. Robe & handbag were for only President's Club members to win. The scarf was awarded for finding a "hidden customer" in territory. All items have brown or beige A's & signed by S.M. Kent (designer for Avon). CMV clutch $10. **CMV Robe $20. CMV Purse $15. CMV Tote $12. CMV Cosmetic $8. CMV Scarf $7. CMV Order Book Cover $5.**

SUNNY MAKE UP CASE 1976-78
Blue vinyl reptile grain case with Avon zipper tag. Inside has clear vinyl pockets to hold make up samples. Won by Reps. for signing up a new Avon Rep. and also sold to Reps. **CMV $6.**

BEACH TOWEL AWARD 1982
32" x 59" size, white, black & red. Given to reps. **CMV $20.**

AWARDS & REPRESENTATIVES GIFTS

These Sales Mates available later this year.

SALES MATES PRIZES 1978
Will be awarded in 1978 for top sales goals. All are tan vinyl with Avon "A" design. Order book cover & pen CMV $3, Tote bag CMV $7, Sample kit CMV $6, Fragrance Demonstrator CMV $4.

JEWELRY DEMONSTRATOR PRIZE 1978
Tan vinyl with "A" design given to Reps. for selling $600 worth of Avon in 3 campaigns. Measures 13" long and 8" wide. **CMV $7.**

PORTFOLIO SHOULDER BAG 1953
Light color linen covered shoulder bag to carry Avon order book and samples. Won by Reps. for placing a $100 order. **CMV $20 mint.**

PRESIDENT'S SERVICE AWARD PURSE 1963
Given to all Reps. who called on 35 or more customers during President's Campaign 1963. Egg shell color vinyl coin purse with 4A design on snap. Box says "Avon Fashion First". **CMV $20 MB.**

PURSE - AVON PLANT TOUR GUIDE 1970
Gray plastic purse with heavy silver chain. 4A silver button on purse. Used by tour guides at Avon Plants. **CMV $20.**

TOTE BAG 1977
White canvas with black nylon straps. Came from Avon in New York. Was not issued to Reps. in U.S. **CMV $25.**

SWEET PICKLES BAG GIFT 1978
Green canvas bag given to district managers on introduction of Sweet Pickle products. **CMV $12.50 bag only.**

TASHA STOWAWAY BAG 1980
Purple shoulder bag given to Reps. Avon tag inside. Pink inside bag. **CMV $15.** Managers also got the same bag without the brass snap on the outside. Same color inside as outside. **CMV $20.**

SALES MATES PRIZES PRESIDENT'S CLUB 1978
All are tan & beige in color, covered with "A" design. Umbrella, Beauty Showcase handbag and jewelry demonstrator given to President's Club Reps. for selling $975 worth of Avon in C4-5-6 1978.
CMV Umbrella $20.
CMV Jewelry Demo Case $7
CMV Handbag $7.

TASHA UMBRELLA "I'M NUMBER ONE" 1980
Tan silk umbrella given Reps. on Flight to Fantasy Trip to Monte Carlo. **CMV $30.**

LIBERTY WEEKEND UMBRELLA 1986
Red & white umbrella. Marked Avon Liberty Weekend. Rare N.Y. Liberty Celebration. **CMV $125.**

APRIL SHOWERS UMBRELLA GIFT 1976
(Left) Beige canvas, wood handle. Avon in blue letters. Given as recommendation prize. **CMV $27.50.**

ADVERTISING UMBRELLA 1977
White Avon box holds brown plastic handle umbrella. Has the names of Avon & magazines & TV shows Avon advertises on. Given to district managers. **CMV $30 MB.**

PRESIDENT'S CELEBRATION UMBRELLA 1977
Marked New York. Given to winning teams. **CMV $35.**

UMBRELLA & BAG AWARD 1980
Tan & brown Avon bag comes with Avon umbrella. Given to Reps. for selling $425 of products in C16-17 1980. **CMV $18.**

TOTE BAG & UMRELLA AWARD 1970
Fawn color leatherette bag & matching coin purse inside. Came with umbrella with tortoise handle. Was not made for Avon only. Must be in Avon box as shown. **CMV $20 for all MB.**

AVON TENNIS UMBRELLA 1980
Only 50 silver nylon with fine wood handle umbrellas were given to press & promoters of Avon tennis matches. Comes in matching silver pouch. Rare. **CMV $125.**

AVON TENNIS CLOTHES BAG 1980
Red & white patch on silver & black nylon travel bag. Comes in small carrying pouch. Given to players of Avon tennis matches. **CMV $35. Rare.**

AVON TENNIS WRISTS BANDS 1980
Pair of white cotton wrist bands used by players in Avon tennis matches. **CMV $4.**
AVON TENNIS HAND TOWEL 1980
White cotton, used by Avon tennis players. **CMV $10.**

EMPLOYEE GIFT 1939
Blue box with Avon's Suffern Plant on box. Holds Tulip label and gold cap of Cotillion Toilet water. CPC label & Cotillion powder sachet. Rare. **CMV $125 MB.**

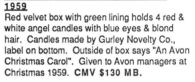

CHRISTMAS CAROL CANDLE SET 1959
Red velvet box with green lining holds 4 red & white angel candles with blue eyes & blond hair. Candles made by Gurley Novelty Co., label on bottom. Outside of box says "An Avon Christmas Carol". Given to Avon managers at Christmas 1959. **CMV $130 MB.**

UMBRELLA LIPSTICK AWARD 1981
White nylon, black & red trim, red plastic handle. Given to Team Leaders. **CMV $25.**

58th ANNIVERSARY GIFT BOX 1944
Holds heart shaped sachet pillow. Given to all Reps. on Avon's 58th anniversary. **CMV $100 MB.**

DESK SET ACHIEVEMENT AWARD 1979
Black plastic note pad & pen. Given to district managers for sales achievement. **CMV $15 with pen.**

ANNIVERSARY ALBUM AWARDS SET 1942

Book type box opens to show 2 satin pillowettes with 56th Anniversary on back of each. One is blue & one pink. Given during Anniversary campaign. **CMV $125.**

56th ANNIVERSARY AWARD 1942

Satin Sachet pillows given to each Rep. who worked her territory for 56 hours during the Anniversary Campaign. Came 2 to a box, in blue & pink. **CMV $30 mint.**

BETSY ROSS RED GIFT SET 1941

Set given to employees of Avon's Suffern Plant as Anniversary campaign gift. Rare. Came with handwritten gift card. **CMV $100 MB.**

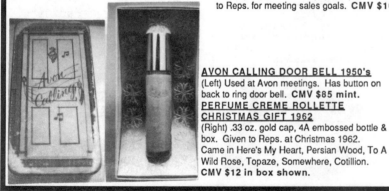

AVON CALLING DOOR BELL 1950's

(Left) Used at Avon meetings. Has button on back to ring door bell. **CMV $85 mint.**
PERFUME CREME ROLLETTE CHRISTMAS GIFT 1962

(Right) .33 oz. gold cap, 4A embossed bottle & box. Given to Reps. at Christmas 1962. Came in Here's My Heart, Persian Wood, To A Wild Rose, Topaze, Somewhere, Cotillion. **CMV $12 in box shown.**

DOOR BELL - DOOR KNOCKER AWARDS 1979

Redwood box with brass Avon Calling door knocker on front, door bell on back side. Given to 5 managers in each division. **CMV $75.**

MANAGER DESK SET AWARD 1972

Has 4A emblem, marble base, 14K gold plated pen. Set made by Cross. **CMV $60. $75 MB.**

DESK SET PRIZE 1973

Brown plastic came with paper & pen. Given to Reps. for meeting sales goals. **CMV $10.**

INKWELL & PEN SET AWARD 1977

Blue & gold display box holds wood base with old glass ink well & 3 feather quill pens & plastic bottle of ink. Avon card about pen set. Avon brass plaque on base. Given for recruiting new Reps. **CMV $45 MB.**

88th ANNIVERSARY DESK SET 1974

White marble base. Black pen. Turquoise & silver 4A says "Avon 88th Anniverary". Given to Reps. for selling $125 worth of Avon. **CMV $15. $20 MB.**

REPRESENTATIVE GIFT CIGARETTE CASE 1961

Siver colored metal case. 4A design & Christmas 1961 on lid. **CMV $47.50.** Also given to managers in gold tone case. **CMV $70.**

DESK VALET - CPC AWARD 1922

Solid bronze. Marked CPC 1922. Awarded to CPC Reps. **CMV $100.**

BIRTHDAY FLOWER GIFT 1981
White Avon box of artificial flowers comes in 4 different kinds. Given to Avon Reps. on their birthday. Box says "Warm Birthday Wishes - Your Friends at Avon". **CMV $5 MB.**

WINNING TEAM DESK SET AWARD 1976
Given for best sales team in district in 1976. White marble base, silver color pen. **CMV $8.**

LETTER OPENER MANAGER AWARD 1975
Red & black box holds wood handle letter opener. Brass Avon lady insignia & K.C. No. 1, 1975 on hand. **CMV $20 MB.**

CIRCLE OF EXCELLENCE LETTER OPENER 1976
Given in Indiana only to C of E Reps. Only 25 were given. Brass plaque & door knocker pin is embedded in black plastic handle. **CMV $40.**

TEDDY BEAR ADDRESS STAMP AWARD 1981
Brown & tan plastic. Says "Avon". Has teddy bear in address imprint. Given to team leaders. **CMV $5 MB.**

QUICK STAMP ADDRESS AWARD 1980
Made of plastic. Has Avon Reps. name & address on it. Given to Reps. for selling $325 in products in C16-17, 1980. **CMV $5.**

NAME STAMP AWARD 1967
Won by Reps. for reaching sales goal in campaign 12. Metal stamp has Avon 4A design on stamp. **CMV $7.**

NAME STAMP 1972
Two-toned blue with name & address. Awarded for entry into President's Club. **CMV $4.**

STEAK KNIFE & CARVING SET 1972
C-12, 1972. In Avon box. **CMV $20 each set MB with sleeve.**

SPOON - PRESIDENT'S CLUB AWARD 1979
(Left) Silver plated serving spoon marked "Avon President's Club 1979". Came in Avon box. **CMV $10 MB.**

CAKE SERVER AWARD 1978
(Right) Silver plated serving spatula. "Avon 92nd Anniversary - President's Club 1978" on spoon. Given to all President's Club members. Special box & card. **CMV $10 MB.**

50th ANNIVERSARY SPOON - 1936
Gold spoon engraved "Compliments Mr. & Mrs. D. H. McConnell - Anniversary 50". The gold on these spoons does not stay very well so many are found silver. **CMV in box gold spoon $100 mint. Silver $50 spoon only. Spoon with gold, mint $75.**

CPC SPOON "STERLING SILVER" 1915

Sold as souvenir at the CPC exhibit at the Panama-Pacific International Exposition. Front reads "Palace of Liberal Arts - Panama-Pacific Exposition Tower of Jewels". Back of spoon reads "CPC 1915 Court of Four Seasons". **CMV $100 with card shown, $75 spoon only.** Was also given to Reps. for selling 12 CPC talcum powders, 1 free for each 12 talcs.

WINDBREAKER 1980

Blue jacket, red & white trim. Sold to Avon employees in Springdale branch for $15. Modeled by Dwight Young. **CMV $15.**

CANDID BLAZER & TIE 1977

Off white blazer with CA on left pocket. Given to division managers only. Came in both male & female sizes. Tie is Candid color with CA on it. Very few of these blazers around. Modeled by Dwight Young. **CMV Blazer $75. CMV Tie $10.**

AVON AWARD SPOONS 1969

6 silver plated demitasse spoons. Each engraved with a design signifying a different fragrance: Occur, Rapture, Unforgettable, Regence, Brocade & Charisma. Each spoon was given in this order for progressively higher sales. A seventh spoon was given to each Rep. in the winning district of each branch. It was engraved "1886-1969" and had a picture of the 1886 Sales Lady. **CMV $45 set MB with sleeve or $5 each spoon. 7th spoon $12.50 in silver envelope.**

AVON RUNNING RAIN COAT 1981

Shown front & back side. Given to people helping in Avon Running Tournament. Red plastic. Modeled by Vera Young. **CMV $10.**

BLAZER JACKET 1977

Blue blazer with 4A design buttons. Inside label says "Made exclusively for the Avon Representative by Family Fashions". Sold to Avon Reps. Red Avon sewn on patch for pocket. **CMV $35.**

SILVERWARE AWARD 1938

Made only for Avon. Each piece marked on back Simeon L. & George H. Rogers Co. Ltd. X-tra. Given for meeting sale goal during Avon's 50th Anniversary. 55 piece set. **CMV set in box. $125 mint.**

CPC SILVERWARE 1920-30's

Used in CPC fatories for employee eating areas. CPC stamped on back of knife, fork & spoons. **CMV $5 each piece.**

AVON REP. BIRTHDAY GIFT 1982

Box says "A birthday gift for you". Satin & lace heart pincushion. Comes with Avon card. Given to Reps. on their birthday. **CMV $5.**

MANAGERS CHRISTMAS GIFT 1980
Red & white scarf and mittens given at Christmas time. **CMV $30 set.**

TOCCARA AWARDS 1981
(Sweater) Dark navy blue with Avon tag. Given for 1st level sales achievement. **CMV $10.**
(Caftan) Lavender & white with Avon Toccara label. Given to 2nd level sales achievement. Came in shiny silver plastic Toccara bag. **CMV $25 in bag.**

CIRCLE OF EXCELLENCE AWARDS 1979
Each item given to managers on C of E trip to Paris 1979.
TRAVEL ALARM CLOCK
(Lower right) Plaque on top says "Circle of Excellence 1979". **CMV $25.**
TOTE BAG
(Upper right) Dark navy blue. Circle of Excellence on front. **CMV $15.**
CIRCLE OF EXCELLENCE YEAR BOOK
(Center) Blue & gold cover shows all C of E winners. **CMV $10.**
FRAGRANCE & FASHION BINDER
White plastic. **CMV $25 with contents.**

AVON SMILE HAT 1978
White hat given to Avon collectors at Houston, Texas, 1978 National Association of Avon Club Convention by Avon Products. Modeled by the late Charlie Crawford. **CMV $15.**

ODYSSEY AWARDS 1980
(Bathrobe) Pink bathrobe given to Reps. for meeting 2nd level sales goals. **CMV $25 in Avon bag.**
(Nightgown) Pink nightgown matches bathrobe. Given to Reps. for meeting 1st level sales goals. **CMV $15 MB.**

TOCCARA PILLOW AWARD 1981
Dark blue satin pillow with Avon card. Given to managers at August Conference. **CMV $15 with Avon card.**
AVON REP. CHRISTMAS GIFT 1981
Red box says "Happy Holidays Avon 1981". Tapestry design address book. Managers book says "District Manager" on front. **$15 MB.** Reps. same except plain on front. **CMV $10 MB.**
HOSTESS APRON
Cotton tapestry design apron given to team leaders who met requirements. **CMV $15.**

CIRCLE OF EXCELLENCE TOWEL 1979
Given to top 250 managers. **CMV $20.**

I'M GOING TO MONTE CARLO MAGNET 1981
(Center) Given to managers. White, red & gold. **CMV $4.**
VALENTINE SUCKER 1981
(Left) Red heart shaped sucker with red tag. Given to Avon managers. **CMV $10.**
NUMBER ONE SCARF AWARD
(Right) Given to team leaders. **CMV $4.**

TOWEL RACK PRIZE AND MILK GLASS SOAP DISH 1972
An exclusive Avon prize. **CMV rack, $5. Soap dish $10.** White glass dish, 2 white hand towels, gold initials, black & brass stand.

AVONS BEST BANNER 1982
(Top) Red & white banner. **CMV $5.**
AVONS BEST SCARF 1982
(Bottom) From Morton Grove branch. Red & white scarf given to managers at Atlanta Conference. **CMV $15.**

PRESIDENTS CAMPAIGN GLACE AWARD 1967
Managers is in script writing with white lined box. **CMV $22.50 MB. $18.50 compact only.** Representatives is in block writing on Presidents Campaign with blue felt lined box. **CMV $10. $12 MB.** Both came in Hawaiian White Ginger box.

SILK SCARF AWARD 1970
Beige & brown silk scarf. 4A design. Given to Avon reps. **CMV $20.**

CIRCLE OF EXCELLENCE BEACH TOWEL 1976
White & brown towel given to managers on C of E Hawaii trip. **CMV $20 mint.**

AVON CURTAINS 1960's
Used to decorate in offices & Avon Plant. **CMV $22.50.**

64TH ANNIVERSARY SCARF 1950
Silk scarf was made only for Avon. Given to representatives for selling 64 pieces of Avon in campaign 9, 1950. Silk scarf has blue border, white center with sketches in turquoise & rose. Some words on scarf say "Long, long ago"; "A thing of beauty is a joy forever"; "The doorway to loveliness". **CMV $50.**

T-SHIRT - AVON RUNNING 1979
Red t-shirt given to each runner in Avon marathon race. **CMV $10.**

FOUNDERS CAMPAIGN ACHIEVE-MENT AWARD SCARF 1941
Blue & white folder holds blue border, white pink & green silk scarf. Shows 1st CPC factory & 1st Avon lady with "The doorway to loveliness" marked under her. Given to reps in 1941. Very rare. **CMV $75 in folder mint, $50 scarf only mint.**

SYMPHONY SCARF 1952
Blue background with pink rose & parts of letters in French. Pure silk. Purchased from store in New York & awarded for selling 36 products in the Prelude to Spring campaign. **CMV $30 mint.**

AVON SCARF 1972
All silk pink, orange & white scarf with 4 big "A" on it. Avon in corner. Made in Italy. Came in silver box. **CMV $12. mint.**

CANDID SCARF GIFT 1976
Silk scarf designed by S.M. Kent in Candid folder. Given to Avon President's Club members. **CMV $7.**

TASHA AWARDS 1980
Monte Carlo scarf, **CMV $20.**
Tasha picture of the late Princess Grace of Monte Carlo with Tasha card. **CMV $20.**
Tasha matches - box & book matches, **CMV $1 each.**
Items were won by reps on Avon trip to Monte Carlo.

4A QUILT 1971
Reversible, ruffled edged, cotton filled comforter in gold, avocado or blue. Given for having a person recommended a a representative appointed. **CMV $50 mint.**
4A QUILT 1969
Pink quilt with white 4A design. **CMV $50 mint.**

4A WALL PLAQUE 1960's
Used at sales meetings. Large size. **CMV $25.**

PRESIDENT'S CLUB APRON 1978
Beige & red canvas apron says "I'd rather be selling Avon". Given to all President's Club reps. Modeled by Grace Powers. **CMV $10.**

WHAT'S COOKING APRON 1977
Blue apron was won by Reps at sales meeting in drawing for getting new Avon ladies. **CMV $7.**

IT'S NOT YOUR MOTHER'S MAKEUP APRON 1977
Light khaki color and orange plastic apron. Used by Avon managers at sales meetings to introduce colorworks. **CMV $10.**

AVON APRON 1948
Aqua in color with white center. Avon in center & pictures of Avon products of 1948. Given to Managers only for sales demo. **CMV $50 mint.**

WALL PLAQUE 1960's
Used at sales meetings. Blue & gold cardboard. **CMV $25.**

MOONWIND MANAGERS DISPLAY 1970
Silver and blue cardboard display. **CMV $10.**

JAM GIFT SET AWARD 1980
Set of 16 small jars of jam with front label "Especially for You from Avon". Given to managers. Was not made only for Avon. **CMV $10.**

AFTER CONFERENCE MINTS 1979
Pink box of fifty 1979 Susan B. Anthony dollar coins with card for Avon managers for Outstanding Recuiting. **CMV $100 MB, with all 1979 coins mint.**

VALENTINE GIFT TO REPRESENTA-TIVES 1976
Whitman Sampler went to all reps. with Avon card. **CMV $3 with card only.**

VALENTINE CANDY 1978
Red and gold heart box. Holds 4 1/2 oz. of chocolates by Bartons. Back of box says "This candy heart selected by Avon and packaged especially for you. Given to Avon reps. **CMV $5 box only. $10 MB full.**

GENERAL MANAGERS HONOR AWARD 1960
(Top) Order book cover in blue. **CMV$8 mint.**
HONOR AWARD ORDER BOOK COVER 1959
(Bottom) Red plastic with gold trim, also had gold pen. **CMV $10.**

ORDER BOOK COVERS 1980-81
Blue plastic. Avon pen inside. Given to all new Avon reps. Gold Avon stamped on face. **CMV $2. Also came wtih Avon stamped upside down. CMV $5.**

TREND SETTERS ORDER BOOK AWARD 1976
(Left) Yellow plastic with 4A design and Avon Trend Setters on front. Given to Avon Trend Setters Reps. **CMV $5.**
TEAM LEADER MIRROR GIFT 1977
(Right) Mirror in red plastic, holder with white star and letters. Given to Avon Team Leaders at Avon luncheon, Dec. 1977. **CMV $4.**

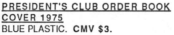

PRESIDENT'S CLUB ORDER BOOK COVER 1975
BLUE PLASTIC. **CMV $3.**

ACHIEVEMENT AWARD ORDER BOOK COVER 1960'S
(Left) Light blue cover. **CMV $7.**
ORDER BOOK -CANADA 1977
(Right) Dark blue plastic. Used by reps in Canda. Came with blue and gold pen and order book. **CMV $5.**

ORDER BOOK COVER 1973
Blue and green design matches delivery bag. Has turqoise and gold pen. Earned for prize points. **CMV $5.**

75 YEAR HONOR AWARD ORDER BOOK 1961
Red with gold letters. **CMV $8 mint.**

PRESIDENT'S CLUB ORDER BOOK COVER 1960
CMV $7.

PRESIDENTS HONOR AWARD ORDER BOOK COVER 1977
Blue plastic with gold trim. **CMV $8.**
REGENCE ORDER BOOK HONOR AWARD 1966
Green plastic with gold trim to match Regence packaging. **CMV $3.**

CHECK COVERS 1973
Red & green plastic check book covers given to Reps. CMV $3 each.

CARD CASES AWARDS 1970'S
President's Club. Pink & turqoise; vinyl. CMV $2.50. Top one Foreign. CMV $5.

BROCADE HONOR AWARD ORDER BOOK COVER 1967
Given to Reps. for calling on customers during introduction of Brocade. Came with Avon pen also. CMV $5. With pen $8.

PRESIDENTS CELEBRATION ORDER BOOK COVER 1977
Red plastic. CMV $3.
PERSONAL POCKET DIARY 1976
Blue plastic cover with Avon pocket diary and calendar inside. CMV $3.

ORDER BOOK COVER & PEN 1976-77
Given to only new Avon Reps. Blue plastic cover and blue and gold pen. CMV $3.

CUSTOMER SERVICE AWARD 1978
Given to Reps. for calling on 60 customers, "red covers" CMV $4 or 100 customers "gold cover" CMV $6. 2-ring binders were used to put Avon customer addresses in.

TERRITORY DIRECTORY 1976
Blue plastic 2-ring binder used by Reps. for customers in their territory. CMV $2.
BOOK MATCHES 1970'S
Gold matches with red Avon rose. Inside says "Welcome your Avon Rep. when she calls". CMV .50.

DIVISION MANAGERS GUIDE 1980-81
1980 red plastic Avon News and 1981 white. Used by managers for training Reps. CMV $10 each.

ARIANE MEMO BOOK 1977
Red cover Memo Book given to Avon Team Leaders when Ariane came out. CMV $7.

CUSTOMER SERVICE AWARD 1980
Leatherette portfolio given to managers; brass corners on outside of maroon cover. CMV $20.

PRESIDENT'S CLUB PORTFOLIO 1981
Maroon with President's Club stationery. CMV $5.
UNIVERSITY OF AVON PORTFOLIO 1979
Maroon training portfolio for managers. CMV $10.

MANAGERS PHOTO ALBUM 1976
Given to managers. Avon 4A on box. CMV $20 MB.

ALBEE STATIONERY NOTES 1980
Box of 1st Avon lady notes with outer sleeve given to President's Club Reps. **CMV $5 MB.**

DISTRICT MANAGERS ORGANIZA-TION GUIDE 1970'S
Dark blue & gold loose leaf binder, contains guide material. **CMV $10.**

CHRISTMAS GIFT FOR AVON REPS. 1980
Ceramic base & green note pad holder signed by William Chaney, Avon President. Given to all Avon Sales Reps. at Christmas 1980. **CMV $10 MB.**

PORTFOLIO 1974
Red plastic, 4A design for Avon Reps. **CMV $3.**

LADY DESK FOLIO 1971
Pink cover holds calendar to be used as a plan guide for sending orders and making appointments. Given for sending a $75 or larger order in. C1-71 **CMV $7.50.**

CELEBRITY AUTOGRAPH BOOK 1965
Not marked Avon. Only in box. **CMV $5. $8.50 MB.**

SUEDE ORDER BOOK COVER AWARD 1977
Brown plastic suede order book cover holds 4 Avon order books. Given to Avon Reps. for reaching sales goals. 1886 Avon lady embossed on front. Was not awarded in all branches. **CMV $10.**

PRESIDENTIAL WINNERS AWARD 1957
Blue felt booklet given to winning district Avon representatives upon touring district Avon plant. **CMV $30.**

MANAGER-REPRESENTATIVE INTRO-DUCTION BOOK 1952
Turqoise & silver booklet. Used by managers to train new Avon Reps. **CMV $10.**

CIRCLE OF EXCELLENCE PASSPORT HOLDERS 1969-80
Given each year. Each marked Circle of Excellence. Given to top managers only for annual C of E trip. Different color each year. **CMV $5 each.**
CIRCLE OF EXCELLENCE PROGRAM
Given to C of E managers at annual C of E celebraion. **CMV $5 each year.**

MANAGERS SALES MEETING NOTE BOOK 1961
Campaign 15,16,17,18 sales meeting plans. Inside front cover says "# so & so of a limited edition for the Management Staff Only". Cover is red satin 12"x20", comes in white box. For you from Avon on cover. **CMV $75 mint.**

NOTE PAD TRENDSETTERS 1976
Clear plastic, Avon on top holder. Trendsetter note pads. Given to managers only. **CMV** **$20.**

AVON COSMETICS MARKETING HIGH-LIGHT BINDER BOOKLET 1970'S
Used by managers. **CMV $5.**

NICE KRISPIES BOX 1980
Small size cereal box given to team leaders. **CMV $6.**

DIAMOND DECADE HONOR ROLL AWARD 1960-70
Silver with blue 4A booklet. Given to managers for outstanding service. **CMV $12.**

TEAM LEADER CARDS 1978
4 different cards given to team leaders, with bears on them. **CMV $1 each.**

PARIS PICTURE GIFT 1978
French print scene by Bernard Picture Co. given to each manager with French printed Avon circle of excellence card & ribbon. **CMV $7.50. Must have Avon card as shown.**

CIRCLE OF EXCELLENCE MATCHES 1977-79
Given to managrs on trip to Paris 1979. White, gold letters. Matches are gold heads. **CMV $5. Also given in 1977.**
GO AHEAD & DREAM MATCHES 1979
White, red letters. Given to managers at September conference. **CMV $2 mint.**

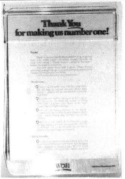

CLIP BOARD MANAGERS GIFT 1979
Front says "Thank You for making us number one". Avon on bottom. Given to managers only. Made of Lucite. **CMV $10.**

AUGUST CONFERNCE PICTURE HOLDER 1978
Tan cover. Given to managers at August conference. **CMV $15.**

DATE BOOK 1979
Rust color date book given out by Avon managers. Inside cover says "A gift from your Avon manager". **CMV $2.**
PENCILS-AVON
1979 Blue marking pen-fine point. **CMV $1.**
1979 Color Up America-red pencil. **CMV $1.**

CALENDAR-PRESIDENT'S CLUB GIFT 1979
Red felt cover calendar with pages of Avon history on inside. Given to President's Club Reps. only. **CMV $4.** Also pictured is President's Club luncheon invitation card. Red. **CMV .50.**

HALL OF FAME PICTURE FRAME AWARD 1987
Leather bound picture frame given to top sales person in each branch. **CMV $40.**

PORTFOLIO AWARD 1984
Left-Red canvass-zippered. Calendar, note pad,calculator,pen. **CMV $15.**
PRESIDENT'S CLUB PORTFOLIO AWARD 1985
Right-Red grained plastic. President's Club writing paper & perncil. **CMV $5.**

FRENCH TULIP ALL YOU NEED KIT AWARD 1986
Red vinyl case holds office supplies. Not marked Avon but box is. Given to Reps. **CMV $20 MB.**
BANK DEPOSIT BAG AWARDS 1985
Both vinyl. 1 red & 1 white. **CMV $3 each.**

PORTFOLIO & CALCULATOR 1984
Red canvas zipper portfolio with small NSC calculator & 1984 calendar & note pad & Avon red pen inside. Given to Reps. **CMV $30.** Calculator also given by itself in red canvas folder. **CMV $15.**

COOK BOOK FOR TEAM LEADERS 1978
Red cover 96 page book given to Team Leaders July 1978. **CMV $10 mint.**

MENU PRESIDENT'S CELEBRATION 1979
Given to President's Club members at their luncheon celebration. **CMV $2.**

AVONOPOLY 1978
Game used by managers at Avon Rep. sales meeting C12-78. Also came with Avon play money of 25 & 50 green notes. **CMV set $12.**

TASHA FLIGHT TO FANTASY VASE 1980
White porcelain vase given to Reps. on Monte Carlo trip. **CMV $40.**
TASHA PASSPORT HOLDER 1980
Given to Reps. on Monte Carlo trip, held luggage tag & misc. Tasha paper items, program, etc. **CMV $20 for all.**

PRESIDENT'S CLUB THANK YOU NOTES 1979
White box with outer sleeve. Both has "President's Club, Avon's Very Best" on lid. Holds 25 thank you notes. Given to President's Club Reps. only. **CMV $5 MB complete set.**

AVON CALLING PHONE INDEX 1971
Given for sending in order of $75 or more. C1-71. **CMV $5.**

WHO'S WHO OF AVON DISTRICT MANAGERS 1977
Red cover book with all Circle of Excellence 1976 winners. 72 pages. **CMV $17.50.**

UNFORGETTABLE INTRODUCTION BROCHURE 1965
Gold cover has red & gold 3D glasses inside cover and 8 pages of introducing new Unforgettable products for Reps only. **CMV $15.**

LUCKY WAGON SWEEPSTAKES GIFT 1970
2 white handkerchiefs with monogram in corner with choice of letters. Given for mens car decanter sales C11-70. In dark blue folder with card. **CMV $7.**

GROW WITH AVON 1974
Avon card with 2 wooden stakes. Many different plants. **CMV $3.**

CARD CARRYING CASE PRIZE 1967
Blue plastic with 4A design and says Avon Cosmetics. Given to Reps. for selling $30 over their sales goals. **CMV $3.**

HANDKERCHIEF GIFT 1965
Pink and white card says "Thank You". Holds white with green and pink design handkerchief given to Reps. for recommendation. **CMV $6 mint with card.**

AVON FUN DOLLARS 1976
Small green paper play five dollar bill. Used by Reps. at meetings. **CMV 50¢.**

CURRIER & IVES COASTERS 1977
Pack of 6 given to Team Leaders at Christmas. Also given to Reps. for recommendation prize. Marked Avon. **CMV $5 pack of 6.**

LINEN TOWEL CALENDAR 1970
Given to all Reps. for sending in an order in C1-1970. Made only for Avon. Measures 15 1/2" x 28 1/2". **CMV $6.50.**

SPRING GARDEN CLUB FLOWER SEED 1978
7 different flower seed packets made up for Avon, given to Reps. at sales meeting. Packaged by James Vick's Seeds. **CMV $1 per pack.**

NOTE PAD PRIZE 1973
Gold plastic with 4A design on front. Has 1973 calendar pad and pen inside. Used by Reps. **CMV $4.**

PICTURE ALBUM AWARD 1966
White Avon box holds large and small picture album and picture frame in brown and gold. Cover says "For you, from Avon". **CMV $45 MB.**

AVON QUEEN CERTIFICATE 1964-65
78th & 79th Anniversary Award Certificates. One red and others blue border. Given to top selling Reps. only. **CMV $10 each.**

MANAGERS INTRODUCTION BOOK 1945
Blue cover, 28 page book, used by Avon Managers to sign up new Avon Reps. 11" x 14" size. Came with clear plastic cover. **CMV $35 mint.**

AVON CHRISTMAS CARD 1976
Green & gold Christmas card. Inside says "From your Avon Representative". Box of 75 cards given to Avon Reps. for recommendation of new Avon lady. **CMV $20 box of 75 mint, or .25 each card mint.**

PLACE MAT AWARD 1966
Plastic place mat showing Avon Daily Need Products. Given to Reps. for meeting sales. **CMV $5.**

PASADENA BRANCH DEDICATION BOOKLET 1947
Gold spiral bound booklet given at opening of Pasadena Branch, Sept. 22-27, 1947. Front says "Avon Serves the Golden West". **CMV $25.**

BEAUTY & FRAGRANCE CALENDAR 1978
Punch out calendar given to special good customers in C24-77 by Avon Reps. Made only for Avon. **CMV $5.** Only given in certain states for test marketing.

TENNIS OFFICIAL BUTTON - 1977
Red futures circuit Avon official button. **CMV $5.**
AVON FUTURES SPONSOR 1980 BUTTON
White - red letters. **CMV $5.**
ROSE PARADE FLOAT DECORATOR BUTTONS
1982 white, 1984 gold. **CMV $10.**
PRESIDENT'S DAY CORPORATE MEDALLION 1983
3" brass medallion with red, white & blue ribbon. **CMV $20.**

BUTTONS
GOING FOR THE GOLD BUTTON 1984
TENNIS CHAMPION SPONSOR 1982
GOOD BYE CHARLIE 1984
100 YEARS BEAUTIFUL AVON
CMV $2. each button.

AVON 100 CUSTOMER SERVICE PIN 1986
Gold & black pin.
AVON 100 YEARS OF BEAUTY PIN 1986
White & black.
WHO'S THE BOSS PIN 1985
Red & white.
WHO COULD SELL AVON PIN 1985
Tan & black.
CMV $2. each.
MUSIC BOX TEAM AWARD 1978
Red painted wood music box made in Japan only for Avon. Brass plate on lid says "You Made Avon Smile". Given to winning team for selling most lipsticks. **CMV $20.**

BUTTONS 1983-85
Misc. buttons given to Avon Reps.
CMV $1.-$2. each.

BUTTONS 1983-85
Misc. buttons given to Avon Reps.
CMV $1.-$2. each.

BUTTONS 1981-85
Misc buttons given to Avon Reps. **CMV $1.-$2. each.**

AVON AWARDS MISC. - 1985-86
ROSE PARADE BUTTON
THE SMILE STARTS HERE BUTTON
LOOK HOW GOOD YOU LOOK KEY CHAIN
AVON ICE SCRAPER
WE THINK YOU'RE BEAUTIFUL MIRROR. CMV $2. each.

BOWLING AVON PATCHES 1981-82
Cloth patches from Baltimore & St. Louis Avon Bowling Tournaments. **CMV $20. ea.**
AVON TENNIS CHAMPIONSHIPS BADGES 1981
1 red & 1 yellow badge. **CMV $20. ea.**
AVON DOUBLE PEN AWARD
White & black & white & blue double pen. **CMV $10.**

CUSTOMERS SERVICE FILE 1969
Turquoise paper box holds file envelopes for Avon lady sales. **CMV $5.**

FILE BOX 1961
(Left) Turquoise cardboard file box with 4A design on lid. **CMV $6 mint.**
DESIGNERS DREAM SWEEPSTAKES AWARD 1971
(Right) C7-1971. White lace handkerchief with note from Avon for sales accomplishments. **CMV $6.50 mint.**

JUNE 15 BUTTON PIN 1971
Bright green to remind customers June 15 was Father's Day. **CMV $3.**
HELLO 1970 BUTTON PIN 1970
Black background with red, yellow & blue letters & numbers. Given to all representatives to tell the world she welcomes successful seventies. **CMV $3.**

EARLY TEAM LEADER RIBBON BADGE 1970's
Yellow badge and ribbon used by Team Leaders at sales meetings. **CMV $5.**
I GOT IT PIN 1978
Gray and white pin given to Reps. at Avon sales meetings. Measures 2 1/4". **CMV $1.**

ZANY BUTTON 1979
Given to Avon Reps. on introduction of Zany Products. **CMV $1.**
TEAM LEADER BUTTON 1979
Given to Avon Reps. **CMV $1.**

I'M THE HEART PIN 1974
Given to Reps. as being the heart of Avon. **CMV $2.**
HI, I'M BUTTON 1981
Says "I'm going to make you feel beautiful". **CMV "$2.**

BUTTON - PINS
1978 Top Horizon 50 pin. **CMV $2.**
1976 Say Yes Yes To No No's. **CMV $1.**
1978 The Smile Starts Here. **CMV $1.**

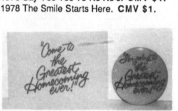

POSTCARD GREATEST HOMECOMING 1978
CMV 50¢.
GREATEST HOMECOMING PIN 1978
CMV $1. Both are yellow & blue. Used for President's Celebration.

AVON 91st BUTTON & RIBBON 1977
(left) Red and white button. **CMV $1, button; & ribbon $2.**
"ASK ME ABOUT THE LOVE OF MY LIFE" BUTTON 1979
(left) White and red button. **CMV $1.**
LUGGAGE TAG 1977
(right) Round white plastic, back side says "The Magic of Avon". **CMV $2.**

CONFERENCE PIN MANAGERS 1946-47
On gold braided rope. **CMV $50 mint.**

4A NAME PIN 1960
Used by Avon Reps. at meetings. 2 1/2" in diameter. **CMV $3.**
COLOR WORKS MAKEUP BUTTONS 1977
Given to Reps. for sales meeting attendance. **CMV $1.**

TEAM LEADER BOOK MARK 1974
Gold & red Book Mark. For Avon Reps. use. **CMV $8.**

ROYAL RIBBON AWARDS 1980
Given to Reps. for sales achievements. Yellow or red ribbon. **CMV $2.** White & blue given with certificate. **CMV $5 each with certificate.** Some dated 1980 and some not.

AVON CARDS AWARD 1980
(right) Silver faced playing cards say 1980 - Avon New York - Las Vegas. Given to Division Managers at Las Vegas conference for Pasadena Branch **CMV $15 MB.**
FRISBEE - AVON 1980
(left) White plastic, blue and red letters. **CMV $10.**

FACE POWDER GOLD KEY 1936
9 1/2" long key is gold on one side with large tulip A & Avon. Back side holds silver face powder sample. CMV label. Given to Reps. only. **CMV $22.50 mint as shown.**

AVON COASTERS 1981
Plastic sheet of 8 white plastic coasters. Had to be cut out. Given to managers. **CMV $5 for sheet of 8.**

FRISBEES - GIFT TO REPS. 1976
White plastic with red letters. **CMV $6.** White with red & green letters. **CMV $8.**

MANAGERS TOOTHBRUSH 1976
Given to managers. Came in different colors. "Avon" on one side; "Prospecting is a habit, too" on other side. **CMV $5.**

CAMEO VANITY SET PRIZE 1965
Made by Syroco only for Avon. Set consists of Cameo brush, 2 combs, vanity mirror, and hand mirror. Given to Reps. for selling 40 cameo lipsticks or compacts for brush and comb. **CMV $7. 76 total for vanity mirror. CMV $13. 100 for hand mirror.**

CHARGE CARD MACHINE 1977
Red plastic, marked Avon. Used by Reps. to take charge cards for Avon Sales. Used only for a short period. **CMV $5.**

McCONNELL FAMILY REUNION COASTERS 1980
Package of 4 white Fiesta Coasters. Center says "James McConnell Family Reunion 1980". Were given at 1st family reunion of David McConnell ancestors since 1948. Very rare. **No price established.**

COSMETIC CASE AWARD 1977
(left) Tan and white plastic zipper purse.
PORTABLE PURSE MIRROR AWARD 1977
(right) Matches purse with mirror. Both given to Reps. by Avon. Both came in plastic bags with Avon on them. **CMV $3 ach. MB only.**

WACKY MONEY BAG 1980
Silver tone bag with red tie string & red $ design. Used at sales meetings. Does not say Avon. **CMV $15.**

LIVE-LAUGH-LOVE TEMPO AWARDS 1979
Given to Reps. on cruise to Caribbean. Red T-Shirt-**CMV $15**
(Left) Picture Cube 1978-Says"New York-Bermuda-Circle of Excellence" **CMV $15.**
(Right) Bahama Stick Pin-In brown felt bag given to Reps. on cruise. Does not say Avon. **CMV $2.**
(Center) Cruise Program -Feb.2-5, 1979. **CMV $2.**

WHAT'S COOKING AVON GIFT 1974
5 yellow plastic scoop, strainer, funnel, egg separator, measurer. Given to Reps. for sales meeting attendance. Made by Geni, a division of Avon. **CMV $2 each.**

TASHA AWARDS 1979
All are pink and purple. (center) Wishing box given to Reps. **CMV $10 MB.**
(right) Dream box with Tasha pin & tray inside given to Managers. **CMV $15 MB.**
(left) Key Chain. **CMV $2.**
(back right) Fan. **CMV $1.**
(back left) Scroll Dream Test. **CMV $1.** All were given to Reps, except Dream box.

JEWELRY WRAP AROUND 1982
Cotton jewelry wrap in lavender box. Box says "You deserve something very special." Given to a few Reps. per district. **CMV $3 MB.**

71ST ANNIVERSARY CAKE 1957
A real cake with 71 on top with Avon card given to managers. Made by Schraffts. **CMV $50.**

AVON DUNCE CAPS 1964-65
Came in several different colors of plastic. Used at sales meetings. 4A design on top and bottom. **CMV $10 each.**

RECORD-HAPPY BIRTHDAY 1980
It's a most unusual day on cover. Given to President's Club Reps. on their birthday. **CMV $5 mint.**

CASTINET AWARD 1975
Given to Circle of Excellence managers only on trip to Spain. Comes with Circle of Excellence orange award card as shown. **CMV $25 MB with card.**

FLIGHT TO FANTASY RECORD 1979
(left) Given to Reps. in C20-79 to introduce Fantasy fragrance. **CMV $3 record and cover mint.**

BON APPETIT COOK BOOK 1979
(right) Given to managers on Circle of Excellence trip to Paris. Avon on front, **CMV $5.**

AVON RECORDS 1970's
Christmas Records, given to Reps. at Christmas. **CMV $3.**
Campaign 21, 1974 Sales Meeting record. **CMV $3.**

AVON CHRISTMAS RECORD 1970
33 1/3 RPM record in blue holder with letter from Avon President Fred Fusse. **CMV $5.**

TEAM LEADER & MANAGERS CHRISTMAS GIFT 1981
Wood case jewelry box with mirror inside says "Avon Team Leader 1981". **CMV $65.**
Same thing given to Avon managers only says "Managers 1981". **CMV $85.**

DOOR KNOCKER RING DISPLAY BOX AWARD 1979
Black ring box with gold tone door knocker on cover. Given to Avon managers. **CMV $30 mint.**

TRAINING RECORDS-FILM STRIPS
Used by managers to show new products at sales meetings. Box came with record and 1 film strip for each record. Have been used for many years by Avon. Many different varieties. **CMV record only $2. $5 set MB.**

RECOMMENDATION PRIZE 1976
Blue plastic case holds 2 order books and an Avon book calculator made by Arizona. Warranty card says "Made for Avon". Given to Reps. for getting 2 new Avon Reps. **CMV $25 mint in working order.**

ROOSTER AWARD 1968
Rooster shape leather covered green glass bottom on wood base. Brass plaque says "Rooster Highest Percent Increase, 4A design & all 7 Avon branches". Given to disrict supervisor. CMV $45.

ARIANE WOMAN PAINTING 1977
25x30 inch original oil painting by Szaro. Used by Avon in Avon Catalog C-22, 1977. CMV not established.

ROSE PARADE JACKETS AWARD 1981-83
Avon Products issued 100 Rose Parade jackets in red to people working with Avon float in '81-'83 parade, rare. Same inscription on front. CMV $100 each.

GATEWAY SPRING COMPETITION AWARD 1977
Lucite man on plastic base & nameplate. Given to managers in Morton Grove branch. CMV $35.

PARKER PEN AWARD SET 1982
2 gold tone Parker pens. Says Avon on side. Given to managers. CMV $35 MB.

MUSK FOR MEN TRAVEL KIT AWARD 1983
Travel kit bag & 2.8 oz. Musk Cologne for men. Comes with Avon letter to reps for meeting sales goals. Bag does not say Avon. CMV $15 MB with letter.

TEAM CAPTAIN AWARD 1972
Awarded to all Team Captains in each district. Thick plastic over lettering with gold frame. CMV $12.

RAIN GEAR COLLECTION AWARDS 1983
Made only for Avon & given to Avon reps for meeting sales goals in 3 levels.
LEVEL 2 WEEKENDER BAG & ACCESSORY BAG
Tan color cotton. Both have Avon Rain Gear tags. CMV $15 set.
LEVEL 3 RAIN GEAR RAINCOAT & UMBRELLA
Tan matching coat & umbrella. Avon tags. Raincoat CMV $25. Umbrealla CMV $25.

PASADENA SUNGLASSES 1982
Blue sunglasses says "Pasadena '82". Made in the shade. CMV $5.
C OF E SALES GROWING BUTTON 1983
Yellow button. CMV $2.
PASADENA NO. 1 BUTTON 1982
White button with red , white & blue ribbon. CMV $2.

YOU DID IT WALLET AWARD 1982
Blue, white & red purse, in red box. Given to reps for $45 increase in sales. **CMV $5 MB.**

TOTE BAG:
9¼" x 4¾" x 12½"

TOTE BAG 1976
Blue brocade bag used by Avon reps to carry demo products. **CMV $3.**

ORDER BOOK & CALCULATOR 1983
Red Avon box has red Avon order book cover with order book, calculator & calendar. 5 reps in each district won them. **CMV $17.50 MB.**

TOTE BAG (WHO COULD SELL AVON) 1983
Beige canvas hand bag, red letters. Given to reps. **CMV $5.**

QUICK STAMP 1982
Red Avon box has pink & white plastic name stamp. **CMV $8 MB.**

TEDDY BEAR AWARD PLAQUE 1980
Certificate in black frame. Given for high sales. **CMV $10.**
TEDDY BEAR RECRUITING AWARD PLAQUE 1980
Ceritficate in black frame. Given for recommendation. **CMV $10.**

BEAUTY SHOWCASE DEMO BAG 1978
Used to carry demo products in by Avon reps. **CMV $3.**

BIG BLACK BOOK 1977
Given to managers. Black foldout clip board. Avon on back. **CMV $5.**

NOTE PAD TOP TEN 1983
Maroon color real leather. Has 4A design on cover. Note pad & telephone directory inside. Given to top ten reps in Newark branch. **CMV $20 mint.**

MANAGERS CHRISTMAS GIFT 1959
Beige box with blue velvet lining holds French hand made bead purse & Majestic cultured pearl necklace. Given to managers at Christmas 1959. Very rare. Set not marked Avon, but valuable. **CMV not established.**

FOOT HILL DIVISION HIGHEST DOLLAR SALES INCREASE AWARD PLAQUE 1982
Wood base plaque given to managers only. **CMV $40.**

JEWELRY BOX AWARD 1965
White box has 2 lids, blue inside, 4A design & says "Bleding Corticelli" inside lid. Given to managers. **CMV $15 box only mint.**

PRESIDENTS HONOR SOCIETY AWARD 1983
Plaque in gold tone glass picture frame. Given to reps for top sales. **CMV $15.**

FEEL LIKE A STAR BUTTON 1981
3" blue & white button. **CMV $2.**

JEWELRY BOX PRESIDENTS SALES COMPETITION AWARD 1983
Black lacquer music box made only for Avon. Bottom says "President Sales Competition 1983". 8"x 4 3/4" size. Given for sales goals. Comes with Avon card. **CMV $25.**

DIRECTOR'S CHAIR AWARD 1980
White folding chair with green seat & back. Back says "You never looked so good". Given to reps for signing up new Avon reps. **CMV $20.**

BEAR PRIDE OF NEWARK AWARD 1982
Small 6" bear hobo name tag with gold tone chain & pendant around neck. Says "Thanks for making us No.1 & 4A design" on 1 side & "District managers are the pride of Newark" on the other side. Bear must have Avon pendant. **CMV $30.**

KEY CHAIN NEW YORK AWARD 1982
I Love Avon's New York on front. Given to group sales leaders at Leadership Circle Celebration in N.Y. **CMV $15.**

NECKTIE 1980'S
Blue necktie with "Avon" in red, white & blue design. Label says "Neatwear Tie London, The Club Tie Specialist". Given to Avon Executives. **CMV $25.**

AVON BEAR SMALL TEDDY AWARD 1979
About 6" high brown bear. Made in Korea, given to managers. **CMV $50.**

KEY CHAIN YOU NEVER LOOKED SO GOOD 1982
White plastic, black letters. Never issued to reps. CMV $5.

CALCULATOR-COLOR UP AMERICA AWARD 1979
(Left) Avon color never looked so good on face of calculator. Came in Avon leatherette case & matching box. Given to Reps. for sales awards. CMV $22.50 MB.

COME COLOR WITH US ANNOUNCEMENT 1979
(Right) Inside has crayola & invitation to meeting. CMV $2.

AVON'S SPRING FEVER 1968
Green felt board with 6 tin painted flowers pins. Managers gave a pin to each representative for recommending a new Avon representative. **$35 complete card mint. Each pin $4.**

MERRI RAT AWARD 1982
(left) White stuffed rat with pink ears & feet, red hat has wood sign around neck "To the best from your N.Y. Buddy". Given to Avon managers just for the hell of it. CMV $20.

TEDDY BEAR SWITCH TO AVON 1982
(right) Small brown & white stuffed bear. Red Avon banner, made by Ruso. Given to winning team in each district. CMV $7.50.

RECOMMENDATION CASIO PRIZE 1980
Casio LC 315 calculator in 4A design black case.

REPRESENTATIVE CHRISTMAS CARD GIFT 1976
White Avon embossed box holds hand screened fold-out glass Christmas card given to all Reps. in 1976. CMV $12 MB.

SWITCH TO AVON BUTTON 1982
Blue pin. CMV $1.

AVON OPPORTUNITY UNLIMITED BUTTON 1982
Yellow button. CMV $1.

LOOK A LITE COMPACT AWARD 1981
Lavender and silver trim. Made only for Avon. Given to Reps. & Managers in blue bag. Card came with it. CMV $15 in bag.

PICTURE YOURSELF MIRROR 1970
Two sided mirror with antiqued gold. Awarded for selling 7 body lotions during campaign 7. CMV $7. $9 MB.

RING THE BELL-MANAGERS GIFT 1963
(Left) 61/2" tall brass bell, black handle. Used by Avon managers at sales meetings. Came with red ribbon & 7 bell shaped cards with Avon on each one. Must have Avon bell cards for value. CMV $60.

WALLET & KEY CASE-MANAGERS GIFT 1976
(Right) Leather wallet & key case given to Avon managers with Avon card on top of box. CMV $15.

KEY CASE AWARD 1971
Blue case with large 4A design. CMV $10.

AVON TENNIS BALLPOINT PEN 1980
Gold tone pen says "Avon Tennis" & has tennis racket on side. Given to Avon tennis match players. Comes in tan suede Avon tennis pouch. **CMV $20 mint.**

ARIANE VASE AWARD 1978
Clear lucite with Ariane Avon on side. CMV $15.

CUSTOMER SERVICE PENCIL 1980
Red & white large pen. **CMV $4.**

DAISY CHAIN JEWELRY & PIN 1971
White and gold earrings, 2 different pins or a daisy topped pen could by chosen by a representative for each person recommended as a representative. Only one gift for each name. **CMV $6 each. Daisy display card $7.**

YOU'RE THE HEART OF AVON AWARD 1986
Calculator, black & silver color. Given to managers. **CMV $50**

PRESIDENT'S CLUB CANDIDATES PEN SET AWARD 1980
Red & gold Avon box holds gold tone pen & pencil set. Inscribed on side of pens, "President's Club Candidate". **CMV $25 MB.**

KEY CASE AWARD 1967
Blue case with gold 4A emblem. Given to Reps. for reaching sales goal in campaign 12. **CMV $10.**

KEY CASE FLASHLIGHT 1970
Red key case with flashlight inside. Not marked Avon. Made only for Avon. Given to Reps. for meeting sales goals. **CMV $5. $8 MB.**

DIVISION MANAGERS TRIBUTE PEN 1969
Silver pen with 4A on clip. Came in blue flannel sleeve & white box. **CMV $35 MB.**

PEN FOR LEADERSHIP AWARD 1969
Silver, black top with olive leaf on top. Garland Pen. Given to Avon Reps. **CMV $15 MB.**

FORUM MONEY PEN AWARD 1977
Clear plastic pen full of chopped up money. **CMV $10.**

15 YEAR PEN SET AWARD 1976
2 Cross 14K gold filled pens engraved "Avon 15 Years" & person's initials. Both pens are in gray felt bags & pink leather pen holder with gold. 4A pen with red ruby in center & gold rose embossed. **CMV $75 MB.**

STERLING CLOCK PEN AWARD 1979
Sterling silver pen with digital clock & calendar inside. Inscribed "Number 1 in $ Inc.", plus name of division. Given to managers only. **CMV $50 MB.**

You've helped us win like you always do, And along with our thanks comes a bear hug for you!

TEDDY BEAR PEN AWARD 1979
Cross chrome pen with small bear marked TL for Team Leader. Avon bear sleeve fits over box. **CMV $27.50 MB.**

PRESIDENT'S CLUB PEN AWARD 1979
Parker 75 silver & gold pen. Inscribed on side, "President's Club 1979". Comes in blue felt Parker case. **CMV $20.**

DIVISION MANAGER'S PEN & PENCIL SET AWARD 1969
Sterling silver pens. 4A emblem on pens. Came in blue brocade Cross pen box. Given to managers only. **CMV $50 set MB, each pen only $20.**

AWARD PENCIL 1950
Deluxe Eversharp, gold color. Given to Reps. for writing 50 or more orders in campaign 2, 1950. 5 inches long with "Avon Woman of Achievement on pencil. **CMV $40 pencil only, $50 MB.**

TOP REPRESENTATIVE PEN GIFT 1975
Brass & black design ball point pen. Small size. Came in red velvet lined, plastic display box & gold sleeve. Given for meeting sales goals. **CMV $10 MB as shown. Pen only $5.**

AVON PEN AWARD 1940'S
Yellow & black plastic, "Avon "on clip. Fountain pen on one end, lead pencil on other end. No information. **CMV $35.**

AVON PENS 1970'S
Blue & silver "Diamond Quarter 1977". **CMV $2.**
Red pen says "Get Write to the Point-Sell Avon". **CMV $2.**

RAIN HAT 1972
Plastic rain hat in pink & white case. Given at Beauty Salons only. **CMV $2.**

DING-DONG AVON CALLING PEN 1974
Given at Christmas. Black & white pen. **CMV $3.**

RADIO AWARD 1985
White, plastic battery powered Blue face. AM-FM in blue sleeve Avon Box. Given to Reps. **CMV $35 MB.**

CHRISTMAS MAGIC PENCIL 1960'S
White pencils from Avon. **CMV $1 each.**

CIGARETTE HOLDER AWARD 1934
Made of solid ivory in velvet lined custom made blue & gold box marked "Avon" inside lid. Green & silver center band. **CMV $75 MB.**

WORLD OF CHRISTMAS-FLOWER PEN AWARD 1970
Small white pen with red, yellow & green holly flower on cap. Given to Avon Reps. **CMV $3.50 mint.**

AVON BRASS MOLD STAMP 1936-53
2" brass mold stamp in reverse says "Avon Products Inc". "Tulip A" in center-New York-Montreal. **Rare-CMV $150.**

84TH ANNIVERSARY FLOWER PENS 1970
Given for sending in an order C-12 84th anniversary. White barrel with red printing with yellow, pink, red, orange or white rose. **CMV $2 each, $3 in cellophane wrapper with card.**

WESTERN CHOICE (STEER HORNS) "MANAGERS" 1967
Managers received the steer horns in a special box with "Avon" embossed all over the box. Was used to show at meetings on introduction of Steer Horns. Rare in this box. **CMV $45 MB as shown.**

RADIO AWARD 1980
Red and white plastic AM-FM Avon radio given 1 to each district manager to give at a drawing. Made by ISIS, in box. **CMV $85 MB.**

PRESIDENT'S CELEBRATION CANDLE HOLDERS 1980
Blue candles in clear glass base. "Avon" on bottom label. Given to all Reps. at banquet. **CMV $12 pair.**

SUGAR 'N SPICE CANDY JAR AWARD 1980
(left) Glass jar full of red candy drops. Yellow neck label. Red Avon sleeve fits over white box. Given to President's Club members. **CMV $6 MB.**

ULTRA WEAR DEMONSTRATOR 1980
(right) Box holds clear plastic box with steel ball to test Ultra Enamel to customers. Given to Avon Reps. in C10-80. **CMV $5 MB.**

ZANY RADIO 1979
Orange and pink Zany bottle shaped AM radio made in Hong Kong for Avon Products. Given to Avon customers in a drawing. Came in pink bag and certificate. **CMV $25 MB, $20 mint in bag complete, radio only $15.**

ZANY BAG AWARD 1979
Given to Reps for ordering 10 Zany products. Orange canvas bag. **CMV $4 mint.**

UNSPOKEN PRESIDENT'S CLUB VELVET BAG 1975
Blue velvet bag with President's Club tag. Came in plastic bag. **CMV $10 bag.**

UNSPOKEN PERFUME VIAL 1975
Blue box holds small 1-5/8" vial Unspoken perfume. Given to Managers only. Outside sleeve on box. **CMV $10 box.**

TOPAZE JEWELRY AWARDS 1960
Awarded for sales of Topaze products. 12 carat gold filled with imported Topaze stones. **CMV necklace-$40-$50 MB, bracelet-$60-$70 MB, earrings $30-$40 MB.**

TOCCARA SWEATER AWARD 1981
(Bottom) Navy blue sweater made by Lady Botany only for Avon. Given to Reps for selling 12 bottles of Toccara cologne spray. **CMV $15.**

TOCCARA CAFTAN AWARD 1982
(Top) Blue, lavender & silver caftan given to Reps for selling 20 bottles of Toccara cologne spray. **CMV $25.**

TIMELESS ULTRA COLOGNE MIST
FOR PRESIDENT'S CLUB ONLY 1974
2 oz. size, gold cap. 1st issue to Avon President's Club members only, had 4A design on bottom under label. Regular issue had Avon on bottom. Box also came with special card saying it was collectors edition, fall 1974. **CMV $6 MB shown.**

TIMELESS MANAGERS GIFT SET 1975
Gold box holds perfume rollette, cologne mist & creme perfume. Given to Avon Mnagers only at introduction of Timeless. **CMV $35 MB.**

SONNET AWARDS 1972
(all earned for selling Cologne Mist)
VANITY TRAY
10" white plastic, gold trim. **CMV $10.**
VANITY BOX
White plastic, gold tirm. **CMV $18 MB.**
THREE PANEL MIRROR
White and gold. **CMV $24 MB.**
HOSTESS ROBE
White satin, gold trim. (won by Presidents Club members only) **CMV $30 MB.**

REGENCE EARRINGS AWARDS 1966
Gold with truqoise settings. Customer service award campaign 14-18, 1966. Has green velvet box. **CMV $60 in box.**
REGENCE NECKLACE AWARDS 1966
Crown performance award. Gold with turqoise setting & gold crown set in center, can also be worn as a pin. Has green velvet box. **CMV $50 MB.**

RAPTURE PIN 1964
(Right) Silver gray in color. **CMV $7. Pin only- $10 on Avon card pictured.**

RAPTURE AWARD BOWL 1965
Fostoria glass bowl with Rapture doves etched in bottom. Given to each Representatives in the winning district during the 79th Anniversary campaign. **CMV $35-MB $40.**

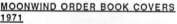

MOONWIND ORDER BOOK COVERS 1971
Dark blue with silver trim. President's Club cover earned for entry into President's Club. Honor Award earned for sales goal. Each came with pen. **CMV $4 Honor cover with pen-$6 President's cover with pen.**

RAPTURE BLOUSE AWARD 1965
Cotton blouse with 2 doves on upper left side of shirt. Came in blue and white. Won by Avon Reps. Modeled by Sally Omann. Avon neck label made by Lady Manhatten. Won by selling 50 Rapture and /or Occur! products. **CMV $20.**

ROSES ROSES AWARDS 1972
ROSES ROSES HOT PLATE 1972
6" square, white Corning Ware with pink and green rose. Given for selling Mist of Roses Cologne. **CMV $12 MB.**
ROSES ROSES GOBLET 1972
Gold trimmed goblet with bouquet of pink artificial roses. Came with card of congratulations. Given for selling Mist of Roses Cologne. **CMV $18 MB.**
ROSES ROSES CLOCK 1972
3" clock by Hamilton, 4 small roses on front. Given for selling Mist of Roses Cologne. **CMV $15 MB.**
ROSES ROSES GOWN 1972
Pink floor length gown with sash. Given for selling Mist of Roses Cologne. **CMV $20 mint. $25 MB.**

ROSES ROSES ORDER BOOK AND PEN 1972
Redesigned size is larger than older Order Books, pink with darker pink rose and green leaves. Given to all President Club members. **CMV $5 mint.**

PATCHWORK CANNISTER AWARD 1972
Level 3. Earned for selling cologne mists. White glass 3 piece cannister set with Patchwork decals. **CMV $25 set MB.**

PATCHWORK BINGO CARD 1973
91/2" paper bingo card used by Reps at meetings. **CMV $2.**

PATCHWORK REFRIGERATOR AWARD 1972
Level 1. Earned by selling cologne mists. White plastic with orange, green, red & yellow patchwork decals. **CMV $10 set-$12 MB.**

PATCHWORK COOKER AWARD 1972
Patchwork design. Level 4. Earned for selling cologne mists. **CMV $30-MB $35.**

PATCHWORK COOKIE JAR AWARD 1972
Level 2. Earned for selling cologne mists. White glass with orange, green, red & yellow. **CMV $12-MB $15.**

IMPERIAL GARDENS AWARDS 1973
Earned for selling certain numbered Cologne Mists for each level.
Level 1 BUD VASE
White china with orange and gold trim. **CMV $8 MB.**
Level 2 TRAY
White plastic with orange and gold trim. **CMV $10, $15 MB.**
Level 3 GINGER JAR
White china with orange and gold trim. **CMV $25 MB.**
Level 4 ROBE
Beige with orangish pink trim and floral sash. **CMV $25 MB.**
FIELD FLOWERS ORDER BOOK COVER & PEN 1971
President's Club. One was given for being eligible for membership. Honor award was earned for sales goal. Cover on left-Canadian President's Club Honor Award. Each came with Avon pen. **CMV $5 each with pen.**

IMPERIAL GARDEN TEA SET 1973
White Bone China with Imperial Garden design. Given to one Representative in each district when her recommendation name was drawn at the Christmas Party. **CMV $175 MB.**

HANA GASA HAPPI-COAT AWARD 1970
Yellow with orange and green flowers. Given when someone a Representative recommended was appointed as a Representative. One size fits all. **CMV $10 mint.**

HANA GASA JEWELRY AWARDS 1970
Enameled pin and clip on earrings are deep red and purple. Given when someone a Representative recommended was appointed as a Representative. **CMV $15 set.**

HANA GASA UMBRELLA 1970
Bamboo painted in Hana Gasa colors. Used at sales meetings at introduction of Hana Gasa. Came in Avon box. Very rare. **CMV $100 in box.**

FIELD FLOWERS UMBRELLA AWARD 1971
(Left) 18" spring green nylon umbrella has cream colored floral-relief handle. Given to Reps for making sales goals. **CMV $10.**

FIELD FLOWERS RAIN CAPE AWARD 1971
(Center) Given to Pres. Club Reps only for making sales quota. Beige with floral sash. **CMV $20.**

FIELD FLOWERS TOTE BAG AWARD 1971
(Right) Cream colored wet looking vinyl tote bag. Field Flowers pattern inside. Given to Reps for achieving sales goal. **CMV $12.**

EMPRISE PURSE AWARD 1977
Black satin purse with jewel snap. Has gold carrying chain inside. Purse does not say Avon on it. Given to Reps for top sales of Emprise products. Came in clear plastic bag marked Avon. Designed by S.M. Kent. **CMV $10 MB.**

EMPRISE NECKLACE GIFT 1977
Gold double E necklace given to Avon Team Leaders to introduce the new fragrance. T.L. on back side and it came in an Avon box. **CMV $10.** District Managers also got one marked D.M. on back and in D.M. Avon box. **CMV $15 MB.** Was also given to Division Managers. **CMV $15 MB.** Emprise money clip for male Reps. **CMV $15 MB.**

ELUSIVE CLUTCH PURSE AWARD 1969
(Left) Pink leather with gold trim. Awarded for selling cologne mists. **CMV $10.**

ORDER BOOK COVER 1969
(Right) Pink plastic with gold "Avon Honor Award" on cover, came with pink & gold pen. **CMV $7.50.**

ELUSIVE BALLAD 1969
(Back) Small black record marked Avon in pink sleeve. **CMV $6.**

ELUSIVE BLOUSE & CUFFLINKS AWARDS 1969
Blouse light lavender silk with label with S.M. Kent signature & Avon. Cufflinks are gold with pink sets. Awarded for selling Elusive cologne mists. **CMV $10 Blouse-$7.50 Cufflinks.**

ELUSIVE PINK & GOLD SCARF AWARDS 1969
Given to Avon sales ladies on first Elusive sales campaign. White box has 4A design & signed by S.M. Kent, designer. **CMV $7.50 MB.**

CHARISMA JEWELRY AWARD 1968
Red & gold necklace, bracelet & earrings. Given for meeting or exceeding a prize goal. **CMV $37.50 set MB-$12 each MB.**

CHARISMA ORDER BOOK COVER 1968
(Back) Introducing Charisma. Came with red pen. **CMV $5-with pen $6.**

CANDID SALES LEADER TROPHY 1977
Wood base with brass plaque with bottle of Candid cologne mist glued in base. Given to 1 Rep in each district who sold the most Candid cologne mists on its introduction. **CMV $12.50.**

CANDID BAG FOR MANAGERS 1976
Maroon and white canvas bag. Back side says Avon, New York, London, Paris, CMV $10.

BIRD OF PARADISE ORDER BOOK COVERS
(Left) Canadian. Presidents Club earned for eligibility into Presidents Club. Honor Award earned for sales goal. Each came with pen in matching design. CMV $5 each with pen.

BIRD OF PARADISE ORDER BOOK COVER 1970
Blue & turquoise, awarded for qualifying for Presidents Club, has matching pen. CMV $7.50.

BIRD OF PARADISE SCARF 1970
Awarded for selling cologne mists. Blue and turquoise silk. CMV $10.

ARIANE ADDRESS BOOK 1977
Red velvet booklet with note pad and address book. Chrome pen has no markings. Given to team leaders. CMV $6.

ARIANE "INCH" NECKLACE 1977
Silver container holds small vial of Ariane cologne. 3 different ones, came in red velvet bag, 1 for Avon Reps with black pull cord on bag. CMV $15 in bag. 1 for President's Club members with PC on back of necklace and silver pull cord, CMV $20 in bag. 1 for Managers, sterling silver, back side says "August Conference", has red pull cord, CMV $50 in bag.

CANDID TOTE BAG 1977
Light colored canvas bag given to Reps for going to C-10 sales meeting. CMV $3. They could also win a Candid matching purse organizer. CMV $3.

AVON 100 DEVOTEE PERFUME AWARD 1986
.33 oz. glass stopper perfume given to Managers. Same as public issue only inscribed on bottom of gold tone container "100 years of Beauty 1886 Avon 1986". CMV $15 MB.

MOONWIND TRAY 1971
(Top Left) Blue glass tray trimmed in silver emblem of Diana in center. Given for selling 10 Moonwind cologne mists during C18-19. CMV $22-MB $25.

MOONWIND JEWELRY BOX 1971
(Bottom Left) Blue & silver. Emblem of Diana on top in silver. Given for selling 20 Moonwind cologne mists in C18-19. CMV $25-30 MB.

MOONWIND ROBE 1971
(Right) Blue, zipper front with silvery trim. Zipper pull is emblem of Diana. Given to President's Club representatives for selling 35 Moonwind cologne mists. CMV $30-MB $45.

BIRD OF PARADISE ROBE 1970
Blue terry cloth robe given to Reps for selling 24 Bird of Paradise 3 oz. cologne mists in C-19-1970. Came in S-M-L sizes. Bird of Paradise on pocket. CMV $35.

BIRD OF PARADISE AWARD JEWELRY 1970
Gold pin, bracelet and earrings with turquoise stones. CMV pin $12, bracelet and earrings $20 MB.

TOCCARA SALES ACHIEVEMENT MIRROR AWARDS 1981
Managers mirror in chrome frame CMV $20. Avon Rep mirror came without frame and is a little larger. CMV $10.

TOCCARA PINS 1981
3 different pins. Same design on face, edges are different. **CMV $10 each.**

TOCCARA NECKLACE AWARD 1981
Toccara design on one side & Avon Toccara 1981 K.C. on back. Sterling Silver pendant & chain in Tiffany bag & box. Given to Division Managers. **CMV $100 MB.**

IMARI 1ST EDITION COLOGNE AWARD 1985
1.2 oz. spray cologne marked First Edition 1985 on bottle. Given only to Reps. **CMV $15.**

FIFTH AVENUE TOTE BAG AWARD 1986
Vinyl bag. Black, white & blue. Given to Reps. **CMV $5.**

FIFTH AVENUE SCARF AWARD 1986
Matches the tote bag. 35x35". **CMV $5.**

FIFTH AVENUE COSMETIC BAG AWARD 1986
White, black & blue vinyl bag given to Reps. **CMV $3.**

CIRCLE OF EXCELLENCE STATIONERY ROME 1983
2 boxes given to all managers on trip to Rome in 1983. **CMV $25 MB set.**

GREAT AMERICAN SELLATHON PRIZES 1981
Name tag, **$1.**
Luggage tag, **$2.**
Menu Presidents Celebration, **$2.**
Portfolio, **$2.**

VIVAGE SCARF AWARD 1985
White, pink, blue, yellow silk scarf. Avon Tag. Given to Reps. **CMV $5.**

DEVOTEE TREASURE BOX AWARD 1986
Brass & glass box mirror bottom. Given to Reps. in black box. **CMV $25 MB.**

VITAMIN SALES RIBBON 1979
Red ribbon for Avon vitamin sales in test market only. **CMV $10.**

PAVIELLE MINK PENCIL AWARD 1983
Red Avon pencil with small mink attached. Given to district managers. **CMV $3.**

COIN GLASS HANDCRAFTED BY FOSTORIA

By Orgreta Simmons

The Fostoria Glass Company began operations in Fostoria, Ohio on Dec. 15, 1887. This site was chosen becase of a promise of very low cost for natural gas for their furnaces. However, the gas field was short-lived and in 1891, Fostoria moved to Moundsville, West Virginia, its present location.

During the first 10 years, Fostoria made pressed ware. About 1897, oil burning lamps were added to the line and soon became a major part of the production. Today, the lamps are highly prized by antique collectors. As electric lights replaced the oil burning lamps, other handmolded items were created, such as dresser sets, table sets containing tumblers, spoon holders, sugar and creamers and upright celery holders.

Early in the century Fostoria realized the importance of fine quality blown stemware along with crystal service. They began to concentrate more on glassware for the home. This was, and still is, produced in the "much higher than average" quality of glassware.

When Coin Glass was first produced, th date of 1887 on coins was used, being the year that the Fostoria Company was founded. On the original pieces of coin glass production, real coins were reproduced. Since this was contrary to law, the U.S. Government quickly stopped production and ordered the molds destroyed. Today, the antique flavor of the stimulated coins and the lovely old shapes produce collectors items to grace contemporary living. Fostoria Coin Glass is now produced in crystal, amber, olive green, blue and ruby. Fostoria for Avon has only been produced in crystal.

Like collectors of Avon coming together and forming the National Associaton of Avon Clubs, likewise, there is a Fostoria Glass Society of America, Inc., a non-profit organization, which furnished much of the information for this article. Fostoria, like Avon, has a colorful past history and is a story all of its own. The plant covers 8 acres of ground and has over 450,000 square feet of floor space. About 420 persons are presently employed and there are 90 employees who have been with Fostoria from 25-40 years. Most employees are highly skilled craftsmen that take great pride in their work.

As traditional with Avon wanting to offer their customers only the best, in 1961, Avon selected Fostoria to produce Avon's 75th Anniversary year memento of the founding of the CPC Company. This was the first Fostoria Coin Glass piece offered by Avon and was the Coin Glass Wedding Bowl. In 1977, for 91st Anniversary of Avon, the Fostoria Company revised the date to 1886 for Avon. This brings up a highly controversial subject about the dates on Coin Glass. Information from Fostoria states that no exclusive items are made for Avon and that Avon does select pieces which are available to Fostoria Dealers around the country. However, for the items selected by Avon, the molds are revised to show the 1886 date. Then, since the molds are owned and retained by Fostoria, the 1886 dates can be found in retail stores on some pieces as Avon does not "own" the 1886 date. For this reason, the cartons and boxes that Fostoria is shipped to Avon Representatives is definite proof that the item is an Avon issue, the collectors should retain the packing box to prove its authenticity status. Each white cardboard box has "Avon" inscribed on it and is your proof that the item came from Avon. However, on the "Coin Glass type" of Fostoria where the Avon motifs are used in lieu of the dated coins, it would appear that these items were made exclusive for Avon you don't need a box to prove that they are Avon.

This article furnished by
Mid America Avon Collectors Club
Ogreta Simmons, Editor
Kansas City, Missouri

Following are some Fostoria Awards given by Avon. There may be others.

1961	Coin Glass Wedding Bowl
1961-72	Coin Glass Covered Compote
1961-72	Coin Glass Oval Center Bowl
1961-72	Coin Glass Candle Holders
1960's	Coin Glass Cake Plate
1960's	Coin Glass Tall Covered Compote
1963	Crystal 77th Anniversary Queen Award (11 1/4" bowl with 4A design)
1964	Coin Glass 78th Anniversary Salt & Pepper, Cruet and Tray
1970	Crystal Creamer and Sugar, Henry Ford Design
1971	Coin Glass Plate
1971	Coin Glass Short Bud Vase
1971	Coin Glass Handled Nappy
1971	Coin Glass Creamer & Sugar
1971	Coin Glass Salt & Pepper
1973	Lead Crystal dessert plate and bowl, set of 4 each
1977	Coin Glass Footed Compote with AVON emblems
1977	Coin Glass Round Center Bowl, AVON emblms
1977	Coin Glass Candle Holders, AVON emblem
1978	Lead Crystal Plates, came in 2 sets of 4 each

1978	Crystal Candy Dish with 4A design. (Christmas gift)
1980	Crystal Team Leader Recruit-A-Thon Bell

Some of the Fostoria items sold by Avon are as follows: (there may be others)

1969	Salt Cellar w/small silver spoon
1973	Perfumed Candle Holder
1974	Covered Compote w/Skin So Soft bath oil capsules
1975	George Washington Goblet Candle Holder
1975	Candlelight Basket Candle Holder
1976	Martha Washington Goblet Candle Holder
1977	Mount Vernon Sauce Pitcher Candle Holder
1977	Hearts and Diamonds, Soap Dish w/soap
1977	Crystal Egg Soap Dish w/egg-shaped soap
1978	Hearts and Diamonds Loving Cup Candle Holder
1978	Hearts and Diamonds Candlestick for 2 sizes of candles
1979	Crystal Pool Floating Candle
1980	Crystal Bud Vase w/scented carnation
1980	Ring Holder
1982	DAD Paper Weight
1983	Images of Love Picture Frame, Paper Weight
1983	MOM Paper Weight

SILVER PHOTO FRAME AWARD 1916
Solid sterling silver frame 4 1/2" high by 3 1/2" wide. Oval band is 1/2" wide, velvet back. Given to Reps. for selling $50 at Christmas. **CMV $350.**

PERFUME ATOMIZER AWARD 1927
Peacock blue opaque crystal bottle with embossed gold top. Silk net over bulb. Given to six Reps. In each district for top sales of gift sets in December, 1927. **CMV $125. BO mint, $165. MB.**

MISSION GARDEN PERFUME AWARD 1923
8" tall cut glass bottle with sterling silver trim, glass stopper. Given to Reps for top sales. Very rare. **CMV $250.**

SILVER TOILET WARE AWARD 1915-1917
Silver plate handle whisk broom made by International Silver Co., and two glass jars with silver plate lids of same design. Hair receiver jar shown with hole in center of lid. Puff jar is same only no hole in lid. Set was given to Reps. for selling $75 order in four month period. **CMV Whisk Broom, $75., Jar $125.**

DIAMOND JUBILEE PEARL AWARD 1933
18" long strand of Coro pearls. 14K white gold clasp with diamond inset. Satin lined box and silver metallic cloth outside. Given to 75 top Reps. in U.S. in July, 1933. **CMV not established.**

PENDANT LAVALLIERE AWARD 1916
Pure gold pendant and chain. Diamond in center of pendant with pearl above. Given to Reps for $150. wholesale order. **CMV $400.**

PRESIDENTS CUP AWARD 1932
81/2" tall silver plate, gold lined. Given to only twenty Reps. in U.S. Engraved on side-winners name, from D.H. McConnell, President California Perfume Co., Inc., July 18, 1932. **CMV $300 mint.**

ELEPHANT CRYSTAL JAR AWARD 1928
6" long and 4" high, wrinkled glass to look like skin. Came filled with Vernafleur Bath Salts. Glass top of elephant lifts off. Given to 36 Reps. for highest sales. This will be considered the 1st decanter Avon ever issued. Very rare. **CMV $300.**

SILVER FRUIT COCKTAIL SET AWARD 1932
Silver plate tray and six silver cocktail bowls. Given for $250. order. **CMV $75. set.**

LAMP AWARDS BY STAFFORDSHIRE 1936
Imported pottery lamps, ivory color with flowers. Shades are shell pink or rose trimmed in rose or gold. Base is gold tone. Given as a pair to top 50 Reps. in U.S. for top sales. **CMV $125. each.**

SILVER TEA SET AWARD 1906
Rogers quadruple silver plate tea set given to CPC reps for selling $100 order. **CMV $300 set.**

TEA SET AWARD 1907
4 piece Rogers quadruple silver plate serving set. Given to Reps. for selling $125 in three months. **CMV $350 set.**

SILVER SHERBET SET AWARD 1932
Silver plate tray and four sherbet bowls. Given for $200 order. **CMV $60 set.**

BROOCH AWARD "GOLD" 1916
Solid gold with one full cut diamond and two pearls. Given to Reps. for $150. wholesale order in four months. **CMV $400.**

SILVER CLOTH BRUSH AWARD 1917
Silver plate back. **CMV $125.**
SILVER HAT BRUSH AWARD 1917
Silver plate back. **CMV $125.**
SILVER JEWEL CASE AWARD 1917
Silver plate jewel box. **CMV $20.** Each piece has the Butler Grey Flower pattern. Each piece was given to Reps for selling $60. in four month period.

TEA SET AWARD 1907
4 piece Rogers quadruple silver plate tea set. Given to Reps. for selling $75. in three months. **CM V $300 set.**

OLIVE DISH CUT GLASS AWARD 1916
8 3/8" long by 4 3/4" wide. Genuine crystal cut glass. Given to Reps. for $30. wholesale order. Made only for CPC. **CMV $200.**

SUGAR & CREAMER AWARD 1913
Glass decorated with sterling silver. Sugar bowl ls 3 1/4" side by 2 3/4" high. Creamer is 4" high by 2 3/4" side. Given to Reps. for selling 40 packages of Laundry Crystals and Starch Dressing. **CMV $100. each piece.**

POCKET WATCH AWARD 1907
14K gold filled watch with either Elgin or Waltham movement. Given to Reps. for $200. order in three months. **CMV $300.**

FLOWER VASE AWARD 1913
Glass vase decorated in sterling silver. Given to Reps. for selling 75 packages of Laundry Crystals and Starch Dressing. **CMV $300.**

CLOCK AWARD "8 DAY" 1913
Eight day Ormuler clock from New Haven Clock Co. Gold plate finish beveled edge glass. 10 3/4" high by 9 1/2" side. Given to Reps. for $100. in sales in three month period. **CMV $750.**

SILVER TOILET SET AWARD 1917
Set holds beveled edge hand mirror of silver plate back and matching silver plate brush and comb. Flower design is Butler Grey pattern. Given to Reps. for selling $96. in four month period in 1917. **CMV $300. set, MB.**

CANDELABRA AWARD 1912-13
Heavy Rogers silver plate. Given to Reps. for selling $75. in four months. **CMV $500.**

CLOCK AWARD "1 DAY" 1913
Ormuler gold plate clock with 2" porcelain dial, 10 3/4" high by 6" side. From New Haven Clock Co. Given to Reps. for $60 in sales in three month period. **CMV $600.**

WATCH AWARD 1906
14dK gold filled case, heavy engraved. Choice of Elgin or Waltham jeweled movement. Choice of small ladies or larger mens watch. **CMV $350. each.**

COMB & BRUSH SET AWARD 1912
Box holds two silver plate brushes and matching comb. Given to Reps. for $75. order in three months. **CMV $300. set MB.**

PUFF & HAIR JAR AWARD 1917
Real cut glass jars with cut glass lids given to Reps. for $50. in sales in January 1917. Given as sets only **CMV $200. each.**

SILVER TOILET SET AWARD 1908
Box holds Rogers silver plated mirror, brush and comb. Given to Reps. for $75. order in three months. **CMV $300. set MB.**

SILVER CANDLESTICK AWARD 1932
Set of two silver plate candlesticks. Given for $50. order. **CMV $40. set.**

CUT GLASS SUGAR & CREAMER AWARD 1917
Real cut glass set given to Reps. for sales of over $50. in February 1917. **CMV $150. each piece.**

LOYALTY BIRTHDAY CELEBRATION AWARD 1934

Three piece W.A. Rogers silver plate tea set given to top 76 Reps. in U.S. during Mr. McConnell's birthday celebration. **CMV $85. set.**

SILVER SUGAR & CREAMER SET AWARD 1932

Silver plate tray and sugar & creamer. Given to Reps. for $85. order. **CMV $75. set.**

SALT & PEPPER AWARD 1931

Chrome plated salt and pepper shakers. Given to Reps. for selling eight jars of Rose Cold Cream in January, 1931. **CMV $30. set MB.**

SILVER PLATTER AWARD 1932

Designed only for Avon. Gold lined center. Given to Reps. for $35. order. Silver plate. **CMV $35.**

CLUTCH POINT PENCIL AWARD 1914

5" long gold filled lead pencil. Given to Reps. for $30. order. **CMV $100.**

ARMY NAVY PEN 1918

Made by Salz Bros. N.Y. Made of Para rubber with 14K gold pen point. Shaped like a bullet. Given to Reps. for $50. order in September, 1918. **CMV $50.**

DINNER DISH SET AWARD 1906

Limoges China, 100 piee set. Given to Reps. for $200. order in three months. **CMV not established.**

DINNER DISH SET AWARD 1905
Made only for CPC. 100 piece set of Limoges
fine china dinnerware. Given to Reps. for a
$200. wholesale order in three months. **CMV
not established.**

CHINAWARE AWARD 1933
A complete set of china dishes could be won
by Reps., a few pieces at a time. Pattern was
made only for Avon. **CMV not established.**

AWARDS - FOREIGN

SILVER CIRCLE PRESENTATION DAY AWARD - AUSTRALIA 1982
Figurine given to Australian Reps for meeting sales goals. **CMV $60.**

TEDDY BEAR CANDLE AWARD - CANADA 1982
(Left) Tan & red bear with white candle & "We're Going All Out To Win" flag on candle. Given to each Team Leader. **CMV $25. mint.**

TEDDY BEAR CLOCK AWARD - CANADA 1981
(Right) Smoke lucite battery operated clock. Given to Team Leaders at August jamboree. **CMV $45.**

PEWTER GOBLETS AWARDS - ENGLAND 1976
Silver pewter goblets came in 3 sizes & were given to Reps for reaching sales goals in 3 steps. **Small CMV $27.50 MB; middle CMV $42.50 MB; large CMV $62.50 MB.** Each came in blue & silver box. 4A design on side of each goblet. They are about 3-4-5 inches in height.

ALBEE AWARD - ENGLAND 1978
Blue & pink figurine of 1st CPC Avon sales lady of 1886. Given to top 10 Reps in each district in England. Bottom says "Florence Albee created exclusively for Avon 1886-1978 Made in England". **CMV $400. MB.**

TEDDY BEAR AWARD - FOREIGN 1980
(Left) French Canadian red shirt. **CMV $40.**
(Right) Australian stuffed teddy bear award in blue shirt. **CMV $50.**

SMILE UMBRELLA, TEAM LEADER - CANADA 1979
White nylon umbrella, red plastic handle. Avon in red. Given to Team Leaders in Canada. **CMV $30. mint.**

FOUR SEASONS AWARD DOLLS - CANADA 1979
Four ceramic dolls of each season in white, blue & beige. Won by Reps. for sales achievement. made only for Avon but does not say Avon on bottom. "Rex Made in Spain" on bottom. Plain cardboard box. **CMV $100. set of 4.**

TEDDY BEAR TEAM LEADER - CANADA 1979
Stuffed teddy bear with French & English Avon tag. Given to Canada Team Leaders. **CMV $35.**

ROSE STEMWARE - CANADA 1976
Given to Reps for meeting sales goals. Each has Avon rose in design. Set consists of: Step 1, 4-5 oz. wine glasses. **CMV $15. set.** Step 2, 4-6 oz. long stem parfait glasses with parfait spoons (spoons say stainless Korea on back). **CMV $25. set.** President's Club, Step 2, 4-20 oz. long stem goblets. **CMV $35. set. CMV complete set $75.**

KVON I.D. PIN - GERMAN 1959-61
(Left) Used 3 years only and name was changed to Avon. Gold and black with 5 pearls. Very rare. **CMV $75.**

SILVER DOOR KNOCKER PIN - EUROPE
Silver Door Knocker pin with black center. 4A design. Came on turquoise Avon card. **CMV $20. on card.**

**PRESIDENT'S CLUB KEY CHAIN - CANADA
1978**
(Left) Clear plastic on gold ring. 4A design.
Given to each President's Club Rep. **CMV
$10.**
**MANAGER'S 90th ANNIVERSARY PIN -
CANADA 1976**
(Right) Sterling silver with 90th on front.
Given to Avon managers. **CMV $25.**

4A OLYMPIC I.D. PIN - GERMANY 1972
Gold color tin stick pin given to German Avon
Reps during Olympics in 1972. **CMV $25.
mint.**

**PRECIOUS MOMENTS MY 1st CALL
AWARD - CANADA 1981**
Same as U.S. issue only inscribed in French.
CMV $40. MB.
**PRECIOUS MOMENTS AWARD "READY
FOR AN AVON DAY" 1981**
Same as U.S. issue only inscribed in French.
Given to Reps. **CMV $30. MB.**

AVON IN CANADA
By Clark Popham

Many of you would like to know how AVON - Canada started.
Following in brief is the story, part history and part from inter-
views to take you back in time to Montreal in 1914.
In 1919, Mr. Charles C. Stewart, 1888-1949, "TIPPIE", moved to
Montreal with his secretary, Miss Murray, and opened the first
Canadian office in the Reed Building. Mr. Stewart was born at
Suffern, New York, grew up in this small town community, and
in 1910 began his life-long career with the Avon Co. then known
as the California Perfume Company. He advanced through a
series of rapid promotions to the position of Secretary to the
Founder of this company, D. H. McConnell, Sr., where he soon
acquired an intimate knowledge and wide vision of the company
and its work. So it was logical that he should be chosen to
assume the managership of the new Canadian Company when it
started in 1914.
Mr. Stewart and Miss Murray with a small ten-person staff set up
the California Perfume Company in a small office in downtown
Montreal.
From the beginning Mr. Stewart built his personality into the
operation of the Canadian Company, his management was a
friendly one, but it also was a steadfast, hardworking one.
Under Mr. Stewart's leadership, Avon of Canada has become
one of Canada's biggest cosmetic companies.
East and west from Montreal the company began to spread
across this great land. In Winnipeg there still lives a lady, now
in her eighty's who worked for the California Perfume Company
back before 1920. She belongs in the vanguard of those ladies,
who like the original Mrs. Albee, should be known as the Mother
of the Canadian Avon Company. Mrs. Marion Verge was employed by the C.P. Co. to recruit and enlist Depot Agents in
Western Canada. Operating out of Winnipeg she would travel
by train and bus to the cities and towns of Manitoba, Sas-
katchewan and Alberta to interview ladies to sell the C.P.C. line
of products. When I spoke to her she was a member of the
Manitoba Avon Bottle Collectors Club and we had a great time
as she reminisced about those days. She would arrive in a
small prairie town and seek out the local rooming house, and
then look for suitable young ladies to employ. Most often she
would find that the landlady of the rooming house was the most
suitable, as she knew everybody in town and was already a
business woman. After a quick training period, she caught the
train or bus and was on to the next town to repeat the process.
Mrs. Verge spent many years on the road for the company
before making her home in Winnipeg and continuing as a
representative herself.
In this way the Company continued to grow with all orders

into Montreal for filling and shipment across the country. Over the years C.P.C. became Avon Canada Ltd. and the Company moved to Pointe Claire, a western suburb of Montreal.
Sales representatives sell not only in the Montreal skyscrapers, but in the glacial-bound territories of northern Canada. Some orders, like those for Newfoundland must travel close to 2,000 miles over land and sea to reach representative's. Besides, the unique physical challenges faced, they must accomodate a market that is 75% English and 25% French. Product labels, brochures, and much of the representative's literature must be printed in both languages. The Company service teams speak both English and French.
Canada manufactures just about all of our present product lines except soap, aerosol and jewelry.

BRACELET TOP TEN AWARD - CANADA 1982
Sterling silver chain & 4A design pendant. Given to top ten President Club reps. White box says "Top Ten District Award Presidents Club 1982". **CMV $75. MB.**

DIAMOND STICK PIN - CANADA 1978
Gold pin with .07 point diamond given to Reps for selling $5,000 in Avon in 6 months. Came in brown velvet box. **CMV $75. MB.**

CHARM BRACELET AWARD - GERMANY 1977
Sterling silver bracelet with possible 8 charms awarded to top selling Reps in Germany. **CMV not established.**

UNSPOKEN AWARD JEWELRY - AUSTRALIA 1977
Sterling silver with blue synthetic aquamarine stones. Earrings, ring & necklace. Each came in blue Avon boxes. **CMV $75. set MB.**

GEMEM'S AWARDS - AUSTRALIA 1979
Necklace with amber color stone. Goldtone. Avon on back. Given to Reps. **CMV $20. MB.** Ring - goldtone, amber color stone. Came in tan felt box. **CMV $25. MB.**

CUSTOMER COUNT DOOR KNOCKER PIN AWARDS - CANADA 1978
Given to Reps for calling on customers. Door knocker design. Pins came with 50, 75 & 100 on pins. 3 different. **CMV 50, $15.; 75, $20.; 100, $25.**

ARIANE NECKLACE PENDANT - CANADA 1978
Given to all Reps in Canada. Dated 1978. **CMV $8.**

AWARD PINS - CANADA 1970s
(Left) Moonwind pin, Sterling silver. **CMV $20.**
(Center) 1977 A Key Pin, goldtone key pin. **CMV $10.**
(Right) 1978 Candid Pin, brass. **CMV $10.** Each of these pins were given to Avon Reps in Canada.

RING AWARD - GERMANY 1977
(Top) Sterling silver ring given to top selling reps in Germany. **CMV not established.**
NECKLACE WISHBONE AWARD - GERMANY 1977
(Bottom) Sterling silver wishbone necklace given to top selling Reps in Germany. **CMV not established.**

CHARM BRACELET AWARD - ENGLAND 1975
Sterling silver bracelet holds 6 silver charms given to Reps for top sales. **CMV $150.**

HEART LOCKET MANAGER'S AWARD - CANADA 1980
(Left) Goldtone locket with tiny diamond chip. Backside inscribed "You're the Heart of Avon". Given to managers only. **CMV $35. MB.**

AVON PIN MANAGERS - CANADA 1980
(Right) Goldtone Avon pin with red enamel center of heart shaped O. Given to managers only. **CMV $25. MB.**

DIAMOND "A" PENDANT NECKLACE - CANADA 1978
10K gold "A" pin with small diamond. Given to 10 top Reps in each division. Came in Keyes brown & gold box. **CMV $75. MB.**

AWARDS - GERMANY
BRACELET 1978
Goldtone marked Avon. Red & black enamel. For high sales. **CMV $16.**

WATCH KEY AWARD 1979
Goldtone watch & chain. Given to Reps for getting new Reps. Avon on back of case. **CMV $55.**

DOOR KNOCKER 1979
Goldtone, small 4A design in center. **CMV $10.**

4A PIN 1978
Silvertone metal. 4A pin given to Reps. **CMV $16.50.**

CHARM BRACELET 1978
Gold chain & 3 charms with pearl, sapphire & diamond in center. Given for top sales. **CMV not established.**

4A PIN - EUROPE 1972
Sterling silver pin with blue stone in center. Given to Avon Reps in Europe. **CMV $15. pin only, $25. MB.**

NO. 1 PENDANT AWARD - CANADA 1977
Gold No. 1 given to all Reps in the winning district of each division for top sales in their division. **CMV $12. MB.**

BIRD OF PARADISE AWARD PIN - CANADA 1972
Gift to Representatives for meeting sales goal of Bird of Paradise products. **CMV $20. MB.**

PRESIDENT'S CAMPAIGN NATIONAL WINNER LOCKET AWARD - CANADA 1969
Sterling silver locket 1" x 3/4" size on 18" silver chain. Given to winning team in each division for top sales. 4A design on front. **CMV $40. MB.**

PRESIDENT'S CAMPAIGN TEAM AWARD - CANADA 1969
Sterling silver pendant on 18" silver chain. Back side says "President 1969" and front has 4A design. Given to all Reps on winning team for top sales. **CMV $25. MB.**

A KEY PIN - CANADA 1977
Small goldtone pin given to Reps for customer list. Blue box. CMV $10. MB.

4A OLYMPIC PIN - EUROPE 1973
Goldtone stick pin. Given to Reps in Europe during 1973 Olympic Games. CMV $40.

EMPRISE PENDANT AWARD - CANADA 1977
10K gold & black "e" pendant given to Rep selling most Emprise products in her district. CMV $40. MB.

TIMELESS AWARDS - CANADA 1975
(Left) Earrings. Gold color, brown center stone. Avon on back. Given to Reps for top sales. CMV $12. MB.
TIMELESS NECKLACE
(Right) Same as earrings. On a long chain. CMV $12. MB.

PRESIDENT'S CAMPAIGN AWARD - CANADA 1969
Sterling silver earrings, brooch and bracelet given to Reps for reaching higher sales goals. 4A design on each piece. CMV earrings $25. MB, brooch $25. MB, bracelet $35. MB.

CANDID NECKLACE AWARD - SPAIN 1981
Goldtone and orange metal. Came in tan felt Avon bag. Given to Avon Reps in Spain. CMV $70.

MANAGER COIN PURSE KEY CHAIN AWARD - FOREIGN 1979
Brass cage coin purse given to Avon managers in Hong Kong. Avon on front of cage. Rare. CMV $50.

AWARD BRACELET - FOREIGN 1973
(Left) Gold chain, first charm with pearl, second charm rose with ruby set. Charms are size of U.S. dime. Awarded for sales goals. CMV $35. each.
MANAGER'S KEY CHAIN - GERMANY 1972
(Right) Made of Sterling silver. Has 4A design on front side. Only 60 were given to Avon managers in Germany for year end conference. CMV $160.

CHRISTMAS PLATE TEAM LEADER GIFT - CANADA 1979
Blue-green pottery plate given to Team Leaders at Christmas 1979. Came with card shown from Avon. CMV $75.

PRESIDENT'S AWARD PLATE - CANADA 1967
Metal plate, 13 1/4 inches. CMV $75.

ANNIVERSARY AWARD PLATE - CANADA 1970
Made of aluminum, given to Reps in C-9-1970. CMV $27.50.

PRESIDENT'S CLUB PLATE - CANADA 1972
Given to all President's Club members. **CMV $25. MB.**

SILVER JUBILEE PLATE - ENGLAND 1977
8-7/8" diameter silver plated plate given to 506 Avon Reps in England, for top sales in their zone in C7-77. Front of plate has the Royal Coat of Arms & Queen Elizabeth II. Silver Jubilee 1952-1977. On back side it has "A Limited Edition Exclusively Created for Avon Representatives". Silver plated plate by Pepper & Hope. Comes in beautiful blue satin lined box. RARE. **CMV $150. MB.**

SILVER JUBILEE PLATE - ENGLAND 1977
In celebrating the 25th anniversary of Queen Elizabeth. Given to Reps for selling 33 pounds (about $50. U.S.) of Avon products in C7-77. **CMV $75. MB.**

PONTESA DISHES AWARD - SPAIN 1976
Set of 4 bowls about 5" across, made by Pontesa & given to Reps in Spain for top sales. Dark pink in color. **CMV $15. MB.** Also came set of 5 bowls & large matching serving bowl for meeting higher sales goals. **CMV $30. set MB.** Gold.

SMILE ORDER BOOK COVER - CANADA 1978
(Left) White plastic and French & English order book inside. **CMV $3.**

CURRIER & IVES AWARD PLATE - CANADA 1977
(Right) Given to Reps for sales. Back side is printed in French & English. **CMV $9. MB.**

CURRIER & IVES AWARDS - EUROPE 1979
Collection made in Bavaria for Avon.
Step 1: Sweets plate, bowl, sugar bowl, cream jug set, cup & saucer. Choice of 1 item for 100 points on above. **CMV $30. each piece.**
Step 2: Choice of 1 for 200 points. Milk jug, biscuit plate or butterdish. **CMV $35. each item.**
Step 3: Choice of 1 for 400 points in sales. Cake stand, coffee pot & tea pot. **CMV $40. each item.**

BELL GIFT
(Bottom Left) Given to Reps at Christmas 1979. **CMV $30. MB.**

POSY VASE
(Bottom Right) Given to Reps for placing an order in C1 and C2-79. **CMV $20.**

PROMISE OF HEAVEN TEA SET AWARD - ENGLAND 1974
21 piece fine English Bone China made only for Avon. Given to top Rep in each zone. **CMV $160. complete set.**

SPRING PROMISE DISH AWARDS - MEXICO 1978
Won for top sales by Mexican Avon reps. Came in 4 steps.
Step 1: gravy boat, salt & pepper shaker, toothpick holder. **CMV $15.**
Step 2: creamer & sugar holder. **CMV $15.**
Step 3: plate & butterdish. **CMV $20.**
Step 4: bowl, coffee pot & bud vase. **CMV $25.**
Made of ceramic by Munoz. All items complete set. **CMV $100.**

MOONWIND AWARDS - CANADA 1971
Blue glass, silver overlay candy dish. Cream and sugar and tray. **CMV $25., jam set $30.**

SILVER CIRCLE AWARDS-EUROPE
COFFEE CUP-GERMANY 1979
(Left) White china with 4A design on cup. Used by employees at Avon plant. CMV $25.
CANDY DISH 1979
(Center) With silver plated base. 1979 in bottom of glass. CMV $35.
CANDY DISH 1978
(Right) Lead crystal dish. Does not say Avon. CMV $25.

10TH ANNIVERSARY HEART OF AVON AWARD-JAPAN 1979
(Left) Box holds white porcelain heart with flower design, bottom says "Heart of Avon Exclusively made for Avon Lady". CMV $45. MB.
BELL CHRISTMAS GIFT-ENGLAND 1979
(Right) White porcelain bell with Currier & Ives design, not marked Avon. White & blue box says "Happy Christmas from Avon". CMV $30. MB.

PRESIDENT'S CLUB CHRISTMAS GIFT-CANADA 1979
(Left) Plastic tree ornament with Noel scene, gold sticker on bottom says Avon's President's Club Gift, 1979. CMV $17.50- MB.
CHRISTMAS GIFT FOR REPS-CANADA 1979
(Right) Fostoria nut bowl with 4A design on bottom. In red & pink Noel box. Came with card from W.E. Griffin, Jr. President of Avon, Canada. CMV $12. MB.

REPRESENTATIVE CHRISTMAS GIFT-AUSTRALIA 1979
Squatty glass decanter says Avon 1979 on bottom. Avon thank you tag around neck. CMV $25. MB.

CHRISTMAS ORNAMENT GIFT-CANADA 1980
Red plastic bulb with Avon sticker on bottom given to President's Club Reps at Christmas. In red Avon box. Comes with 1980 Avon card. CMV $15. MB.

SMILE COFFEE CUP AWARD-CANADA 1979
Set of 6 given to Reps for signing up new Reps in Canada. Came in plain cardboard box. CMV $30. set of 6 MB-$5. each cup.

TRY ME MIRROR AWARD-JAPAN 1980
Goldtone mirror case in brown felt sleeve. White box. Given to Reps in Japan. CMV $15. MB.

CHRISTMAS ORNAMENT GIFT-CANADA 1980
Red plastic bulb with Avon sticker on bottom given to President's Club Reps at Christmas. In red Avon box. Comes with 1980 Avon card. CMV $15. MB.

CREAM & SUGAR AWARD-ENGLAND 1973
White porcelain with green, pink, blue flowers on side. Given to Reps in England. Does not say Avon. Came in plain box. CMV $10. set.

PRESIDENT'S AWARD SPOON HOLDER-CANADA 1967
Gold & turquoise spoon holder. Holds 12 spoons from Oneida Silver with crest of each province on each spoon & 1 for Canada crest. Top says 1867-1967 on one side & Avon President's Award 1967 on other side. Awarded to President's Club Reps only. CMV $125. complete, mint.

AUSTRALIAN AWARDS ARIANE NOTE PAD 1979
Red velvet. CMV $15.
ARIANE INCH
In black bag. CMV $10.
SERENITY CLOCK AWARD
Small white plastic clock made in Germany by Jerger. Has blue serenity flowers on face. CMV $25.
PRESIDENT'S CLUB SILVER PLATED COVERED DISH
Top flips open, glass dish inside. Given to Reps. "Avon President's Club" inscribed on top. CMV $55.

PROMISE OF HEAVEN AWARD-ENGLAND 1974

First step for selling 7 cream sachets won the 9" high white porcelain vase. **CMV $22.50** Second step for selling 15 cream sachets won the white clock, 3 1/2" high x 3 1/4" wide. **CMV $25.** Third step for selling 25 cream sahets won the blue, white & gold electric lamp. **CMV $50.**

ALBEE PICTURE AWARD-CANADA 1982

Rayon & silk picture of Mrs. Albee 1st Avon Lady. French & English on back label. Given to Canada Team Leaders only. **CMV $50. MB**

TEAM LEADER AWARD TRAY-CANADA 1983

12 1/4" size. Chrome plated brass tray. Last gift given to Team Leaders in Canada. **CMV $30.**

PRESIDENT'S AWARD PLATE-CANADA 1967

7 1/2" size aluminum plate. Given to Presidents Club members in Canada. **CMV $85.**

ARKLOW "TEA GARDEN" TABLEWARE AWARD-CANADA 1980

20 piece Honey Stone set with Tea Garden flower design. Given to Reps for sales goals. 3 levels.
COFFEE CUPS
Level 1, set of 4. **CMV $10.**
SOUP & SALAD BOWLS
Level 2, 4 each. **CMV $20 set.**
DINNER PLATES & SMALL SAUCERS
Level 3, 4 each. **CMV $30 set.**

PRESIDENTS CLUB GLASSES-CANADA 1983

Set of 6 glasses with 4A around top of glass. Box sleeve says "You're better than ever" in English & French. Given to Presidents Club reps. **CMV $20 set of 6 with box & sleeve.**

SMILE GLASSES AWARD-AUSTRALIA 1982

Box of 4 smile drink glasses. Given to Australian Avon reps. **CMV $20 set MB.**

CANADIAN KITCHEN AWARD-CANADA 1974

Same as American Patchwork awards only Canada label. White ceramic. 4 levels.
STORAGE JARS
Level 1, set of 2. **CMV $12.**
COOKIE JAR
Level 2. **CMV $15.**
CANNISTER SET
Level 3, 3 ceramic jars. **CMV $25 set.**
PRESSURE COOKER
Level 4. **CMV $35.**

IMPERIAL GARDEN AWARDS-CANADA 1974

Each is white ceramic & orange flowers. Given to Reps in Canada for sales achievement.
BUD VASE
5 3/4" high. **CMV $10.**
CERAMIC VASE
7" hign. **CMV $16.**
GINGER JAR
10 3/4" high. **CMV $25.**

CLOCK PEN-CANADA 1982

Silver tone pen says "Avon 1982" in red letters on side LED clock in top half of pen. Hook is for changing battery. **CMV $25 MB.**

MUSIC BOX AWARD-CANADA 1982
Wood music box in blue color. Wood trim, gold tassel on key. Bottom label says "President's Club Avon 1982" Club Du President. Made in Italy. **CMV $50.**

PEN SET PRESIDENT'S CLUB-CANADA 1980
(Left) Clear & white plastic. 1980 4A pin embedded in plastic base. "President's Club 1980" on pen. Came in green & gold box & Avon card. **CMV $25. MB.**

TERRITORY RECORD COVER-CANADA 1977
(Right) Blue plastic with gold door knocker. **CMV $2.**

87TH ANNIVERSARY AWARD CLOCK-CANADA 1973
(Left) White plastic with roses. Made by Phinney Walker, Germany. **CMV $10.**

PRESIDENT'S CLUB ORDER BOOK COVER-CANADA
Winter scene on front. **CMV $5.**

FIELD FLOWERS DESK SET-CANADA
Given to Reps. **CMV $20. MB.**

MOONWIND CLOCK AWARD-GERMANY 1973
(Left) Given to German Avon Reps for top sales. Blue & silver. Moonwind on clock face. **CMV $40.**

DESK PEN SET AWARD-CANADA 1967
(Right) Black pen. Clear plastic base with 4A design & British Columbia crest on base with 50c Canadian coin inside clear base. Only 1 per district given to Reps only. **CMV $30.**

WATCH AVON AWARD-GERMANY 1978
17 jewel date watch with 4A design on face. Leather strap. Given to Avon reps in Germany. Avon on back. **CMV $80. mint.**

PRESIDENT'S CLUB WATCH-CANADA 1978
Gruen watch in black case & box with President's Club on face of watch in English & French & 4A design. Won for $5,000. in sales in 9 campaigns. **CMV $125 MB.**

CHRISTMAS GIFT COLOGNE-CANADA 1975
Given to all Reps in Canada at Christmas 1975. Box has outside sleeve that says in English & French "Especially for you from Avon". **CMV $17. as shown with sleeve, MB.**

CHRISTMAS GIFT-GERMANY 1971
Blue & silver box holds ribbed glass perfume rollette, silver cap in Moonwind. Given to Avon Reps at Christmas 1971. **CMV $22.50 MB.**

TIMELESS GIFT SET AWARD-CANADA 1977
Gold box given to Avon Reps in Canada for sales of Timeless products. Outside sleeve came in English & French. **CMV $22.50 MB.**

CARD FILE-CANADA 1975
For Avon ladies, green and gold. Field Flowers. **CMV $7.**

PROMISE OF HEAVEN ORDER BOOK - ENGLAND 1974
White plastic order book cover used by Avon Reps. CMV $10. Each piece is decorated in Promise of Heaven design.

CHRISTMAS GIFT COLOGNE - CANADA 1974
3 oz. bottle of cologne never sold to public, given to all Reps at Christmas 1974 in Canada. Red lined gold box. Outside sleeve says in French & English "A Gift to You from Avon". CMV $22.50 MB as shown.

ROSE STICK PIN CHRISTMAS GIFT - CANADA 1981
Real preserved rose given to Canadian Avon Reps. Comes in red and white box with description of rose. CMV $20. MB.

TEAM LEADER HATS AWARDS - CANADA 1982
2 different hats, 1 red trim, 1 blue trim. Given to Team Leaders in Canada. CMV $5. each.

PRESIDENT'S CLUB BATHROOM SET AWARD - CANADA 1979
Beige plastic set consists of trinket box, cotton box, tissue box & beauty box with mirror. Given for best increase in sales. Designed by M. H. in Italy. CMV $65. set MB.

SILK ROSE PRESIDENT'S CLUB GIFT - CANADA 1979
Blown glass vial 7" high with red silk rose given to all Pesidents Club in Canada. Came in gold box. Came with card from R.J. Fairholm, Avon Products. CMV $15.

CATALOG FOLDER - MEXICO 1979
Blue vinyl folder used by Reps. CMV $5.
CALENDAR - EUROPE 1980
Foldout Avon calendar. CMV $4.

TEAM LEADER ORGANIZER - CANADA 1978
Blue plastic, for Reps in Canada. CMV $5.

SMILE PRODUCTS - ENGLAND
SMILE TOTE BAG 1979
Plastic coated cloth bag. Smile on back. CMV $7.50.
SMILE BALLONS
CMV 50c.
SMILE WITH AVON BUTTON 1979
CMV $2.
OPERATION SMILE TAPE & FILM SET 1979
Cassette and film used by managers at sales meetings. CMV $10. MB.

MAKE-UP BINDER - JAPAN 1979
White plastic 2 ring binder marked Avon. CMV $10.
CIRCLE OF DESTINCTION ORDER BOOK COVER - MEXICO 1979
Tan plastic cover. Same as our President's Club in U.S. CMV $10.

DIARY, JEWEL PIN CLUB - JAPAN 1979
Vinyl covered Avon diary given to Japanese Reps. CMV $15.
CIRCLE OF EXCELLENCE ORDER BOOK COVER - MEXICO 1979
Vinyl covered order book. Name on front Circulo de Distincion. CMV $5.

SNACK SET AWARD - CANADA 1982
Set of 4 chrome plated servers. Pie server & candy dish, 1st level; candy dish & bread tray, 2nd level; tiered snack tray, 3rd level. Avon label on bottom of each tray. **CMV $50. Set of 4.**

UMBRELLA SMILE AWARD - CANADA 1980
White with red & black design. Given to Team Leaders. **CMV $25.**

TEAM LEADER BILLFOLD & CALCULATOR - CANADA 1983
Maroon color leatherette has Cities 3660 calculator. Avon on billfold only. **CMV $15.**

HOT PLATE AWARD - CANADA 1980
White ceramic, red & green holly design. Green & red box sleeve. Given to Presidents Club Reps at Christmas 1980. Box in French and English. **CMV $15. MB.**

UMBRELLA AWARD - CANADA 1982
Tan umbrella with wood handle. Black letters, red stripe. Given to Team Leaders. **CMV $25.**

TOCCARA AWARDS - CANADA 1982
Royal blue tote bag. **CMV $10.** Cosmetic bag. **CMV $5.** Lavender lighted compact. **CMV $10.**

PARADISE ISLAND HAT AWARD - CANADA 1983
Straw hat with pink Avon band. Given to Presidents Club members on trip to Bahamas. **CMV $5.**
PARADISE AUTOGRAPH BOOK
CMV $5.

UMBRELLA AWARD - EUROPE 1983
White nylon with Avon in black & red all over. Black plastic handle. Given to Avon reps in Europe. **CMV $30.**

CLOCK - MRS. ALBEE AWARD - CANADA 1983
(Left) Brass quartz clock. 10 given in each district for top sales. Mrs. Albee face on clock. **CMV $150.**
CLOCK 5TH QUARTER CAMPIONS - CANADA 1983
(Right) Same brass clock as above only all brass clock face. Made by Equity in Hong Kong. Plaque on top says "5th Quarter Champions, Niagara Division 1983". Only 16 given for signing up most new Avon reps. **CMV $125.**

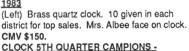

REP. CHRISTMAS GIFT - CANADA 1973
Tan and white card holds tan silk "A" scarf given to all Canada Reps at Christmas. **CMV $20. mint in card. Scarf only $12.**

PRESIDENTS CLUB PIN - CANADA 1982-83
Gold tone stick pin, 4A design cut out in center. English or French. Given to top reps. **CMV $10. MB.**

JEWELRY CASE AWARDS - CANADA 1972
Given to Presidents Club members only for sales goals on introduction of Avon Jewelry in Canada. 1st level award was travel case. **CMV $16.** 2nd level award was Deluxe Jewelry Case, on bottom of picture. Avon rose inside of lid. **CMV $22.50.**

MANAGERS BLAZER - CANADA 1980
Maroon blazer with goldtone Avon buttons and 4A gold emblem on pocket. Given to managers for meeting appointment goals. Modeled by Ruth Hershberger. **CMV $150.**

JEWELRY CASE AWARDS - CANADA 1972
Given to Reps on meeting sales goals on introduction of Avon Jewelry in Canada. Avon rose inside lid on both. 1st level is ring case. **CMV $12.** 2nd level is jewel case. **CMV $17.50.**

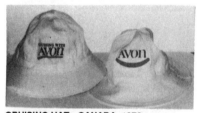

CRUISING HAT - CANADA 1978
White and black hat. Given to each team leader in Canada. **CMV $5.**
SMILE HAT - CANADA 1979
White, red and black hat given to team leader in Canada. **CMV $5.**

SWEATER AWARD - CANADA 1981
White sweater. Avon in red. Given to managers in Canada. **CMV $25.**
SCARF & TOQUE SET AWARD - CANADA 1981
Red and white stocking cap and scarf. Both marked Avon. Given to Reps for new recommendation. **CMV $25. set or $12.50 each.**
MITTENS AWARD - CANADA 1981
Red and white. **CMV $10.** Modeled by Vera Young.

CAPUCCI SCARF 1975
Brown and rust color silk scarf given to Reps in Germany for sales. Came in color matching envelope. **CMV $10.**

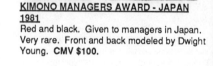

KIMONO MANAGERS AWARD - JAPAN 1981
Red and black. Given to managers in Japan. Very rare. Front and back modeled by Dwight Young. **CMV $100.**

4A TOWEL AWARDS - CANADA 1978-79
Reps. could win 1st level 4A face cloth. **CMV $5. MB.** 2nd hand towels. **CMV $7. MB.** 3rd bath towels. **CMV $10. MB each.** 4th bath sheets. **CMV $20. MB each.** Each came in white or brown. Each had 4A design on towel and came in Avon box. Boxes have French on one side and English on other.

SMILE NECK SCARF - CANADA 1979
Red and white, black letters. made in Canada. Given to managers only. **CMV $25.**

AWARDS - GERMANY 1977
CLUTCH
Gray and brown. "A" all over it. Came with calculator. **CMV $32.50 with calculator.**
ARIANE INCH 1978
Silvertone dated 1978, has red plastic dabber. In red bag. **CMV $15.**
SCARF AND PURSE 1977
Brown and tan. **CMV $12. scarf, $20. purse.**

AVON NUMBER 1 SCARF AWARD - ENGLAND 1979
Given to top Reps in England. **CMV $15.**

TOWEL AWARDS - GERMANY 1978
Rust and beige color towels with doves on towels. Tag says "Made in Belguim by Santens for Avon". large and small towels. **CMV $10. small, $15. large.**

RECOMMENDATION PRIZE - GERMANY 1977
Terrycloth, plastic lined bags. Green or pink with 4A design. **CMV $7. each.**

CANDID AWARDS - CANADA 1978
Candid Scarf, Step 1. **CMV $6.** Candid Scarf Clip, Step 2. **CMV $9.** Candid Umbrella, Step 3. **CMV $22.50.**

LIVE, LAUGH, LOVE TEMPO AWARDS - CANADA 1979
Beige and red design. Level 1 - terry hat. **CMV $5.** Level 2 - lounger. **CMV $20.** Level 3 - terry warm-up. **CMV $30.**

SIGNATURE COLLECTION AWARDS - CANADA 1976
Scarf, clutch purse, hand bag and large tote bag not shown, size 16 1/2" x 14 1/2". Each is brown and tan canvas. **CMV complete set is $45.** 1976 Order Book also shown. Inside cover says Avon's 90th Anniversary Sales Achievement Award. **CMV $4.**

TIMELESS AWARD SET - SPAIN 1976
Set given to Reps. in Spain for selling Timeless cologne mist . Set consists of leather overnight case, leather manicure set, travel clock made by Blessing and Avon on face, in leather case, and leather jewelry case. **CMV $80. complete set.**

TRAVEL BAG AWARD - CANADA 1978
Beige canvas, navy trim bag given to winning team Reps for sales in C14-78. **CMV $5.**

COLOGNE TEST SET - ENGLAND 1979
White box has 5 samples. **CMV $20. MB.**
AWARD BAG - ENGLAND 1979
Suede hand tote bag. Avon tag. **CMV $12.**

SALES ACHIEVEMENT AWARD BAGS - CANADA 1974
Tan canvas with brown leather trim. Given to Reps for top sales. Clutch, handbag, medium tote and large tote. All 4 as set. **CMV $45.**

RECORD CHRISTMAS GIFT - CANADA 1978
Record album given to all Canadian Avon Reps at Christmas. Record is marked "Avon Presents A Christmas Concert by Boston Pops". **CMV $8. mint.**

CANDID AWARD BAG - MEXICO 1978
Given to Mexican Avon Reps for top sales. **CMV $15.**

SMILE BEACH BALL - ENGLAND 1979
Given to Reps in England. Orange and white plastic. **CMV $5.**

CALENDAR - JAPAN 1979
CMV $5.
CALENDAR - JAPAN 1980
CMV $5.

PEN & PENCIL SET - CANADA 1974
Black and red Papermate pen box holds 2 pens with 4A inscribed. Given to Presidents Club Reps. **CMV $35. set MB.**

SMILE PEN AWARD - CANADA 1978
White and black pen with black silk ribbon. Given to Reps for selling $400. in Avon in C6-C7 in 1978. Came in white Avon box. **CMV $12. MB.**

CHRISTMAS GIFT - CANADA 1981
Embroidered rayon and silk picture of Mrs. Albee, 1st Avon lady. French and English Avon label on back. Given to team leaders. **CMV $50. MB only.**

PARKER PEN PRESIDENTS CLUB - CANADA 1979
Blue and gold box holds Parker 75 Pen inscribed on side (Presidents Club 1979). **CMV $25. MB.**

SALES BAG - EUROPE 1976
Gray bag, brown "A" design. Used by Avon Reps in Germany for deliveries. **CMV $20.**

ADVENT AVON CALENDAR - GERMAN 1972
Given to Reps for getting a new Rep for Avon.
CMV $5.

CALENDAR - GERMAN 1972
Cloth roll up calendar, says Avon on bottom.
CMV $10.
AVON CALENDAR - GERMAN 1973
Cloth roll up calendar, does not say Avon on it.
CMV $10. Both were given to Reps for
sending in orders in C-1.

CHRISTMAS CARD GIFT - CANADA 1976
Brown and beige card, 1st issue from Avon.
Given to all reps at Christmas. 4A design on
white card. Winter scene on inside. **CMV $5.**

AVON CHRISTMAS CARDS - GERMANY 1975
Avon on inside and 4A design on front. **CMV $2.**

CHRISTMAS CARD AND WRAPPING PAPER - EUROPE 1979
Card. **CMV $3., wrapping paper $4.**

CHRISTMAS CARD GIFT - CANADA 1977
2nd issue gold fold out large card with Sugar
Bush scene inside. 4A design on outside of
card and envelope. Given to all Reps at
Christmas. **CMV $4.**

COLORING BOOK - EUROPE 1970
CMV $5.

CHARISMA PORTFOLIO - CANADA 1968
Avon Christmas Award on cover Order Book,
pencil. Date pads. **CMV $8.**

REPS. CHRISTMAS GIFT - CANADA 1971
Green Seasons Greetings envelope holds four
8" x 10" size pictures to frame with a letter from
Canada's Avon President. Given to all Reps at
Christmas. **CMV $20. complete, mint.**

CHRISTMAS AVON CARD - GERMANY 1978
Gray card, Avon '78 on inside. **CMV $2. in
envelope.**

REP. CHRISTMAS GIFT - CANADA 1972
Green box holds Christmas card with black
and red rose print on inside to be cut out and
put in small gold picture frame. "Made in
Austria" on back. Inside card says "From
Avon" and signed by Avon President from
Canada. Given to all Canadian Avon Reps at
Christmas **CMV $20. MB.**

AVON 100 MANAGERS BLAZER - CANADA 1986
Blue blazer, goldtone buttons say Avon 100. Given to managers. **CMV $100.**

AVON 100 CENTENNIAL GOLD RECORD - CANADA 1986
Gold 45 RPM record in goldtone frame. Given to managers. **CMV $100.**

COFFEE MUG AWARD - CANADA 1982
Set of two ceramic coffee mugs given as a bonus for recommendations by Canadian Avon Reps. **CMV $15.**

AVON 100 LITHOGRAPH - CANADA
Limited edition of 2600 in pencil. Framed in chrome frame & glass 13" x 16" size. 1st CPC Factory, Mr. McConnell and Mrs. Albee in print. **CMV $100.**

AVON 100 BOTTLE COLLECTORS PLATE - ENGLAND
White ceramic plate made for Avon Bottle collectors club in England. Limited edition. 1886-1986 date. **CMV $30.**

TOP 10 DIVISION AWARDS - CANADA SILVER PLATED TEA SET
1 set to a Division for 1st place winner plus the silver plated candle stick lamps. 2nd place winners got the Tea Set. 3rd place, silver plated tray in satin lined box. All are engraved "Top 10 Division Award - Presidents Club 1986". **CMV Tea Set, $100. MB. CMV Candle Sticks, $80. MB. CMV Tray, $35. MB.**

AVON 100 TREASURE CHEST AWARD - CANADA 1986
Beveled glass box with brass trim. Bottom gold label says "Avon 100 A Year To Remember. Also in French. Given to Reps for $300. order. **CMV $20.**

VILLAGE FOLKS KITCHENWARE AWARDS - CANADA 1986
All ceramic. Given for sales goals.
Level 1 - Salt and Pepper Shakers. **CMV $10.**
Level 2 - Sugar and Creamer. **CMV $15.**
Level 3 - Cookie Jar. **CMV $20.**
Level 4 - Milk Pitcher, 4 coffee cups and Honey Jar. **CMV $30.**
Complete set, **CMV $75. MB.**

CANDY DISH AWARD - GERMANY 1977
White porcelain with pink flowers. Bottom Avon label made only for Avon. Given to German Avon Reps. **CMV $30.**

PRESIDENTS CLUB PIN - CANADA 1982
Goldtone 4A with "82" on it. Blue box - white 82 dated sleeve. **CMV $10. MB.**

PRESIDENTS CLUB PIN - CANADA 1986
Goldtone stick pin says Presidents Club Avon 1886-1986. Only 7,000 given. **CMV $15.**

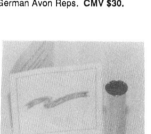

BUD VASE - PC - CANADA 1983
Small chrome bud vase with 4A design on base. Given at Presidents Club celebration dinner. Comes with Avon card. **CMV $10.**

SILVER CIRCLE PENDANT AWARD - AUSTRALIA 1986
Small 4A silvertone pendant and silver chain. Given for top sales. **CMV $25. MB.**

AVON 100 PIN SILVERTONE - CANADA 1986
Only 2,190 winners. Given to Avon Reps in Canada. **CMV $20.**

KEY WATCH AWARD - GERMANY 1981
2" long gold tone key watch on neck chain. Back says "Avon 1HR ERFOLG MiT". Given to Avon managers in Germany. Comes in black velvet box. **CMV $150. MB.**

AVON 100 PIN GOLDTONE - CANADA 1986
Only 1,200 winners to Avon Reps. 2 simulated diamonds. **CMV $30.**

AVON 100 WINE GLASSES AND WINE AWARD - CANADA 1986
750 ml bottle of Avon 100 Bordeux white wine. 3,000 bottles made. 27,000 Avon 100 glasses made. **CMV $35. wine full. CMV $8. each glass.**

"A" NECKLACE AWARD - CANADA 1983
Avon box holds goldtone chain & Avon "A" with ruby color stone. Given to Avon Reps for sales goal. **CMV $10. MB.**

PRESIDENTS CLUB PEN - CANADA 1987
Goldtone pin in French. Says 'Club du President'. Rose with small pearl. **CMV $15.**

AVON 100 EARRINGS & NECKLACE AWARDS - JAPAN 1986
All goldtone with Statue of Liberty and Avon 100 Anniversary on back. Given to Reps in Japan. **CMV $35. set.**

AVON 100 BLUE LAPIS AWARDS - CANADA 1986
Bracelet and necklace given to Reps for Night Oddyssey sales. Blue beads & gold tone. **CMV $10. Bracelet MB, $15. Necklace MB.**

NORTHAMPTON. ENGLAND AVON PLANT PLATE 1981
8" porcelain plate for opening new Avon plant at Northampton, England, 2 July 1981. Made by Wedgewood & numbered. Great Oak on face. **CMV $100.**

PRESIDENTS CLUB ALBEE PLATE - CANADA 1987
Ceramic plate given to Presidents Club Reps in Canada. Says on back "Mrs. Albee Comes to Call". **CMV $40.**

CHRISTMAS GIFT PLATE - GERMANY 1981
White porcelain plate given to German Avon Reps for Christmas gift in 1981. Avon & numbered on back. Rare. **CMV $125.**

AVON 100 PRESIDENTS CLUB MINI PLATE - CANADA 1986
Small plate plaque. Gold rose and Avon 1886-1986 in center. **CMV $10.**

AVON 100 ALBEE PLAQUE - CANADA 1986
Goldtone with Albee design. Given for Centennial celebration. **CMV $65.**

AVON 100 MIRROR TRAY AWARD - CANADA 1986
Mirror and Lucite tray. "Avon 100 1886-1986 A Year to Remember" on back. **CMV $25.**

AVON 100 CENTENNIAL AWARDS - CANADA 1986
AVON 100 ORDER BOOK
Step 1: Maroon vinyl, gold letters. 15,000 given. **CMV $8.**
AVON 100 BUSINESS PORTFOLIO
Step 2: Maroon vinyl, came with mini Avon calculator. **CMV $20.** 5,000 given.
AVON 100 PURSE, UMBRELLA & SCARF
Step 3: Matching organizer purse with Centennial scarf & umbrella. 1,500 given.
Purse: **CMV $20.**
Umbrella: **CMV $20.**
Scarf: **CMV $5.**

AVON 100 BROCHURE - CANADA 1986
Only 80,000 printed. Campaign 1 - 1986 product brochure. **CMV $5.**

PRESIDENTS CLUB PEN & PENCIL SET AWARD - CANADA 1983
Black, gold & tan lined box holds pair of Quill white pen & pencil set. Avon 4A emblem on top of pens. Outer sleeve on box. **CMV $35. MB.**

PRESIDENTS CLUB COIN PURSE AWARD - CANADA 1984
Avon box in French and English holds tan leather coin purse. **CMV $10. MB.**

AVON 100 T-SHIRT - CANADA 1986
White T-shirt "Avon 100" on it. Given to Reps. 30,000 made in all sizes. **CMV $10.**

AVON 100 CENTENNIAL SCARF - CANADA 1986
Bonus recommendation gift to Reps. **CMV $6.**

20th ANNIVERSARY COIN PURSE AWARD - ENGLAND 1979
Gold tan mesh coin purse & brass 4A coin with Avon 20 on one side. **CMV $25.**

AVON 100 MANAGERS WATCH - CANADA 1986
Goldtone watch. Avon on face. Given to managers in Canada. **CMV $75.**

1957-1973 STOCKHOLDER'S XMAS GIFTS - Stockholders gifts were special packaged Avon items sent to each share holder of Avon Stock at Christmas each year. A special stockholders greeting card was sent with each gift & a stockholders gift is not mint or complete without this card. They were first sent in 1957 & discontinued at Christmas 1973. They are considered quite hard to find.
There are only 2 years of stockholders gifts not shown. If you have any of the following 2 complete sets with card, please contact Bud Hastin. 1957 set had Persian Wood Perfume Mist & Beauty Dust. 1959 set had Topaze Spray Perfume & Cologne Mist. Also listed as After Shower for Men. This could be 1 complete set or 2 different. 1 for men & 1 for women. Also listed for 1960 is 8 oz. Spice After Shave Lotion. This again sounds like 2 different items for 1960. All the other years are pictured & priced.

STOCKHOLDER'S GIFTS

STOCKHOLDERS GIFT 1958
Satin lined box with large ribbon across lid and stockholders card. Holds Here's My Heart beauty dust, sachet lotion & Top Style lipstick. **CMV $65. MB.**

STOCKHOLDERS GIFT 1964
White flip open box with 4A design on both sides of lid, holds 4A after shave and Rapture 2 oz. cologne. With stockholders card. **CMV $60. MB.**

REGENCE COLOGNE MIST STOCKHOLDERS GIFT 1966
White, green and gold box. Given to stockholders on introduction of Regence, says "Your introduction to a fragrance masterpiece by Avon". **CMV $40. MB.**

TOPAZE TREASURE STOCKHOLDERS GIFT 1960

Yellow & gold satin lined box holds Topaze Beauty Dust & 2 oz. cologne. Came with stockholders card. This was a general issue gift that was also sold. **CMV $40. MB., $55. MB with stockholders card.**

STOCKHOLDERS GIFT 1961

Box with stockholders Christmas card, holds Cotillion beauty dust, cream sachet & cologne mist. This set is same as 1961-62 Cotillion Debut, only with special card. **CMV $60. MB.**

STOCKHOLDERS GIFT 1962

Flip open box with Avon printed all over lid. Holds Bay Rum jug after shave & Skin So Soft bud vase. With stockholders card. **CMV $65. MB.**

STOCKHOLDERS GIFT 1963

Box opens in center with double lid to show 3 oz. Occur! cologne mist & Tribute after shave. Stockholders card. **CMV $50. MB.**

STOCKHOLDERS MEETING GIFTS

A special wrapped Avon product is given to each stockholder attending the Annual Avon Stockholders Meeting. Each gift comes with a special card which states "With the compliments of the Board of Directors, Officers and Employees of Avon Products, Inc". **CMV $15. to $20. each mint with card only.**

STOCKHOLDERS GIFT 1965

Box with stockholders card & Just Two set. **CMV $80. MB.**

STOCKHOLDERS GIFT 1967

Brown brocade design box holds 1st Edition Book after shave & Brocade 4 oz. cologne. **CMV $40. MB.**

STOCKHOLDERS GIFT 1968

A special gift given to Avon stockholders. Short pony in Windjammer & Charisma Cologne Mist, set in white foam. **CMV set $32.50 MB.**

STOCKHOLDERS GIFT 1971

White foam box with blue felt band. Contains Moonwind Cologne Mist. **CMV $25. MB with card.**

IMPERIAL GARDENS STOCKHOLDERS GIFT 1973

Cream sachet in white styrofoam with orange & gold ribbon. Also has card. **CMV $18. MB.**

STOCKHOLDERS GIFT 1970
Bird of Paradise Cologne Mist in foam box. Gold band around box. Came with card from Avon as Christmas gift to stockholders. **CMV $22.50 MB with card only.**

DEEP WOODS STOCKHODERS GIFT 1972
Brown foam box shaped like a log, card on top, with brown ribbon and gold sticker, contains Deep Woods Cologne. **CMV $25. MB.**

STOCKHOLDERS GIFT 1969
Pink foam box holds Elusive Cologne Mist & Perfume Rollette. Ribbon around box. **CMV $27.50 MB.**

NATIONAL ASSOCIATION AVON COLLECTOR'S AVON CLUB BOTTLES & NAAC COLLECTABLES.

SOLD ONLY TO MEMBERS OF NAAC CLUBS

NAAC and club bottle offers not affilliated with Avon Products, Inc.

CLUB BOTTLES-PLATES-CONVENTION BOTTLES-BELLS

What are they? Where do you get them? Club bottles are made for Avon collectors and are sold thru any of the more than 100 Avon Collectors Clubs throughout the United States and Canada. These clubs are all members of the National Association of Avon collectors (N.A.A.C.). Club bottles or plates are sold for a period of 60 days only and only the amount sold in that time is made. At the end of the sale period, the order is placed with the factory. It usually takes around 4 months to get them manufactured and shipped to the collector. Each bottle is numbered with the quantity made. All club bottles are hand painted porcelain of the finest quality. If you do not have an Avon Club in your area belonging to the N.A.A.C. we invite you to join the Avon Times to be eligible to purchase all club bottles as they come out at the lowest possible price. $15.00 yearly dues ($18.00 for Canada, U.S. funds money orders only from Canada). Send to:

AVON TIMES
Box 9868
Kansas City, Missouri 64134

All N.A.A.C. Avon club & convention bottles & bells 1972 to 1986 were designed, created & manufactured by Bud Hastin. Bud has created over 100 different hand painted porcelain bottles & figurines. They have become very collectable over the years. All are very limited editions.

2nd NAAC McCONNELL CLUB BOTTLE 1973
2nd annual Club Botle issued by the NAAC Clubs in honor of Mr. & Mrs. D. H. McConnell, founders of Avon. Registration certificate goes with the bottle. 5,604 bottles were sold & numbered. OSP $11.95. **CMV $80.**

1st ANNUAL NAAC AVON CLUB BOTTLE 1st AVON LADY 1972

7" high, hand painted porcelain bottle. Made for Avon Club members only belonging to the National Association of Avon Collectors. 1st NAAC Club bottle issued. Made in image of first CPC saleslady. Each bottle is numbered. Released in June 1972. Total issue was 2,870. Bottle made and issued by National Association of Avon Collectors. OSP $10.95. **CMV $250.** 18 made with red hair & green purse. **CMV $600. for a redhead.** No registration certificates were issued with the '72 Club Bottle. 4 bottles had blue lettering on bottle. All others had black letters. **CMV blue letter bottom $700.** 1972 factory sample of 1st lady sold by mistake. Same as above only no lettering on bottom & neck is flush where cork fits top of bottle. No raised lip for cork as regular production was. Bottle has letter from Bud Hastin as 1 of a kind sample. **CMV $500.**

NAAC MINI McCONNELL & CPC FACTORY 1978

(Left) Miniature size figurines of the 1886 CPC Factory and Mr. & Mrs. McConnell the founders of Avon. Issued by the National Association of Avon Clubs. Only 1,200 sets were sold. OSP $16.95. Original set came with McConnell & factory 2nd from right. Factory was too large so issued a second smaller factory on left. 1,200 small factories made. **CMV set with 1 factory & McConnell $35. CMV with both factories in center $55.**

NAAC CPC FACTORY CLUB BOTTLE 1974

(Right) 3rd annual club bottle issued by the NAAC Clubs in honor of the 1st California Perfume Co. Factory in 1886. Came with a registration card. 4,691 bottles were made, the mold was broken at 3rd annual NAAC Convention June 22, 1974 in Kansas City. OSP $11.95. **CMV $55.**

5th ANNUAL NAAC AVON CLUB BOTTLE 1976

(Left) In the image of the 1896 CPC Avon lady. Blue dress, black bag, and blue feather in hat. Black hair. 5,622 were made. Came with registration card and numbered on the bottom. OSP $12.95. **CMV $45.**

BLOND AVON LADY 1976

(Right) Of the 5,622 regular issue 1896 lady, 120 had blond hair. **CMV $225. on blond, rare.**

4th ANNUAL NAAC CLUB BOTTLE 1975

The modern day Avon Lady is the 1975 Club bottle from the NAAC. Blue hand painted porcelain. Each bottle is numbered on bottom & came with registration card. 6,232 were made. OSP $12.45. **CMV $40.**

NAAC CLUB BOTTLE 1906 AVON LADY 1977

6th annual club bottle issued by the National Association of Avon Clubs. Made of porcelain and hand painted in the image of the 1906 Avon lady. She stands 7 1/2" high with yellow dress, brown hat and carrying the CPC Avon sales case of the period. Only 5,517 were made & sold for $12.95 each. Came with NAAC registration certificate and is numbered on the bottom. **CMV $40. MB.** 100 sample bottles were given to each NAAC Club and are the same only they are numbered and marked club sample on bottom. **CMV $110. sample bottle.**

NAAC CLUB BOTTLE 1978

7th annual club bottle made in the image of the 1916 CPC Avon lady. She stands 7 1/2" high with a rust colored hat and coat. Brown hair. Only 5,022 were made. The bottle is numbered on the bottom and comes with a registration certificate. Made of hand painted porcelain. OSP $13.95. **CMV $35.** Club sample was marked on bottom of 125 club bottles given to each club in the NAAC. Sample bottles are same as regular issue only marked club sample. **CMV $105.**

NAAC CLUB BOTTLE 1936 AVON LADY 1980
(Left) 9th annual club bottle. Purple dress, black bag. 7 1/2" high. 4,479 were made & sold & numbered on the bottom as total sold. Did not come with certificate. Bottom cork. OSP $14.95. **CMV $30.** Same bottle came with blue bag & marked club sample on bottom. 155 club samples were made & given to to NAAC clubs. **CMV $120. blue bag club sample.**

NAAC CLUB BOTTLE 1946 AVON LADY 1981
(Right) 10th annual club bottle. Only 3,589 sold and made. Green dress, black bag, cork in bottom. OSP $15.95. **CMV $30.** 140 sample club bottles made and marked club sample on bottom. **CMV $105.**

NAAC CLUB BOTTLE 1926 AVON LADY 1979
8th annual club bottle. Purple & black. Brown hat & shoes. 4,749 were made & numbered on bottom. Came with certificate that says 4,725. Actual count is 4,749. OSP $14.95. **CMV $40.** 150 club samples were issued to NAAC Clubs. Bottom is marked club sample. **CMV sample $105.**

NAAC 1st CONVENTION BOTTLE 1980
Sold only to NAAC club members. 1st in an annual series of NAAC Convention bottles to commemorate the annual NAAC Convention held in Spokane, Washington in 1980. 7 1/2" high, lavender dress of 1890s style. Hand painted porcelain. This bottle is the only one in the series that the cork is in the head, and 7 1/2" size. All rest are 5 1/2" size starting in 1981. The rest of the series will have a cork in the bottom to present a prettier bottle. Only 3,593 were made & sold. OSP $14.95. **CMV $30.**

NAAC CLUB BOTTLE 1956 AVON LADY 1982
(Left) 11th annual club bottle for NAAC club members. 7 1/2" high, red dress, bottom cork. Only 3,000 made & sold. OSP $17. **CMV $30.** 150 club sample 1956 lady bottles made & marked on bottom. **CMV $100. for club sample.**

NAAC CLUB BOTTLE 1966 AVON LADY 1983
(Right) 12th annual club bottle. 7 1/2" high, hand painted porcelain bottle made only for the National Association of Avon Collectors in the image of dress of the 1966 Avon lady. She wears a black & white striped dress. Blue bag. 2,350 made, bottom cork. OSP $18. **CMV $35.** A new club bottle is issued each year to NAAC members only. 100 club samples made. **CMV $100.**

NAAC CLUB BOTTLE 1984 AVON REPRESENTATIVE 1984
13th annual club bottle 7 1/2" high, hand painted porcelain. Gray pants suit, pink blouse, red hair. Brown bag says Avon. Bottom cork. Choice of a white or black representative. SSP $20. 1,133 white rep bottles were made. **CMV $30. MB.** 1,070 black reps made. **CMV $35. MB.**

NAAC CLUB BOTTLE "MR. AVON" 1985
7 1/2" high porcelain bottle. 14th & last in club bottle series. Only 1,800 made. SSP $20. **CMV $30. MB.**

7th NAAC CONVENTION BOTTLE & BELL 1986
5 1/2" high porcelain bottle. Black dress, red hair on 100 club samples. **CMV $75.** Regular issue has red dress, black trim. Only 1,800 made. SSP $18. **CMV $25.**

7th NAAC CONVENTION BELL 1986
Same as regular issue bottle only bell with dress colors reversed. Only 500 made by Bud Hastin. SSP $20. **CMV $30.**

NAAC CONVENTION BOTTLE & BELL 1987
5 1/2" high porcelain bottle. 8th in series. 750 made for Chicago Avon Collector Convention. Hand painted porcelain, light blue, dark blue trim. SSP $20. **CMV $25.**
CONVENTION BELL
Same only dress color reversed. Only 300 made. **CMV $30.**

NAAC 1st CONVENTION BOTTLE RE-ISSUE 1982
Same as 1980 bottle only is 5 1/2" high to match rest of series in size. Only 1,775 reissue bottles made. Reissued bottles sold in 1982. Cork in bottom. OSP $15. **CMV $35.** 150 club sample bottles were made & marked in the bottom of the 5 1/2" size. **CMV $100.**
4th NAAC CONVENTION BELL 1980
(Left) 5 1/2" high porcelain bell same as bottle only dress colors reversed. Issued in 1984. Only 500 made by Bud Hastin. SSP $20. **CMV $30.**
6th NAAC CONVENTION BOTTLE & BELL 1985
(Right) Seattle, WA. Avon Convention. 5 1/2" porcelain bottle. Pink dress with dark pink trim. 1,800 made. SSP $18. **CMV $25.**
NAAC CONVENTION BELL 1985
Is same as bottle only dress color reversed. Only 500 bells made & sold by Bud Hastin. SSP $20. **CMV $30.** 15 bells were painted same as convention bottle by mistake & came in bottle boxes. Some have no inside labels. Rare. **CMV $125.**

NAAC 2nd CONVENTION BOTTLE 1981
Long Beach, CA Convention. 5 1/2" high hand painted porcelain bottle. Yellow & green dress of the 1800s style. Second in a series of 11 bottles of the 1800s style. Only 3,128 were made & sold to NAAC club members. SSP $15. **CMV $30.**
CONVENTION CLUB SAMPLE 1981
140 club sample bottles were made for NAAC clubs. Each marked club sample on bottom & numbered 140 edition. **CMV $100. club sample.**
5th NAAC CONVENTION BELL 1981
Same as bottle only has green dress. 500 made & sold in 1984. SSP $20. **CMV $30.**

NAAC 3rd CONVENTION BOTTLE 1982
(Left) 3rd in a series of 1800s style dress. Blue dress, pink bag & hat rim, blond hair. 5 1/2" high porcelain. Only 2,205 bottles were made & sold to NAAC convention was held in Las Vegas, Nevada. SSP $15. **CMV $30. mint.** No club samples were made.
NAAC CONVENTION BELL 1982
(Right) 1st issue - only 500 bells made in the same shape as the 1982 convention bottles. Only the dress colors are reversed. Pink dress & blue trim. You had to attend the 11th Annual NAAC Convention in Las Vegas, June 22-27, 1982 to get a bell. SSP $12. **CMV $65.**

NAAC 4th CONVENTION BOTTLE 1983
5 1/2" high, bottom cork. Rust & brown color hand painted porcelain. 4th in a series of Avon ladies of the 1800s to commemorate the NAAC Avon Collectors Convention in Wilmington, DE in June 1983. Only 1,875 made. Total number sold marked on bottom. SSP $15. **CMV $30.** 150 club samples made & marked club sample. 1 of 150 on bottom. **CMV $100.**
2nd NAAC CONVENTION BELL 1983
Same as 1983 Convention bottle only dress colors are reversed and bottom is open as bell. Bottom label, only 500 made. SSP $15. **CMV $40.** Bells created and sold by Bud Hastin.

NAAC 5th CONVENTION BOTTLE 1984
5 1/2" high porcelain bottle, bottom cork. Brown dress, yellow and black umbrella. 1,650 made. 5th in a series of 11 convention bottles to be sold thru NAAC clubs of the Avon ladies of the 1890s for NAAC Avon Collectors 13th Annual Convention in Kansas City, MO June 1984. SSP $15. **CMV $30.** 100 NAAC Club Samples made and marked Club Sample on bottom. 1 of 100. **CMV $100. club samples.**
3rd NAAC CONVENTION BELL 1984
Same as 1984 NAAC Convention bottle only dress & umbrella colors reversed & bottom is open as bell. Bottom label. Only 500 made for Kansas City, NAAC Convention. Bells created & sold by Bud Hastin. SSP $16. **CMV $35.**

NAAC PLATE 1983
9" porcelain plate of the 1946 Avon Lady on face. Only 1,125 made. Label on back. SSP $25. **CMV $35.**
NAAC BOARD MEMBER PLATE 1983
Same as regular issue only back has special label marked "NAAC Board Member Sample". Only 7 made with each board member's name on back. **CMV $100.**

NAAC PLATE 1974
1st in an annual series of plates. Clear crystal thumb print plate with blue & red background. Only 790 plates were made. OSP $12.95. **CMV $50.**
NAAC BOARD MEMBER PLATE 1974
Same as regular issue only have Board Member on plate. **CMV $135.**

3rd ANNUAL NAAC 5 YEAR AVON COLLECTORS PLATE 1976
9 3/8" porcelain plate showing the 1st 4 NAAC club bottles. 1755 were made. OSP $13.95. **CMV $35.**

NAAC CONVENTION PLATE 1975
Only 250 made for 4th annual NAAC Convention, Anaheim, Calif. OSP $12.95. **CMV $25.**

NAAC SAMPLE PLATE 1975
(Left) Sample plate never issued to general public. 84 were made and sent to each Avon Collectors Club in NAAC, numbered on the back. **CMV $100. each.**
2nd ANNUAL NAAC PLATE 1975
(Right) General issue plate Mr. & Mrs. McConnell founders of Avon in center, gold 2 inch band around edge. OSP $12.95. **CMV $35. MB.**

NAAC PLATE 1984
Limited edition 9" porcelain plate 1956 Avon Lady. 8th in series. SSP $26. **CMV $35.**

NAAC 6 YEAR PLATE 1977
1886 Avon lady on plate. Made by AVON Products for the National Association of Avon Clubs. A beautiful china plate. Total of 5,000 were made with 1,500 gold rimmed, and numbered. **CMV $60. MB.** 3,500 were silver rimmed and not numbered. **CMV $32.50.** 7 plates marked board member. **CMV $125. MB.**

PLATE - NAAC BOARD MEMBER 1975
(Left) 2" wide gold edge marked board member. Only 7 were issued, This was a general issue plate. **CMV $130.**
PLATE - NAAC BOARD MEMBER 1975
(Right) White plate with small gold edge marked board member. Only 7 were made. This plate was never issued to public. **CMV $130. MB.**

NAAC PLATE 1985
9th in series. 9" plate of 1966 Avon Lady. Limited edition. SSP $26. **CMV $35.**

NAAC ROSE BOWL PLATE 1987
9" porcelain plate. 1st in a series of Avon Floats in the annual Rose Bowl Parade. Floats in the annual Rose Bowl Parade. Less than 2,000 made. No NAAC plate was made in 1986. SSP $25. **CMV $25.**

NAAC 7 YEAR PLATE 1978
Made by Avon Products for the National Association of Avon Clubs. A beautiful china plate with a decal of the 1906 Avon Sales Lady. Only 5,000 were made. OSP $14.95. 2,310 were gold rimmed plates. **CMV $45. MB.** 2,690 are silver rimmed plates. **CMV $35. MB.** 7 made for board members. **CMV $125. MB.** Rare issue plate with backward printing on back. **CMV $60. MB.**

NAAC PLATE 1926 AVON LADY 1981
Limited edition of 2,000. Gold rim. Marked on back. OSP $20. **CMV $35. MB.**
NAAC BOARD MEMBER PLATE 1981
Same plate as above only back is marked 1981 board member sample. Only 7 were made this way for NAAC board of directors. **CMV $100. MB.**

NAAC CUP PLATES 1984-86
Sold at Annual Avon Convention. 1st issue 1984 in Kansas City. Light yellow glass. 2nd issue 1985 - Seattle, Wa. Green glass. 3rd issue 1986 - Nashville, Tn. Red glass. All under 500 issued. **CMV $15. each.**

NAAC PLATE 1896 AVON LADY 1979
Limited edition of 5,000. Made by Avon Products exclusively for the NAAC. Came with gold edge & numbered back. **CMV $37.50 MB.** Silver edge and no number. **CMV $27.50 MB.** OSP $14.95 sold only by NAAC clubs. 7 plates made - marked board members. **CMV $125.**

NAAC PLATE 1916 AVON LADY 1980
Limited edition of 4,000. Came with gold edge & number on the back. 2.060 made. **CMV $30. Or silver edge, 1,940 made & no number $30. MB.** Made by Avon Products exclusively for the NAAC. OSP $14.95. 7 plates made marked board members. **CMV $125.**

NAAC PLATE 1982
Only 2,000 made and numbered. 6th in a series of the 1936 Avon lady. SSP $25. **CMV $35.**

NAAC CONVENTION GOBLETS 1976-83
Different color goblet sold each year at NAAC Convention. 1st year, red, 1976, 276 made. **CMV $60.** 1977, blue, 560 made. **CMV $30.** 1978, smoke, 560 made. **CMV $20.** 1979, clear, 576 made. **CMV $15.** 1980, purple, 576 made. **CMV $15.** OSP was $4. to $6. each. 1978-83 a special marked goblet given to each NAAC delegate. **CMV $25.** Less than 100 delegate goblets made each year. Special marked goblets were made for each 7 NAAC board members. **CMV for board member goblets $100. each year.** 1981 - 684 goblets made. **CMV $15.** 1982 - 700 made. **CMV $15.** 1983 - 322 made. **CMV $25.** 1983 is last year goblets made.

NAAC CONVENTION BANQUET MIRROR 1974
(Left) Yellow and black, mirror on back. Convention held in Kansas City, Mo. June 22, 1974. **CMV $15.**

NAAC CONVENTION BANQUET MIRROR 1975
(Right) Blue and black, mirror on back. Convention held in Anaheim, Calif. June 21, 1975. **CMV $10.** Both were given to each person attending the annual NAAC Avon Convention Banquet.

NAAC CONVENTION BANQUET MIRROR 1976
(Left) 5th annual Avon collectors convention mirror in white with blue letters. Held in Cincinnati, Ohio, June 25-27, 1976. Mirror on back. **CMV $10.**

NAAC CONVENTION BANQUET MIRROR 1977
(Right) 6th annual Avon collectors convention mirror in blue with yellow letters. Mirror on back. Hollywood, Florida, June, 1977. **CMV $10.**

NAAC NASHVILE CONVENTION MIRROR 1986
Only 400 made. Red buttons with white letters. Mirror back. 15th Annual. **CMV $5.**

NAAC CHICAGO CONVENTION MIRROR 1987
400 made. White button, red letters, blue design. Given at 16th NAAC Convention banquet. **CMV $5.**

NAAC CONVENTION MIRROR & BUTTON 1984-85
1984 - yellow - Kansas City, Mo. Convention. 1985 - green - Seattle, Wa. Convention. Both less than 350 issued. **CMV mirror $10. each. CMV buttons $3.**

NAAC CONVENTION BANQUET MIRROR 1983
Only 500 small mirrors for the 12th annual Avon Collectors Convention in Wilmington, De, 1983. **CMV $10.**

NAAC CONVENTION BANQUET MIRROR 1978
(Left) Purple with mirror on back. Given to over 500 who attended the Avon Collectors Convention Banquet in Houston, Texas, June 1978. **CMV $10.**

NAAC CONVENTION BANQUET MIRROR 1979
(Right) White & red, mirror on back. Given to over 500 people attending the annual Avon Collectors Convention Banquet in St. Louis, Mo, June 1979. **CMV $10.**

NAAC CONVENTION BANQUET MIRROR 1980-82
Only 500 of each made for annual NAAC Convention Banquet. 1980 - Spokane, Washington, 1981 - Queen Mary, Long Beach, Ca. 1982. - Las Vegas, Nevada. **CMV $10. ea.**

NAAC CONVENTION MIRROR 1972
Only 300 made. given at banquet, also some were made with pins instead of mirrors. These were dealers badges. **CMV $25. each.**

NAAC KEY CHAIN 1983
Red & white with black pen insert. Given to Delaware convention attendees from Avon Products. Only 500 made. **CMV $5. each.**

GOLD COAST ("BUD HASTIN") CLUB BOTTLE 1974
Issued in honor of Mr. Bud Hastin for his contribution to the field of Avon collecting. 1st in an annual series. Only 2,340 bottles were made. Bottle is 8 1/2" high, white pants, maroon coat, black turtle neck shirt, black shoes. Few were made with white shirt. Rare. OSP $11.95. **CMV black shirt $60. CMV white shirt $115.**

PRESIDENTS GOLD SET 1980
Set of six different U.S. Presidents Bust, with
antique brush gold finish. Only 250 sets made
& issued by Bud Hastin Avon Club. OSP $70.
set. **CMV $130. MB set.**

**AVON ENCYCLOPEDIA COVER SHEET
REJECTS 1976**
30,000 covers for the 1976 Avon Encyclopedia
were printed with the word Encyclopedia
spelled encylopedia. The covers were never
used but about 200 sheets were given to
collectors with 4 covers and backs printed on a
sheet. These sheets are rare. The rest of the
covers were destroyed. **CMV $15. each
sheet.**

AVON LADY MINI SET NO. 2 1977
1,265 sets of 11 miniature Avon ladies of the
1886-1900 period. Issued by the Bud Hastin
National Avon Club (now called Avon Times) in
1977. Set came in special display box. Came
with numbered registration certificate. Sold
only to Bud Hastin's National Avon Club
members. OSP $60. set. **CMV $130. MB.**

CLINT GOLD COAST CLUB BOTTLE 1977
7-5/8" tall. Blue pants, shirt, jacket. Black
shoes, brown hair. 1,264 made & numbered
on the bottom. Came with registration card.
4th Annual Club bottle. OSP $13.95. **CMV
$32.50.**

**BICENTENNIAL MINI AVON LADY SET NO.
1 1976**
10 exact replicas in 3" high miniature figurines
of the larger NAAC Club bottles. Issued by the
Bud Hastin National Avon Club (now called
Avon Times). 1775 sets were made and came
with a numbered registration certificate. OSP
$60. for set of 10. **CMV $135. MB.**

PRESIDENTS 1978
A set of 6 3" high bust figurines of the 1st five
presidents of the United States, plus Lincoln.
Only 1,050 sets made. Hand painted porcelain
and came with a numbered registration card.
Sold only to members of the Bud Hastin
National Avon Club. OSP for set of 6 $40.
CMV $85.
PRESIDENTS ALL WHITE 1978
Same set as painted presidents above only all
white porcelain. Only 150 sets made. OSP
$40. **CMV $160.**

MINI REDHEAD SET 1977
965 sets of Something Old - Something New made. Issued by Bud Hastin's National Avon Club with registration card. 3 1/2" high, 1886 Avon lady on left has green purse and red hair. 1975 Avon lady on right has red hair & Avon Calling is misspelled on base of figurine. OSP $12. set. Sold as set only. **CMV $35.**

WORLD WIDE JO OLSEN AVON CLUB BOTTLE 1975
(Left) Light blue dress, black hair. 1,102 bottles sold. Made in the image of Jo Olsen for her contribution to Avon collecting. OSP $12.95. **CMV $40.**

GOLD COAST RON PRICE CLUB BOTTLE 1975
(Right) Green suit, brown hair and shoes. Holding book "Testing 1-2-3". 1,096 bottles sold. Made in the image of Mr. Ron Price for his contribution to the field of Avon collecting. Mr. Ron Price was a member of the Board of Directors of the NAAC. Mr. Price passed away in 1977. OSP $12.95. **CMV $40.**

GOLD COAST MINIS 1976
A set of 3 miniature figurines 3 1/2" high in the image of Bud Hastin, Jo Olsen and Ron Price. 914 sets were sold at $18. per set. **CMV $40. per set.**

BUD HASTIN NATIONAL AVON CLUB BOTTLE 1976
2nd issue. Hand painted porcelain made in the image of Mr. Dale Robinson, past director of National Association of Avon Clubs. 1,000 bottles made & numbered. OSP $14.95. **CMV $40.**

AVON ENCYCLOPEDIA HARD BOUND COLLECTORS EDITION 1974-75
Only 1,000 special limited collectors editions were printed. Blue hard bound cover with gold stamped letters on front. Each is signed and numbered by Bud Hastin. OSP $20. **CMV $32.50 mint.**

AVON ENCYCLOPEDIA HARD BOUND 2nd COLLECTORS EDITION 1976-77
Only 500 special limited collectors editions were printed. Maroon hard bound cover with gold stamped letters on front. Each book is numbered and signed by Bud Hastin. OSP $20. **CMV $30. mint.** 6 hard bounds were found with all pages upside down. Each was signed by Bud Hastin as 1 of 6 rare upside down books. Very rare. **CMV $40.**

AVON ENCYCLOPEDIA HARD BOUND 3rd COLLECTORS EDITION 1979
Only 350 special limited hard bound covers with gold letters on front. Each book was signed and numbered by Bud Hastin. OSP $22.50. **CMV $30.**

BUD HASTIN NATIONAL AVON CLUB BOTTLE 1974
1st issue club bottle by Bud Hastin Avon Club (now called Avon Times) is a 3-piece Avon Family Scene. 3 separate bottles showing the Man, Child & Woman Avon Collectors. 1,091 sets sold. OSP $45. per set. Sold in sets only. **CMV $145.**

MID AMERICA NAAC CONVENTION PLATE 1972
(Left) Clear glass with frosted lettering, 134 were made for the 1st annual NAAC Convention in Kansas City, Kansas, June 1972. This plate was not made until 1975. OSP $12.95. **CMV $30.**

CENTRAL VALLEY NAAC CONVENTION PLATE 1973
(Right) Clear glass, frosted lettering. 124 were made and sold for 2nd annual NAAC Convention at Sacremento, Calif. This plate was not made until 1975. OSP $12.95. **CMV $30.**

NAAC CONVENTION DELEGATE PLATE 1977
White china plate with the date & place of 6 NAAC Annual Conventions. Given to each NAAC Club delegate attending the convention "85 plates". **CMV $50.** 7 board member plates were made the same only marked Board Member. **CMV $75.**

NAAC CONVENTION PLATES 1975-83
Made by Mid-America Avon Club as the official NAAC Convention souvenir plate each year. Very low issue on each. All are etched clear glass & signed by the artist. OSP was $12.95 each. 1975 Orange County, CA - **CMV $30.** 1977 Hollywood, FL - **CMV $30.** 1978 Houston, TX - **CMV $25.** 1979 St. Louis, MO - **CMV $25.** 1980 Spokane, WA - **CMV $25.** 1981 Long Beach, CA - **CMV $25.** 1982 Las Vegas, NV - **CMV $25.** 1983 Wilmington, DE - **CMV $25.**

MID-AMERICAN NAAC CONVENTION PLATE 1974
(Left) Crystal plate with frosted inscription made in honor of the 3rd NAAC Convention by Mid-America Club. 225 were made. OSP $12.95. **CMV $30.**

QUEEN CITY NAAC CONVENTION PLATE 1976
(Right) Clear glass with frosted letters. OSP $12.95. **CMV $25.**

BETSY ROSS MOLD 1976
(Left) Very rare steel mold given to Avon Collectors at 1976 NAAC Convention. Mold was cut into 5 pieces. Must have a letter form Avon Products stating it is 1 of a kind. **CMV $500. with letter.**

ANNIVERSARY KEEPSAKE MOLD BASE 1976
(Right) Steel base of Avons anniversary keepsake mold given to National Association of Avon Clubs by Avon Products and auctioned off to Avon collectors. The numbers (17) and 5,215 on bottom. **CMV $500.**

CALIFORNIA PERFUME ANNIVERSARY KEEPSAKE MOLD 1975
This is the actual steel mold Avon used to make the 1975 Anniversary bottle. Mr. Art Goodwin from Avon Products, Inc. New York presented this mold cut into 5 separate pieces to the National Association of Avon Clubs at the 4th annual NAAC Convention banquet at Anaheim, Calif. June 19, 1975. The mold was auctioned off bringing several hudreds of dollars on each piece. This is the 1st time an Avon mold has been destroyed & given to the general public. Very rare. **CMV $600. each piece.**

ST. LOUIE BLUE PERFUME 1979
Small glass bottle, white cap. Special perfume made & given by Mid-America Avon Club & NAAC at NAAC Convention in St. Louis, June 1979. 231 bottles with registration card & envelope. **CMV $20.** mint & about 120 bottles only given without envelope & card. **CMV $10. BO.**

NAAC CONVENTION SOUVENIRS 1979
Each item was sold or given to collectors at annual St. Louis NAAC Convention. Most are very limited & hard to find. Luggage tag. **CMV $2..** Pen, brass. **CMV $2.** Monthly minder Christmas 1980. **CMV $5.** Matches, NAAC. **CMV 50c.**

BESTSY ROSS NAAC CONVENTION SOUVENIR 1976
Given by Avon Products to all collectors touring Avon plant in Springdale, Ohio, June 24, 1976. Special NAAC label on bottom. **CMV $17.50 with special label.**

THE KING II "FOR MEN" 1975
(Left) Special label reads "Souvenir, June 19, 1975 NAAC Tour Monrovia Avon Plant". Given to each male taking the Avon plant tour at NAAC Convention, Monrovia, California. Only 150 bottles have this label. **CMV $17.50.**

SKIP-A-ROPE "FOR LADIES" 1975
(Right) Same special label given to all ladies on same tour. **CMV $17.50.**

NAAC FREEDOM DOCUMENTS 1976
Souvenir booklet sold by NAAC at Cincinnati, Ohio, June 20-27, 1976. **CMV $5. mint.**

NAAC STATIONERY 1974-75
Blue box with NAAC logo on top. Back of NAAC. Only 214 boxes of stationery made & each is numbered. OSP $7. **CMV $20. MB.**

NAAC AVON CHESS BOARD 1975-76
21 1/2" square plastic chess board made for the Avon chess pieces. Silver & brown checker top with black rim border & back. NAAC logo in center, silver over black. 105 were made for sample to each NAAC club with center gold logo over black. 1,500 are numbered & last 1,000 are not numbered on back. **CMV gold logo $200. MB, regular issue silver logo with number $70. MB., black border no number $50. MB.** OSP $19.95 MB. Also came brown border with large black logo in center. **CMV $40. MB.** Last one to be issued had brown border & small logos in center, brown back. **CMV $40.**

NAAC CONVENTION SOUVENIRS 1973
A few souvenir items were sold at the convention. They are: Matchbook, black letters on yellow cover (**CMV $1.**); a yellow Ball Point Pen, with black lettering (**CMV $1.**); a green Pennant with yellow letters that read "NAAC Convention 73" (**CMV $1.50**).

NAAC CONVENTION SOUVENIRS 1978
Convention Packet, green plastic. **CMV $8.** Monthly Minder 1979. **CMV $5.** Magnifying Glass. **CMV $1.** All items given or sold at Houston, Texas, 1978 NAAC Convention.

NAAC CONVENTION SOUVENIRS 1974
Pin. **CMV $2.** Each year the mold for the annual NAAC club bottle is broken at the NAAC banquet and distributed to each person attending. 1974 piece of mold and card for NAAC club bottle. Distributed at convention banquet. Overland Park, Kansas, June 22, 1974. **CMV $10.** 1975 piece of mold and card for NAAC club bottle. Distributed at convention banquet Anaheim, California, June 21, 1975. **CMV $10.**

NAAC CONVENTION BANQUET RIBBON 1973
(Left) Blue ribbon, rare. **CMV $10.**
NAAC CLUB BOTTLE MOLD PIECE 1973
(Right) Piece of mold from 1973 NAAC club bottle & card. **CMV $10.**

NAAC COLLECTABLES
PLAYING CARDS 1978
CMV $4.
CONVENTION TRAY 1984
Glass tray given by Avon Products to NAAC Convention. Marked "Avon Welcomes NAAC to Kansas City, Mo. Convention, June 19-24, 1984". **CMV $10.**
CONVENTION CARD HOLDER 1985
Brass business card holder given by Avon Products to NAAC Convention in Seattle, Washington, marked "Avon Welcomes NAAC Convention, July 1-7, 1985. **CMV $10.**
NAAC CHRISTMAS ORNAMENT 1985
1st in series. Clear glass center, brass chain rim. Marked "NAAC 1985". **CMV $10.**

NAAC CONVENTION SOUVENIRS 1975
Given to each delegate & board member at NAAC convention in Anaheim, California, June 19, 1975. Blue engraved plastic packet holds package of NAAC stationery, memo pad - blue (250 made. **CMV $5.**), perfumed nips on engraved card (250 made. **CMV $5.**), and yellow delegate ribbon, Board Member nominee gray ribbon, National Director red ribbon, Chairman purple ribbon, Board Member green ribbon, Historian white ribbon. **CMV $10. each ribbon.**

CONVENTION DELEGATES RBBON 1973
(Left) Red ribbon with a red rosette was given to all delegates. Gold printing reads "Official Delegate National Association Avon Clubs Convention Sacramento, California, June 22, 1973". **CMV $8.**
CONVENTION BOARD MEMBER RIBBON 1973
(Not Shown) Same as the delegate ribbon only in blue instead of red. Board Member replaced the Official Delegate on the ribbon. **CMV $15.**
CONVENTION NATIONAL CHAIRMAN RIBBON 1973
(Right) Same as the Delegate ribbon only in maroon instead of red. Only one of these ribbons was made. It is owned by Mr. Bud Hastin. No value established.
NAAC CONVENTION SOUVENIR BADGE 1972
(Center) Round, light blue background with first CPC Lady in center. Has pin back. **CMV $10.**

QUICK REFERENCE INDEX
AN AID TO FINDING CATEGORIES QUICKLY

ALPHABETICAL INDEX

If you cannot find the items your are looking for in the Alphabetical Index,
check the Quick Reference Index in which it falls.

This book was typeset on Macintosh Plus™ computers using
PageMaker 2.0™ Desktop publishing software.

Typesetting furnished by:

LaserPrint
Desktop Publishing
4700 S. Maryland Pkwy. Suite 1
Las Vegas, Nevada 89119
(702) 736-4064

Owners: Derryl Rice &
                               Robert Sandberg

Typesetters: Stacy Carlson
                               Tiffany Riner
                               Heidi Wasmund
                               Lori Mohr

Proofreaders: Kathy Duley
                               Lori Mohr
                               Bud Hastin

**Photograph Paste-up
and Layout:**   Bud Hastin